COLLEGE ALGEBRA

FIFTH EDITION

COLLEGE ALGEBRA
A CONTEMPORARY APPROACH

William L. Hart PH.D.
UNIVERSITY OF MINNESOTA

D. C. HEATH AND COMPANY
Boston, Chicago, Englewood, San Francisco, Atlanta, Dallas

LIBRARY OF CONGRESS CATALOG CARD NUMBER: 66-23815

Copyright © 1966 by D. C. Heath and Company

Printed in the United States of America

PRINTED OCTOBER, 1966

Preface

General Viewpoints

This book is designed for students who have studied geometry and substantial algebra at the secondary level. A few sections require moderate acquaintance with trigonometry, but the corresponding content can be omitted without inconvenience if desirable. The author has aimed to prepare a flexible text suitable for either a three-hour or a five-hour course for one semester in *college algebra, where a substantial amount of plane analytic geometry is integrated with appropriate algebraic content*. Also, for the advantage of superior students, the book offers a *generous amount of supplementary material*. The text was planned to prepare students efficiently for a later course in analytic geometry and calculus, or for courses of a quantitative nature in the biological and social sciences.

Each edition of the author's *College Algebra* has featured, and sometimes has initiated, advances in the maturity level and modifications of the content of the corresponding course. Thus, the preceding or *Fourth Edition** introduced for the first time, in an elementary American text, a modern postulational presentation of probability. In the preparation of this *Fifth Edition,*† contemporary new ideas as to content were analyzed critically. The author has accepted those features about which he believes that a consensus has been reached and justified, or about which he is convinced that such agreement should be encouraged by his text. Also, as in previous editions of his *College Algebra*, he has not hesitated to present original innovations as to content and methods. The book thus provides *a substantial course in college algebra, couched in the best contemporary form, and enriched by related analytic geometry and a selection of new topics with recognized value*.

Special Features

● **The efficient but relatively brief preliminary review,** which may be covered leisurely, may be telescoped by use of the review exercises, or may be omitted and then serve for later references as to facts and elementary terminology.

---

* Published in 1953.
† And also in the preparation of the author's expanded text, *Algebra, Elementary Functions, and Probability;* D. C. Heath and Company (1965). That text includes almost all of the content of *College Algebra, Fifth Edition*, without some of its devices to permit flexibility in the level of sophistication. In addition, that text includes more chapters on *finite mathematics, a treatment of analytic trigonometry; some vector analysis; an introduction to analytic geometry in three dimensions.*

● **The fresh viewpoints introduced for parts of intermediate algebra** which are given brief mature discussion.

● **The numerous devices for creating flexibility,** which permit the teacher to raise or lower the level of sophistication of his course as desired by use of supplementary content* in the body of the text, final problems in the carefully graded exercises, and numerous notes with some exercises in the Appendix.

● **Early and continued emphasis on inequalities** in one and in two variables.

● **Integration of the analytic geometry of the straight line** with corresponding elementary algebraic content.

● **The treatment of the equations of conics,** occurring first in the chapter on quadratic functions and equations in two variables, involving:

A brief descriptive discussion of the equations of the conics in simplest positions.

Optional sections deriving equations for the conics from their definitions as loci.

An extensive note in the Appendix discussing translation of axes and corresponding equations for conics.

● **The sophisticated foundation for the real and complex systems of numbers** in supplementary content:

An axiomatic foundation for real numbers in the Appendix, introducing the concepts of a *group* and a *field*.

An optional foundation for complex numbers as ordered pairs of real numbers, in addition to a more elementary foundation, in the body of the text.

● **An augmented treatment of probability defined on a modern postulational basis,**† with simple introduction of the concepts of a *random variable,* a *probability distribution,* a *Bernoulli space,* and supplementary content about *conditional probability, Bayes' Rule,* and *dependent or independent events.*

● **Emphasis on matrix language and methods** in the study of systems of linear equations, with solution by *diagonalization of matrices* as well as by use of determinants.

● **A foundation for determinants by reference to inversions of indices** in the Appendix.

● **A substantial introduction to the algebra of matrices,** leading to the *inverse of a matrix and a simple proof of Cramer's Rule,* in the Appendix, with corresponding exercises for the student.

* Marked with a black star, ★.
† The chapter simplifies, and expands in optional content, the author's pioneering introduction of modern probability in *College Algebra, Fourth Edition.*

● **A complete discussion of linear programming with two independent variables** in an optional chapter.

● **An intuitional introduction to limits of sequences,** with application to a few simple infinite series, infinite geometric progressions, and the *definition of irrational numbers as endless decimals.*

● **An optional sophisticated foundation for the logarithm function** as the inverse of the exponential function, where a^x is defined, for $a > 0$ and any real x, as the *limit* of a sequence of powers of a with exponents which are terminating decimals.

● **The sensible attitude about sets,** *involving use of set language, and the simple operations on sets* from the very start,* avoiding any attempt to make set algebra and set symbolism an end by itself, and emphasizing the indispensable role of considerable set language in probability and the discussion of systems of inequalities.

● **Continuation of the high standards in regard to logical structure** of previous editions of the author's *College Algebra,* by emphasis on definitions, clear statements of theorems, with formal proofs, and occasional demands for proofs and counterexamples in exercises.

Pedagogical Aids

The book employs devices common to all of the author's texts to assist both the teacher and the student.

Illustrative examples are used profusely.

The problem material for the student is extensive.

Review or miscellaneous exercises occur frequently.

The problems in exercises are arranged in order of difficulty.

Answers are given in the text for almost all of the odd-numbered problems; answers to the even-numbered problems are available in a separate pamphlet when requested by the instructor.

William L. Hart
University of Minnesota

---

* To simplify consideration of the essential elementary algebra of sets, the text defines *union* (∪) and *intersection* (∩) for *any number* (possibly an infinite number) of sets, instead of for just *two* sets, as would be done if a foundation for set theory, with ∪ and ∩ as *binary operations,* were a primary objective. The definitions in the text are those which must be used in the study of probability where the sample space is *not finite,* and in various other mathematical situations where infinitely many sets are involved.

Contents

CHAPTER EIGHT

Theory of Equations

CHAPTER NINE

Exponential and Logarithmic Functions

CHAPTER FOURTEEN

Introduction to Linear Programming

Appendix

Tables

COLLEGE ALGEBRA

Chapter **1** Basic Review*

1. Real numbers and decimals

Any number system which we shall consider will consist of abstract† elements called *numbers*, for which two operations called *addition* and *multiplication* are defined. Until specified later, we shall be concerned with the system of real numbers. A written symbol representing a number is called a **numeral,** or simply a **number symbol.** The number represented by a numeral may be called its *value*. If x is a symbol for a number, we may refer to it as *"the number x."*

Illustration 1. The symbols 5, $(3 + 2)$, $\sqrt{25}$, and *five* are symbols for the same number.

In this text, it is assumed that the student has become familiar with the system, R, of real numbers, which consist of the *positive numbers*, the *negative numbers*, and *zero*, which is not called either positive or negative. We shall review various definitions and terminology about R.

In writing symbols for real numbers, we frequently use a place system with base 10, the symbol 0, and the Hindu-Arabic numerals (1, 2, 3, 4, 5, 6, 7, 8, 9). This method is referred to as the decimal system of numerals. Any number symbol written by this method is called a *decimal*. Also, if the context prevents ambiguity, the number represented by the decimal may itself be called a decimal. We sometimes refer to the symbols (0, 1, 2, 3, 4, 5, 6, 7, 8, 9) as digits, or figures.

Illustration 2. The decimal 326.148 is defined by

$$326.148 = 3(10^2) + 2(10) + 6 + \frac{1}{10} + \frac{4}{10^2} + \frac{8}{10^3}.$$

---

* The teacher may desire to use merely the seven review exercises scattered through the chapter. Some of the most familiar terminology of elementary algebra will be employed freely without review.

† That is, no specific realization as physical objects is attached to the elements.

Sometimes, it is convenient to visualize each decimal as having an endless succession of digits in the places to the right of the decimal point. Then, the decimal is referred to as an *endless* or *infinite* decimal (where we shall prefer the name *endless*). It is proved at a more advanced level that *every real number can be represented by an endless decimal.* Or, the real numbers can be referred to as the set of all decimals—positive, negative, or zero.

With any decimal now considered as endless, a **terminating decimal** is one with zero in each place to the right of a certain decimal place; these zeros usually are omitted in writing the number symbol.

Illustration 3. 35.675, or 35.675000 · · · , is a terminating decimal. Also, $\frac{5}{4} = 1.25$, a terminating decimal.

A **repeating decimal** is one whose digits to the right of a specified place consist of endless repetitions of certain digits in a given order. To indicate that a decimal is of the repeating type, we may write the repeating digits just once, with a dot over each digit. A decimal which is not of repeating type will be referred to as a nonrepeating decimal.

Illustration 4. $\frac{1}{3} = .333 · · · $, *a repeating decimal.* We may write simply $\frac{1}{3} = .\dot{3}$. Similarly,

$$\frac{1}{7} = .142857'142857'142857 · · · , \textit{a repeating decimal.}$$

Or, $\frac{1}{7} = .\dot{1}4285\dot{7}$. Also, $\frac{5}{6} = .8\dot{3}$.

$$\pi = 3.14159 · · · , \textit{an endless but not a repeating decimal.}$$

The system R includes the endless set of integers,

$$· · · -5, -4, -3, -2, -1, 0, 1, 2, 3, 4, 5, · · · .$$

Also, the numbers of R are classified as either *rational* numbers or *irrational* numbers, according to the following definitions.

DEFINITION I. *A real number N is said to be a **rational number** if and only if there exist integers p and $q \neq 0$ such that $N = p/q$.*

If p is any integer, then $p = p/1$, and thus p is a rational number.

Illustration 5. 3, 0, $\frac{5}{17}$, and $-\frac{3}{5}$ are rational numbers.

DEFINITION II. *A real number is said to be an **irrational number** if it is not a rational number.*

A sound foundation for the introduction of irrational numbers cannot be given at an elementary level. As an intuitional basis for appreciation, we may state that an irrational number is a real number which is not a rational number, but *can be approximated as closely as desired by rational numbers.*

Any terminating decimal represents a rational number. Thus, 35.78 = 3578/100. Later, we shall discuss why any repeating decimal represents a rational number. Thus, $.41\dot{6} = \frac{5}{12}$. Also, we observe that some rational numbers may be represented by terminating decimals. Thus, $\frac{3}{4} = .75$. If the decimal symbol for a rational number is not a terminating decimal, it will be proved later in the text that the number is equal to an endless repeating decimal. We conclude, then, that the rational numbers consist of those represented by all endless repeating decimals (including the terminating decimals), while the irrational numbers are those represented by all endless nonrepeating decimals. From the decimal representation of an irrational number, N, we can obtain rational numbers (terminating decimals) approximating N as closely as we please.

Illustration 6. In Note 1 of the Appendix, it is proved that $\sqrt{2}$ is an irrational number. Improving decimal approximations to $\sqrt{2}$ can be obtained to as many decimal places as we please by the square root process of arithmetic. Thus, $\sqrt{2} = 1.4142 \cdots$, where no formula is available for the digit in the kth decimal place. An approximation to $\sqrt{2}$ to three decimal places is 1.414, or 1414/1000, a rational number.

Frequently, it may be very difficult, or impossible, to learn whether or not a number, specified in some fashion, is rational or irrational, even though it may be feasible to compute the number to any desired number of decimal places. Thus, with π described as the ratio of the circumference of a circle to its diameter, a proof that π is an irrational number requires use of extremely advanced mathematics.

Note 1. Until otherwise stated in a later section, the word *number* will refer to a *real number*. A reference to a *particular number* will mean a number represented by an explicit numeral, such as -3, and thus not represented by a literal number symbol such as x or b, which might be allowed to assume various values. In this text, any letter used without a qualifying description will represent a number.

2. Addition and multiplication

Two fundamental operations on numbers in R are defined in accordance with the following statements.

For any two numbers a and b in R, there exists in R just one number called the **sum** *of a and b, and represented by $(a + b)$.*

For any two numbers a and b in R, there exists in R just one number called the **product** *of a times b, and represented by ab.*

The operation of finding a sum $(a + b)$ is called **addition.** The operation of finding a product ab is called **multiplication,** and each of a and b is called a **factor** of the product. Each of these operations is called a **binary operation** because it applies to just *two* numbers. Since $(a + b)$ is in R, we say that the number system R is *closed under addition.* Since ab is in R, we say that R is *closed under multiplication.*

The student should recall the following *theorems*, which we shall call *laws*, about addition and multiplication of real numbers.

I. *Multiplication is* **commutative,** *or the product of two numbers is the same in whatever order they are multiplied. That is,* $ab = ba$.

II. *Multiplication is* **associative.** *That is,*

$$(ab)c = a(bc). \tag{1}$$

III. *Addition is* **commutative,** *or the sum of two numbers is the same in whatever order they are added. That is,* $a + b = b + a$.

IV. *Addition is* **associative.** *That is,*

$$a + (b + c) = (a + b) + c. \tag{2}$$

V. *Multiplication is* **distributive** *with respect to addition. That is,*

$$a(b + c) = ab + ac. \tag{3}$$

On account of Law II, we may speak of the product of *any number* of numbers, although multiplication is originally defined for just *two* numbers. Thus, for three numbers, we define the product *abc* as the common value of the products in (1); we remark that the product is the same in whatever order the factors are grouped (or, *associated*) in exhibiting *abc* as a product of just two numbers. Similarly, because of Law IV, we may speak of the sum of *any number* of numbers. Thus, for *a*, *b*, and *c*, we define the sum $(a + b + c)$ as the common value of any one of the sums in (2).

At one stage of the student's experience in more elementary mathematics (perhaps in advanced arithmetic), the available system, S, of numbers consisted of just zero and the positive numbers, where the name *positive* was not yet employed, but will be used now by us in connection with S. For a brief span, let us act *as if S is our number system*, with operations of addition and multiplication obeying Laws I–V. In the remainder of this section and in Section 3, we propose expanding S to include negative numbers, in order to give a background for manipulation of the signs "+" and "−" with real numbers.*

For every number x of S, we introduce a number x' with the following property assigned in addition:

$$x + x' = 0. \tag{4}$$

Illustration 1. If $x = 0$, then the number $x' = 0$ satisfies (4). Hence, if $x = 0$, no new number need be introduced to satisfy (4). If $x = 4$, we have defined x' to satisfy

$$4 + x' = 0. \tag{5}$$

Since S contains no number x' (0 or positive) satisfying (5), it is necessary to introduce a *new* number x' to satisfy (5).

* For an axiomatic discussion of all real numbers (omitting irrational numbers), see Note 2 in the Appendix.

In Illustration 1, we have a background for the statement that, in (4), *for every positive number x we have introduced a new number x′*, which we agree to call a **negative number**. Then, we define the system, R, of real numbers as consisting of zero and the positive numbers of S, and the negative numbers defined by (4). In (4), we observe one result for addition in R: by the definition of the negative number $x′$, the sum of x and $x′$ is 0. Also, in R, it is necessary to define all other possible sums and products where any number occurs which is negative. We shall proceed by use of merely (4), the usual properties of 0 and 1 in addition and multiplication, and the assumption that addition and multiplication in R obey Laws I–V.

DEFINITION III. *If a is any number in R, then a number b in R is called an* **additive inverse** *of a in case*

$$a + b = 0. \tag{6}$$

If $a + b = 0$ then $b + a = 0$, by Law III. Therefore, if b is an additive inverse of a then a is an additive inverse of b. If x is a positive number, then the corresponding number $x′$ of (4) is an additive inverse of x. Hence, by the first sentence in this paragraph, x is an additive inverse of the negative number $x′$. Also, 0 is an additive inverse of 0 because $0 + 0 = 0$. Thus, *each number of R has an additive inverse.* In Problem 68 on page 17, the student will be asked to prove that *there is just one additive inverse for each number in R.* Hereafter, for any number a in R,

$$\left.\begin{array}{c} -a \text{ *will represent the additive inverse of a, or*} \\ a + (-a) = 0. \end{array}\right\} \tag{7}$$

In particular, since the negative number $x′$ in (4) is the additive inverse of the positive number x, we have $x′ = -x$. That is,

$$\left.\begin{array}{l} \textit{for each positive number x, a corresponding} \\ \textbf{negative number } -x \textit{ has been defined, with} \\ x + (-x) = 0. \end{array}\right\} \tag{8}$$

In (7), since $-a$ is the additive inverse of a, then a is the additive inverse of $-a$, or

$$a = -(-a). \tag{9}$$

With $a = 1$ in (7), we obtain $\qquad 1 + (-1) = 0. \tag{10}$

For any number a in R, on multiplying a in turn by each side of (10), on account of Law V we obtain

$$[1 + (-1)] \cdot a = 0 \cdot a, \quad \textit{or} \quad a + (-1) \cdot a = 0. \tag{11}$$

Hence, by reference to (6), we see that $(-1) \cdot a$ is the *additive inverse of a.* Or, from (7),

$$-a = (-1) \cdot a. \tag{12}$$

Illustration 2. With $x = 4$ in (8), $\qquad\qquad 4 + (-4) = 0.$

From (9) with $a = 3$, $\qquad\qquad\qquad\qquad 3 = -(-3).$

From (12) with $a = 5$, $\qquad\qquad\qquad\quad -5 = (-1) \cdot 5.$

In the future, we shall usually replace the name "*additive inverse of a*" in (7) by "*negative of a*," as follows:

$\qquad$ *For any real number a, the* **negative** *of a is defined as* $-a$. $\qquad$ (13)

Illustration 3. The negative of 0 is 0 because 0 is the additive inverse of 0; or, $-0 = 0$. The negative of any real number x is $-x$, and the negative of $-x$ is $-(-x)$, or x, because of (9). On account of (7), we observe that *the sum of any number and its negative is zero.* The negative integers are $(-1, -2, -3, \cdots)$.

In Laws I–V, and elsewhere in arithmetic and algebra, we have used "+" to indicate the operation of addition. Now, consider the true statement

$$0 + a = a. \qquad (14)$$

Thus, it will be reasonable to consider "$+a$" as an abbreviation for $(0 + a)$, and then write $+a = a$ if we please. Hence, we reach the following conclusion:

$\left\{\begin{array}{l}\text{\textit{Attaching "}+\text{" at the left of the symbol, N, for a number gives a}}\\\text{\textit{new symbol for the same number, or}}\ \boldsymbol{N = +N = (+1) \cdot N.}\end{array}\right\}$ $\quad$ (15)

Illustration 4. The positive integers may be written as

$$(1, 2, 3, \cdots) \quad or \quad (+1, +2, +3, \cdots).$$

By reference to (12), we make the following observation:

$\left\{\begin{array}{l}\text{\textit{Attaching "}-\text{" at the left of the symbol, N,}}\\\text{\textit{for a number gives a symbol for}}\ (-1) \cdot N,\ \textit{or}\\\qquad\quad \boldsymbol{-N = (-1) \cdot N.}\end{array}\right\}$ $\quad$ (16)

In view of preceding remarks, *we agree to think of any symbol for a number as having a sign "+" or "−" at the left,* where "+" can be inserted if desired, and will be understood without being written if no sign is visible.

Illustration 5. The number symbol $3ab$ can be written $+3ab$.

In (12), let $a = 1$ on the left, and write $a = +1$ on the right. Then,

$$-1 = (-1) \cdot (+1). \qquad (17)$$

In (9), let $a = 1$. Then, by use of (12) on the right in (9),

$$1 = -(-1) = (-1) \cdot (-1), \quad or \quad +1 = (-1) \cdot (-1). \qquad (18)$$

To represent the product of a given set of numbers, we write their symbols side by side. We separate each symbol from any neighboring symbol by parentheses, or a sign of multiplication, if this is necessary to prevent ambiguity.

Illustration 6. The product of x, b, -2, and 5 is represented by $(5)(-2)bx$. The product of 3, 5, and -7 is represented by $3(5)(-7)$, or by $3 \cdot 5 \cdot (-7)$.

Illustration 7. If we desire to insert a second sign, $+$ or $-$, at the left of a symbol such as $-3x$, where a sign already is present, it is essential, first, to enclose the symbol in parentheses. Thus, to insert the sign $+$, we write $+(-3x)$, which means $(+1) \cdot (-1) \cdot 3x$.

The following laws of signs in multiplication are consequences of the facts that $(-1) \cdot (-1) = +1$, $(+1) \cdot (+1) = +1$, and $(-1) \cdot (+1) = -1$. In forming a product of two numbers:

$$\left(\begin{array}{l} \textit{If their symbols bear } \textbf{like signs,} \textit{ this} \\ \textit{creates a } \textbf{plus sign} \textit{ for the product.} \end{array}\right) \tag{19}$$

$$\left(\begin{array}{l} \textit{If their symbols bear } \textbf{unlike signs,} \textit{ this} \\ \textit{creates a } \textbf{minus sign} \textit{ for the product.} \end{array}\right) \tag{20}$$

Illustration 8. $(-3) \cdot (+5) = -15$, because

$$(-3) \cdot (+5) = (-1) \cdot (3) \cdot (+1) \cdot (5) = (-1) \cdot (+1) \cdot 15 = -15.$$

Similarly, $(-2a) \cdot (-3c) = +6ac$, because

$$(-2a) \cdot (-3c) = (-1) \cdot (2a) \cdot (-1) \cdot (3c) = [(-1) \cdot (-1)] \cdot 6ac = (+1)(6ac).$$

3. Division and subtraction

DEFINITION IV. *To* **divide** *b by c, where $c \neq 0$, means to find x so that $b = cx$. Then, we call b the* **dividend,** *c the* **divisor,** *and x the* **quotient** *of b divided by c.*

We use $b \div c$, or $\dfrac{b}{c}$, or b/c for the quotient of b divided by c. Occasionally we refer to this quotient as *the* **ratio** *of b to c,* written $b : c$. Thus,

$$b \div c = b : c,$$

which we read *"b divided by c is equal to the ratio of b to c."* From more elementary courses in algebra, we accept without proof the theorem that, for any b and c with $c \neq 0$, there exists *just one number x such that $x = b \div c$.*

The laws of signs stated in (19) and (20) above for a product of two numbers apply also with *"product of two numbers,"* changed to *"quotient of one number divided by another."*

Illustration 1. $\qquad \dfrac{15}{-45} = \dfrac{+15}{-45} = -\dfrac{1}{3} \cdot \qquad 5 : 7 = \dfrac{5}{7} \cdot$

Each of the operations of multiplication and division is referred to as the *inverse* of the other operation, because multiplication and then division of a number b by $c \neq 0$, or these operations in reverse order, leave b unchanged.

DEFINITION V. *To subtract c from b means to find a number x such that*

$$b = x + c. \tag{1}$$

Temporarily, let us act as if this is our first contact with subtraction in the system of real numbers. We then ask: Does (1) have a solution x for every b and c, is x unique, and what is its value?

THEOREM I. *For any real numbers b and c, equation* (1) *is true for just one value of x, where*

$$x = b + (-c). \tag{2}$$

Or, to subtract c from b, we add $-c$ to b.

Proof. 1. **IF** x satisfies (1), then x satisfies the equation obtained on adding $-c$ to both sides of (1), which gives

$$b + (-c) = x + c + (-c) = x + [c + (-c)], \text{ or} \tag{3}$$
$$b + (-c) = x + 0 = x.$$

In (3), notice that we used Law IV of page 6, and the fact that $-c$ is the *additive inverse of c*. Hence, the only possible value of x to satisfy (1) is shown in (2).

2. It remains to verify that (2) satisfies (1). On substituting from (2) in the right-hand side of (1), we obtain

$$x + c = b + (-c) + c = b + [(-c) + c] = b + 0 = b.$$

Therefore, (2) satisfies (1), and is the only value of x with this property. Hence, we have proved Theorem I.

Hereafter, the result of subtracting c from b, or the number x in (2), will be called the **difference** of b and c.

Illustration 2. Since $-(-4) = 4$, the difference of 7 and -4, or the result of subtracting -4 from 7 is

$$7 + [-(-4)] = 7 + 4 = 11.$$

Now, we make the following agreement:

$$[b + (-c)] \quad \text{will be written} \quad (b - c), \tag{4}$$

when we desire. That is,

$$\text{the difference of } b \text{ and } c \text{ is } (b - c). \tag{5}$$

We have no basis for *proving* that $b + (-c) = b - c$ for all b and c in R, and thus (4) is a *definition* of $(b - c)$. The agreement (4) is convenient because we obtain the same formal expression for the difference of b and c as in arithmetic, where only positive numbers and zero were involved, and "$-$" was the sign for subtraction. Thus, the use of "$-$" in arithmetic is consistent with (5).

If c is *added* to b, and then is *subtracted* from the sum, or if these operations are performed in reverse order, the operations cancel each other, and b is obtained as the final result. Thus,

$$b + c + (-c) = b + [c + (-c)] = b + 0 = b.$$

Hence, each of the operations of addition and subtraction is called the *inverse* of the other operation.

Note 1. We call *addition, subtraction, multiplication,* and *division* the **fundamental operations** of algebra.

Recall our agreement on page 8 that any symbol for a number may be considered to have an attached sign, $+$ or $-$, at the left. Then, we make the following agreement about representing a sum.

$$\left\{\begin{array}{l}\textit{To represent the sum of a set of numbers, write their symbols}\\ \textit{with their attached signs in a line, where ``+'' is supplied}\\ \textit{for any symbol whose sign is not written originally.}\end{array}\right\} \quad (6)$$

For any sum represented as in (6), each symbol with its attached sign is called a **term** of the sum. In using (6), we may omit any sign "$+$" at the extreme left.

Illustration 3. To represent the sum of a, b, and c, first altered to a, $+b$, and $+c$, we write $(a + b + c)$. Hence, (6) is consistent with the symbol for a sum on page 6.

Illustration 4. By agreement (6), to represent the sum of b and $-c$ we write $(b - c)$. Hence, (6) is consistent with (4). Agreement (6) extends (4) to more elaborate cases. Thus, the sum of $-5a$, $-3b$, and 6 is represented by

$$-5a - 3b + 6, \quad meaning \quad (-5a) + (-3b) + 6.$$

4. Absolute values

The terminology of the following definition is extremely important in many fields of mathematics.

DEFINITION VI. *The **absolute value** of a positive number or zero is the number itself. The absolute value of a negative number is its negative.*

We use $|H|$ to represent the "*absolute value of H.*" Thus,

$$|H| = H \text{ if } H \text{ is zero or positive;} \quad (1)$$
$$|H| = -H \text{ if } H \text{ is negative.} \quad (2)$$

Illustration 1. $|0| = 0.$ $|-5| = -(-5) = 5.$ $|\frac{4}{3}| = \frac{4}{3}.$

Illustration 2. If b is positive, c is negative, and $b = |c|$, then $b = -c$, and hence

$$c + b = c + (-c) = 0.$$

In terms of absolute values, we can phrase conveniently the definitions of the sum and the product of any two real numbers. In references below to the number system of arithmetic, we mean the system, S, consisting of *zero and the positive numbers*. We assume that the results of addition and multiplication for any numbers of S are known. The words *"larger"* and *"smaller"* will be used with the meanings met in arithmetic. For any real number b, recall that $|b|$ is positive or zero, and hence addition and multiplication of absolute values can be considered as applied to numbers in S.

A. To calculate a product *of real numbers, multiply the absolute values of the factors to find the absolute value of the product; then, multiply the resulting absolute value by $+1$ or by -1 according as there are an even or an odd number of negative factors.*

B. Calculation of a sum $(b + c)$.

1. *If b and c are nonnegative, the sum is the same as specified for $(b + c)$ in arithmetic.*

2. *If b and c are both negative, add their absolute values and multiply the result by -1.*

3. *If just one of b and c is negative, subtract the smaller* of the absolute values $|b|$ and $|c|$ from the larger.* Then, multiply the resulting number by $+1$ or by -1 according as the number, b or c, with the larger absolute value is positive or negative.*

Illustration 3. By use of A,

$$(-5) \cdot 8 = (-1) \cdot |-5| \cdot |8| = -40;$$
$$(-5)(3)(-7) = (+1) \cdot |-5| \cdot |3| \cdot |-7| = 105.$$

Illustration 4. By use of B,

$$(-4) + (-12) = (-1) \cdot (4 + 12) = -16;$$
$$(-12) + 4 = -(|-12| - |4|) = -(12 - 4) = -8.$$

It is expected that previous experience permits the student to operate quickly with real numbers. The solutions in Illustrations 3 and 4 were expanded in order to illustrate the details of A and B.

From (1) and (2), we see that $H = 0$ if and only if $|H| = 0$. Now, consider a product bc; from A, $|bc| = |b| \cdot |c|$. Hence, $bc = 0$ if and only if $|b| \cdot |c| = 0$, which occurs if and only if $\{|b| = 0 \quad or \quad |c| = 0\}$,† which is equivalent to $\{b = 0 \quad or \quad c = 0\}$. Thus, we have the following useful result.

$$bc = 0 \quad \textit{if and only if} \quad \{b = 0 \quad \textbf{or} \quad c = 0\}. \tag{3}$$

* If $|b| = |c|$, the larger and smaller values are equal.
† Let E and F represent meaningful statements. Then, to say that $\{E \text{ or } F\}$ is true means that one of the following possibilities is met: E *is true and* F *is false; both E and F are true; E is false and F is true.*

Similarly, a product of any number of factors is equal to zero if and only if at least one of the factors is zero.

Note 1. Recall that we defined $b \div c$ with the stipulation that $c \neq 0$. It is advisable to consider why this agreement was made. Thus, suppose that $b \div 0$ were defined as some number d; then, we would have $b = 0 \times d = 0$, which is impossible if $b \neq 0$. If $b = 0$ and $b \div 0 = d$, then we would have $0 = 0 \times d$, which is true for every number d. Hence, $0 \div 0$ could represent *any* number d, and thus would be ambiguous. Therefore, we consider $b \div 0$ as useless, and never employ 0 as a divisor; or, **division by zero is not allowed.** However, no exception arises in dividing zero by other numbers, in adding or subtracting zero, or in multiplying by zero. Thus, if N is any number,

$$N \times 0 = 0; \quad N + 0 = N; \quad N - 0 = N; \quad \frac{0}{C} = 0 \ \textit{if } C \neq 0.$$

5. Signs of grouping

Parentheses, ( ), brackets, [ ], braces, { }, and the vinculum, ‾, are used frequently to enclose terms whose sum is to act as a single term in some algebraic operation. In general, the word *parentheses* will refer to any one of these symbols of grouping.

Illustration 1. Doubt arises as to the meaning of $(9 - 6 \div 3)$. Does it mean $(9 - 6) \div 3$, which is equal to 1, or $9 - (6 \div 3)$, which is equal to $(9 - 2)$ or 7? Use of parentheses eliminates ambiguity.

A factor multiplying a sum within parentheses should be used to multiply each term of the sum, because of Law V on page 6. Also, recall that "$+$" or "$-$" at the left of a symbol for a number indicates multiplication by $+1$ or -1, respectively. These facts justify the following statements.

I. *In removing or inserting parentheses preceded by a* **plus** *sign, rewrite the included terms* **unchanged.**

II. *In removing or inserting parentheses preceded by a* **minus** *sign, rewrite the included terms with their* **signs changed.**

Illustration 2. $-(-2 + 5x - y) = (-1)(-2 + 5x - y) = 2 - 5x + y.$

If a symbol of grouping encloses other symbols of grouping, remove them by removing the *innermost* symbol first, etc. Usually, we enclose parentheses within brackets; brackets within braces.

Illustration 3. $-[3y - (2x - 5)] = -(3y - 2x + 5) = -3y + 2x - 5.$

In a sum, two products with the same literal part are called **similar terms,** or **like terms.** In a term such as $6abc$, the particular number, 6, multiplying the other factors is called the **numerical coefficient,** or simply the *coefficient*. *To collect terms* in a sum means *to collect similar terms*, where use is made of Law V on page 6 to justify the following routine.

III. *To collect similar terms, add their numerical coefficients and multiply the result by the common factor.*

Illustration 4. $\qquad -9ab + ab = ab(-9 + 1) = -8ab.$

The difference of $(3a - 5y - 8)$ and $(3y - 2a - 6)$ is

$$(3a - 5y - 8) - (3y - 2a - 6) = 5a - 8y - 2.$$

6. Real number scale and inequality relations

In this text, the word *length*, or the unqualified word *distance* will refer to a nonnegative number which is the measure of some distance, or straight line segment, between two points. On a horizontal line, as in Figure 1, we now

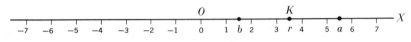

Figure 1

select a point O, to be called the **origin**, and let it represent the number 0. Also, we choose a unit for measuring distances on the line OX. Then, if p is any *positive* number, let it be represented by the point on OX which is at p units of distance from O to the *right*. Let the negative number $-p$ be represented by the point on OX which is at p units of distance from O to the *left*. Thus, each real number is represented by a point on OX. Conversely, if K is any point, not O, on OX, and if K is at a distance h from O, then there exists just one number r which is represented by K, where $r = h$ if K is to the right of O, and $r = -h$ if K is to the left of O. Hence, we say that there is a *one-to-one correspondence* between the points on OX and real numbers. Hereafter, if r is any real number, we may refer to the *"point r,"* meaning the point representing r on OX. We call OX, as in Figure 1, a **number scale.**

DEFINITION VII. *To say that b is **less than** a or that a is **greater than** b means that $(a - b)$ is positive.*

We use the inequality sign "$<$" for "*is less than*" and "$>$" for "*is greater than.*" Thus,

$$b < a \quad means\ that \quad (a - b)\ is\ \textbf{positive.} \tag{1}$$

We refer to "$a < b$" as an *inequality relation*, or simply an *inequality*.

Illustration 1. We have $4 < 6$ because $(6 - 4) = 2$, which is positive.

$-7 < -3$ because $-3 - (-7) = -3 + 7 = 4$, which is positive.

$-10 < 0$ because $0 - (-10) = 0 + 10 = 10$, which is positive.

We emphasize that "$p > 0$" means that $(p - 0)$, or p, is *positive:*

$$p > 0 \quad means\ that \quad p\ is\ positive. \tag{2}$$

To say that $H < 0$ means that $(0 - H)$, or $-H$, is *positive;* hence, $-(-H)$, or H, is *negative:*

$$H < 0 \quad \textit{means that} \quad H \textit{ is negative.} \tag{3}$$

Let b and r be two numbers, with representations on the number scale in Figure 1 on page 14. On account of the nature of the scale, to state that b *is to the left of* r, as in Figure 1, means that $r = b + p$ where p is positive, and hence $r - b = p$. Thus, on account of (1),

$$\left\{ \begin{array}{l} b < r \textit{ means that } b \textit{ is to the} \\ \textit{left of } r \textit{ on the number scale.} \end{array} \right\} \tag{4}$$

7. Elementary operations on fractions

Suppose that each of a, b, c, and d is a positive integer or 0, with $b \neq 0$ and $d \neq 0$. When rational numbers were introduced into the number system in more elementary mathematics, the following equations were specified as *definitions* of equality, multiplication, and addition, respectively, for the rational numbers a/b and c/d.

$$\frac{a}{b} = \frac{c}{d} \quad \textit{means that} \quad ad = bc. \tag{1}$$

$$\frac{a}{b} \cdot \frac{c}{d} = \frac{ac}{bd}. \tag{2}$$

$$\frac{a}{b} + \frac{c}{d} = \frac{ad + bc}{bd}. \tag{3}$$

Then, a detailed study of the number system, through the stage of introduction of positive irrational numbers, and finally negative rational and irrational numbers, shows that (1), (2), and (3) remain true if a, b, c, and d are any real numbers, with $b \neq 0$ and $d \neq 0$. We accept this fact. Then, the following familiar results I and II can be proved by use of (1) and (2).

I. *The value of a fraction is not altered if both numerator and denominator are multiplied (or divided) by the same number, not zero. That is, if $k \neq 0$ and $b \neq 0$,*

$$\frac{a}{b} = \frac{ka}{kb}. \tag{4}$$

Proof. Since $a(kb) = b(ka)$, it is seen that (4) is true because (1) is true. On reading (4) from right to left, it follows that *division* of both numerator and denominator by k on the right does not change the value of the fraction.

Illustration 1.
$$\frac{5}{7} = \frac{5 \times 3}{7 \times 3} = \frac{15}{21}.$$

$$\frac{36}{84} = \frac{36 \div 12}{84 \div 12} = \frac{3}{7}.$$

In particular, from (4), both numerator and denominator of a fraction may be multiplied by -1 without altering the value of the fraction. Thus,

$$\frac{-3}{-4} = \frac{(-1)(-3)}{(-1)(-4)} = \frac{3}{4}.$$

II. *To divide one fraction by another, not zero, invert the divisor and multiply the dividend by this inverted divisor. That is, if no one of b, c, and d is zero,*

$$\frac{a}{b} \div \frac{c}{d} = \frac{ad}{bc}. \tag{5}$$

Proof of (5). By Definition IV on page 9, the left-hand side of (5) represents a unique number x such that $(c/d)x = a/b$. By use of (2) and (4),

$$\frac{c}{d} \cdot \frac{ad}{bc} = \frac{acd}{bcd} = \frac{a}{b},$$

and hence (5) is true.

By use of the fact that any number N can be written as a fraction $N/1$, we obtain the following result.

III. *To multiply a fraction by a number, multiply the numerator by the number. To divide a fraction by a number, not zero, multiply the denominator by the number.*

Illustration 2.
$$c\left(\frac{a}{b}\right) = \frac{c}{1} \cdot \frac{a}{b} = \frac{ac}{b}. \qquad 7 \cdot \frac{5}{6} = \frac{35}{6}.$$

$$\frac{a}{b} \div c = \frac{a}{b} \div \frac{c}{1} = \frac{a}{b} \cdot \frac{1}{c} = \frac{a}{bc}. \qquad 4 \div (3\tfrac{2}{7}) = 4 \div \frac{23}{7} = \frac{4}{1} \cdot \frac{7}{23} = \frac{28}{23}.$$

If just the numerator, or denominator, of a fraction is multiplied by -1, the sign before the fraction must be *changed*. These actions are equivalent to multiplying by *two* factors -1, whose product is $+1$, and thus the value of the fraction is not altered.

Illustration 3.
$$\frac{a-3}{2} = -\frac{(-1)(a-3)}{2} = -\frac{3-a}{2}.$$

EXERCISE 1

Compute the expression, if possible. Otherwise, remove any signs of grouping and collect similar terms.

1. $-(-5)$.   **2.** $0(-5+7)$.   **3.** $-7(-4)(6)$.   **4.** $-3(16-9)$.

5. $-(2a - 5b + c)$.   **6.** $-2(8a - 3b - c)$.   **7.** $-13x + 8x$.

8. $2(a - 3b) - 5(b - 2a) + 3(-a - 3b)$.

9. $-[4a - (2a + 3)]$.   **10.** $9 - [z - (6 - 3z)]$.

11. $2y - \{5 + [3 - 2(y - 2)]\}$.   **12.** $-\{2b - [6 - (3b - 4)]\}$.

Rewrite, with the two terms at the right placed within parentheses preceded by a minus sign.

13. $2a - 3 - c + 5b$.   **14.** $16 - 4a + 3c - b$.

15. State the absolute value of 17; -46; $-\frac{3}{4}$; -1.48.

16. Read the symbol and specify its value: $|-36|$; $|0|$; $|-1.3|$.

17. Write the negative of 7; -4; $-\frac{2}{3}$; -8; 0.

18. Write in a line the sum of $(3a - 5y - 3)$ multiplied by 2, and $(-5a + 7y - 5)$ multiplied by -3; remove parentheses and collect terms.

Construct a real number scale. Read the inequality, check it by use of (1) on page 14, and verify the inequality on your scale.

19. $5 < 9$.   **20.** $0 < 7$.   **21.** $-3 < 0$.   **22.** $-3 < 8$.

Decide which sign, $<$ or $>$, should be placed between the numbers.

23. $7, 9$.   **24.** $-5, -9$.   **25.** $0, -6$.   **26.** $8, -10$.

Read the inequalities and check them.

27. $|-7| < |8|$ and $-7 < 8$.   **28.** $|-8| > 3$, but $-8 < 3$.

Divide, to express the rational number as a repeating decimal.

29. $\frac{5}{9}$.   **30.** $\frac{7}{12}$.   **31.** $\frac{5}{16}$.   **32.** $\frac{2}{7}$.   **33.** $\frac{4}{13}$.

Express the result by use of a fraction in lowest terms.

34. $\dfrac{77}{121}$.   **35.** $\dfrac{4}{-7}$.   **36.** $\dfrac{-3}{-12}$.   **37.** $-\dfrac{78}{-26}$.   **38.** $\dfrac{4}{5} \cdot \dfrac{3}{8}$.

39. $(2\frac{1}{7}) \cdot \left(\dfrac{21}{7}\right)$.   **40.** $\dfrac{5}{6} \div \dfrac{15}{4}$.   **41.** $7(\frac{3}{8})$.   **42.** $\dfrac{8}{15} \div 2$.

43. $15 \div \dfrac{12}{7}$.   **44.** $\dfrac{3x}{4} \div 1\frac{3}{4}$.   **45.** $a \div \dfrac{2}{3}$.   **46.** $\dfrac{27a}{6ad}$.

47. $-\dfrac{5ad}{-a}$.   **48.** $(4\frac{5}{9}) \div \dfrac{x}{3}$.   **49.** $\dfrac{14}{15} \div 2a$.   **50.** $b \div \dfrac{ab}{6}$.

51. $\dfrac{\frac{2}{5}}{\frac{4}{15}}$.   **52.** $\dfrac{\frac{7}{3}}{\frac{4}{18}}$.   **53.** $\dfrac{-\frac{8}{9c}}{\frac{4d}{5c}}$.   **54.** $\dfrac{\frac{12a}{5b}}{\frac{8a}{15}}$.   **55.** $\dfrac{-\frac{3}{a}}{\frac{12}{ax}}$.

56. $\dfrac{\frac{15}{7}}{6}$.   **57.** $\dfrac{\frac{14}{5}}{10}$.   **58.** $\dfrac{\frac{3h}{k}}{6}$.   **59.** $\dfrac{\frac{4w}{9d}}{2w}$.

60. $6 \div \dfrac{3}{2}$.   **61.** $5 \div \dfrac{4}{7}$.   **62.** $5 \div \dfrac{3}{10}$.   **63.** $5d \div \dfrac{3d}{c}$.

64. $\frac{2}{3} \div c$.   **65.** $\frac{4}{5} \div 2b$.   **66.** $\frac{3}{8} \div \frac{1}{2}c$.   **67.** $\frac{8}{5} \div kd$.

68. Refer to Definition III on page 7, and recall that each real number a has *at least one* additive inverse. Represent any additive inverse of a by a' at present. Then, add a' to each side of (6) on page 7, and prove that $b = a'$, by use of Laws III and IV on page 6. Thus, prove that a has *just one* additive inverse.

8. Nonnegative integral exponents

By definition, if m is a positive integer, then $a^m = a \cdot a \cdot a \cdots a$, to m factors. We call a^m the __mth power__ of the __base__ a and m the __exponent__ of the power. By definition, $a^1 = a$. Hence, when the exponent is 1, we shall usually omit it. We call a^2 the __square__ of a and a^3 the __cube__ of a. Until later, any literal number symbol occurring in an exponent will represent a positive integer. The following *theorems* about exponents are called the *laws of exponents*.

I. *Law of exponents for multiplication:* $a^m a^n = a^{m+n}$.

Proof. 1. By definition, $\qquad a^m = a \cdot a \cdots a;$ *(m factors)*

$$a^n = a \cdot a \cdot a \cdots a. \qquad \textit{(n factors)}$$

2. Hence, $a^m a^n = (a \cdot a \cdots a)(a \cdot a \cdot a \cdots a) = a^{m+n}$. *[(m + n) factors a]*

II. *Law for finding a power of a power:* $(a^m)^n = a^{mn}$.

Proof. 1. $\qquad\qquad (a^m)^n = a^m \cdot a^m \cdots a^m;$ *(n factors a^m)*

(By Law I) $\qquad\qquad\quad = a^{m+m+\cdots+m}.$ *(n terms m)*

2. Since $(m + m + \cdots + m)$ to n terms is equal to mn, $(a^m)^n = a^{mn}$.

III. *Laws of exponents for division: if $a \neq 0$,*

$$\frac{a^m}{a^m} = 1; \qquad \frac{a^m}{a^n} = a^{m-n} \text{ (if } m > n\text{)}; \qquad \frac{a^m}{a^n} = \frac{1}{a^{n-m}} \text{ (if } n > m\text{)}.$$

Proof, for the case $n > m$. By the definition of a^m and a^n,

$$\frac{a^m}{a^n} = \frac{\overset{1 \cdot 1 \cdots 1}{\cancel{a} \cdot \cancel{a} \cdots \cancel{a}}}{\underset{1 \cdot 1 \cdots 1}{a \cdot a \cdots a \cdot \cancel{a} \cdot \cancel{a} \cdots \cancel{a}}}; \qquad \begin{matrix}\textit{(m factors)} \\ \textit{(n factors)}\end{matrix}$$

$$[(n - m) \text{ factors } a] \qquad = \frac{1}{a \cdot a \cdots a} = \frac{1}{a^{n-m}}.$$

IV. *Law for finding a power of a product:* $(ab)^n = a^n b^n$.

Law IV extends to products of any number of factors. Thus,

$$(abc)^n = a^n b^n c^n.$$

V. *Law for finding a power of a quotient:* $\qquad \left(\dfrac{a}{b}\right)^n = \dfrac{a^n}{b^n}.$

Illustration 1. $\quad \dfrac{a^5}{a^5} = 1. \qquad \dfrac{a^{10}}{a^2} = a^8. \qquad \dfrac{a^4}{a^7} = \dfrac{1}{a^3}.$

Illustration 2. $\quad \left(\dfrac{3}{2}\right)^4 = \dfrac{3^4}{2^4} = \dfrac{81}{16}. \qquad \left(\dfrac{4cd^2}{3x}\right)^2 = \dfrac{(4cd^2)^2}{(3x)^2} = \dfrac{16c^2d^4}{9x^2}.$

Illustration 3. $\quad \dfrac{-15a^3x^5}{10ax^9} = -\dfrac{3}{2} \cdot \dfrac{a^3}{a} \cdot \dfrac{x^5}{x^9} = -\dfrac{3a^{3-1}}{2x^{9-5}} = -\dfrac{3a^2}{2x^4}.$

The student may prove the preceding laws IV and V in the next exercise.

Suppose that we wish to use zero as an exponent, and that a^0 is to obey the law of exponents for multiplication. Then, if n is any positive integer, and $a \neq 0$,

$$a^0 a^n = a^{0+n} = a^n, \quad or \quad a^0 a^n = a^n, \quad so\ that \quad a^0 = \frac{a^n}{a^n} = 1.$$

Hence, if $a \neq 0$, we define a^0 as follows: $\qquad a^0 = 1.$ $\qquad$ (1)

Hereafter, until otherwise specified, any exponent which occurs will be a nonnegative integer.

9. Sets, variables, and constants

In referring to a *set* of things, we take **"set"** as an undefined term. Each object in a set will be called an **element** or a **member** of it. For any set A, we imply that we have the means to recognize whether or not any specified object belongs to A. A **subset** S of a set A is a set consisting of some (possibly all) of the members of A. If a set T has just n elements, where n is a nonnegative integer, we call T a *finite set*. If T is not a finite set, T is said to be an *infinite set*. Then, corresponding to any positive integer n, there exist *more than n elements* in T.

Illustration 1. We may refer to the set, T, of members of the United States Senate. The two senators from Illinois form a subset of T.

Illustration 2. The set, T, of all integers, and the set, R, of all real numbers are infinite sets. The set, P, of all positive integers is a subset of T, and of R. The set, A, of all rational numbers and the set, L, of all irrational numbers are infinite sets.

If S is a subset of the set T, we say that S is *included* in T, and write "$S \subset T$," read "*S is included in T.*" We have $T \subset T$. If all members of S are members of T, and if all members of T are also members of S, then S and T consist of the *same members* and we write $S = T$. Above, with $n = 0$, we implicitly introduced the so-called **empty set, or null set,** with *no* members, to be represented by $\emptyset$. We agree to say that $\emptyset$ is a subset of every set. If $S \subset T$ and $S \neq T$, we say that S is a **proper subset** of T. Then, there is *at least one element* of T which is *not* in S.

Illustration 3. In Illustration 2, $P \subset T$ and P is a proper subset of T. If H is the set $\{1, 2, 3, 4, 5, 6, 7, 8, 9, 10, 11, 12\}$, then the set $\{1, 2, 3\}$ is a proper subset of H.

Note 1. At this point in the text, the preceding introduction to sets is sufficient for our purposes. Added content about sets will be introduced where desirable.

A **variable** is a symbol, such as x, which may represent any particular element of a *non-empty set*, S, of elements (not necessarily numbers). We call S the **domain** of the variable x; each element of S is called a *value* of x, where value does not necessarily refer to a number. In this text, unless otherwise specified, the domain of any variable will be a set of numbers.

Illustration 4. We may use y to represent any person in the United States. Then, its population is the domain of the variable y.

Illustration 5. Let S be the set of all numbers $x < 2$. We could also define S as the set of all numbers $u < 2$. Thus, the letter, x or u, chosen as the symbol for an arbitrary number in S is of no importance.

In a given discussion, a **constant** is a number symbol representing a fixed number. A letter, such as b, which is a constant also may be called a variable whose domain consists of *just one number*. When a variable is mentioned, we shall infer that it is not a constant, unless otherwise specified.

In this text, except where otherwise implied, any literal number symbol, such as x, is understood to be a variable whose domain is the set of *all real numbers* x for which the expression involved has meaning.

Illustration 6. In the formula $A = \pi r^2$ for the area,* A, of a circle of radius r, if we think of all circles, then A and r are variables and π is a constant.

10. Monomials and polynomials

A **monomial** in certain variables x, y, z, $\cdots$ is defined as a nonzero constant, called the **coefficient** of the monomial, multiplied by powers of the variables where the exponents are nonnegative integers. If each exponent is zero, the monomial is merely a *constant, not zero*. A sum of monomials in the variables is called a **polynomial** in them. A polynomial is called a **binomial** or a **trinomial** according as the polynomial is the sum of two or of three monomials, respectively. The **degree of a monomial** in a set of variables is the sum of the exponents of their powers which are factors of the monomial. The **degree of a polynomial** in the variables is the degree of the monomial of *highest degree* in the polynomial. A polynomial of the *first degree* in any set of variables is said to be **linear** in them.

Illustration 1. Let a, b, and c be constants, not zero, and all other letters represent variables. Then $7ax^3y^2$ is a monomial of degree 5 in x and y, with the coefficient $7a$. The polynomial $5a + 3bxy^2 + 2cy^3z^2$ is of degree 5 in x, y, and z; if we decide temporarily to consider x and z also as constants, the polynomial then is said to be of degree 3 in y alone. Since $x^0 = 1$ if $x \neq 0$, any constant $b \neq 0$ can be thought of as being of degree zero in x, because $b = bx^0$. The polynomial $(3x + 5)$ is linear in x.

---

* Whenever we use a symbol for a concrete quantity, the symbol will represent a number which is the measure of the quantity in terms of an appropriate unit.

11. Square roots

If $r^2 = A$, we call r a **square root** of A. If A is positive, then A is found to have *two* square roots, one positive and one negative, with equal absolute values. The positive square root is denoted by the radical $+\sqrt{A}$ or simply $\sqrt{A}$, and the negative square root by $-\sqrt{A}$. Unless otherwise stated, we read "$\sqrt{A}$" as "*the square root of A,*" with the implicit understanding that we are referring to the *positive* square root of A.

Illustration 1. 16 has the square roots ± 4, read "plus and minus 4," because $4^2 = 16$ and $(-4)^2 = 16$. We have $4 = \sqrt{16}$ and $-4 = -\sqrt{16}$.

Any square root, r, of *zero* satisfies the condition $r^2 = 0$. Hence, one square root of 0 is 0 because $0^2 = 0$. If $r \neq 0$, then $r \cdot r \neq 0$, or $r^2 \neq 0$, because of (3) on page 12. Hence, the *only* square root of zero is 0, and we write $\sqrt{0} = 0$.

If $A < 0$, and r is a square root of A, then $r^2 = A$. But, if r is a real number not zero, then $r^2 > 0$, and hence *no real number r satisfies $r^2 = A$ when $A < 0$.* Or, *a negative number A has no real square root.* On page 33, we shall introduce a new variety of number, called an *imaginary number*, in order that a negative number A will have square roots, which will be imaginary numbers.

If $A > 0$, by the definition of $\sqrt{A}$ we have

$$(\sqrt{A})^2 = A. \tag{1}$$

If $x \neq 0$, then the two square roots of x^2 are $\pm x$ because $(x)^2 = x^2$ and $(-x)^2 = x^2$. Hence, if $x > 0$ then the *positive* square root of x^2 is $\sqrt{x^2} = x$. If $x < 0$, the *positive* square root of x^2 is

$$\sqrt{x^2} = -x, \qquad or \qquad \sqrt{x^2} = |x| \qquad (when\ x < 0).$$

Illustration 2. $\sqrt{(-5)^2} = \sqrt{25} = 5 = |-5|$. $(\sqrt{198})^2 = 198$.

In this text, to state that a *rational number** is a *perfect square* means that the number is *the square of a rational number*. A monomial, or a quotient of monomials, where each coefficient is a rational number, is said to be a **perfect square** if it is the square of some expression of the same type.

Illustration 3. $25a^2b^4$ is a perfect square, because $25a^2b^4 = (5ab^2)^2$. Also, $25a^2b^4/16x^6$ is a perfect square because

$$\left(\frac{5ab^2}{4x^3}\right)^2 = \frac{25a^2b^4}{16x^6}.$$

Until otherwise specified, in any radical $\sqrt{A}$, we shall suppose that the numerical coefficients are positive, that all literal number symbols represent positive numbers, and that A is a perfect square of one of the types previously

---

* Sometimes, "*perfect square*" is restricted to mean an *integer* which is a perfect square. In this text, in factoring, we shall sometimes allow coefficients in polynomials to be rational numbers, and hence our usage for "*perfect square*" will be convenient.

mentioned. In such a perfect square, any exponent for a literal number symbol is an *even* integer because, in squaring, exponents are multiplied by 2.

SUMMARY. *To find (or extract) the square root of a monomial which is a perfect square, divide each exponent by 2 and multiply by the square root of the numerical coefficient.*

Illustration 4. $\sqrt{16x^4y^8} = \sqrt{16}\sqrt{x^4y^8} = 4x^2y^4$, *because*

$$(4x^2y^4)^2 = 4^2x^4y^8 = 16x^4y^8.$$

We verify that, if N and D are positive,

$$\sqrt{\frac{N}{D}} = \frac{\sqrt{N}}{\sqrt{D}} \qquad because \qquad \left(\frac{\sqrt{N}}{\sqrt{D}}\right)^2 = \frac{(\sqrt{N})^2}{(\sqrt{D})^2} = \frac{N}{D}.$$

Hence, *to obtain the square root of a fraction, find the square root of the numerator and of the denominator, and divide.*

Illustration 5. $$\sqrt{\frac{100a^6}{9x^4y^8}} = \frac{\sqrt{100a^6}}{\sqrt{9x^4y^8}} = \frac{10a^3}{3x^2y^4}.$$

If H and K are positive,

$$\sqrt{HK} = \sqrt{H}\sqrt{K} \qquad because \qquad (\sqrt{H})^2(\sqrt{K})^2 = HK.$$

Hence, if a radicand A is a product of perfect square factors, we may find $\sqrt{A}$ by multiplying the square roots of the factors. The details of this method are similar to those met in the Summary above.

Illustration 6. $\sqrt{25x^2y^{10}} = \sqrt{25}\sqrt{x^2}\sqrt{y^{10}} = 5xy^5$.

$$\sqrt{\tfrac{4}{49}x^4w^6} = \sqrt{\tfrac{4}{49}}\sqrt{x^4}\sqrt{w^6} = \tfrac{2}{7}x^2w^3.$$

12. Multiplication and division of polynomials

To form the product of two polynomials, on account of the distributive law for multiplication we may multiply one of them by each term of the other and collect similar terms. Before multiplying, if many terms are involved, the polynomials should be arranged in ascending (or descending) powers of one variable.

Illustration 1. To multiply $(x^2 + 3x^3 - x - 2)(2x + 3)$:

$$
\begin{array}{l}
 3x^3 + x^2 - x - 2 \\
(Multiply) \underline{ 2x + 3} \\
 6x^4 + 2x^3 - 2x^2 - 4x \qquad (Multiplying\ by\ 2x) \\
 \underline{9x^3 + 3x^2 - 3x - 6} \qquad (Multiplying\ by\ 3) \\
(Add) 6x^4 + 11x^3 + x^2 - 7x - 6 = product.
\end{array}
$$

When we defined $b \div c$, its value was called the *quotient*. Sometimes, the word quotient refers to a *"partial quotient."* If the context does not make this meaning clear, the qualifying word *"partial"* should be used.

Illustration 2. We find $259 \div 17 = 15\frac{4}{17}$; the quotient is $15\frac{4}{17}$. Also, we might say that the *quotient* (meaning *partial quotient*) is 15 and the remainder is 4. Then,

$$259 = (17 \times 15) + 4. \tag{1}$$

At any stage of the usual long division process in arithmetic, or algebra, the remainder and partial quotient satisfy

$$\frac{\text{dividend}}{\text{divisor}} = \textbf{(partial quotient)} + \frac{\text{remainder}}{\text{divisor}}, \ or \tag{2}$$

$$\textbf{dividend} = \textbf{(partial quotient)(divisor)} + \textbf{remainder.} \tag{3}$$

Equation (1) is an illustration of (3), which will be called the *fundamental equation of division.*

To divide a polynomial by a single term, divide each term of the polynomial by the divisor and combine the results.

Illustration 3.
$$\frac{4a^2b^4 - 8a^2b - 2b^2}{-2ab^3} = \frac{4a^2b^4}{-2ab^3} - \frac{8a^2b}{-2ab^3} - \frac{2b^2}{-2ab^3}$$
$$= -2ab + \frac{4a}{b^2} + \frac{1}{ab}.$$

To divide one polynomial by another, first we arrange them in descending powers of some common variable.

EXAMPLE 1. Divide: $\qquad (4x^3 - 9x - 8x^2 + 7) \div (2x - 3)$.

Solution. Arrange the dividend in descending powers of x. Then, since $(4x^3 \div 2x) = 2x^2$, this is the first term of the quotient; etc.

$$
\begin{array}{l}
2x^2(2x - 3) \rightarrow (Subtract) \\
[(-2x^2) \div 2x] = -x. \\
-x(2x - 3) \rightarrow (Subtract) \\
[(-12x) \div 2x] = -6. \\
-6(2x - 3) \rightarrow (Subtract)
\end{array}
$$

$$
\require{enclose}
\begin{array}{r}
2x^2 - x - 6 \ (Quotient) \\
(Divisor)\ 2x - 3 \enclose{longdiv}{4x^3 - 8x^2 - 9x + 7}\ (Dividend) \\
4x^3 - 6x^2 \\
\hline
-2x^2 - 9x \\
-2x^2 + 3x \\
\hline
-12x + 7 \\
-12x + 18 \\
\hline
-11 \ (Remainder)
\end{array}
$$

Conclusion. From equation (2),

$$\frac{4x^3 - 8x^2 - 9x + 7}{2x - 3} = 2x^2 - x - 6 - \frac{11}{2x - 3}. \tag{4}$$

13. Products of binomials

In calculating products mentally, the following formulas are useful. They will be referred to as Types I–VI in this chapter, and should be verified.

Illustration 1. $(a + b)^2 = (a + b)(a + b)$
$$= a(a + b) + b(a + b) = a^2 + 2ab + b^2.$$

I. $a(x + y) = ax + ay.$

II. $(x + y)(x - y) = x^2 - y^2.$

III. $(a + b)^2 = a^2 + 2ab + b^2.$

IV. $(a - b)^2 = a^2 - 2ab + b^2.$

V. $(x + a)(x + b) = x^2 + (ax + bx) + ab.$

VI. $(ax + b)(cx + d) = acx^2 + (adx + bcx) + bd.$

Illustration 2.

$$(3x + 2y)^2 = (3x)^2 + 2(3x)(2y) + (2y)^2 = 9x^2 + 12xy + 4y^2.$$

In Types V and VI, we refer to $(ax + bx)$ and $(adx + bcx)$ as *the sum of the cross products.*

Illustration 3. $(2x - 7h)(3x + 2h) = 6x^2 - 17hx - 14h^2,$ because the sum of the cross products is $-21hx + 4hx$, or $-17hx$.

Illustration 4. $(x^2 - 2y)(x^2 + 2y)(x^4 + 4y^2)$
$$= [(x^2 - 2y)(x^2 + 2y)](x^4 + 4y^2) = (x^4 - 4y^2)(x^4 + 4y^2) \quad \text{(Type II)}$$
$$= (x^4)^2 - (4y^2)^2 = x^8 - 16y^4.$$

EXERCISE 2

If no literal number symbol is involved, compute the value of the expression. Otherwise, carry out the indicated operation by use of the laws of exponents.

1. $(-1)^6$.   2. $(-5)^3$.   3. $(\frac{1}{3})^4$.   4. $(\frac{2}{5})^3$.   5. $(\frac{3}{4})^4$.

6. $(2^2)^3$.   7. $(10^4)^3$.   8. $2^3 2^0$.   9. $[3(2^2)]^2$.   10. $-2(-5)^3$.

11. $a^5 a^4$.   12. $a^h a^{2k}$.   13. $u u^7$.   14. $(a^3)^5$.   15. $(a^2 x)^3$.

16. $\left(\dfrac{c}{d}\right)^3$.   17. $\left(\dfrac{h}{2}\right)^5$.   18. $\left(\dfrac{3}{a}\right)^4$.   19. $\left(\dfrac{x^2}{y^3}\right)^2$.   20. $\left(\dfrac{a^3}{b^2}\right)^4$.

21. $\dfrac{y^3}{y}$.   22. $\dfrac{a^2}{a^8}$.   23. $\dfrac{x}{x^4}$.   24. $\dfrac{5r}{25r^3}$.   25. $\dfrac{a^3 b^8}{ab^9}$.

26. $(-a^3 x^2)^4$.   27. $(-3x^2 y)^0$.   28. $(2wx^3)^4$.   29. $4y^2(2x^2 y)$.

30. $-8m^3 n(-2m^2 n^2)$.   31. $4hr^2(-2h^4 r)$.   32. $-6c^2 d^3(-2cd)$.

33. $(3 - 5x^2)(2 + 3x^2)$.   34. $(ay - 2z)(3ay + 4z)$.

35. $(2 + x)(3 - 4x - x^2)$.   36. $(c + 2)(2c - 5 - 3c^2)$.

37. $(x^n - 3y^k)(x^{2n} + 3x^n y^k + 9y^{2k})$.

Find the two square roots of the number, or the specified root, by inspection.

38. 49. **39.** 121. **40.** $\frac{25}{9}$. **41.** 100. **42.** 196.

43. $\sqrt{\frac{49}{64}}$. **44.** $\sqrt{16h^2}$. **45.** $\sqrt{49z^6}$. **46.** $\sqrt{9x^2y^4}$.

47. $\sqrt{\frac{64}{w^6}}$. **48.** $\sqrt{\frac{121}{y^6}}$. **49.** $\sqrt{\frac{81a^2}{y^4z^2}}$. **50.** $\sqrt{\frac{b^2x^4}{81y^6}}$.

51. Square each quantity: $\sqrt{37x}$; $\sqrt{142a^5}$; $\sqrt{659z^3}$.

Express as a sum of fractions in lowest terms.

52. $(6 - 2uv + 18u^3v^3) \div 12u^4v$. **53.** $(x^2y^5 - 3xy^3 + 2x^2y^4) \div 6x^3y^6$.

Divide, and summarize as in (4) on page 23.

54. $(x^3 + 4x^2 + x - 6) \div (x + 2)$. **55.** $(4x^3 - 8x^2 + 13x - 5) \div (2x - 1)$.

56. $(8y^3 - 18y^2 - 6 + 11y) \div (4y^2 - 3y + 2)$.

57. $(x^4 - 4x^3 + 3x^2 - 4x + 12) \div (x - 3)$.

Expand and collect terms, performing as much of the work as possible mentally.

58. $(b - k)(b + k)$. **59.** $(h + k)^2$. **60.** $(c + 4)(c - 4)$.

61. $(a - 3x)(a + 3x)$. **62.** $(2x - y)^2$. **63.** $(8 + x)(3 - x)$.

64. $(5 - 2y)(5 + 2y)$. **65.** $(3 + 2r)(3 - 5r)$.

66. $(2c + x)^2$. **67.** $(3x - 5)^2$. **68.** $(x^2 - y)^2$. **69.** $(3x + y^3)^2$.

70. $[3(2a + b)]^2$. **71.** $[x(2 + x)]^2$. **72.** $[2(a - 3b)]^2$.

73. $(x^2 - 2y)(x^2 + 2y)(x^4 + 4y^2)$. **74.** $[(x + y) + 2]^2$.

75. $[2 + (a + b)]^2$. **76.** $[(x + y) - 3][(x + y) + 3]$.

77. $(a + w + 4)(a + w - 4)$. **78.** $(a + b - x)(a + b + x)$.

79. Expand $(x + y + z)^2$ and state the result in words.

80. Prove Laws IV and V on page 18.

81. If T represents the set $\{1, 2, 3, 4\}$, write out all proper nonempty subsets of T.

14. Terminology about factoring

In any reference to *factors* of a polynomial, two possible sets of factors will be considered essentially the same if those of one set differ at most in signs from those of the other set.

A positive integer is said to be *prime* if it is *greater than* 1 and has no integer as a factor except itself or 1.

Illustration 1. 2, 3, 5, 7, 11, etc., are prime numbers.

In our discussion of factoring, any expression involving a variable, or any factor mentioned, will be a polynomial with integers as coefficients. Such an expression will be called *prime* if it has no factor of similar type except itself or 1. No simple rule can be stated for determining whether or not an expression is prime. *To factor a polynomial* will mean to express it as a product of positive integral powers of distinct *prime* factors.

Illustration 2. $4x^4 - 4b^2x^2 = 4x^2(x^2 - b^2) = 4x^2(x - b)(x + b)$.

Illustration 3.   We shall say that $(x - y)$ is prime although

$$x - y = (\sqrt{x} + \sqrt{y})(\sqrt{x} - \sqrt{y}),$$

because these factors are not polynomials. Other prime polynomials are $(x + y)$, $(x^2 + y^2)$, $(x^2 + xy + y^2)$, and $(x^2 - xy + y^2)$.

Each of Types I–IV of Section 13 on page 24 becomes a formula for factoring when read *from right to left*. Thus, from Type I with three terms, we obtain

I. $$ax + ay + az = a(x + y + z),$$

which is useful in removing a common factor from the terms of a polynomial. The student should read II, III, and IV on page 24 from right to left, in words.

Illustration 4.   From II, *the difference of two squares is equal to the product of the sum and the difference of their square roots.* Thus,

$$x^2 - 9 = (x - 3)(x + 3).$$

Illustration 5.   The right-hand sides of III and IV are *perfect square trinomials.* In such a trinomial, *two terms are perfect squares and the third term is plus (or minus) twice the product of the square roots of the other terms.*

Illustration 6.   From III, $9x^2 + 24xz + 16z^2 = (3x + 4z)^2$.

Certain trinomials of the form* $gx^2 + hx + k$ can be factored by a trial and error method based on Types V and VI on page 24.

EXAMPLE 1.   Factor: $15x^2 + 2x - 8$.

Solution.   1. We wish to find a, b, c, and d so that

$$(ax + b)(cx + d) = acx^2 + (ad + bc)x + bd = 15x^2 + 2x - 8.$$

2. Hence, $ac = 15$, $bd = -8$, and the sum of the cross products is $2x$. After various unsatisfactory trials, we finally select $a = 3$, $c = 5$, $b = -2$, and $d = 4$, and verify that

$$15x^2 + 2x - 8 = (3x - 2)(5x + 4).$$

15. Cube of a binomial

We verify that

$$(x + y)^3 = x^3 + 3x^2y + 3xy^2 + y^3; \tag{1}$$
$$(x - y)^3 = x^3 - 3x^2y + 3xy^2 - y^3. \tag{2}$$

---

* If g, h, and k were chosen at random, without a common factor, the trinomial would probably be prime. Later, we shall discuss a condition which g, h, and k satisfy when and only when the trinomial is *not* prime.

Illustration 1. From (1), with $x = 2a$ and $y = b$,
$$(2a + b)^3 = (2a)^3 + 3(2a)^2(b) + 3(2a)(b)^2 + b^3$$
$$= 8a^3 + 12a^2b + 6ab^2 + b^3.$$

Memorize

16. The sum and the difference of two like powers

By multiplication on the right in (1) and (2) below, we verify the factors of the sum, and of the difference, of two cubes.

$$a^3 - b^3 = (a - b)(a^2 + ab + b^2); \qquad (1)$$
$$a^3 + b^3 = (a + b)(a^2 - ab + b^2). \qquad (2)$$

Illustration 1. By use of (1), read from right to left, with $b = 3$,
$$(a - 3)(a^2 + 3a + 9) = a^3 - 3^3 = a^3 - 27.$$

Illustration 2. From (2) with $a = 3x$ and $b = 2y$,
$$27x^3 + 8y^3 = (3x)^3 + (2y)^3$$
$$= (3x + 2y)(9x^2 - 6xy + 4y^2).$$

Illustration 3. $\qquad y^6 - 19y^3 - 216 = (y^3 - 27)(y^3 + 8)$
$$= (y - 3)(y^2 + 3y + 9)(y + 2)(y^2 - 2y + 4).$$

A monomial, whose coefficient is a rational number, is said to be a **perfect nth power** if it is the nth power of a monomial of the same type. In a perfect nth power, each exponent has n as a factor because, in raising a monomial to the nth power, each original exponent is multiplied by n.

Illustration 4. $\qquad 8a^6b^6$ *is a perfect cube,* $(2a^2b^2)^3$.

In factoring a sum $a^n \pm b^n$, where a^n and b^n are perfect nth powers, we start as in (3) and (4) below, when they apply.

$$\begin{cases} \textit{If } n \textit{ is even, commence factoring } (a^n - b^n) \textit{ by} \\ \textit{recognizing it as the difference of two squares.} \end{cases} \qquad (3)$$

Illustration 5. $\qquad x^6 - y^6 = (x^3)^2 - (y^3)^2 = (x^3 - y^3)(x^3 + y^3)$
$$= (x - y)(x^2 + xy + y^2)(x + y)(x^2 - xy + y^2).$$

$$\begin{cases} \textit{If } n \textit{ is odd and has 3 as a factor, commence factoring} \\ (a^n \pm b^n) \textit{ as a sum or a difference of two cubes.} \end{cases} \qquad (4)$$

Illustration 6. $x^9 + y^9 = (x^3)^3 + (y^3)^3 = (x^3 + y^3)(x^6 - x^3y^3 + y^6)$
$$= (x + y)(x^2 - xy + y^2)(x^6 - x^3y^3 + y^6).$$

We have met special cases of the following facts (A)–(E). Any special case can be verified by dividing $(a^n \pm b^n)$ by the indicated linear factor, $(a + b)$ or $(a - b)$. General proofs of the facts will be met in Problem 18 on page 202. Factors obtained by (A)–(E) are not necessarily prime. Hence, **the student should continue to emphasize (3) and (4) in place of (A)–(E).**

Memorize

A. *For every positive integer* n, $(a^n - b^n)$ *has* $(a - b)$ *as a factor. In other words,* $(a^n - b^n)$ *is exactly divisible by* $(a - b)$; *in the quotient, all coefficients are* $+1$, *and the sum of the exponents of* a *and* b *is* $(n - 1)$ *in each term.*

Illustration 7. $a^4 - b^4 = (a - b)(a^3 + a^2b + ab^2 + b^3)$.

FORGET IT!

B. *If* n *is even,* $(a^n - b^n)$ *has* $(a + b)$ *as a factor.*

Illustration 8. $a^4 - b^4 = (a + b)(a^3 - a^2b + ab^2 - b^3)$.

C. *If* n *is odd,* $(a^n + b^n)$ *has* $(a + b)$ *as a factor.*

Illustration 9. $a^3 + b^3 = (a + b)(a^2 - ab + b^2)$.

D. *If* n *is even,* $(a^n + b^n)$ *does not have either* $(a + b)$ *or* $(a - b)$ *as a factor.*

Illustration 10. $(a^2 + b^2)$ *and* $(a^4 + b^4)$ *are prime.* $(a^6 + b^6)$ *is not prime, but does not have either* $(a + b)$ *or* $(a - b)$ *as a factor:*

$$a^6 + b^6 = (a^2 + b^2)(a^4 - a^2b^2 + b^4).$$

E. *When* $(a^n + b^n)$ *or* $(a^n - b^n)$ *has* $(a + b)$ *as a factor and is divided by* $(a + b)$, *the coefficients in the quotient are alternately* $+1$ *and* -1; *the sum of the exponents of* a *and* b *is* $(n - 1)$ *in each term of the quotient.*

EXERCISE 3

Factor each polynomial which is not prime. If fractions occur, leave the factors in the form which arises most naturally by use of the standard methods.

1. $-ax + bx$.
2. $3ab + 2a - 5a^2$.
3. $-4at + t^2 - ct^3$.
4. $4a^2 - 9b^2$.
5. $1 - 25x^2$.
6. $9z^2 - \frac{1}{4}$.
7. $\frac{1}{9} - w^2$.
8. $25w^2 - c^2d^2$.
9. $36a^2b^2 - 64x^2$.
10. $25 - 10x + x^2$.
11. $a^2 + 4a + 4$.
12. $y^2 - 6y + 9$.
13. $d^2 + 2dy + y^2$.
14. $u^2 - 8u + 16$.
15. $a^2 - 14ab + 49b^2$.
16. $15 - 8x + x^2$.
17. $12 - 7y + y^2$.
18. $z^2 - 5z + 6$.
19. $27 + 6w - w^2$.
20. $4 - 3y - y^2$.
21. $16 - 6a - a^2$.
22. $2x^2 + 3xy - 5y^2$.
23. $3a^2 + 8a + 5$.
24. $2x^2 + 7xy + 3y^2$.
25. $5a^2 + 14ab + 9b^2$.
26. $3x^2 + 7ax - 6a^2$.
27. $3x^2 + 5xy + 2y^2$.
28. $8w^2 + 14wz - 15z^2$.
29. $8x^4 - 10x^3 + 3x^2$.
30. $2x^4 - x^3 - 6x^2$.
31. $3h(w - z) - (w - z)$.
32. $2x(h - 2k) + 3hy - 6ky$.
33. $4hx - 4bh - 8cx + 8bc$.
34. $3bw - 3bz - 4aw + 4az$.
35. $(x^3 - 2x^2) - (x - 2)$.
36. $ax^2 + bx^2 + ad^2 + bd^2$.
37. $8a^2c - 18c^3$.
38. $x^4 - \frac{1}{16}y^4$.
39. $81c^4 - 16d^4$.
40. $4a^2 + 12a + 9 - 25x^2$.
41. $y^2 + 2yz + z^2 - 4x^2$.
42. $9y^2 - (4x^2 + 20x + 25)$.
43. $9w^2 - 4a^2 - 4ab - b^2$.
44. $d^3 - y^3$.
45. $z^3 + 1000$.
46. $1 - v^3$.
47. $216x^3 - y^3z^3$.

48. $h^3 + z^3$. **49.** $8x^3 - 125y^3$. **50.** $16 + x^4$. **51.** $x^3 - 343y^3$.
52. $a^5 - c^5$. **53.** $y^4 - 81$. **54.** $h^9 + k^9$. **55.** $a^3 - 27x^6$.
56. $4x^4 + 1$. **57.** $a^6 - 64$. **58.** $u^{3h} + v^3$. **59.** $16x^4 - y^8$.

Expand by use of formulas from Sections 15 and 16.

60. $(u - v)(u^2 + uv + v^2)$. **61.** $(1 - 3x)(1 + 3x + 9x^2)$.
62. $(c + d)^3$. **63.** $(5 - y)^3$. **64.** $(y - 3x)^3$. **65.** $(c + 3b^2)^3$.
66. $(2 + y)^3$. **67.** $(2x + w)^3$. **68.** $(a - b^2)^3$. **69.** $(c - 6z^3)^3$.

Divide by long division, and check by Section 16.

70. $\dfrac{a^3 - h^3}{a - h}$. **71.** $\dfrac{x^3 + 8y^3}{x + 2y}$. **72.** $\dfrac{x^4 - y^4}{x - y}$. **73.** $\dfrac{x^5 + y^5}{x + y}$.

17. Fractions in lowest terms

In the remainder of this chapter, in any fraction which is mentioned, the numerator and denominator will be polynomials in one or more variables. To reduce such a fraction to lowest terms, the numerator and denominator should be factored, if possible, and then should be divided by each common factor.

Illustration 1. After factoring below, the denominator was multiplied by -1, with a compensating multiplication of the fraction by -1, to show identical factors. Then, the numerator and denominator were divided by the common factor, where use was made of result I on page 15.

$$\frac{x^2 - 9}{12 + 2x - 2x^2} = \frac{(x - 3)(x + 3)}{2(3 - x)(2 + x)} = -\frac{(x - 3)(x + 3)}{2(x - 3)(2 + x)} = -\frac{x + 3}{2(x + 2)}.$$

18. Addition of fractions

Consider a sum of fractions with a common denominator. To express such a sum as a single fraction, we first form the sum of the numerators, *each enclosed within parentheses preceded by the sign at the left of its fraction*, and divide by the common denominator. Then, we simplify the numerator.

Illustration 1. $\quad \dfrac{5 - 2x}{3x^2 + 5} - \dfrac{1 - 4x}{3x^2 + 5} - \dfrac{6}{3x^2 + 5}$

$$= \frac{5 - 2x - (1 - 4x) - 6}{3x^2 + 5} = \frac{5 - 2x - 1 + 4x - 6}{3x^2 + 5} = \frac{2x - 2}{3x^2 + 5}.$$

The **lowest common multiple (LCM)** of two or more polynomials is defined as the polynomial of lowest degree in the variables, with coefficients of the smallest absolute values, which has each polynomial as a factor. In remarks about a LCM, we shall assume that the coefficients are integers in all polynomials. To find a LCM, first factor the given polynomials. Two results for a LCM which differ only in sign will be considered essentially identical.

Illustration 2. The LCM of

$$2(3 - x)(3 + x), \quad 4(x - 3)(x - 1), \quad and \quad 3(x - 3)^2$$

is $4 \cdot 3(x - 3)^2(x + 3)(x - 1)$. We did not consider $(3 - x)$ and $(x - 3)$ essentially distinct, because $x - 3 = -(3 - x)$.

The **lowest common denominator (LCD)** of two or more fractions is defined as the LCM *of their denominators*. Now, consider a sum of fractions, and perhaps a polynomial, which we shall think of as a fraction with denominator 1. To express such a sum as a single fraction, we first alter the given fractions to new forms where each denominator is the LCD of the given fractions, as follows, and then form the sum of the new fractions.

To find the LCD, factor each denominator and form the product of all different prime factors, giving to each factor the largest exponent with which it appears in any denominator.

For each fraction, divide the LCD by the denominator and then multiply both numerator and denominator by the resulting quotient, to express the fraction as an equal one having the LCD.

As a partial check on the determination of a LCD, notice that it should have each given denominator as a factor.

Illustration 3. In the following addition, we multiply by -1 in the second denominator to exhibit identical variable factors in denominators:

$$\frac{5}{9c - 6d} + \frac{7}{4d - 6c} = \frac{5}{3(3c - 2d)} - \frac{7}{6c - 4d} = \frac{5}{3(3c - 2d)} - \frac{7}{2(3c - 2d)}$$

$$= \frac{(5 \cdot 2) - (7 \cdot 3)}{3 \cdot 2(3c - 2d)} = -\frac{11}{6(3c - 2d)}.$$

EXAMPLE 1. Express as a single fraction: $\dfrac{4x}{x^2 - 9} - \dfrac{3x}{x^2 + x - 6}.$

Solution. 1. $x^2 - 9 = (x - 3)(x + 3)$; $x^2 + x - 6 = (x + 3)(x - 2)$. Hence, LCD $= (x - 3)(x + 3)(x - 2)$.

2. In the 1st fraction, $\qquad\qquad$ LCD $\div (x^2 - 9) = x - 2.$

3. In the 2d fraction, $\qquad\qquad$ LCD $\div (x^2 + x - 6) = x - 3.$

4. Multiply both numerator and denominator by $(x - 2)$ and by $(x - 3)$, respectively, in the corresponding fractions:

$$\frac{4x}{x^2 - 9} - \frac{3x}{x^2 + x - 6}$$

$$= \frac{4x(x - 2)}{(x - 3)(x + 3)(x - 2)} - \frac{3x(x - 3)}{(x - 3)(x + 3)(x - 2)}$$

$$= \frac{4x(x - 2) - 3x(x - 3)}{(x - 3)(x + 3)(x - 2)} = \frac{x^2 + x}{(x - 3)(x + 3)(x - 2)}.$$

Note 1. The **highest common factor (HCF)** of two or more polynomials is the polynomial of highest degree, with largest integral coefficients, which is a factor of each of the given polynomials. To find a HCF, we first factor the polynomials. Thus, the HCF of

$$6(x-1)^2(x-3)(x+2) \quad and \quad 15(x-1)(x-3)^3(x+2)^2$$

is $3(x-1)(x-3)(x+2)$.

19. Multiplication and division of fractions

A **simple fraction** is one without any fraction in its numerator or denominator. Before multiplying simple fractions, or dividing one simple fraction by another, it is desirable to factor the numerators and denominators, if possible. We recall (2) of page 15 and (5) of page 16 in multiplying fractions, or in dividing one fraction by another. A fraction is called a **complex fraction** if one or more fractions occur in the numerator and denominator of the given fraction.

Illustration 1. $\dfrac{\dfrac{2x^2+7x-15}{2x^2-3x-14}}{\dfrac{8x-12}{2x^2-19x+42}} = \dfrac{2x^2+7x-15}{2x^2-3x-14} \cdot \dfrac{2x^2-19x+42}{8x-12}$

$$= \frac{(2x-3)(x+5)}{(2x-7)(x+2)} \cdot \frac{(2x-7)(x-6)}{4(2x-3)} = \frac{(x+5)(x-6)}{4(x+2)} \cdot$$

Illustration 2. $\dfrac{2x-4}{x^2-5} \div (x-2) = \dfrac{2x-4}{x^2-5} \div \dfrac{x-2}{1}$

$$= \frac{2(x-2)}{x^2-5} \cdot \frac{1}{x-2} = \frac{2}{x^2-5} \cdot$$

Suppose that an expression is the sum of a polynomial and one or more fractions. Then, the sum should be expressed as a single fraction before multiplying or dividing by the expression, or simplifying any fraction where the expression is the numerator or denominator.

Illustration 3. $\dfrac{\dfrac{a-a^2}{a^2-1}}{\dfrac{a}{a+1}-a} = \dfrac{\dfrac{a-a^2}{a^2-1}}{\dfrac{a-a(a+1)}{a+1}} = -\dfrac{\dfrac{a-a^2}{a^2-1}}{\dfrac{a^2}{a+1}}$

$$= -\frac{a(1-a)}{(a-1)(a+1)} \cdot \frac{a+1}{a^2} = -\frac{1-a}{a(a-1)} = \frac{1}{a} \cdot$$

The **reciprocal** of a number H is defined as $1/H$.

Illustration 4. The reciprocal of 3 is $\frac{1}{3}$; of $\frac{3}{4}$ is $1 \div \frac{3}{4} = \frac{4}{3}$. *The reciprocal of a fraction is the fraction inverted, because*

$$1 \div \frac{a}{b} = 1 \cdot \frac{b}{a} = \frac{b}{a} \cdot$$

Illustration 5. To *divide* a number N by H is equivalent to *multiplying by the reciprocal* of H, because

$$\frac{N}{H} = N \cdot \frac{1}{H}.$$

EXERCISE 4

Obtain the result as a simple fraction in lowest terms.

1. $\dfrac{2x-3}{5} - \dfrac{3-5x}{35}.$

2. $\dfrac{3-2x}{4} - \dfrac{4-5x}{6}.$

3. $3u - \dfrac{3-4u}{12}.$

4. $\dfrac{3}{2x^2} - \dfrac{5}{7xy^3}.$

5. $\dfrac{4}{3a^2} - \dfrac{5y-1}{5ab}.$

6. $\dfrac{3}{2xy} - \dfrac{4x-y}{4x^2y^3}.$

7. $\dfrac{2-x}{3x^2y} - \dfrac{4-3y}{2xy^2}.$

8. $\dfrac{3}{2(a-b)} - \dfrac{2}{5(a-b)}.$

9. $\dfrac{3}{7x+7y} - \dfrac{2}{5(x+y)}.$

10. $\dfrac{4}{3x-3y} - \dfrac{2}{5x-5y}.$

11. $-\dfrac{2x-3}{6x+6} - \dfrac{5}{3x}.$

12. $\dfrac{3}{2x-4y} - \dfrac{5}{x^2-4y^2}.$

13. $\dfrac{3x}{2x+2y} + \dfrac{4}{x^2-y^2}.$

14. $\dfrac{5}{4x-x^2} + \dfrac{10}{3x^2-48}.$

15. $\dfrac{5x}{x+4} - \dfrac{4x^2+2x-1}{x^2+x-12}.$

16. $\dfrac{2x+1}{x^2+4x-60} - \dfrac{2}{x-6}.$

17. $\dfrac{1}{3n-3} - \dfrac{n+6}{n^2+3n-4}.$

18. $\dfrac{a-2}{a^2-16} - \dfrac{a+2}{a^2+8a+16}.$

19. $\dfrac{3x-5x^2}{4x^2+12x+9} - \dfrac{x-3}{4x+6}.$

20. $\dfrac{2a-3}{2a^2-18} - \dfrac{4}{3a^2-11a+6}.$

21. $\dfrac{4x^2+1}{4x^2-1} - \dfrac{1+2x}{2x-1} - \dfrac{5x+3}{2x+1}.$

22. $\dfrac{x^2+5}{8x^3-27} - \dfrac{3x+2}{2x-3}.$

23. Find the reciprocal of 5; of $-\frac{4}{7}$; of $3c/d$.

24. $\dfrac{2a-2x}{3c+9d} \cdot \dfrac{c+3d}{a-x}.$

25. $(y^2-9) \cdot \dfrac{y+2}{y^2+3y}.$

26. $\dfrac{2a-ab}{4d-ad} \cdot \dfrac{4k-ak}{2c-bc}.$

27. $\dfrac{2x-2y}{6x+3y} \cdot \dfrac{4x^2-y^2}{(x-y)^2}.$

28. $\dfrac{h^2-9}{3x-3y} \cdot \dfrac{(x^2-y^2)}{h^2-6h+9}.$

29. $\dfrac{\dfrac{x^2-25y^2}{2x-6}}{\dfrac{x^2+5xy}{x^2-9}}.$

30. $\dfrac{\dfrac{u^2-v^2}{(a+3b)^2}}{\dfrac{cu-cv}{a^2+3ab}}.$

31. $\dfrac{\dfrac{2}{y}-\dfrac{3}{x}}{\dfrac{4}{y^2}-\dfrac{9}{x^2}}.$

32. $\dfrac{1-\dfrac{3}{ab}}{b^2-\dfrac{9}{a^2}}.$

33. $\dfrac{3x-bx}{5h-hx} \div \dfrac{3c-bc}{4w-wx}.$

34. $\dfrac{6x-4a}{4x^2-9y^2} \div \dfrac{2a-3x}{2x+3y}.$

35. $\dfrac{25-9x^2}{x+3} \div (5x-3x^2).$

36. $\dfrac{a^2+2ab+b^2}{2a-3b} \div (b^2-a^2).$

37. $\dfrac{\dfrac{3x-1}{9x^2-1}}{4x+5}$. 38. $\dfrac{\dfrac{ax+bx}{b^2-a^2}}{3x}$. 39. $\dfrac{\dfrac{x^2-16}{x^2-4x}}{x-1}$. 40. $\dfrac{\dfrac{h^2-x^2}{ch-cx}}{5w}$.

41. $\dfrac{100-\dfrac{9}{a^2b^2}}{2a+\dfrac{3}{5b}}$. 42. $\dfrac{1-\dfrac{4a}{2a+b}}{1-\dfrac{2a}{2a+b}}$. 43. $\dfrac{\dfrac{1}{4x}-\dfrac{x^2}{4}}{\dfrac{1}{2x}-\dfrac{x}{2}}$. 44. $\dfrac{ab-\dfrac{8}{a^2b^2}}{a^2-\dfrac{4}{b^2}}$.

45. $(b^2-a^2) \div \dfrac{a^2+2ab+b^2}{2a-3b}$. 46. $(ax+ay^2) \div \dfrac{x^2+2xy^2+y^4}{x-y^2}$.

20. Elementary foundation for complex numbers

Suppose that P is positive. Then, by definition, to state that *"r is a square root of the negative number $-P$"* means that $r^2 = -P$. But, r^2 is positive or zero if r is any real number, and hence $-P$ can have *no real number r as a square root.* In particular, -1 has no real square root. Therefore, we shall expand the system, R, of real numbers by introducing numbers of a new type which will serve as square roots of negative numbers, and also will be available for other important purposes.

Let $\sqrt{-1}$ be introduced as a symbol for a *new number*, to be called an *imaginary number*, and also to be represented by i. Let T be a new system of numbers consisting of *all numbers of the system, R, of real numbers together with i.* In T, we define the product of i by itself to be a real number as follows, in various notations:

$$\sqrt{-1}\sqrt{-1} = -1, \quad or \quad i \cdot i = -1, \quad or \quad i^2 = -1.$$

Thus, with T as the number system, -1 has the square root i. If a and b are any real numbers, we join to T the new number bi, to represent the *product* of b and i, and the new number $(a + bi)$ to represent the *sum* of a and bi. This expansion of T produces a system C which may be described as the *set of all numbers $(a + bi)$, where a and b are real.* We call C the system of **complex numbers.***

For any real numbers (a, b), the number $(a + bi)$ is called a **complex number,** whose **real part** is a and **imaginary part** is b. If $a = 0$ and $b \neq 0$, we call $(a + bi)$ an **imaginary number.** Any real number a is considered, now, as a complex number where the imaginary part is zero, and we permit writing $a + 0i = a$. In particular, $0 + 0i = 0$. Also, we write $(0 + bi)$ simply as bi when $b \neq 0$. We shall call i the **imaginary unit.**

Illustration 1. $(2 - 3i)$ is a complex number. The real number 6 can be thought of as $(6 + 0i)$. The number $(0 + 5i)$, or simply $5i$, is an imaginary number. We may refer to $(2 - 3i)$ also as a **non-real** number.

---

* The type of foundation for C presented in this section was chosen in the interest of brevity in the preliminary review for the course. A different foundation will be presented in Chapter 7.

In the complex number system C, addition and multiplication are *defined* by the following statements, where all letters except i represent real numbers.

$$(a + bi) + (c + di) = (a + c) + (b + d)i. \tag{1}$$

$$(a + bi)(c + di) = (ac - bd) + (bc + ad)i. \tag{2}$$

Division for complex numbers will not be introduced until they are considered again in Chapter 7. If N is a complex number, we agree that $+N$ will mean $(+1) \cdot N$, and $-N$ will mean $(-1) \cdot N$.

By use of (1), it is very simple to show that addition for complex numbers obeys the commutative and associative Laws III and IV of page 6, as restated for complex numbers. By use of (1) and (2), moderate details prove that multiplication obeys Laws I and II of page 6, and multiplication and addition obey Law V of page 6. The proofs will be outlined, for performance by the student in the next exercise. Proofs of Laws I–V will be met again in Chapter 7 from a different viewpoint. With the assumption that it has been proved that Laws I–V are obeyed in C, there no longer is any reason for memorizing the right-hand sides of (1) and (2). Thus, (1) is obtained by removing parentheses on the left and collecting real and imaginary parts. By use of the distributive Law V, and the associative Law II for multiplication, we obtain the right-hand side of (2) when we use $i^2 = -1$. Thus,

$$(a + bi)(c + di) = ac + adi + bci + bdi^2 \tag{3}$$
$$= (ac - bd) + (ad + bc)i.$$

Hence, in multiplying particular complex numbers, we may proceed directly as in (3), without referring to (2).

Illustration 2. $\qquad (-5i)^2 = (-5i)(-5i) = 25i^2 = -25.$

From (2), $\quad (3 + 5i)(2 - 6i) = (6 + 30) + (10 - 18)i = 36 - 8i.$

Or, $\quad (3 + 5i)(2 - 6i) = 6 - 18i + 10i - 30i^2 = 36 - 8i.$

Illustration 3. The number $-i$ as well as i is a square root of -1 because

$$(-i)^2 = [(-1) \cdot i]^2 = (-1)^2 i^2 = i^2 = -1.$$

If P is any positive number, we verify that

$$(i\sqrt{P})^2 = i^2(P) = (-1) \cdot P = -P; \quad (-i\sqrt{P})^2 = -P.$$

Hence, $-P$ has the two square roots $\pm i\sqrt{P}$. Hereafter, we shall let $\sqrt{-P}$, or $(-P)^{\frac{1}{2}}$, represent the particular square root $i\sqrt{P}$. Then, $-P$ has the two square roots $\pm\sqrt{-P}$, or $\pm i\sqrt{P}$. Thus, we should proceed as follows in dealing with the square root of a negative number:

$$\sqrt{-P} = \sqrt{(-1)P} = \sqrt{-1}\sqrt{P} = i\sqrt{P}.$$

Illustration 4. The square roots of -5 are $\pm i\sqrt{5}$.

Illustration 5. $\qquad \sqrt{-4}\sqrt{-9} = (i\sqrt{4})(i\sqrt{9}) = i^2 \cdot 6 = -6.$

Illustration 6. By use of the associative Law II of page 6 for multiplication, i^n has a well-defined meaning for every positive integer n, and positive integral powers of i obey the law of exponents in multiplication. Thus, since $i^2 = -1$,

$$i^3 = i^2 \cdot i = (-1)i = -i; \quad i^4 = i^2 i^2 = (-1)^2 = +1;$$
$$i^9 = i^4 \cdot i^4 \cdot i = (+1)^2 \cdot i = i.$$

We notice that any positive integral power of i is equal to either i, $-i$, 1, or -1. Also, if $n > 4$, then i^n can be found quickly by recalling that $i^4 = 1$.

Note 1. Unless otherwise stated, any literal number symbol will represent a real number, except that hereafter i always will represent $\sqrt{-1}$.

21. Roots of any order

We call R a *square root* of A if $R^2 = A$ and a *cube root* of A if $R^3 = A$. If n is any positive integer,

$$\textbf{R is an \textit{n}th root of A if } R^n = A. \tag{1}$$

Illustration 1. The only nth root of 0 is 0. 2 is a 5th root of 32 because $2^5 = 32$. -3 is a cube root of -27.

The following facts will be proved in Chapter 7.

1. *Every real number A, not zero, has just n distinct nth roots, some or all of which may be non-real numbers.*

2. *If n is* **even,** *every positive number A has just* **two** *real nth roots, one positive and one negative, with equal absolute values.*

3. *If n is* **odd,** *every real number A has just* **one** *real nth root, which is positive when A is positive and negative when A is negative.*

4. *If n is* **even** *and A is* **negative, all** *nth roots of A are non-real numbers.*

If A is *positive,* its *positive* nth root is called the **principal nth root** of A. If A is *negative* and n is *odd,* the *negative* nth root of A is called its *principal nth root.* If A is *zero,* its only nth root, 0, is called the *principal nth root of A.*

Illustration 2. The real 4th roots of 81 are ± 3, and $+3$ is the principal 4th root. The principal cube root of $+125$ is $+5$, and of -125 is -5. All 4th roots of -16 are non-real numbers.

Illustration 3. The real cube root of 8 is 2. On page 196, it will be shown that 8 also has the non-real cube roots $(-1 \pm \sqrt{-3})$, or $(-1 \pm i\sqrt{3})$.

The **radical** $\sqrt[n]{A}$, which we read "*the nth root of A,*" is used to denote the *principal nth root* of A if it has a real nth root, and to denote any convenient nth root of A if all nth roots are non-real. In $\sqrt[n]{A}$, the positive integer n is called the **index** or **order** of the radical, and A is called its **radicand.** When $n = 2$, we omit writing the index and use $\sqrt{A}$ instead of $\sqrt[2]{A}$.

I. $\sqrt[n]{A}$ *is positive if* A *is positive.*

II. $\sqrt[n]{A}$ *is negative if* A *is negative and* n *is odd.*

III. $\sqrt[n]{A}$ *is non-real if* A *is negative and* n *is even.*

Illustration 4. $\sqrt[4]{81} = 3$; $\sqrt[3]{-8} = -2$; $\sqrt[4]{-8}$ is non-real. The two real 4th roots of 16 are $\pm\sqrt[4]{16}$, or ±2.

By the definition of an nth root, $\qquad\qquad (\sqrt[n]{A})^n = A.$ $\qquad$ (2)

Illustration 5. $\qquad (\sqrt{3})^2 = 3.$ $\quad (\sqrt[7]{169})^7 = 169.$ $\quad (\sqrt[5]{2cd^3})^5 = 2cd^3.$

In this book, unless otherwise stated, if the index of a radical is an *even* integer, all literal number symbols in the radicand not used as exponents represent positive numbers, which are such that the radicand is positive. With this agreement, for every positive integer n we have* $\sqrt[n]{a^n} = a.$

Recall that N is said to be a *rational* number if there exist integers p and q, where $q \neq 0$, such that $N = p/q$; if N is real and is not rational, then N is called an *irrational number.* If $\sqrt[n]{A}$ is rational, from (2) we find that A must be the nth power of a rational number, and hence also is rational. Moreover, if A is *not* the nth power of a rational number, it follows that $\sqrt[n]{A}$ is irrational.

Illustration 6. $\sqrt{3}$ is irrational. $\sqrt[6]{64}$ is not irrational: $\sqrt[6]{64} = \sqrt[6]{2^6} = 2.$

22. Elementary properties of radicals

The following results I and II were met earlier. To verify III, IV, and V, we raise each side of each equality to the nth power.

I. $(\sqrt[n]{a})^n = a.$

II. $\sqrt[n]{a^n} = a.$ $\qquad (a > 0$ *if* n *is even*)

III. $\sqrt[n]{ab} = \sqrt[n]{a}\sqrt[n]{b}.$

IV. $\sqrt[n]{\dfrac{a}{b}} = \dfrac{\sqrt[n]{a}}{\sqrt[n]{b}}.$ $\qquad (b \neq 0)$

V. *If* m, n, *and* m/n *are positive integers,* $\qquad\qquad \sqrt[n]{a^m} = a^{\frac{m}{n}}.$

Illustration 1. $\sqrt[3]{ab} = \sqrt[3]{a}\sqrt[3]{b}.$ $\quad \sqrt[3]{a^{12}} = a^{\frac{12}{3}} = a^4,$ *because* $(a^4)^3 = a^{12}.$

Illustration 2. $\qquad \sqrt[4]{\dfrac{81}{16}} = \dfrac{\sqrt[4]{3^4}}{\sqrt[4]{2^4}} = \dfrac{3}{2}.$ $\qquad \sqrt[3]{\dfrac{125y^9}{8x^6}} = \dfrac{\sqrt[3]{5^3}\sqrt[3]{y^9}}{\sqrt[3]{2^3}\sqrt[3]{x^6}} = \dfrac{5y^3}{2x^2}.$

An algebraic expression is said to be **rational** in certain variables if it can be written as a fraction whose numerator and denominator are polynomials in the variables. If the expression is *not rational* in the variables, it is said to be **irrational** in them.

---

* If $a < 0$ and n is even, then $a^n > 0$ and the positive nth root of a^n is $-a$, or $\sqrt[n]{a^n} = -a$. This case is ruled out by the agreement above. For any a, $\sqrt[n]{a^n} = |a|$ if n is even.

Illustration 3. Since $x^3 - 2x = \dfrac{x^3 - 2x}{1}$, hence $(x^3 - 2x)$ is rational in x.

$(x^3 - 3a^2)/(x + a)$ is rational in a and x. $\sqrt{3x + y}$ is irrational in x and y.

Hereafter in this chapter, in any radical $\sqrt[n]{A}$, we shall assume that A is *rational* in any variables which may be present, and that the coefficients are *rational numbers* in any polynomial which is involved. A rational expression of this variety will be called a **perfect nth power** if the expression is the nth power of some rational expression of the same type. Suppose that a perfect nth power has been expressed as a product of powers of distinct prime factors. Then, the exponent for each of these powers has n as a factor because, in obtaining an nth power, each exponent of any power *is multiplied by n*.

Illustration 4. Since $32y^{15} = (2y^3)^5$, then $32y^{15}$ is a perfect 5th power: $\sqrt[5]{32y^{15}} = \sqrt[5]{(2y^3)^5} = 2y^3$. By II and III, $\sqrt[3]{8x^3y^9} = \sqrt[3]{8}\sqrt[3]{x^3}\sqrt[3]{y^9} = 2xy^3$.

23. Rational numbers as exponents

We introduce powers with positive rational exponents as substitutes for radicals in many situations. Consider the possibility of exponents of the type m/n, where m and n are positive integers. If exponents of this variety are to obey the laws of exponents, then, for instance, we should have $(a^{\frac{5}{3}})^3 = a^{3 \cdot (\frac{5}{3})} = a^5$, and thus $a^{\frac{5}{3}}$ should be a *cube root* of a^5. Accordingly, *we define $a^{\frac{m}{n}}$ to be the* **principal nth root of a^m**, or

$$a^{\frac{m}{n}} = \sqrt[n]{a^m}; \tag{1}$$

[*when* $m = 1$ *in* (1)]
$$a^{\frac{1}{n}} = \sqrt[n]{a}. \tag{2}$$

When m/n is an integer, (1) is consistent with V on page 36.

Illustration 1. $8^{\frac{1}{3}} = \sqrt[3]{8} = 2.$ $(-8)^{\frac{1}{3}} = \sqrt[3]{-8} = -2.$ $x^{\frac{8}{3}} = \sqrt[3]{x^8}.$
$8^{\frac{2}{3}} = \sqrt[3]{8^2} = \sqrt[3]{64} = 4.$ $(-8)^{\frac{2}{3}} = \sqrt[3]{(-8)^2} = \sqrt[3]{64} = 4.$

THEOREM II. $a^{\frac{m}{n}}$ *is the mth power of the nth root of a, or*

$$a^{\frac{m}{n}} = (\sqrt[n]{a})^m. \tag{3}$$

Proof. 1. $(\sqrt[n]{a})^m$ is an nth root of a^m because

$$[(\sqrt[n]{a})^m]^n = [(\sqrt[n]{a})^n]^m = (a)^m = a^m.$$

2. $(\sqrt[n]{a})^m$ in (3), and $(\sqrt[n]{a^m})$, or $a^{\frac{m}{n}}$, have the *same absolute value* because each is a real nth root of a^m. Both of the symbols represent *positive numbers if* $a > 0$, because the principal nth root of a positive number is positive; hence, in this case, (3) is true. If $a < 0$ then, by a previous agreement, n is *odd;* hence each side of (3) is *positive*, or each side is *negative*, according as m is *even* or *odd*.

Therefore, again, the numbers on the two sides of (3) are equal, because the numbers have the same absolute value. Thus, in all cases, (3) is true.

From (1) and (3), we obtain two methods for calculating $a^{\frac{m}{n}}$, when a is known.

Illustration 2. By use of (3), $\qquad 64^{\frac{5}{6}} = (\sqrt[6]{64})^5 = 2^5 = 32.$

Also, from (1), $\qquad\qquad 64^{\frac{5}{6}} = \sqrt[6]{(2^6)^5} = \sqrt[6]{2^{30}} = 2^5 = 32.$

If a negative exponent is to obey the laws of exponents, and if p is any positive rational number, we should have $a^p a^{-p} = a^0 = 1$. Hence, *we define* a^{-p} *as follows when* $a \neq 0$:

$$a^{-p} = \frac{1}{a^p}. \tag{4}$$

By use of (4), $a^p a^{-p} = 1$ so that, besides (4), we have

$$a^p = \frac{1}{a^{-p}}. \tag{5}$$

Hereafter, until otherwise specified in a later chapter, we shall restrict exponents of powers to be *positive or negative rational numbers, or zero.*

Illustration 3. $\qquad\qquad a^{-3} = 1/a^3; \quad a^5 = 1/a^{-5}.$

From (4) and (5), we remark that each of a^p and a^{-p} is the *reciprocal* of the other power. As a consequence of (4) and (5), we have the following result.

$$\left\{ \begin{array}{l} \textit{Suppose that a certain power, say } a^h, \textit{ is a factor of one term (numerator} \\ \textit{or denominator) of a fraction. Then, we obtain an equal fraction} \\ \textit{by dividing that term by } a^h \textit{ and multiplying the other term by } a^{-h}. \end{array} \right\} \quad (6)$$

Illustration 4. $\quad \dfrac{a}{bx^h} = \dfrac{ax^{-h}}{b},\quad$ *because* $\quad \dfrac{a}{bx^h} = \dfrac{a}{\dfrac{b}{x^{-h}}} = a \cdot \dfrac{x^{-h}}{b} = \dfrac{ax^{-h}}{b}.$

$\dfrac{3a^{-2}b^3}{c^{-3}a^4} = \dfrac{3b^3c^3}{a^2a^4} = \dfrac{3b^3c^3}{a^6},\quad$ *because* $\quad \dfrac{3a^{-2}b^3}{c^{-3}a^4} = \dfrac{\dfrac{3b^3}{a^2}}{\dfrac{a^4}{c^3}} = \dfrac{3b^3}{a^2} \cdot \dfrac{c^3}{a^4} = \dfrac{3b^3c^3}{a^6}.$

In Note 3 of the Appendix, it is indicated how to prove that Laws I–V for integral exponents on page 18 apply when the exponents are allowed to be any rational numbers, positive, negative, or zero. Hereafter we shall make use of this result. *To simplify* an expression involving exponents will mean to apply Laws I–V and to eliminate zero or negative exponents, unless otherwise specified.

Illustration 5. $\qquad\qquad (x^6)^{\frac{2}{3}} = x^4. \qquad x^{\frac{1}{4}}x^{\frac{2}{3}} = x^{\frac{1}{4}+\frac{2}{3}} = x^{\frac{11}{12}}.$

$$(-\tfrac{1}{125})^{-\frac{2}{3}} = [(-\tfrac{1}{5})^3]^{-\frac{2}{3}} = (-\tfrac{1}{5})^{-2} = \frac{1}{(-\tfrac{1}{5})^2} = \frac{1}{\tfrac{1}{25}} = 25.$$

EXERCISE 5

1. State the principal square root of 121; $\frac{4}{49}$; $\frac{25}{36}$.
2. State the principal cube root of -8; 27; $-\frac{1}{64}$; -216.
3. State the principal 4th root of 625; $10,000$; 256; $-.0001$.

Find the power of the radical, or the indicated root, or calculate.

4. $\sqrt{a^2}$, if $a < 0$.   5. $\sqrt{a^4 b^2}$.   6. $\sqrt[3]{y^3}$.   7. $\sqrt[6]{3^6}$.

8. $\sqrt[4]{2^4}$.   9. $\sqrt[4]{81}$.   10. $(\sqrt{29})^2$.   11. $(\sqrt[5]{57})^5$.

12. $(\sqrt[3]{-19})^3$.   13. $(\sqrt[5]{3ab^3})^5$.   14. $\sqrt[3]{-8}$.   15. $\sqrt[3]{-27}$.

16. $\sqrt[3]{-216}$.   17. $\sqrt[4]{625}$.   18. $\sqrt[3]{64}$.   19. $\sqrt[4]{16}$.

20. $\sqrt[5]{-1}$.   21. $\sqrt[3]{1000}$.   22. $\sqrt[4]{10,000}$.   23. $\sqrt{900}$.

24. $\sqrt{\frac{9}{16}}$.   25. $\sqrt{\frac{36}{49}}$.   26. $\sqrt[3]{8y^3}$.   27. $\sqrt[3]{27h^3}$.

28. $\sqrt[3]{\frac{27}{64}}$.   29. $\sqrt[3]{\frac{1000}{27}}$.   30. $\sqrt[3]{\frac{8}{27}}$.   31. $\sqrt[4]{\frac{81}{16}}$.

32. $\sqrt{y^4 w^6}$.   33. $\sqrt[3]{a^9 b^6}$.   34. $\sqrt[3]{-x^3}$.   35. $\sqrt[3]{-27x^3}$.

36. $\sqrt[3]{-8x^3 y^{12}}$.   37. $\sqrt[5]{-32a^{10}}$.   38. $\sqrt[3]{8a^6 y^9}$.   39. $\sqrt[4]{.0625}$.

40. $\sqrt[3]{\frac{-64}{a^6 b^9}}$.   41. $\sqrt[4]{\frac{16x^4}{a^4 b^8}}$.   42. $\sqrt{\frac{9a^4}{25y^8}}$.   43. $\sqrt[3]{\frac{216}{x^6 b^3}}$.

44. 8^{-1}.   45. 35^0.   46. 28^{-1}.   47. $81^{\frac{1}{4}}$.   48. $144^{\frac{1}{2}}$.

49. 5^{-2}.   50. 4^{-3}.   51. 6^{-3}.   52. $32^{\frac{1}{5}}$.   53. $16^{\frac{1}{4}}$.

54. $(\frac{1}{49})^{\frac{1}{2}}$.   55. $121^{\frac{1}{2}}$.   56. $(\frac{1}{27})^{\frac{1}{3}}$.   57. $(-8)^{\frac{1}{3}}$.   58. $216^{\frac{1}{3}}$.

59. $9^{-\frac{1}{2}}$.   60. $27^{-\frac{1}{3}}$.   61. $4^{-\frac{1}{2}}$.   62. $(\frac{2}{3})^{-1}$.   63. $(\frac{1}{5})^{-1}$.

64. $16^{\frac{3}{2}}$.   65. $144^{\frac{3}{2}}$.   66. $8^{\frac{4}{3}}$.   67. $81^{\frac{3}{4}}$.   68. $36^{\frac{3}{2}}$.

69. $125^{\frac{4}{3}}$.   70. $16^{\frac{5}{4}}$.   71. $(\frac{25}{9})^{\frac{5}{2}}$.   72. $(-8)^{\frac{2}{3}}$.   73. $(\frac{1}{4})^{\frac{3}{2}}$.

74. Express with positive exponents: x^{-4}; $5y^{-3}$; $x^2 y^{-4}$; $4x^{-3}y$.

Write without denominators by use of negative exponents.

75. $\dfrac{2}{y^3}$.   76. $\dfrac{3}{x^5}$.   77. $\dfrac{x}{4}$.   78. $\dfrac{y^2}{3}$.   79. $\dfrac{2a^3}{9y^4}$.   80. $\dfrac{5x^{\frac{1}{2}}}{y^3}$.

Express any radical as a power, and each rational power as a radical.

81. $6x^{\frac{2}{5}}$.   82. $ax^{\frac{2}{3}}$.   83. $bx^{\frac{3}{4}}$.   84. $\sqrt[4]{x^5}$.   85. $\sqrt[3]{x^7}$.

86. $\sqrt[9]{y^{12}}$.   87. $\sqrt[5]{x^{10}}$.   88. $\sqrt[4]{a^6}$.   89. $(3a)^{\frac{3}{2}}$.   90. $(2x^3)^{\frac{2}{3}}$.

Express without negative exponents and simplify.

91. $2^{-1} - 3^{-1}$.   92. $4^{-1} + 5^{-2}$.   93. $2^{-3} + 4^{-2}$.   94. $a^{-1} + b^{-1}$.

95. $\dfrac{5^{-1}}{2^{-1} + 3^{-1}}$.   96. $\dfrac{2^{-1} + 3^{-2}}{4^{-1}}$.   97. $\dfrac{5(2^{-1}) + 6^{-1}}{3^{-1} + 2^{-1}}$.   98. $\dfrac{a^{-1}}{b^{-1} + c^{-1}}$.

99. $a^{\frac{1}{3}} a^3$.   100. $x^{\frac{2}{3}} x^{\frac{3}{4}}$.   101. $y^4 y^0 y$.   102. $(x^{\frac{2}{3}})^6$.   103. $(2^6)^{\frac{4}{3}}$.

104. $x^0 x^{\frac{5}{4}}$.   105. $(3^4)^{\frac{3}{2}}$.   106. $(4y)^{-2}$.   107. $(3x)^{-4}$.   108. $(a^{-2}y)^2$.

109. $\dfrac{a^4}{a^{\frac{3}{2}}}$.   110. $\dfrac{x^2}{x^{\frac{2}{3}}}$.   111. $\dfrac{a^2}{a^{\frac{7}{3}}}$.   112. $\dfrac{b^{-3} y^4}{b^2 y^{-2}}$.   113. $\dfrac{x^{-2} y^3}{y^{-1} x^4}$.

Express by use of the imaginary unit i.

114. $\sqrt{-4}$.   **115.** $\sqrt{-49}$.   **116.** $\sqrt{-36}$.   **117.** $\sqrt{-17}$.   **118.** $\sqrt{-\frac{1}{4}}$.

119. $\sqrt{-\frac{1}{9}}$.   **120.** $\sqrt{-\frac{36}{49}}$.   **121.** $\sqrt{-a^2}$.   **122.** $\sqrt{-4c^2}$.   **123.** $\sqrt{-\frac{121}{25}}$

Specify the two square roots of the number.

124. -100.   **125.** $-\frac{4}{25}$.   **126.** -81.   **127.** $-\frac{25}{16}$.   **128.** -144.

Perform indicated operations and simplify by use of $i^2 = -1$.

129. $(2 - i)(2 + i)$.   **130.** $(2i + 3)(5i - 2)$.   **131.** $(3 + 4i)(2 + i)$.

132. $i^2 \cdot i^3$.   **133.** i^6.   **134.** i^{11}.   **135.** i^5.   **136.** i^9.

137. $\sqrt{-4}\sqrt{-144}$.   **138.** $\sqrt{-16}\sqrt{-49}$.   **139.** $\left(\sqrt{-16}\right)^2$.

140. $(2 - 3i)(-4 + 5\sqrt{-1})$.   **141.** $(-2 + 2\sqrt{-1})(3 + \sqrt{-9})$.

142. Prove Laws I, III, V, and II of page 6 for addition and multiplication of complex numbers by calculating the two sides of the equation in each of the following cases, with the aid of (1) and (2) on page 34. Also, prove Law IV.

$$(a + bi)(c + di) = (c + di)(a + bi);$$
$$(a + bi) + (c + di) = (c + di) + (a + bi);$$
$$(a + bi)[(c + di) + (h + ki)] = (a + bi)(c + di) + (a + bi)(h + ki);$$
$$(a + bi) \cdot [(c + di)(h + ki)] = (c + di) \cdot [(a + bi)(h + ki)].$$

24. Elementary operations on radicals

In the following operations, it should be recalled that, in a radical $\sqrt[n]{A}$ where n is *even*, we have agreed that, at present, all literal number symbols in A represent *positive numbers* such that A always is positive.

To remove a factor which is a perfect nth power from the radicand in a radical $\sqrt[n]{A}$, use $\sqrt[n]{ab} = \sqrt[n]{a}\sqrt[n]{b}$.

Illustration 1. $\sqrt{147} = \sqrt{49 \cdot 3} = \sqrt{49}\sqrt{3} = 7\sqrt{3} = 7(1.732) = 12.124.$

$$\sqrt[5]{64a^{11}c^9} = \sqrt[5]{32}\sqrt[5]{2}\sqrt[5]{a^{10}}\sqrt[5]{a}\sqrt[5]{c^5}\sqrt[5]{c^4} = 2a^2c\sqrt[5]{2ac^4}.$$

The product or quotient of two radicals of the same order can be expressed as a single radical, by use of $\sqrt[n]{ab} = \sqrt[n]{a}\sqrt[n]{b}$ and $\sqrt[n]{a/b} = \sqrt[n]{a}/\sqrt[n]{b}$.

Illustration 2. $2\sqrt{3}(5\sqrt{6}) = 10\sqrt{3}\sqrt{6} = 10\sqrt{18} = 10\sqrt{9}\sqrt{2} = 30\sqrt{2}.$

$$\frac{\sqrt{3}}{\sqrt{5}} = \sqrt{\frac{3}{5}}. \qquad \frac{\sqrt[3]{ab}}{\sqrt[3]{b^5}} = \sqrt[3]{\frac{ab}{b^5}} = \sqrt[3]{\frac{a}{b^4}} = \frac{\sqrt[3]{a}}{b\sqrt[3]{b}} = \frac{1}{b}\sqrt[3]{\frac{a}{b}}.$$

Illustration 3. $\qquad \sqrt[3]{3a + \frac{5}{x^3}} = \sqrt[3]{\frac{3ax^3 + 5}{x^3}} = \frac{\sqrt[3]{3ax^3 + 5}}{x}.$

$$(\sqrt{2} + \sqrt{3})(2\sqrt{2} + 5\sqrt{3}) = 2(\sqrt{2})^2 + 2\sqrt{2}\sqrt{3} + 5\sqrt{2}\sqrt{3} + 5(\sqrt{3})^2$$
$$= 4 + 2\sqrt{6} + 5\sqrt{6} + 15 = 19 + 7\sqrt{6}.$$

25. Rationalization of denominators

To rationalize a denominator in a radical of order n, after the radicand has been expressed as a simple fraction, *multiply both numerator and denominator of the radicand by the simplest expression which will make the denominator a perfect nth power.* If the radical is a *square* root, we make the denominator a perfect *square;* if a *cube* root, we make the denominator a perfect *cube.*

Illustration 1. $\quad \sqrt{\dfrac{3}{7}} = \sqrt{\dfrac{3 \cdot 7}{7^2}} = \dfrac{\sqrt{21}}{7} = \dfrac{4.583}{7} = .655.$ (Table I)

Illustration 2. $\quad \sqrt[3]{\dfrac{3}{4}} = \sqrt[3]{\dfrac{3 \cdot 2}{4 \cdot 2}} = \dfrac{\sqrt[3]{6}}{\sqrt[3]{8}} = \dfrac{\sqrt[3]{6}}{2}.$

If a denominator has the form $a\sqrt{b} - c\sqrt{d}$, we can rationalize it by multiplying by $a\sqrt{b} + c\sqrt{d}$.

Illustration 3. $\quad \dfrac{3\sqrt{2} - \sqrt{3}}{2\sqrt{2} - \sqrt{3}} = \dfrac{3\sqrt{2} - \sqrt{3}}{2\sqrt{2} - \sqrt{3}} \cdot \dfrac{2\sqrt{2} + \sqrt{3}}{2\sqrt{2} + \sqrt{3}}$

$$= \dfrac{6(\sqrt{2})^2 + (3 - 2)\sqrt{6} - (\sqrt{3})^2}{(2\sqrt{2})^2 - (\sqrt{3})^2}$$

$$= \dfrac{9 + \sqrt{6}}{8 - 3} = \dfrac{9 + 2.449}{5} = 2.290.$$

26. Operations on radicals by use of exponents

Any algebraic operations involving powers, roots, products, or quotients of radicals can be performed by expressing each radical as a power with a rational exponent, and then simplifying by use of the laws of exponents. If a result in terms of powers with rational exponents is acceptable, practically all operations are simple to perform. We shall adopt this attitude in the following illustrations. Frequently, in later mathematics, the exponential form has advantages as compared to the radical form.

Illustration 1. $\quad \sqrt[3]{\sqrt[4]{3xy}} = [(3xy)^{\frac{1}{4}}]^{\frac{1}{3}} = (3xy)^{\frac{1}{12}} = 3^{\frac{1}{12}}x^{\frac{1}{12}}y^{\frac{1}{12}}.$

Illustration 2. $\quad (2\sqrt[3]{5x})^4 = 2^4[(5x)^{\frac{1}{3}}]^4 = 2^4 5^{\frac{4}{3}}x^{\frac{4}{3}}.$

Illustration 3. $\quad \dfrac{\sqrt[3]{4b^2x}}{\sqrt{3ab}} = \dfrac{4^{\frac{1}{3}}b^{\frac{2}{3}}x^{\frac{1}{3}}}{3^{\frac{1}{2}}a^{\frac{1}{2}}b^{\frac{1}{2}}} = \dfrac{4^{\frac{1}{3}}b^{\frac{1}{6}}x^{\frac{1}{3}}}{3^{\frac{1}{2}}a^{\frac{1}{2}}}.$

27. Changing from rational exponents to radicals

Suppose that the powers in a product involve rational exponents which are not integers. Then, we may express the product by use of a single radical as follows:

1. *Express each exponent as an integer plus a fraction with absolute value less than 1. Then alter the fractions to new forms with their LCD as the new denominator, say it is n.*

2. *Write the given product as a product of two factors, where one factor involves just integral exponents, and the other factor is a product of powers with rational exponents having the denominator n. Then change this second factor to a radical of order n.*

Illustration 1. $\quad 5y^{\frac{2}{3}}z^{\frac{5}{2}} = 5z^2y^{\frac{2}{3}}z^{\frac{1}{2}} = 5z^2y^{\frac{4}{6}}z^{\frac{3}{6}} = 5z^2(y^4z^3)^{\frac{1}{6}} = 5z^2\sqrt[6]{y^4z^3}.$

The following operations on radicals may arise:

To find a power or a root of a radical.

To find the product or quotient of two radicals of different orders.

To reduce the order of a radical when possible.

We may perform the preceding operations by use of fractional exponents. If desired, the final exponential form then can be changed to a radical form as in (1) and (2) above. In any final radical, rationalize the denominator.

Illustration 2. $\qquad \sqrt[6]{25w^4} = [(5w^2)^2]^{\frac{1}{6}} = (5w^2)^{\frac{1}{3}} = \sqrt[3]{5w^2}.$

$$\sqrt[5]{\sqrt[3]{u}} = (u^{\frac{1}{3}})^{\frac{1}{5}} = u^{\frac{1}{15}} = \sqrt[15]{u}.$$

$$\sqrt[3]{a^2}\sqrt[4]{a^3} = a^{\frac{2}{3}}a^{\frac{3}{4}} = a^{\frac{8}{12}}a^{\frac{9}{12}} = a^{\frac{17}{12}} = a\sqrt[12]{a^5}.$$

EXERCISE 6

Simplify by removing perfect powers from the radicand.

1. $\sqrt{27}.$ 2. $\sqrt{50}.$ 3. $\sqrt{300}.$ 4. $\sqrt[3]{y^8}.$ 5. $\sqrt[4]{z^{19}}.$ 6. $\sqrt[4]{16z^6}.$

7. $\sqrt{18x^3y^4}.$ 8. $\sqrt{75x^4y^9}.$ 9. $\sqrt[5]{-x^6y^7}.$ 10. $\sqrt[3]{-128a^9}.$

11. $\sqrt{\dfrac{81u^5}{25v^5}}.$ 12. $\sqrt[4]{\dfrac{16a^2b^6}{81u^4v^5}}.$ 13. $\sqrt[3]{\dfrac{-27x^3}{4y^6}}.$ 14. $\sqrt[3]{-\dfrac{16a^7}{x^3y^4}}.$

Simplify and collect terms, exhibiting any common radical factor.

15. $\sqrt{3}\sqrt{2}.$ 16. $\sqrt{5}\sqrt{2}.$ 17. $\sqrt[3]{2}\sqrt[3]{12}.$ 18. $\sqrt[4]{3}\sqrt[4]{27}.$

19. $\dfrac{\sqrt{15}}{\sqrt{3}}.$ 20. $\dfrac{\sqrt{15x}}{\sqrt{3x}}.$ 21. $\dfrac{\sqrt{2a}}{\sqrt{8c}}.$ 22. $\dfrac{\sqrt[3]{44}}{\sqrt[3]{11}}.$

23. $\sqrt{5x}\sqrt{20x}.$ 24. $\sqrt{y}\sqrt{3y}\sqrt{15y^3}.$ 25. $\sqrt[3]{4x^2}\sqrt[3]{6x^2y^4}.$

26. $(\sqrt{5} - 2\sqrt{3})(2\sqrt{5} - \sqrt{3}).$ 27. $(\sqrt{6} - 2\sqrt{3})(2\sqrt{6} + \sqrt{3}).$

Rationalize the denominator. Compute, by use of Table I if possible.

28. $\sqrt{\frac{1}{3}}.$ 29. $\sqrt{\frac{1}{5}}.$ 30. $\sqrt{\frac{2}{5}}.$ 31. $\sqrt[3]{\frac{3}{25}}.$ 32. $\sqrt[3]{\frac{4}{25}}.$ 33. $\sqrt[3]{\frac{3}{100}}.$

34. $\dfrac{1}{\sqrt{7}}.$ 35. $\dfrac{1}{\sqrt{10}}.$ 36. $\dfrac{5}{\sqrt{3}}.$ 37. $\dfrac{3}{\sqrt[3]{36}}.$ 38. $\dfrac{1}{\sqrt[3]{100}}.$ 39. $\dfrac{\sqrt[3]{14}}{\sqrt[3]{63}}.$

Rationalize the denominator and simplify exponents.

40. $\dfrac{1-\sqrt{2}}{2+\sqrt{3}}$.

41. $\dfrac{\sqrt{3}+2\sqrt{2}}{3\sqrt{2}+2\sqrt{3}}$.

42. $\dfrac{\sqrt{5}+\sqrt{2}}{3\sqrt{2}-\sqrt{5}}$.

43. $\sqrt{\dfrac{a}{2}}$.

44. $\sqrt{\dfrac{3x}{5}}$.

45. $\sqrt{\dfrac{2c}{a}}$.

46. $\sqrt[3]{\dfrac{3cd}{16x^2}}$.

47. $\sqrt[3]{\dfrac{c}{3d^2}}$.

48. $\sqrt{x^{-3}}$.

49. $\sqrt[4]{a^{-3}}$.

50. $\sqrt[3]{a^{-5}}$.

51. $\sqrt{x^2y^{-3}}$.

52. $\sqrt{\frac{1}{3}x^{-5}}$.

53. $\sqrt{\dfrac{a}{2}-\dfrac{5}{x}}$.

54. $\sqrt{\dfrac{3}{a}-\dfrac{4}{5b^2}}$.

55. $\sqrt{\dfrac{2}{x}+\dfrac{x}{2b}}$.

56. $\sqrt{4+\dfrac{9}{25x^4}}$.

Change to simplest radical form.

57. $a^{\frac13}a^{\frac15}$.

58. $2a^{\frac34}b^{\frac13}$.

59. $a^2b^{\frac73}$.

60. $x^{\frac27}y^{\frac92}$.

61. $xy^{\frac53}z^{\frac72}$.

Express by use of exponents. Place the final answer in radical form.

62. $\sqrt[8]{y^2}$.

63. $\sqrt[6]{z^3}$.

64. $\sqrt[4]{b^2}$.

65. $\sqrt[6]{u^4}$.

66. $\sqrt[10]{x^5}$.

67. $\sqrt[4]{16}$.

68. $\sqrt[6]{64}$.

69. $\sqrt[8]{4x^2}$.

70. $\sqrt[6]{16x^4}$.

71. $\sqrt[9]{27a^3}$.

Factor any integer involved. Express in a final exponential form and also in a final radical form with any denominator rationlized.

72. $(\sqrt[4]{x})^3$.

73. $(\sqrt[4]{z})^6$.

74. $(\sqrt[4]{y})^8$.

75. $(\sqrt[3]{3})^4$.

76. $(\sqrt[5]{a})^4$.

77. $(\sqrt[3]{7})^5$.

78. $(\sqrt{3})^5$.

79. $(\sqrt{6})^7$.

80. $(\sqrt{2a})^3$.

81. $(\sqrt[3]{2a})^2$.

82. $(\sqrt{2x^5})^3$.

83. $(\sqrt[3]{5a})^4$.

84. $\sqrt[4]{\sqrt{x}}$.

85. $\sqrt{\sqrt[4]{a}}$.

86. $\sqrt[5]{\sqrt[3]{z}}$.

87. $\sqrt[3]{\sqrt[3]{x}}$.

88. $(2\sqrt{3})^4$.

89. $\sqrt[3]{\sqrt[4]{a^3}}$.

90. $\sqrt{\sqrt[3]{a^4}}$.

91. $\sqrt[4]{\sqrt[3]{a^8}}$.

92. $\sqrt[3]{x}\sqrt{x}$.

93. $\sqrt[4]{2}\sqrt{2}$.

94. $\sqrt[4]{y}\sqrt[3]{y}$.

95. $\sqrt[5]{x}\sqrt{x}$.

96. $\sqrt[3]{3}\sqrt[4]{27}$.

97. $\sqrt[3]{2}\sqrt[5]{16}$.

98. $\sqrt[3]{4}\sqrt[4]{8}$.

99. $\sqrt[4]{\frac{4}{25}}$.

100. $\dfrac{\sqrt[3]{x}}{\sqrt{x}}$.

101. $\dfrac{\sqrt{a}}{\sqrt[4]{a}}$.

102. $\dfrac{\sqrt[3]{y}}{\sqrt[4]{y}}$.

103. $\dfrac{\sqrt[3]{b}}{\sqrt{b}}$.

104. $\dfrac{\sqrt{5}}{\sqrt[4]{25}}$.

105. $\sqrt[4]{\frac{9}{25}}$.

106. $\sqrt[6]{\frac{8}{27}}$.

107. $\sqrt[3]{\frac14 x^{-5}}$.

108. $\sqrt[5]{\frac19 x^{-3}}$.

109. $\sqrt{x^{-5}}$.

110. $\sqrt[3]{cd^4}\div\sqrt{cd}$.

111. $\sqrt[4]{a^2d^3}\div\sqrt{ad}$.

112. $2\sqrt{xy}\div\sqrt[3]{xy^2}$.

113. $\sqrt[3]{81x^{-4}}$.

114. $\sqrt[6]{216}$.

115. $\sqrt[3]{\sqrt[4]{27x^3}}$.

116. $\sqrt{4\sqrt[3]{9u^2}}$.

117. $\sqrt[3]{y^{-3}+x^{-3}}$.

118. $\sqrt{\sqrt{\sqrt{x}}}$.

119. $\sqrt[3]{\sqrt[3]{\sqrt{a}}}$.

120. $\sqrt[5]{\sqrt[3]{\sqrt{8}}}$.

28. Terminology for equations

An **equation** is a statement that two numbers are equal. The two numbers are called the sides, or members, of the equation. An **open equation** is one involving at least one variable. If an equation is written without use of a literal number symbol, the equation is true or false as it stands.

Illustration 1. The equations $3=\sqrt{9}$ and $3=2+1$ are true statements, while $5=\sqrt{36}$ is a false statement. If x is a variable, then $3+2x=4$ is an open equation, which is a true statement if $x=\frac12$, and is false for all other values of x.

DEFINITION VIII. *A* **solution** *of an open equation consists of a value of each variable in the equation, such that it is a true statement when each variable is assigned the specified value. Then, these values of the variables are said to satisfy the equation.* **To solve** *it means to find all of its solutions.*

A solution of an equation in a single variable also is called a **root** of the equation. Any reference to a solution of an equation will imply that it is an open equation. Hereafter, unless otherwise indicated, the unqualified word *equation* will refer to an *open equation*. For brevity, the set of all solutions of an equation may be called its **solution set.** *

Illustration 2. The equation $3x + 5 = 11$ has just one solution, $x = 2$; the solution set consists of just the number 2. The equation $2x^2 - x = 1$, or $(2x + 1)(x - 1) = 0$, has the solutions $x = -\frac{1}{2}$ and $x = 1$, or the solution set $\{-\frac{1}{2}, 1\}$. A graph of this solution set on the number scale in Figure 2 consists of just two points, indicated by black dots. We shall refer to these two points as *the graph of the equation in one dimension.*†

Figure 2

Illustration 3. By Definition VIII, if x and y are variables, a solution of $x + y = 3$ is a pair of corresponding values of x and y which satisfy the equation. Thus, $(x = 2, y = 1)$ is a solution. If x takes on any value in the given equation, it determines a corresponding value for y so that (x, y) satisfies the equation. Thus, if $x = 6$, we find $6 + y = 3$ or $y = -3$, and $(x = 6, y = -3)$ is a solution of $x + y = 3$. Hence, this equation has infinitely many solutions, or its solution set consists of infinitely many pairs of numbers.

An equation is said to be **inconsistent** if it has no solution, and otherwise is said to be **consistent.** A **conditional equation** is one which is *not* satisfied by *all* values of the variables. If an equation, open or not, is satisfied by all values of any variables involved, the equation is referred to as an **identity,** or an **identical equation.** Two open equations are said to be **equivalent** if they have the same solutions.

Illustration 4. Sometimes, to indicate that an equation is an identity, we use "≡" instead of "=" to specify the equality of the members. Thus, the following equation is indicated as an identity: $x^2 - 4 \equiv (x - 2)(x + 2)$.

Illustration 5. The equations $x + 3 = 2$ and $x(x + 3) = 2x$ are not equivalent, because the second equation has the root $x = 0$, which is not a root of the first equation.

Operations on an equation which lead to equivalent equations are developed by recollection of the following familiar facts.

---

* Sometimes called the equation's *truth set*, because the equation becomes a true statement if the variables are given the values in a solution.
† In contrast to a later notion of a graph of such an equation in two dimensions.

A. *If the same number is added to (or subtracted from) equal numbers, the results are equal.*

B. *If equal numbers are multiplied (or divided) by the same number, not zero, the results are equal.*

THEOREM III. *Let $U = V$ represent a given equation. Let H and K be number symbols, which may involve any variable present in U and V, with $K \neq 0$ for all values of the variables in their domains.* Then, the equation $U = V$ is equivalent to*

$$U + H = V + H \qquad \text{and to} \qquad U - H = V - H; \qquad (1)$$

$$UK = VK \qquad \text{and to} \qquad \frac{U}{K} = \frac{V}{K}. \qquad (2)$$

Proof of (1). (*Phrased as if just one variable x is involved.*) If $x = c$ satisfies $U = V$, then fact A above shows that $x = c$ satisfies $U + H = V + H$. Conversely, suppose that $x = c$ satisfies $U + H = V + H$; then, by A, if $x = c$ and if H is subtracted from both sides of $U + H = V + H$, we obtain $U = V$, which shows that $x = c$ is a solution of $U = V$. Thus, $U = V$ and $U + H = V + H$ have the same solutions, or are equivalent. Similar remarks, using A and B, apply to the other three equations in (1) and (2).

In Theorem III, we have justified the familiar operations of *addition (or subtraction) of the same number,* and *multiplication (or division) by the same number,* not zero, on both sides of an equation, in solving it.

A **polynomial equation** is one in which each member is a *polynomial* in the variables, or is *zero.*† A **linear equation** in one variable, x, is a polynomial equation which is equivalent to $ax = b$, where a and b are constants and $a \neq 0$. Thus, the equation has just one solution, $x = b/a$.

EXAMPLE 1. Solve the equation: $\dfrac{x - 4}{3} - \dfrac{x - 3}{2} = \dfrac{3 + x}{10} - 2.$ \hfill (3)

Solution. 1. The LCD is 30. Multiply both sides by 30:

$$10(x - 4) - 15(x - 3) = 3(3 + x) - 60; \ or, \qquad (4)$$

$$-5x + 5 = 3x - 51. \qquad (5)$$

2. Subtract $3x$ and 5 from both sides:

$$-5x - 3x = -51 - 5; \qquad -8x = -56. \qquad (6)$$

3. Divide both sides by -8: \hfill $x = 7.$ \hfill (7)

By Theorem III, each of equations (4)–(7) is equivalent to (3), and hence (3) has just the single solution $x = 7$.

---

* Review the definition of *domain of a variable* on page 20.

† On page 20, a monomial is defined as a *nonzero* constant times integral powers of the variables. Then 0 itself is *not* called a monomial. Also, 0 is *not* called a polynomial. This feature of terminology will be met again on page 198, but is not important at present.

EXAMPLE 2.   Solve for x if $a + b \neq 0$: $b(b + x) = a^2 - ax$.

Solution.   1. Expand: $b^2 + bx = a^2 - ax$.

2. Add ax; subtract b^2: $ax + bx = a^2 - b^2$.

3. Factor: $x(a + b) = (a - b)(a + b)$

4. Divide by $(a + b)$:* $x = a - b$.

In (2) on page 45, the multiplier or divisor, K, for both sides of an equation was stated to be different from zero at all values of any variables in the equation. If this condition is not met, the new equations in (2) may not be equivalent to the given equation. Hence, the following warnings are important (stated for an equation involving just one variable, but applicable in case more than one variable is involved).

Caution 1.   *If both sides of an equation in one variable, x, are divided by a common factor involving x, the new equation obtained may have fewer roots than the original equation. In particular, if the factor is equal to zero at any value x = c, this is a root of the original equation, but not necessarily of the new equation.*

Caution 2.   *If both sides of an equation in a single variable x are multiplied by a factor involving x, the new equation thus obtained may have more solutions than the original equation.*

Illustration 6.   By substitution, we verify that $x = 1$ and $x = 2$ are roots of $x^2 - 3x + 2 = 0$. On dividing both sides by $(x - 2)$, we obtain

$$\frac{x^2 - 3x + 2}{x - 2} = 0, \quad or \quad \frac{(x - 2)(x - 1)}{x - 2} = 0, \quad or \quad x - 1 = 0,$$

which has *just one* root, $x = 1$. The root $x = 2$ was lost by the division. Hence, we avoid such an operation in solving an equation.

Illustration 7.   Consider the equation $x - 3 = 0$.   (8)

Multiply both sides by $(x - 2)$ in (8):

$$(x - 2)(x - 3) = 0 \quad or \quad x^2 - 5x + 6 = 0. \qquad (9)$$

By substitution, we verify that (9) has the roots $x = 2$ and $x = 3$, whereas (8) has just the solution $x = 3$; the root $x = 2$ of (9) was brought in by the multiplier $(x - 2)$. If $x - 2 \neq 0$, we can state that, if (9) is true, then (8) is true as a consequence of dividing both sides of (9) by $(x - 2)$. But, when $x - 2 = 0$, we cannot argue that the truth of (9) implies the truth of (8), because we cannot divide by $(x - 2)$ in (9) to obtain (8).

* At this point we use the fact that $a + b \neq 0$. Similarly, in any problem in the exercises, the student will assume that the constants are not allowed to have values which make any denominator zero in the solution.

A value of the variable, such as $x = 2$ in Illustration 7, which satisfies a derived equation, but not the original equation, is called an **extraneous root.** Whenever an operation of the type mentioned in Caution 2 is employed, test all values obtained to reject extraneous roots, if any.

EXAMPLE 3.   Solve: $\dfrac{x}{x^2 - 1} - \dfrac{1}{x^2 - 1} + \dfrac{2}{x + 1} = 0.$

Solution.   The LCD is $x^2 - 1$; multiply both sides by $x^2 - 1$:

$$x - 1 + 2(x - 1) = 0; \quad 3x = 3; \quad or \quad x = 1.$$

Test.   Since $x = 1$ makes $x^2 - 1 = 0$ in the given denominators, $x = 1$ *cannot be accepted as a root* because division by zero is not admissible. Hence, 1 is an extraneous root and the given equation has *no root.*

EXERCISE 7

Solve, and check by substitution.

1. $\frac{2}{3} - 5y = -3y - \frac{2}{15}.$

2. $.23 - z = .95 - 3z.$

3. $\dfrac{3x}{2} - \dfrac{3x}{5} = \dfrac{3}{5}.$

4. $\dfrac{4x}{9} - \dfrac{3}{5} = \dfrac{5x}{6} - \dfrac{13}{10}.$

5. $.17x - .362 = .028 - .09x.$

6. $4.088 + .03x = 3x - .07.$

7. $\dfrac{4 - 2x}{3} = \dfrac{21}{12} - \dfrac{5x - 3}{4}.$

8. $\dfrac{33}{10} + \dfrac{2x + 9}{5} = -\dfrac{3x - 5}{4}.$

Solve for h, t, x, y, or z, whichever appears. The other letters represent numbers which, for the moment, are assumed to be known.

9. $2ay - 5c = 3by + 4a.$

10. $7x - d = 5ax + 8.$

11. $\dfrac{2b}{c} - \dfrac{3x}{a} = 0.$

12. $\dfrac{a^2 x}{3} - 2a^3 = 0.$

13. $\dfrac{A}{4} - \dfrac{3x}{BC} = 0.$

14. $3z - 18 = az - 2a^2.$

15. $c^2 y - ck = b^2 y - bk.$

16. $25a^2 x - 5ab = d^2 x - bd.$

17. $4z - b^3 = 64 - bz.$

18. $2adx + 9c^2 + d^2 = 6cd + 6acx.$

19. $27 + ay - a^2 y = a^3 - 6y.$

20. $\dfrac{2}{3x} - \dfrac{3}{x} + \dfrac{5}{2x} = 1 - \dfrac{11}{6x}.$

21. $\dfrac{1 + 4t}{t - 1} - \dfrac{20t}{5t - 6} = 0.$

22. $\dfrac{2t}{t - 2} = 2 + \dfrac{5}{t}.$

23. $\dfrac{x}{3x + 3} = \dfrac{x + 3}{3x + 6}.$

24. $\dfrac{4}{14 - 3h} = \dfrac{1}{1 - 2h}.$

25. $\dfrac{2}{t^2 + t} = \dfrac{1}{t^2 - 1}.$

26. $\dfrac{z + 3}{z + 1} = \dfrac{z^2 + 9z + 20}{z^2 - z - 2}.$

27. $\dfrac{2x - 1}{1 + 3x} = \dfrac{2x^2 + x + 14}{3x^2 - 5x - 2}.$

28. $\dfrac{1 + 2y}{y - 4} = \dfrac{4y^2 + 5y}{2y^2 - 7y - 4}.$

29. $\dfrac{x + 6}{x - 2} - \dfrac{x + 3}{x - 10} = \dfrac{11}{x^2 - 12x + 20}.$

30. $\dfrac{2}{3z + 2} + \dfrac{2}{9z^2 - 4} = \dfrac{3z}{9z^2 - 4}.$

31. $\dfrac{z - 1}{z + 2} - \dfrac{4z - 3}{2z + 3} = \dfrac{7 - 2z^2}{2z^2 + 7z + 6}.$

32. In the Fahrenheit-centigrade equation, $5F = 9C + 160$, solve for C in terms of F. Then, use the formula to find C corresponding to the following values of $F°$: (a) $32°$; (b) $212°$; (c) $80°$.

Note 1. Recall that the word *percent*, represented by %, means *hundredths*. That is, if r is the value of $h\%$, then $r = h/100$, and $h = 100r$. Thus, $4\% = .04$. If a number M is described by $M = Nr$, that is, if r is the *ratio of M to N*, we sometimes say that M is expressed as a **percentage** of N, with r as the **rate** and N as the **base** for the percentage. Thus,

$$M = Nr, \quad or \quad percentage = (base) \cdot (rate); \tag{1}$$

$$r = \frac{M}{N}, \quad or \quad rate = \frac{percentage}{base}. \tag{2}$$

33. Express 375 as a percentage of 500, and state the rate in percent form.

34. Find the number of residents in a city where 13% of the population, or 962 people, had influenza.

35. How many gallons of a mixture containing 80% alcohol should be added to 5 gallons of a 20% solution to give a 30% solution?

Note 2. Recall that a *ratio* $a : b$ is defined as a fraction, a/b. A **proportion** is a statement that two ratios are equal. The proportion $a : b = c : d$ is read "*a is to b as c is to d*," and we say that the four numbers a, b, c, and d *form a proportion.*

$$a : b = c : d \quad means \; that \quad \frac{a}{b} = \frac{c}{d}. \tag{3}$$

In a proportion $a : b = c : d$, the first and fourth numbers, a and d, are called the **extremes,** and the second and third, b and c, are called the **means** of the proportion. If a proportion involves a single variable, x, and if we are requested to solve the proportion, we use (3) and solve the resulting equation by standard methods.

Solve the equation.

36. $(2 - y) : (3 + 2y) = 4 : 3.$ **37.** $(2x - 1) : 3x = 2 : 5.$

38. $(2x - 1) : (1 + 4x) = (1 + 2x) : (4x + 3).$

Solve by writing a proportion involving a single variable.

39. A line 20 inches long is divided into two parts whose lengths have the ratio $3 : 7$. Find the lengths of the parts.

40. Divide 80 into two parts such that the ratio of one part, decreased by 4, to the other part, decreased by 8, is $1 : 3$.

41. The sides of a triangle are 10, 9, and 15 inches long. In a similar triangle, the longest side is 21 inches long. Find the other sides.

Solve the equation.

42. $|2x - 3| = 4.$ **43.** $|x - 3| = 2.$ **44.** $|12 - 4x| = 3.$

Chapter 2 Sets and Linear Inequalities in One Variable

29. Origin of analytic geometry

In the year 1637, the French mathematician and philosopher RENÉ
DESCARTES (1596–1650) established a landmark in the field of mathematics
by publishing a book entitled *la Géométrie*. In it, he introduced the notion of
the equation of a curve and related analytical methods into the study of
geometry. Later, similar methods were extended to the field of geometry in
space of three dimensions (solid geometry). The resulting combination of
analysis and geometry is referred to now as *analytic geometry*. For contrast,
the study of geometry by purely geometric means, essentially as in parts of
high school geometry, is called *synthetic geometry*. A proper development of
algebra at any level requires simultaneous treatment of various parts of analytic
geometry, in order to illuminate, and sometimes to aid, the algebra. Also, the
achievements of Descartes smoothed the road leading to the invention of the
indispensable mathematical discipline called *calculus* by SIR ISAAC NEWTON
(1642–1727) and GOTTFRIED WILHELM LEIBNIZ (1646–1716). Their work
appeared late in the 17th century, and forms a cornerstone of modern mathematics. Part of the present chapter is devoted to first steps in the development
of analytic geometry. Other aspects of the subject will be presented in proper
settings with corresponding topics of algebra.

30. Directed line segments

Let us consider geometry restricted to a given line *l*, on which a unit for
measuring lengths has been specified. From page 14, recall that we shall use
the word *length* or the unqualified word *distance* to refer to a *nonnegative*

49

number which is the measure of some distance in terms of the given unit of length. By the distance between two points, we shall mean the length of the line segment joining them.

A line l is said to be a *directed line* if it is agreed that one direction on l is called positive, with the opposite direction negative, as in Figure 3. Also, directed distances on l in the corresponding directions will be taken positive and negative, respectively, and a direction is assigned to each line segment on l. To indicate that a segment is directed or traced from a point A to B on l, the segment is named AB. Then, we shall let $\overline{AB}$ represent the *directed distance* from A to B, and may call $\overline{AB}$ the *value* of AB. Thus, if A and B coincide, $\overline{AB} = 0$. If AB has positive direction, then $\overline{AB}$ is positive and is the length of the segment.

If AB has negative direction, then $\overline{AB}$ is the negative of the length of AB. In any case, the absolute value of $\overline{AB}$ is the length of AB:

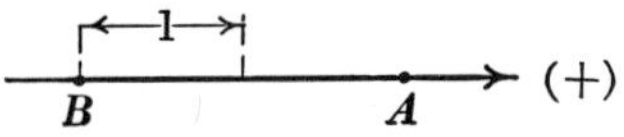

Figure 3

$$|\overline{AB}| = \text{(length of segment } AB\text{).} \qquad (1)$$

If a segment is directed from B to A, we refer to the segment as BA. Since AB and BA have opposite directions,

$$\overline{AB} = -\overline{BA} \qquad or \qquad \overline{AB} + \overline{BA} = 0. \qquad (2)$$

Illustration 1. In Figure 3, the positive direction is indicated on the line by an arrowhead (a common usage); then

$$\overline{AB} = -2; \quad \overline{BA} = 2; \quad |\overline{AB}| = |\overline{BA}| = 2.$$

We use the concept of a directed line segment in the representation of real numbers on a linear scale. Thus, in Figure 4, let OX be a directed line with

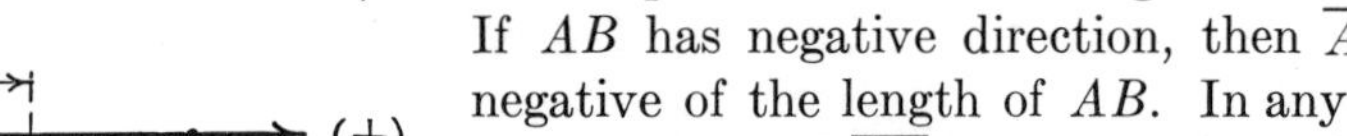

Figure 4

the positive direction to the right. If x is any real number, we associate it with that point P on the scale for which $x = \overline{OP}$, where $\overline{OP}$ is positive or negative according as P is to the *right* or the *left*, respectively, from O. On the real number scale OX, we shall call O the **origin,** and x the **coordinate** of P. We shall use "$P:(x)$" to abbreviate "*point P with coordinate x.*"

Figure 5    Figure 6

For any three points A, B, and C on a directed line, as in Figures 5 and 6,

$$\overline{AB} + \overline{BC} = \overline{AC}. \qquad (3)$$

In (3), if we think of the *value* of each segment as *the measure of travel in a specified direction*, then (3) simply states the fact that travel *from A to B*, followed by travel *from B to C*, is equivalent to travel *from A to C*.

Illustration 2. In Figure 4 on page 50, $\overline{AB} = 7$, $\overline{BC} = -5$, and $\overline{AC} = 2$. We verify that $7 + (-5) = 2$, as stated in (3).

THEOREM I. *If $P_1:(x_1)$ and $P_2:(x_2)$ are on a number scale, then*

$$\overline{P_1P_2} = x_2 - x_1; \tag{4}$$

$$\text{(length of } P_1P_2\text{)} = |\overline{P_1P_2}| = |x_2 - x_1|. \tag{5}$$

Proof of (4). In Figure 4, $\overline{OP_1} = x_1$, $\overline{OP_2} = x_2$, and $\overline{P_1O} = -\overline{OP_1}$. On applying (3) to (P_1, O, P_2) in that order, we obtain

$$\overline{P_1P_2} = \overline{P_1O} + \overline{OP_2} = \overline{OP_2} - \overline{OP_1} = x_2 - x_1.$$

Illustration 3. In Figure 4, the coordinates of B and C are 2 and -3, respectively. From (4), $\overline{BC} = -3 - 2 = -5$; $|\overline{BC}| = |-3 - 2| = 5$.

We use the number scale as a background for geometrical language where each *number* may be talked of as a *point*. Thus, to remark that b *is close to* c will mean that *the scale distance* $|b - c|$ *is small*.

On page 14, we defined "$b < c$" to mean that $(c - b)$ is *positive*. Suppose, now, that b and c are represented on a number scale, as in Figure 7, and that $b < c$. We recall that $(c - b)$ is the value of the directed line segment *from b to c* on the scale; since $(c - b)$ is positive, the line segment is directed to the *right*. Thus, we have proved that the following geometrical interpretation of "$b < c$" is correct (as accepted informally on page 15):

Figure 7

$b < c$ *means that b is to the* **left** *of c on the number scale.* (6)

If no agreement is made as to positive and negative directions on a line l, it is said to be undirected. Then, all distances measured on l are positive, and we may use either AB or BA for a segment of l with A and B as endpoints. In this case, either $\overline{AB}$ or $\overline{BA}$ is the length of AB. If we refer to a directed segment AB on a line where, previously, no positive direction has been assigned, we agree that AB has positive direction.

Let any number x_1 be represented on a number scale by point P_1, as in Figure 4 on page 50. We note that $|x_1|$ is the measure of the length of segment OP_1, or $|x_1| = |\overline{OP_1}|$. Then, if x_1 and x_2 are any two numbers, the student should verify with the aid of Figure 4 that

$$|x_1 + x_2| \leq |x_1| + |x_2|. \tag{7}$$

To check (7), the following mutually exclusive possibilities should be considered: (a) neither x_1 nor x_2 negative; (b) neither positive; (c) one negative and one positive. In (7), the sign "$=$" applies in (a) and (b), and the sign "$<$" in (c).

EXERCISE 8

Read the symbol in words and find its value.

1. $|3|$.　　　2. $|-4|$.　　　3. $|-2|$.　　　4. $|-6|^2$.　　　5. $|-2|^3$.

6. Mark $A:(2)$, $B:(-3)$, $C:(-6)$, and $D:(-8)$ on a number scale and compute $\overline{AB}$, $\overline{CD}$, $|\overline{BC}|$, and $\overline{DA}$.

Plot the points on a scale. Find $\overline{AB}$, $\overline{BC}$, and $\overline{AC}$ by use of (4) in Section 30, and check $\overline{AB} + \overline{BC} = \overline{AC}$. Also, compute $|\overline{AB}| + |\overline{BC}|$ and $|\overline{AC}|$.

7. $A:(-7)$; $B:(-3)$; $C:(-1)$.　　　　8. $A:(9)$; $B:(-1)$; $C:(-5)$.

9. $A:(-2)$; $B:(-6)$; $C:(0)$.　　　　10. $A:(8)$; $B:(-6)$; $C:(-3)$.

11. $A:(-5)$; $B:(7)$; $C:(2)$.　　　　12. $A:(9)$; $B:(-8)$; $C:(0)$.

Insert the proper sign, $<$ or $>$, between the numbers.

13. 2 and 5.　　　14. -12 and 3.　　　15. -3 and 0.　　　16. -4 and -7.

Think of the number x on a number scale and state the given fact by an inequality.

17. x is positive; negative.　　　　18. x is to the left of -4.

19. x is to the right of 6.　　　　20. x is to the right of -3.

Verify (7) on page 51 for the indicated numbers x_1 and x_2.

21. $x_1 = 5$; $x_2 = 7$.　　　　22. $x_1 = -3$; $x_2 = -5$.

23. $x_1 = -4$; $x_2 = 6$.　　　　24. $x_1 = -4$; $x_2 = 7$.

31. Terminology for numerical statements

In this text, sometimes it will be convenient to use the name **numerical statement** to refer to any variety of assertion concerning equality or inequality about certain numbers. We define an **open numerical statement** as a statement involving at least one variable. Thus, a numerical statement may be simply a single equation, or a single inequality, or a system of equations, or a system of inequalities, or may involve both equalities and inequalities. A numerical statement may be true or false as it stands; or, it may be true for just some values of the variables, or for all values of the variables.

In Definition VIII for the solution of an equation on page 44, let the word *"equation"* be changed to *"numerical statement."* Then, the definition applies unchanged otherwise. Similarly, the definitions of the following items for an equation on page 44 apply to a *"numerical statement:"*

$$\left.\begin{array}{l}\text{\textbf{solution set} } \textit{for a numerical statement;} \\ \text{\textbf{to solve} } \textit{a numerical statement;} \\ \textit{a } \textbf{consistent,} \textit{ or an } \textbf{inconsistent } \textit{numerical statement;} \\ \textit{a } \textbf{conditional,} \textit{ or an } \textbf{identical } \textit{numerical statement;} \\ \textbf{equivalent } \textit{numerical statements.} \end{array}\right\} \quad (1)$$

The student should write the definition for each item in (1) by changing *"equation"* to *"numerical statement"* in the discussion on page 44.

Illustration 1. The inequality $x^2 < 0$ is inconsistent, or has no solution, because x^2 is positive or zero for all real values of x. The inequality $x^2 \geq 0$ is an identical inequality (sometimes called an **absolute inequality**) for the reason mentioned in the preceding sentence.

Illustration 2. The solutions of $x < 3$ consist of all numbers represented by the points on a number scale to the left of the point 3. Thus, the solution set of $x < 3$ consists of infinitely many numbers.

DEFINITION I. *The **graph** (in one-dimension) of a numerical statement involving a single variable x is the set of points on a number scale representing the values of x in the solution set, S, of the statement.*

Illustration 3. In Figure 8, the heavy part of the number scale, omitting the circled point 3, is the graph of $x < 3$. In Figure 2 on page 44, we observed that the graph of $2x^2 - x = 1$ consists of just two points on the scale.

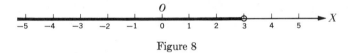

Figure 8

Illustration 4. A numerical statement may consist of two or more equations, or inequalities, considered as simultaneous conditions. Thus,

$$(x = 3 \quad and \quad x < 2)$$

is an *inconsistent* numerical statement involving a variable x. The statement

$$2 < x < 5 \quad means \quad (2 < x \quad and \quad x < 5). \tag{2}$$

In (2), any number x lying between the points 2 and 5 on the number scale satisfies the statement. We refer to (2) as a *system of two inequalities*, or a *pair of simultaneous inequalities* in x. We may refer to the numerical statement

$$(x - y = 5 \quad and \quad x + 2y = 2) \tag{3}$$

as a *system of two equations*, or as *two simultaneous equations* in the variables x and y. By methods met in elementary algebra, and to be reviewed briefly later, (3) is found to have just one solution, $(x = 4, y = -1)$.

Note 1. We have agreed that, occasionally, it will be convenient to employ a single name,* such as *numerical statement*, to cover a large class of mathematical statements for which some similar concepts are considered. However, inherent distinctions between *equations* and *inequalities*, and the importance of their individual roles, makes it essential to emphasize consideration of equations and inequalities separately.

If M is a set of real numbers, let us define **the graph of M on a number scale** as the set of points representing the numbers in M. Then, Definition I can be restated as follows: *the graph on a number scale of a numerical statement in the variable x is the graph of the solution set of the statement.*

---

* Instead of the name *numerical statement*, sometimes we find the name *sentence* used, with a somewhat more inclusive meaning.

32. Equivalent inequalities

From page 14, recall that, if b and c are any real numbers, then

$$b < c \qquad \textit{means that} \qquad (c - b) \textit{ is } \textbf{positive.} \qquad (1)$$

THEOREM II. *If b, c, and h are any real numbers, then*

$$b < c \qquad \textit{if and only if} \qquad \textbf{\textit{b}} + \textbf{\textit{h}} < \textbf{\textit{c}} + \textbf{\textit{h}}. \qquad (2)$$

Proof. 1. Suppose that $b < c$, and let $c - b = p$. Then, $p > 0$. Hence, we obtain

$$(c + h) - (b + h) = c - b = p > 0.$$

Therefore, by (1), we see that $b + h < c + h$ if $b < c$.

2. Now, suppose that $b + h < c + h$. Then, if $-h$ is added to both sides, the first part of this proof shows that the new inequality thus obtained will be true, or

$$b + h - h < c + h - h, \qquad or \qquad b < c.$$

Thus, if either inequality in (2) is true, the other inequality also is true.

THEOREM III. *If b, c, and r are any real numbers, where $r > 0$, then*

$$b < c \qquad \textit{if and only if} \qquad \textbf{\textit{rb}} < \textbf{\textit{rc}}. \qquad (3)$$

Proof. 1. Assume that $b < c$ and let $c - b = p$, where $p > 0$ because of (1). Then,

$$rc - rb = r(c - b) = rp > 0,$$

because $r > 0$ and $p > 0$. Hence, $rb < rc$.

2. Assume that $rb < rc$. Then, by Step 1 of this proof, if both sides are multiplied by $1/r$, the new inequality thus obtained is true, or

$$\frac{1}{r}(rb) < \frac{1}{r}(rc), \qquad or \qquad b < c.$$

Hence, if either inequality in (3) is true, we see that the other inequality also is true.

THEOREM IV. *If b, c, and r are any real numbers, where $r < 0$, then*

$$b < c \qquad \textit{if and only if} \qquad \textbf{\textit{rb}} > \textbf{\textit{rc}}. \qquad (4)$$

That is, if both sides of an inequality are multiplied by a negative number, an equivalent inequality is obtained by reversing the sign of inequality.

Proof. 1. Assume that $b < c$, and let $(c - b) = p$. Then

$$rb - rc = r(b - c) = -rp > 0,$$

because both $-r$ and p are positive. Hence, $rc < rb$.

2. Assume that $rc < rb$. By Step 1 of this proof, if both sides of this inequality are multiplied by the negative number $1/r$, the inequality sign must be reversed, to obtain a true inequality, and thus

$$\frac{1}{r}(rc) > \frac{1}{r}(rb), \quad or \quad b < c.$$

Hence, if either inequality in (4) is true, the other inequality also is true, when $r < 0$.

Illustration 1. If $b < c$ then $-2c < -2b$.

THEOREM V. *If b, c, and d are any real numbers, where $b < c$ and $c < d$, then $b < d$.*

Proof. We have $(c - b) > 0$ and $(d - c) > 0$. Hence,

$$d - b = d - c + c - b = (d - c) + (c - b) > 0.$$

Therefore, because of (1), we have $b < d$.

Illustration 2. From Theorem V, since $-3 < 5$ and $5 < 9$, we find that $-3 < 9$.

Suppose, now, that U, V, H, P, and N are number symbols involving the same variables. Also, assume that $P > 0$ and $N < 0$ for all values of the variables. Then, the statement $U < V$ is an open inequality, which may have solutions, or $U < V$ may become a true inequality when the variables are assigned certain values. Then, as a consequence of Theorems II–IV, we shall obtain the following results.

$\left\lvert\begin{array}{l} \textit{The open inequality } \boldsymbol{U} < \boldsymbol{V} \textit{ is } \textbf{equivalent} \textit{ to (has the} \\ \textit{same solutions as) each of the following inequalities:} \end{array}\right\rvert$

$$U + H < V + H; \quad PU < PV; \quad NU > NV. \tag{5}$$

At this point, for convenience in the discussion, suppose that just one variable, x, is involved in (5). Suppose that $x = c$ is a solution of $U < V$. Then, with $x = c$ in U, V, and H, we have particular numbers U, V, and H to which Theorem II applies. Thus, $U < V$ at $x = c$ if and only if $U + H < V + H$. In other words, the open inequalities $U < V$ and $U + H < V + H$ have the *same solutions*, or are *equivalent*. Similarly, by use of Theorems III and IV, the open inequality $U < V$ is seen to be equivalent to each of the inequalities $PU < PV$ and $NU > NV$.

Note 1. If $U < V$ is replaced above by $U \leqq V$, and then "$<$" is changed to "$\leqq$" in (5), the equivalence statement about (5) remains true. This insertion of "$=$" is legitimate because, when "$=$" applies, the equivalence is a consequence of Theorem III about equations on page 45. The student should focus particularly on the reversal of the inequality sign from $U < V$ to $NU > NV$.

If U and V are polynomials in a variable x, then the inequality $U < V$ is said to be linear in x in case $U < V$ is equivalent to an inequality of the form

$$ax < b, \tag{6}$$

(or, equally well, $ax > b$), where a and b are constants and $a \neq 0$. To *solve* a linear inequality in x means to obtain a simple description of the solution set for the inequality, in the form

$$x < k \quad or \quad k < x. \tag{7}$$

We arrive at (7) for any linear inequality by use of operations leading to equivalent inequalities, as listed in (5). In (6) and (7), we might have "$\leq$" in place of "$<$," without any change in the verbal remarks.

EXAMPLE 1. Solve: $$\frac{7x}{3} - 1 < 17 - \frac{2x}{3}. \tag{8}$$

Solution. 1. Multiply both sides by 3:

$$7x - 3 < 51 - 2x. \tag{9}$$

2. Add $(3 + 2x)$ to both sides: $\qquad\qquad 9x < 54.$ (10)

3. Divide by 9: $\qquad\qquad\qquad\qquad x < 6.$ (11)

Because of (5), inequality (8) is equivalent to (9), then to (10), and finally to (11). Thus, the solution set for (8) consists of all numbers less than 6. The graph of (8) on a number scale would consist of that part of the number scale to the left of, and not including the point representing 6.

33. Identical, or absolute, inequalities

To prove that a specified open inequality is true for *all* values of any variable involved, it is sometimes convenient to proceed as follows.

Suggestive analysis. *Assume that the specified inequality is true. Proceed from it, by operations yielding equivalent inequalities, until a more simple inequality is obtained, which can be verified to be identically true. (This analysis is* **not** *part of the "proof.")*

Proof. *Start with the final simple inequality mentioned above and, from it, by reversal of preceding operations, attempt to derive the given inequality.*

In carrying out the suggestive analysis, some of the operations involved may not be of the types indicated in (5) on page 55. Hence, the demonstration mentioned above may not be a mere routine inspection of preceding steps.

EXAMPLE 1. Prove that, if $x \neq 1$ and $x > 0$, $\qquad \dfrac{1}{x} + x > 2.$ (1)

Solution.   1. *Suggestive part.*   **IF** the inequality is true, then

(multiply by x) $$1 + x^2 > 2x; \tag{2}$$

(subtract $2x$) $$1 - 2x + x^2 > 0, \quad or \quad (1 - x)^2 > 0. \tag{3}$$

2. *Proof.*   For all values of $x \neq 1$,

$$(1 - x)^2 > 0, \quad or \quad 1 - 2x + x^2 > 0. \tag{4}$$

On adding $2x$ to both sides of (4), we obtain the equivalent inequality

$$1 + x^2 > 2x. \tag{5}$$

Now, assume that $x > 0$. Then, for all $x \neq 1$ where $x > 0$, we obtain an inequality equivalent to (5) on dividing both sides by x. Since this operation yields (1), we have proved that (1) is true for all values of $x \neq 1$ if $x > 0$.

EXERCISE 9

Graph the inequality on a number scale.

1. $x < 2.$ **2.** $-3 \leqq x.$ **3.** $4x \leqq 9.$

Solve the inequality.   Then, obtain its graph on a number scale, drawing a small circle around any endpoint not included in the graph.

4. $3x - 15 < 0.$ **5.** $2x + 7 > 15.$ **6.** $\frac{2}{3}x - 7 < 4.$

7. $13 - 5x < 0.$ **8.** $7 - 2x > 3x.$ **9.** $\frac{1}{4}x - 3 < 2x.$

10. $2x - 3 < 5x + 7.$ **11.** $3x - \frac{2}{3} > \frac{5}{2}x - 4.$

12. $3x - \frac{2}{3} > \frac{2}{5}x + 1.$ **13.** $\frac{2}{5}x - 3 \leqq 4x - 6.$

14. $\frac{2}{5}x - \frac{2}{3} \leqq \frac{3}{4}x - \frac{17}{5}.$ **15.** $\frac{7}{2} - \frac{4}{3}x \leqq -\frac{5}{2} - \frac{10}{3}x.$

Solve for x in terms of the constants a and b.

16. $3x - a < b + 2x.$ **17.** $\frac{3}{2}a + 2bx \leqq ax - \frac{3}{5}b.$

If the variable x has the specified domain, prove that the inequality is true for all values of x.   It may be convenient to use (1) on page 54.

18. If $x > 1$, prove that $x < x^2$.   **19.** If $0 < x < 1$, prove that $x > x^3$.

20. If $0 < x < 1$ and n is a positive integer, prove that $x^n \leqq x$.

21. If $x > 1$ and n is a positive integer, prove that $x \leqq x^n$.

22. If $x + y > 0$ and $x \neq y$, prove that $\dfrac{x + y}{2} > \dfrac{2xy}{x + y}.$

If $x > 0$, $y > 0$, and $x \neq y$, prove the inequality.

23. $\dfrac{x + y}{2} > \sqrt{xy}.$ **24.** $\dfrac{x}{y} + \dfrac{y}{x} > 2.$ **25.** $\dfrac{2xy}{x + y} < \sqrt{xy}.$

26. Prove that $a^2 + b^2 \geqq 2ab$, for all values of a and b.

27. If $A > 0$ and $B > 0$, prove that the inequality $A > B$ is equivalent to (1) $A^2 > B^2$; (2) $A^3 > B^3$; (3) $A^n > B^n$, where n is a positive integer.

28. If $0 < A < B$ and $0 < U < V$, prove that $AU < BV$.

29. If $A < B$ and $C < D$, prove that $A + C < B + D$.

30. Prove that, if $A < B$ and $A + C < B + D$, it is *not* always true that $C < D$.

Comment. On many occasions in mathematics, the need arises for proof that a conjectured theorem is NOT true. Any theorem can be represented by *"H implies C,"* where H is the hypothesis and C is the conclusion. To prove that the theorem is not true, it may be convenient to exhibit a special example of the situation involved where the hypothesis H *is true* and the conclusion C *is false.* This would show that C *is not always true when* H *is true,* and hence would disprove the theorem. An example as just described then is called a **counterexample.** In Problem 30, the student should search for a counterexample where $A < B$, $A + C < B + D$, and $C \geqq D$.

34. Certain terminology concerning sets*

In order to represent a finite set of elements, we may merely list symbols for them, enclosed within braces as a standard notation indicating that a set is being described. This device may be called the **roster method** for describing a set.

Illustration 1. The set of all integers from 3 to 10 inclusive is represented by $\{3, 4, 5, 6, 7, 8, 9, 10\}$.

Either a finite or an infinite set, T, of elements (not necessarily numbers) may be described by introducing a variable, say r, whose domain is T, and specifying a condition on r which is satisfied if and only if r is in T.

Illustration 2. The infinite set, T, of all numbers between -1 and 4 can be represented as follows:

$$T = \{x \mid -1 < x < 4\}. \tag{1}$$

In (1), the vertical rule is read *"such that."* Then, (1) is read as follows:

T *is the set of all numbers x such that* $-1 < x < 4$.

Illustration 3. Let T be the set of all solutions (infinitely many) of the equation $x + 2y = 3$. Then, we may write

$$T = \{(x, y) \mid x + 2y = 3\}, \tag{2}$$

read *"T is the set of pairs of numbers (x, y) such that x + 2y = 3."* Thus, $(1, 1)$ is an element in T.

Sometimes it is said that **set builder notation** is employed when a symbol such as that on the right in (1) or (2) is used.

If r is a variable whose domain is a certain set T, and if the nature of T is well known, we may write simply

$$T = \{all\ r\}, \tag{3}$$

* Section 9 on page 19 should be reviewed.

which can be read *"T is the set of all elements r."* In this text, as a rule we shall use either the roster notation, as in Illustration 1, or (3), or simply a clear definition in words, without special symbolism, in describing a set of elements.

In the following discussion, we shall suppose that all sets to be mentioned are subsets of a certain set T, to be called the *basic space* or the *universal set*, or the *universe*. For instance, T might consist of all real numbers.

DEFINITION II. *If T is the basic space, the* **complement,** *H', of any set H is the set of elements of T which are not in H.*

Although the elements of T are thought of at present as abstract objects r, let us visualize them as points in a plane. Also, let T be thought of as all points of the plane inside some simple closed curve, such as C in Figure 9. Then, let H be the set of points inside some curve, as in Figure 9 where H is not cross-hatched. With this representation, the complement of H is the set H' which *is cross-hatched* in T. This interpretation of a set as points in a plane is extremely useful; a corresponding figure like Figure 9 sometimes is called a **Venn diagram.**

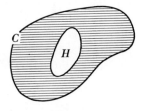
Figure 9

Illustration 4. Let T be the set of all pupils in a class consisting of 15 boys and 10 girls. Let H be the subset of T consisting of the boys in the class. Then the complement, H', of H is the subset of T consisting of the girls in the class.

Illustration 5. If S is the set of points covered by horizontal rulings in Figure 10, and T is the whole plane, then S' is indicated by the radial lines.

Figure 10

DEFINITION III. *The* **union** *of any number of sets is the set consisting of all elements which are in one or more of the sets.*

If A and B are sets, *"the union of A and B"* is represented by *"$A \cup B$."* The order in which the sets are described is of no importance in Definition III. Thus, $A \cup B = B \cup A$. The union of three sets, A, B, and C is represented by $A \cup B \cup C$, or any similar expression with the letters in any desired order. The symbol "$\cup$" may be read *"union"* wherever met.

Illustration 6. Let T be the set of all points in the plane in Figure 11, and let A and B represent the sets of points indicated by the vertical and horizontal rulings, respectively. Then $A \cup B$ consists of all ruled points; this set includes some points which are in *both sets*, and thus have double rulings. In general, $A \cup B$ consists of all elements in A alone, or in B alone, or in both A and B.

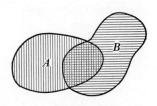
Figure 11

DEFINITION IV. *The* **intersection** *of any number of given sets is the set of elements belonging to all of the given sets.*

If A and B are sets, *"the intersection of A and B"* is denoted by *"$A \cap B$"*; it consists of all elements in *both A and B.* In Figure 11 on page 59, $A \cap B$ consists of all points in the doubly ruled region. To denote *"the intersection of A, B, and C,"* we write $A \cap B \cap C$, where the order of the letters is immaterial. The symbol *"$\cap$"* may be read *"intersection"* wher-ever met.

Illustration 7. In Figure 12, let A be the set of all points on the circle, and let B represent the set of points on the line. Then $A \cap B$ consists of just the two points P and Q where the line and circle intersect. Thus, the concept of the intersection of sets is consistent with the meaning previously as-signed to intersection of loci in geometry.

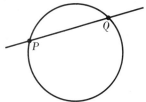

Figure 12

DEFINITION V. *To say that two sets A and B are* **mutually exclusive,** *or* **disjoint,** *means that they have no element in common, or $A \cap B = \emptyset$. To say that certain sets A, B, C, $\cdots$ are mutually exclusive, means that the intersection of any two of the sets is the empty set, $\emptyset$.*

Illustration 8. In Figure 13, A and B are mutually exclusive sets of points in the plane.

Figure 13

Illustration 9. In a group, T, of people, let H be the subset consisting of those with blue eyes who have brown hair, and K be the subset composed of those having brown eyes. Then, $H \cap K = \emptyset$, or H and K are mutually exclusive.

DEFINITION VI. *The* **difference** *of two sets A and B, represented by $A \setminus B$, and read "A slash B," is the set of all points of A which are not in B.*

We may refer to "$\setminus$" as a sign for *set subtraction.* It is important to notice that this operation is not so simple as subtraction of numbers in ordinary algebra.

Illustration 10. For any set H in the basic space T, we have $H' = T \setminus H$. In Figure 14, where A is the set of points inside the outer curve and B is the set inside the inner curve, $A \setminus B$ is the set of points covered just by vertical rulings. If we let $W = A \setminus B$, then $A = W \cup B$, because $W \cup B$ merely replaces those points of A which were re-moved by subtracting B. In Figure 14, $B \setminus A = \emptyset$, because all points of B are in A; in this case, we do *not* have $B = \emptyset \cup A$ because $\emptyset \cup A = A$ and $B \neq A$.

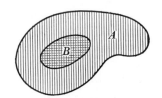

Figure 14

The preceding operations on sets, and the definitions of equality, $=$, and inclusion, $\subset$, for sets on page 19 offer a basis for an algebra of sets. In this algebra, the roles played by $\cup$, $\cap$, $\setminus$, $\subset$, and $\emptyset$ would resemble those played by $+$, $\times$, $-$, $\leqq$, and 0 in ordinary algebra. However, many peculiarities are exhibited by the operations of set algebra, as compared to the operations of ordinary algebra.

Illustration 11. With $\cup$ thought of as analogous to "$+$" and $\cap$ as analogous to "$\times$," we realize the possibility of differences between set algebra and ordinary algebra by observing the following easily verified results.

$$A \cup A = A; \quad A \cap A = A; \quad (A \cap B) \subset A;$$
$$\textit{if } A \subset B \quad \textit{then} \quad A \cup B = B.$$

Also, recall the last sentence in Illustration 10, where $B \setminus A = \emptyset$ but $B \neq \emptyset \cup A$; that is, "$\setminus$" and $\emptyset$ do *not* act like "$-$" and 0 in this instance.

The following simple laws of set algebra will prove sufficient for our needs in this text. The basic space for sets is T. We shall use mainly (4), (5), and (6).

(Commutative laws): $\quad\quad A \cup B = B \cup A; \quad A \cap B = B \cap A.$ $\quad\quad$ (4)

(Associative law for $\cup$): $\quad A \cup B \cup C = (A \cup B) \cup C = A \cup (B \cup C).$ $\quad$ (5)

(Associative law for $\cap$): $\quad A \cap B \cap C = (A \cap B) \cap C = A \cap (B \cap C).$ $\quad$ (6)

($\cap$ is distributive with respect to $\cup$):

$$A \cap (B \cup C) = (A \cap B) \cup (A \cap C). \tag{7}$$

($\cup$ is distributive with respect to $\cap$):

$$A \cup (B \cap C) = (A \cup B) \cap (A \cup C). \tag{8}$$

(Properties of empty set): $\quad\quad\quad A \cup \emptyset = A; \quad A \cap \emptyset = \emptyset.$ $\quad\quad$ (9)

(Transitive property of $\subset$): $\quad$ "$A \subset B$ and $B \subset C$" *implies* $A \subset C.$ $\quad$ (10)

(T acts like a unit in intersections): $\quad\quad T \cap A = A \cap T = A.$ $\quad\quad$ (11)

The results in (4) are a consequence of the fact that no specific order is assigned to the sets mentioned in the Definitions III and IV for *union* and *intersection*. In (5), each of the three expressions can be described as *"the set of all elements of the universe which are in A, or B, or C"*; hence, (5) is true. Similarly, the three expressions in (6) have the same description in words, so that (6) is true. The student should check the simple results in (9), (10), and (11) by reference to the definitions of $\emptyset$, $\cup$, $\cap$, and $\subset$.

To establish the fact that two specified subsets A and B of the universe, T, are equal, or the same, we try to prove that each element α of A is in B, and also that each element β of B is in A. The student will not be requested to carry out such demonstrations in this text except in supplementary work, but the method is illustrated by the following proof of (7). A similar proof would apply for (8).

★*Proof* of (7). 1. If α is an element in $A \cap B$, then α is in A and B, and hence is in $(B \cup C)$; therefore α is in $A \cap (B \cup C)$. Similarly, if α is in $A \cap C$, then α is in C and hence is in $B \cup C$; therefore, α is in $A \cap (B \cup C)$. Thus, any element in the right-hand set in (7) is in the set on the left.

2. Suppose that α is in $A \cap (B \cup C)$. Then, α is in A. Also, α is in $B \cup C$ and hence is in B alone or in C alone or in both B and C. Hence, α is in *both* A *and* B, or in *both* A *and* C. That is, α is in $(A \cap B) \cup (A \cap C)$, or each element α in the set on the left in (7) is in the set on the right. Hence, (7) is a true set equality.

Illustration 12. In Figure 15, for sets A, B, and C in the plane, $A \cap (B \cap C)$, or $(A \cap C) \cap B$, or $(B \cap C) \cap A$, etc., is represented by the region which is dotted and also is crossed by both vertical and horizontal lines.

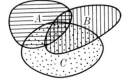

Figure 15

35. Systems of inequalities

In (2) on page 53, we remarked that a statement such as

$$A < B < C \qquad (1)$$

should be read $\qquad A < B \qquad and \qquad B < C, \qquad (2)$

which will be referred to as a *system* of inequalities, or as two *simultaneous inequalities*. If A, B, and C involve just one variable, x, let U, V, and W represent the solution sets of $A < B$, $B < C$, and (1), respectively; let G, H, and K be their corresponding graphs (sets of points) on a number scale. Then, W consists of all solutions *in both U and V; K consists of all points on a number scale *in both G and H*. Thus, from Definition IV on page 60,

$$W = U \cap V \qquad and \qquad K = G \cap H.$$

Illustration 1. Consider $\qquad -2 < x \leqq 3, \qquad (3)$

which means $\qquad -2 < x \qquad and \qquad x \leqq 3. \qquad (4)$

The graph G of $-2 < x$ in Figure 16 consists of all points to the right of point -2; the graph H of $x \leqq 3$ consists of 3 and all points to the left of 3. The graph K of (3), where $K = G \cap H$, consists of the points on the interval from -2 to 3, excluding -2 and including 3, shown by a black dot. The boundary points -2 and 3 of the interval are called its *endpoints*.

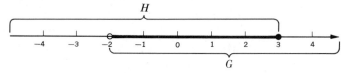

Figure 16

A finite interval of numbers on a number scale is called a **closed interval** if it includes its endpoints; an **open interval** if neither endpoint is included; a **half-open** or **half-closed interval** if just one endpoint is included. In Illustration 1, the graph of (3) is a half-open interval.

Illustration 2. Let A represent the interval of numbers x on a number scale, as in Figure 17, such that $-4 < x \leqq 2$. Let B represent all x such

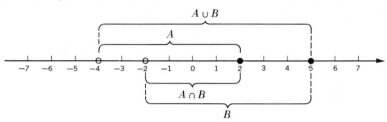

Figure 17

that $-2 < x \leqq 5$. That is,

$$A = \{x \mid -4 < x \leqq 2\}; \quad B = \{x \mid -2 < x \leqq 5\}.$$

Then, in Figure 17, $A \cap B$ is a half-open interval RQ, and $A \cup B$ is a half-open interval PS, where RQ and PS, thought of as sets of points representing values of x, are described as follows:

$$RQ = \{x \mid -2 < x \leqq 2\}; \quad PS = \{x \mid -4 < x \leqq 5\}.$$

Illustration 3. If $p > 0$, consider the inequality $|x| \leqq p$, where x is a variable. On a number scale, as in Figure 18, if some point S represents a particular number x, then the length of OS is equal to $|x|$. Hence, if $|x| \leqq p$, the distance of S from the origin, O, is at most p. Thus, $|x| \leqq p$ is equivalent to

$$-p \leqq x \leqq p, \quad or \quad (-p \leqq x \quad and \quad x \leqq p). \tag{5}$$

The graph of $|x| \leqq p$ is the closed interval with endpoints $\pm p$.

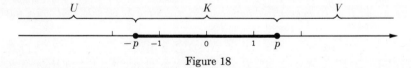

Figure 18

Illustration 4. With x as a variable,

$$|x| > p \quad \textit{is equivalent to} \quad (x < -p \quad or \quad x > p). \tag{6}$$

In Figure 18, the graph, U, of $x < -p$ consists of all points x to the left of $-p$ on the number scale. We may describe this infinite set of points as "all $x < -p$," or as the *infinite interval* (not including $-p$) extending from "*minus infinity to* $-p$," which we abbreviate by writing "$-\infty$ to $-p$," where of course "∞" is not used as a number. Similarly, the graph, V, of $p < x$ is the infinite interval extending from p to plus infinity $(+\infty)$, not including p. The graph, W, of $|x| > p$ from (6) consists of all points *"in U or in V."* Thus, by Definition III on page 59, $W = U \cup V$. If K represents the graph of $|x| \leqq p$ in Figure 18, and if the universe, T, for sets is the whole number scale, then $K \cup W = T$; thus K and W are complementary sets, or $K = W'$ and $K' = W$. In terminology about infinite intervals as just met, the whole number scale can be described as the infinite interval from $-\infty$ to $+\infty$.

EXERCISE 10

In Problems 1–3, the universe, T, consists of all integers.

1. If $A = \{1, 2, 3 \cdots, 10\}$ and $B = \{5, 6, 7, 8, \cdots, 20\}$, list the elements of
   $A \cap B;\quad A \cup B;\quad A \setminus B;\quad B \setminus A;\quad A \cup T;\quad B \cap T.$

2. If A is the set of all even positive integers, describe the complement, A', of the set A.

3. With A and B as in Problem 1, and $C = \{8, 9, 10, \cdots, 25\}$, find

   $$A \cup (B \cap C);\quad A \cap (B \cup C);\quad A \cup B \cup C;\quad A \cap B \cap C.$$

4. With the universe consisting of the children of ages less than 21 years in a given city, let the set of children with ages less than 11 years be A, the set with ages between 6 and 15 be B, and the set with ages between 5 and 21 be C. Describe $A \cup B; B \cup C; A \cap C; A \cap B; (A \cup B) \cap C$.

Let x be a variable, and obtain the graph, K, of the statement on a number scale. Also, by use of inequalities, define two sets, U and V, of points on the scale so that $K = U \cap V$.

5. $-1 < x < 4$.   6. $-3 \leqq x \leqq 0$.   7. $-4 < x \leqq 6$.

Let x be a variable, and obtain the graph, W, of the statement on a number scale. Also, by use of inequalities, define two sets, G and H, of points on the scale so that $W = G \cup H$ or $W = G \cap H$.

8. $|x| \leqq 3$.   9. $|x| \geqq 3$.   10. $|x| \geqq 4$.   11. $|x| < 4$.

Let the basic space or universe of points, T, be the whole number scale. For the specified subsets A and B of T, as described by inequalities, exhibit the requested sets on a number scale and describe them by use of inequalities.

12. $A = \{x \mid -3 \leqq x < 5\}; B = \{x \mid 2 \leqq x \leqq 8\}$. Find $A \cup B; A \cap B$.
13. $A = \{x \mid -4 < x \leqq 3\}; B = \{x \mid 0 < x \leqq 6\}$. Find $A \cup B; A \cap B$.
14. $A = \{x \mid x < 4\}; B = \{x \mid -1 < x\}$. Find $A \cup B; A \cap B$.
15. $A = \{x \mid x \leqq 3\}; B = \{x \mid 1 < x\}$. Find $A \cap B$.
16. $A = \{x \mid x \leqq 3\}; B = \{x \mid 4 < x\}$. Find $A \cap B; A \cup B$.
17. $A = \{x \mid x \leqq 5\}; B = \{x \mid -5 \leqq x\}$. Find $A \cap B$.
18. $A = \{x \mid x > 5\}; B = \{x \mid x < -5\}$. Find $A \cup B; A \cap B$.

★19. With A and B as in Problem 14, and $C = \{x \mid 2 \leqq x \leqq 5\}$, find

$$(A \cap B) \cup C;\quad A \cap B \cap C;\quad A \cup B \cup C.$$

★20. With A and B as in Problem 12, and $C = \{x \mid 3 \leq x \leq 9\}$, find

$(A \cup B) \cap C;$ $(A \cup C) \cap B;$ $(A \cap B) \cup C;$ $A \cap B \cap C;$ $A \cup B \cup C.$

★21. Prove (8) on page 61 by a suitable verbal argument.

36. Solution of systems of linear inequalities in x

In order to solve a compound statement such as $A < B < C$, involving just one variable x, it is advisable, first, to express the statement as a system of two inequalities, and then to solve each of the inequalities separately. The intersection of their solution sets is the solution set of $A < B < C$. We note that a statement of this nature may be inconsistent.

EXAMPLE 1. Solve: $\qquad 4 - x < 3x - 2 \leq x + 8.$ $\qquad$ (1)

Solution. 1. Statement (1) is equivalent to

$\qquad$ (a) $4 - x < 3x - 2$ $\quad$ *and* $\quad$ (b) $3x - 2 \leq x + 8.$ $\qquad$ (2)

2. Solution of (a). We obtain

$$6 < 4x, \qquad or \qquad \tfrac{3}{2} < x.$$

3. Solution of (b). We obtain

$$2x \leq 10, \qquad or \qquad x \leq 5.$$

4. In Figure 19, the graph G of $\tfrac{3}{2} < x$ is the infinite interval to the right of

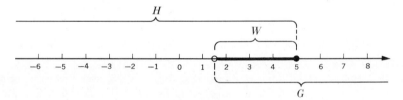

Figure 19

$\tfrac{3}{2}$ on the scale; the graph H of $x \leq 5$ is the infinite interval from $-\infty$ to 5, inclusive, on the scale. Let W be the graph of (1), or (2). Then, $W = G \cap H$, and W consists of all points x on the scale where $\tfrac{3}{2} < x \leq 5$. This half-open interval of numbers constitutes the solution set of (1).

EXAMPLE 2. Solve: $\qquad |x + 1| < 3.$ $\qquad$ (3)

Solution. 1. Statement (3) is equivalent to

$\qquad -3 < x + 1 < 3,$ $\quad$ *or* $\quad$ $(-4 < x$ $\quad$ *and* $\quad$ $x < 2).$ $\qquad$ (4)

2. The solution set for (3) is the intersection of the solution sets for the simultaneous simple inequalities in (4). This intersection is the open interval of numbers x where $-4 < x < 2$.

EXERCISE 11

Solve the statement and indicate its graph on a number scale.

1. $1 < 3x - 5 \leqq 4$.

2. $4 - x < 3x - 2 \leqq x + 4$.

3. $5 \leqq 3 + 2x < 7$.

4. $7 < 2x - 1 \leqq 2 - x$.

5. $8 < 3x < 7 - 2x$.

6. $\frac{1}{3} + 2x < 3x - 5 < -4 + x$.

7. $\frac{5}{2}x - 4 < 3x - \frac{2}{3} < x + \frac{1}{4}$.

8. $\frac{2}{5}x + 1 \leqq 3x - \frac{2}{3} < x + 5$.

9. $|x + 2| < 3$.   **10.** $|x - 3| < 4$.   **11.** $|x - 4| \geqq 3$.   **12.** $|x - a| < r$.

Note 1. From (5) on page 51, $|x_2 - x_1|$ is the distance on a number scale between the points representing x_1 and x_2. Hence, $|x - a| < r$ states that the variable x satisfies the inequality in case the distance between a and x on the scale is less than r. Thus, the graph of $|x - a| < r$ is the open interval of the scale with center at a and length $2r$.

EXERCISE 12

Review of Chapter 2

1. Read the symbol in words and find its value: $|-3|^3$; $|-4|^2$.

2. Mark $A:(-2)$, $B:(4)$, $C:(-5)$, and $D:(7)$ on a number scale. Compute $\overline{AC}$; $\overline{BD}$; $|\overline{DA}|$. Verify $\overline{AC} = \overline{AB} + \overline{BC}$.

3. In Problem 2, compute $\overline{BA}$, $|\overline{CD}|$, and $\overline{DC}$ by use of (4) and (5) on page 51.

4. Insert the proper inequality sign between (a) -4 and 2; (b) 5 and -8.

Solve the statement and indicate its graph on a number scale.

5. $\frac{2}{3}x - \frac{5}{6} \leqq \frac{1}{4}x + \frac{5}{3}$.

6. $\frac{4}{5} - \frac{2}{3}x < 2 - \frac{1}{15}x$.

7. $x - 1 < 3x - 2 \leqq x + 5$.

8. $x + 2 < 2x - 3 < \frac{1}{3}x + 2$.

Let T be the set consisting of all integers, and let all sets be subsets of T. With the given sets A, B, and C, describe the set requested in the problem.

9. If A consists of all integers x such that $3 \leqq x < 15$, and B consists of all x such that $-4 \leqq x < 12$, describe $A \cup B$; $A \cap B$; $A \setminus B$; $B \setminus A$.

10. If C consists of all integers x such that $-6 < x \leqq 8$, and A and B are the sets of Problem 9, describe

$$A \cup B \cup C; \quad A \cap B \cap C; \quad A \cup (B \cap C); \quad B \cup (A \cap C); \quad C \cap (A \cup B).$$

Let x be a variable, and obtain the graph, K, of the statement on a number scale. By use of inequalities, define two intervals, A and B, of points on the scale such that $K = A \cap B$, or such that $K = A \cup B$, whichever may be possible.

11. $-3 < x \leqq 2$.   **12.** $-2 \leqq x \leqq 0$.   **13.** $|x| \leqq 6$.

14. $|x| > 3$.   **15.** $|x - 2| > 1$.   **16.** $|x + 2| \leqq 3$.

17. Describe, by use of words without set builder notation or inequality symbols, the set $A = \{x \mid |x - 3| < 2\}$.

★**18.** If (x_1, y_1, x_2, y_2) are any four numbers, prove that

$$\sqrt{(x_1 + x_2)^2 + (y_1 + y_2)^2} \leqq \sqrt{x_1^2 + y_1^2} + \sqrt{x_2^2 + y_2^2}.$$

Chapter 3 Functions; Linear Statements in Two Variables

37. Coordinates in a plane

A pair of elements x and y is said to be an **ordered pair** in case each element is assigned to a specific place in two available locations. If two symbols are written with a comma between them, we shall call the corresponding elements the first and second *components* of the pair. Two ordered pairs of symbols (a, b) and (c, d) are considered *identical* if and only if a and c represent the same element and b and d represent the same element. Thus, the ordered pairs of numbers (a, b) and (c, d) are identical if and only if $a = c$ and $b = d$. To initiate analytic geometry in a plane, we shall associate an ordered pair of numbers, called *coordinates*, with each point in the plane.

Consider a given plane subject to any one of the customary sets of postulates involved in Euclidean geometry at the high school level. In this plane, we draw two perpendicular lines, each called a *coordinate axis*, with one axis, OX, horizontal and the other, OY, vertical in the typical Figure 20. We agree that the axes and lines parallel to them will be *directed lines*, with the positive direction to the *right* parallel to OX, and *upward* parallel to OY. On each axis, we establish a number scale with O as the origin. We choose *arbitrarily* a unit for scale distance on OX, and a unit for scale distance on OY, where these units are *not necessarily equal*. For coordinates, we shall measure distances in the plane parallel to OX in terms of the scale unit on OX, and parallel to OY in the scale unit on OY. Let P be any point in the given plane. Then, by definition:

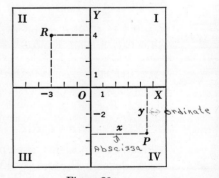

Figure 20

67

The horizontal coordinate, or **abscissa,** *of P is the directed distance x, measured parallel to OX, from the vertical axis OY to P.*

The vertical coordinate, or **ordinate,** *of P is the directed distance y, measured parallel to OY, from the horizontal axis OX to P.*

The abscissa and ordinate of P together are called its **rectangular coordinates.** We shall use *"P:(x, y)"* to mean *"P with coordinates (x, y),"* and read *"P:(x, y)"* as *"P, x, y."* Rectangular coordinates establish a one-to-one correspondence between all ordered pairs of real numbers and the points in the plane. The intersection, $O:(0, 0)$, of the axes is called the **origin** of coordinates. The axes divide the plane into four **quadrants,** numbered I, II, III, and IV, counterclockwise from OX.

Illustration 1. To plot $R:(-3, 4)$, erect a perpendicular to OX at $x = -3$ and go 4 units upward to reach R, in Figure 20.

Recall that a geometric *locus* is a set of all points satisfying a specified condition.

Illustration 2. The locus of all points $P:(x, y)$ with $x = 5$ is the line perpendicular to OX and 5 units to the right of OY.

Note 1. *"To find a point"* usually means *"to find its coordinates."*

Hereafter in this text, unless otherwise specified, in any reference to an xy-plane, it will be implied that the scale units on the axes possibly are unequal. We make the following agreement.

$$\left\{ \begin{array}{l} \textit{If the scale units on the coordinate axes in an} \\ \textit{xy-plane are equal, this unit also applies in} \\ \textit{measuring distance in any direction in the plane.} \end{array} \right\} \quad (1)$$

The **projection** of a point P on a line l is defined as the foot of the perpendicular from P to l.

Illustration 3. In Figure 20 on **page 67,** the projection of $R:(-3, 4)$ on OX is $(-3, 0)$ and on OY is $(0, 4)$. The projection of any point $P:(x, y)$ on OX is $(x, 0)$ and on OY is $(0, y)$.

Note 2. If A and B are any two points, at present *"AB"* will refer to the segment AB of the line through A and B, as on page 50.

THEOREM I. *Suppose that the scale units on the coordinate axes are equal in an xy-plane. Then, the distance, d, between $P_1:(x_1, y_1)$ and $P_2:(x_2, y_2)$, or the length of P_1P_2, is given by*

$$d = |\overline{P_1P_2}| = \sqrt{(x_2 - x_1)^2 + (y_2 - y_1)^2}. \quad (2)$$

Proof. 1. In Figure 21 on page 69, let H be the intersection of perpendiculars to OY through P_1, and to OX through P_2. Then, in triangle P_1HP_2, by the Pythagorean theorem we obtain

$$d^2 = (\overline{P_1P_2})^2 = (\overline{P_1H})^2 + (\overline{HP_2})^2.$$

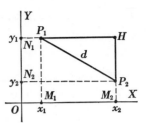

2. From (4) on page 51,

$$\overline{P_1H} = \overline{M_1M_2} = x_2 - x_1;$$
$$\overline{HP_2} = \overline{N_1N_2} = y_2 - y_1.$$

Hence, $\qquad d^2 = (x_2 - x_1)^2 + (y_2 - y_1)^2.$

On extracting square roots we obtain (2).

Figure 21

Since $|\overline{P_1P_2}| = |\overline{P_2P_1}|$, and also because (2) involves *squares* of differences, the *order* of P_1, P_2 in (2) is immaterial. In (2), $|\overline{P_1P_2}|$ can be rewritten merely $\overline{P_1P_2}$ if P_1P_2 is undirected, and hence has a nonnegative value.

Illustration 4. From (2), the distance between $A:(2, -8)$ and $B:(-3, 4)$

is $\qquad \overline{AB} = \sqrt{(-3 - 2)^2 + [4 - (-8)]^2} = \sqrt{25 + 144} = 13.$

The distance d of $P:(x, y)$ from the origin $O:(0, 0)$ is called the **radius vector** of P and is found from (2):

$$d = \sqrt{x^2 + y^2}. \tag{3}$$

EXAMPLE 1. Find the point on OX equidistant from $A:(5, 4)$ and $B:(-2, 3)$ in a plane where a single unit of length applies as in (1).

Solution. 1. Let the unknown point be $P:(x, 0)$, in Figure 22. Then $|\overline{PA}| = |\overline{PB}|$. This occurs if and only if $(\overline{PA})^2 = (\overline{PB})^2$. From (2),

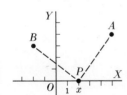

$$(\overline{PA})^2 = (5 - x)^2 + 4^2; \tag{4}$$
$$(\overline{PB})^2 = (x + 2)^2 + 3^2. \tag{5}$$

2. From (4) and (5),

$$25 - 10x + x^2 + 16 = x^2 + 4x + 4 + 9.$$

Figure 22 $\qquad$ Therefore, $14x = 28$ or $x = 2$. The point is $P:(2, 0)$.

EXERCISE 13

Find the other vertex of a rectangle with the given vertices.

1. $(3, 4)$; $(-5, 4)$; $(3, -1)$. $\qquad\qquad$ 2. $(-2, -1)$; $(3, -1)$; $(3, 2)$.

3. A line l through $(2, -3)$ is perpendicular to OY. What is true about the ordinates of all points on l?

Describe and construct the locus of a point $P:(x, y)$ satisfying the condition.

4. The abscissa is -3. $\qquad\qquad$ 5. The ordinate is -4.

Plot the point and its projections M and N on OX and OY, respectively.

6. $(3, 7)$. $\qquad$ 7. $(-2, 4)$. $\qquad$ 8. $(-2, -5)$. $\qquad$ 9. $(8, -7)$.

If A represents the first point and B the second, find $\overline{AB}$ and $|\overline{AB}|$.

10. $(0, 8); (0, 5)$.   **11.** $(8, 4); (2, 4)$.   **12.** $(-1, 3); (-1, 5)$.

13. $(2, 2); (9, 2)$.   **14.** $(3, 4); (3, -12)$.   **15.** $(x_1, y_1); (x_1, y_2)$.

In the following problems, the scale units on the coordinate axes are equal.

Find the distance between the points, or an expression for it.

16. $(1, 2); (3, 6)$.   **17.** $(5, 0); (0, 12)$.   **18.** $(3, 7); (-6, 7)$.

19. $(7, 2); (2, 14)$.   **20.** $(-1, -3); (2, 1)$.   **21.** $(0, 0); (4, 7)$.

22. $(0, 3); (4, 0)$.   **23.** $(-2, 5); (-2, -1)$.   **24.** $(x, y); (3, -4)$.

Prove that the triangle with the given vertices is isosceles.

25. $(-2, 8); (-1, 1); (3, 3)$.   **26.** $(3, -1); (3, -3); (7, -2)$.

Prove that the triangle with the given vertices is equilateral.

27. $(-2, 0); (8, 0); (3, 5\sqrt{3})$.   **28.** $(0, 2); (0, -6); (4\sqrt{3}, -2)$.

Prove that the points are the vertices of a right triangle.

29. $(-1, -1); (1, 0); (-2, 6)$.   **30.** $(3, 2); (5, 3); (0, 8)$.

31. Find y if $(-3, y)$ is equidistant from $(-3, 2)$ and $(5, 6)$.

32. Find a point on OX equidistant from $(-1, 1)$ and $(3, 5)$.

38. Inclination and slope*

Let l be a nonhorizontal line in an xy-plane. Then, regardless of the scale units chosen on the coordinate axes, we define the **inclination** of l as that angle ψ, less than 180°, through which the x-axis must be rotated counterclockwise about its intersection with l in order to coincide with l. If l is horizontal, its inclination is defined as $\psi = 0°$. Thus, in any case, we have $0° \leqq \psi < 180°$, as illustrated in Figures 23 and 24.

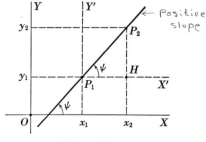
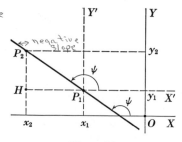

Figure 23   Figure 24

Note 1. The *whole line* through two points A and B will be referred to as AB when there is no danger of confusion with the *segment AB*.

---

* The student should review the definitions of the trigonometric functions of angles, particularly the tangent of an angle, on page 383.

THEOREM II. *Let $P_1:(x_1, y_1)$ and $P_2:(x_2, y_2)$ be distinct points on a non-vertical line l in an xy-plane with equal scale units on the axes. Then, if ψ is the inclination of l,*

$$\begin{Bmatrix} \textit{the scale units are} \\ \textit{equal on OX and OY} \end{Bmatrix} \qquad \tan \psi = \frac{y_2 - y_1}{x_2 - x_1}. \qquad (1)$$

Proof. 1. The order in which we label P_1 and P_2 is immaterial in (1). Hence, we assign subscripts to P_1 and P_2 so that $x_1 < x_2$ if $\psi < 90°$ and $x_2 < x_1$ if $\psi > 90°$, as in Figures 23 and 24. Then, the following discussion applies to either figure.

2. With respect to the lines P_1X' and P_1Y' as *new $x'y'$-axes*, and with the same unit for distance as in the xy-system, the coordinates of P_2 are

$$x' = \overline{P_1H} = x_2 - x_1 \qquad and \qquad y' = \overline{HP_2} = y_2 - y_1. \qquad (2)$$

Hence, by the definition of the tangent function on page 383, $\tan \psi = y'/x'$, which gives (1).

Note 2. If the scale unit for x is v inches and for y is w inches (possibly $v \neq w$), in Figure 23 we obtain, in inches, $\overline{P_1H} = v(x_2 - x_1)$ and $\overline{HP_2} = w(y_2 - y_1)$, so that

$$\begin{Bmatrix} \textit{x-unit, v inches;} \\ \textit{y-unit, w inches} \end{Bmatrix} \qquad \tan \psi = \frac{w}{v} \cdot \frac{y_2 - y_1}{x_2 - x_1}. \qquad (3)$$

From (1) or (3), $(y_2 - y_1)/(x_2 - x_1)$ is a constant for all choices of P_1 and P_2 on l because ψ is a constant. Then, we give the fraction a name as follows.

DEFINITION I. *The* **slope,** *m, of a nonvertical line l in any xy-plane is the ratio of the change in the vertical coordinate to the change in the horizontal coordinate as we move on l from any point $P_1:(x_1, y_1)$ to a distinct point $P_2:(x_2, y_2)$, or*

$$\begin{Bmatrix} \textit{in any} \\ \textit{xy-plane} \end{Bmatrix} \qquad \textbf{slope} = m = \frac{y_2 - y_1}{x_2 - x_1}. \qquad (4)$$

From (1) and (4),

(equal *scale units on axes)* $\qquad\qquad m = \tan \psi. \qquad (5)$

Illustration 1. To find the slope of the line through $A:(2, -5)$ and $B:(-3, 4)$, use (4) with A as P_1 and B as P_2, or with B as P_1, etc.:

$$m = \frac{4 - (-5)}{-3 - 2} = -\frac{9}{5} \qquad or \qquad m = \frac{-5 - 4}{2 - (-3)} = -\frac{9}{5}.$$

Recall that $\tan \psi > 0$ if $0° < \psi < 90°$; $\tan \psi < 0$ if $90° < \psi < 180°$.

Note 3. In the remainder of this section, we restrict the major discussion to an xy-plane where the scale units on the axes are *equal,* so that (1) and (5) are true. The discussion applies with minor changes to *any* xy-plane if (3) is used in place of (1).

From (5), $\tan\psi > 0$ or the slope of a line l is *positive* if and only if $0° < \psi < 90°$, and is *negative* if and only if $90° < \psi < 180°$. If $\psi = 90°$ so that l is vertical, we have not defined the notion of slope for l, or **a vertical line has no slope;** this corresponds to the fact that $\tan 90°$ does not exist. If l varies so as to approach a limiting vertical position, then $|m|$ grows large without bound or, briefly, m *becomes infinite*, because $|\tan\psi|$ becomes infinite as ψ approaches $90°$ as a limit. On account of the preceding remarks, although a vertical line has no slope in the ordinary sense, it is sometimes said that *a vertical line has infinite slope.*

Illustration 2. The slope of l is positive if, colloquially, l slopes upward to the right ($\psi < 90°$), and is negative if l slopes downward to the right ($\psi > 90°$). If l is horizontal, the slope of l is zero. If l is vertical, l has no slope.

Illustration 3. From (5), if $\psi = 45°$, the slope is $m = \tan 45° = 1$. If $\psi = 117°$, from Table IV we find $m = \tan 117° = -\tan 63° = -1.963$. If $m = -.8$, then $\tan\psi = -.800$ and hence ψ is obtuse; from Table IV,

$$\tan 38.7° = .800; \quad hence \quad \psi = 180° - 38.7° = 141.3°.$$

Note 4. From (4), $\qquad$ *(slope of a nonvertical line l)* $= \dfrac{\text{rise}}{\text{run}}$, $\qquad$ (6)

where the *rise*, $(y_2 - y_1)$, and the *run*, $(x_2 - x_1)$, are measured from any point $P_1:(x_1, y_1)$ to any distinct point $P_2:(x_2, y_2)$ on l.

THEOREM III. *In any xy-plane, two lines l_1 and l_2 with slopes m_1 and m_2, respectively, are parallel if and only if $m_1 = m_2$.*

Proof. Let ψ_1 and ψ_2 be the inclinations of l_1 and l_2, respectively. Lines l_1 and l_2 are parallel if and only if $\psi_1 = \psi_2$. This is equivalent to stating that $\tan\psi_1 = \tan\psi_2$, which is equivalent to $m_1 = m_2$.

EXAMPLE 1. With $A:(2, 3)$, $B:(4, 6)$, $C:(-3, 1)$, and $D:(-1, 4)$, determine whether or not line AB is parallel to line CD.

Solution. The slopes m_1 and m_2 of AB and CD, respectively, are

$$m_1 = \frac{6 - 3}{4 - 2} = \frac{3}{2}; \qquad m_2 = \frac{4 - 1}{-1 + 3} = \frac{3}{2} = m_1.$$

Hence, AB is parallel to CD.

THEOREM IV. *In any xy-plane, if A, B, and C are distinct points where the lines AB and BC have the slopes m_1 and m_2, respectively, then A, B, and C are collinear (lie on a line) if and only if $m_1 = m_2$.*

Proof. To say that A, B, and C *lie on a line* is equivalent to stating that lines AB and BC *coincide*, which means that they are *parallel*. By Theorem III, AB and BC coincide if and only if $m_1 = m_2$, which proves Theorem IV.

Illustration 4. To prove that $A:(2,3)$, $B:(5,1)$, and $C:(11,-3)$ are collinear, we compute

$$(\textit{slope of } AB) = \frac{3-1}{2-5} = -\frac{2}{3}; \quad (\textit{slope of } BC) = -\frac{3+1}{11-5} = -\frac{2}{3}.$$

Hence, the points are collinear.

In considering an angle formed by two lines in an xy-plane, for simplicity we agree that the scale units on the coordinate axes will be taken *equal*, so that $\tan \psi = m$ as in (5) on page 71. This agreement will apply also in discussing perpendicularity or inclinations of lines, unless otherwise implied.

THEOREM V. *If lines l_1 and l_2 have slopes m_1 and m_2, respectively, then l_1 and l_2 are perpendicular if and only if the slopes are negative reciprocals, or*

$$\boldsymbol{m_1 = -\frac{1}{m_2}}, \quad or \quad \boldsymbol{m_2 = -\frac{1}{m_1}}, \quad or \quad \boldsymbol{m_1 m_2 = -1.} \quad (7)$$

Proof. We are given that l_1 and l_2 have slopes. Let the inclinations of l_1 and l_2 be ψ_1 and ψ_2, respectively, where the notation is chosen so that $\psi_1 \leqq \psi_2$. To say that "*l_1 and l_2 have slopes and are perpendicular*" is equivalent to saying that "*$\psi_2 = \psi_1 + 90°$ and $\psi_1 \neq 0$,*" as in Figure 25. Since ψ_2 and $(\psi_1 + 90°)$ both lie on the domain from 90° to 180°, we have $\psi_2 = \psi_1 + 90°$ if and only if

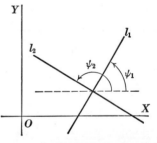

$$m_2 = \tan \psi_2 = \tan (\psi_1 + 90°), \text{ or*}$$

$$m_2 = -\cot \psi_1 = -\frac{1}{\tan \psi_1} = -\frac{1}{m_1}.$$

Hence, l_1 and l_2 are perpendicular if and only if $m_2 = -1/m_1$.

Figure 25

Illustration 5. Line l_1 through $(-2, 1)$ and $(2, 3)$ is perpendicular to line l_2 through $(-1, 4)$ and $(2, -2)$ because

$$m_1 = \frac{3-1}{2+2} = \frac{1}{2}; \quad m_2 = \frac{-2-4}{2+1} = -2 = -\frac{1}{m_1}.$$

EXERCISE 14

Find the slope of the line with the given inclination.

1. 73°.   2. 96°.   3. $\frac{3}{4}\pi$.†   4. $\frac{2}{3}\pi$.   5. $\frac{1}{4}\pi$.   6. $\frac{5}{6}\pi$.

Find the inclination, in degrees, corresponding to the given slope.

7. $m = 3$.   8. $m = .554$.   9. $m = -2$.   10. $m = -.325$.

* Recall the trigonometric identity $\tan (\theta + 90°) = -\cot \theta$.
† When there is no indication of degree measure for an angle, the value is understood to be stated in radian measure. See page 384.

Find the slope of the line through the given points.

11. $(2, 3)$; $(7, 10)$.   **12.** $(-2, 4)$; $(4, -3)$.   **13.** $(-4, -7)$; $(-3, -4)$.

14. $(1, 4)$; $(5, 6)$.   **15.** $(0, -3)$; $(-2, 5)$.   **16.** $(6, -4)$; $(2, -3)$.

Prove that lines AB and CD are parallel, or that they are perpendicular.

17. $A:(3, 5)$; $B:(1, 1)$; $C:(-2, 1)$; $D:(-1, 3)$.

18. $A:(-1, -2)$; $B:(-2, -4)$; $C:(2, -3)$; $D:(0, -2)$.

19. $A:(1, 5)$; $B:(1, 2)$; $C:(2, -4)$; $D:(3, -4)$.

Prove that the points are collinear.

20. $(2, 3)$; $(3, 5)$; $(1, 1)$.   **21.** $(-2, 1)$; $(0, 2)$; $(4, 4)$.

22. $(0, 3)$; $(1, 6)$; $(-1, 0)$.   **23.** $(-3, -5)$; $(1, -6)$; $(-7, -4)$.

Prove the result if the scale units on the axes are equal.

24. $(-4, 1)$, $(2, 4)$, $(5, -2)$, and $(-1, -5)$ are vertices of a square.

25. $(1, 0)$, $(-2, 6)$, and $(-1, -1)$ are vertices of a right triangle.

Find x, or y, if the points are collinear.

26. $(3, 4)$; $(2, 6)$; $(x, 3)$.   **27.** $(3, -2)$; $(1, -3)$; $(2, y)$.

28. Prove by use of slopes that the points $(-2, 1)$, $(-1, -2)$, $(2, 2)$, and $(3, -1)$ are the vertices of a parallelogram.

29. In an xy-plane where a single unit is used for all distances, prove that the following points are the vertices of a rhombus: $(1, -1)$, $(2, 3)$, $(5, 0)$, $(6, 4)$.

39. Graph of an equation in two variables

Consider an equation in two variables, x with the domain H and y with the domain K, where H and K possibly do not consist entirely of real numbers. By Definition VIII on page 44, a *solution* of the equation is a *pair of corresponding values of x and y*, or is an *ordered pair* of numbers (x, y), which satisfy the equation. Hereafter in this chapter, we shall assume that the domain of any variable consists of real numbers. Then, the solution set for an equation in two variables is a set of *ordered pairs of real numbers*. At present, in any equation which we consider, each member will be a polynomial in the variables.

Illustration 1. In $3x - 5y = 15$, if $y = 0$ then $x = 5$ in order to satisfy the equation; thus $(5, 0)$ is a solution of it. Another solution is $(8\frac{1}{3}, 2)$, with $y = 2$. The given equation has infinitely many solutions obtained similarly.

Suppose that each solution (x, y) of an equation in x and y is taken as the coordinates of a point in an xy-plane. This leads to the following terminology.

DEFINITION II.* *The* **graph** *or* **locus** *of an equation in two variables x and y is the set of points whose coordinates (x, y) satisfy the equation.*

---

* This definition extends without alteration if the word *equation* is replaced by *any numerical statement*, in two variables. See Section 31 on page 52.

Suppose that T is *any* set of ordered pairs of real numbers (x, y) and let us define the *graph of* T as the set of points in an xy-plane whose coordinates are number pairs in T. Then, in place of Definition II, we may say that **the graph of an equation in x and y is the graph of the solution set for the equation.** The graph is drawn through points corresponding to representative solutions (x, y).

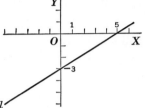

Illustration 2. To graph $3x - 5y = 15$, we compute the following solutions. The graph, in Figure 26, is seen to be a straight line, l.

$x =$	-5	-2	0	5	6
$y =$	-6	$-4\frac{1}{5}$	-3	0	$\frac{3}{5}$

Figure 26

To say that an equation is **linear,** or of the *first degree* in x and y, means that the equation is equivalent to one of the form $Ax + By + C = 0$, where A and B are constants not both zero. In Figure 26, we illustrated the fact (to be proved later) that *the graph of a linear equation in x and y is a line.*

The **x-intercepts** of a graph in an xy-plane are the values of x at the points where the graph meets the x-axis; the **y-intercepts** are the values of y where the graph meets the y-axis. Intercepts are useful in graphing. We obtain the intercepts of the graph of an equation in x and y as follows:

1. *To find the x-intercepts, place $y = 0$ and solve for x.*

2. *To find the y-intercepts, place $x = 0$ and solve for y.*

Illustration 3. To graph $3x - 5y = 15$, we place $x = 0$ and find $y = -3$, the y-intercept. The x-intercept is $x = 5$. The graph is in Figure 26.

Illustration 4. We may look upon $x - 8 = 0$ as a linear equation in x and y where y has the coefficient zero. Then, the graph of $x - 8 = 0$ in an xy-plane has an x-intercept, $x = 8$, but no y-intercept because we cannot have $x = 0$. Hence, the graph is the line perpendicular to the x-axis where $x = 8$.

Illustration 5. To graph $y - x^2 + 2x + 1 = 0$, we solve for y to obtain $y = x^2 - 2x - 1$; then we assign values to x and compute y to obtain solutions (x, y). The graph, in Figure 27, is called a **parabola.** Sometimes we refer to an equation by giving it the name of its graph. In Figure 27, we observe the *parabola* $y = x^2 - 2x - 1$.

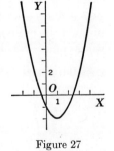

$x =$	-2	0	1	2	4
$y =$	7	-1	-2	-1	7

Figure 27

An equation of a locus in an xy-plane is an equation in x and y whose graph is the given locus.

If we can find one equation for a locus, then we can write infinitely many equivalent equations for it. As a rule, we refer to the particular one of these equations with which we deal as **THE** equation of the locus.

Illustration 6. The locus of $3x - 5y = 15$ is the line l in Figure 26, page 75. This line also is the locus of the equivalent equation $6x - 10y = 30$.

Either the *equation of a locus* in an xy-plane or the *locus of an equation* in x and y is determined by the following conditions.

A. *If $P:(x, y)$ is on the locus, the coordinates (x, y) of P satisfy the equation.*

B. *If $P:(x, y)$ is not on the locus, then (x, y) does not satisfy the equation.*

EXERCISE 15

Graph each equation in an xy-plane.

1. $3x + 2y = 6$.
2. $3y - 4x - 12 = 0$.
3. $3x + 7y = 0$.
4. $x - 5 = 0$.
5. $y = -7$.
6. $x + y = 0$.
7. $3x - 4 = 0$.
8. $4x + 5y + 20 = 0$.
9. $2y + 9 = 0$.
10. $5x = 3y$.

Graph the equation with $x = 2$ used in the table of values.

11. $y = x^2 - 4x - 5$.
12. $y = 3 + 4x - x^2$.
13. $y = 3 - 8x + 2x^2$.

Graph the equation with $y = -2$ used in the table of values.

14. $x = y^2 + 4y - 5$.
15. $x = 7 - 8y - 2y^2$.
16. $2x - 8y = 2y^2 + 5$.

17. Make verbal statements to prove that $3x^2 + y^2 = -5$ has no graph.
18. Prove that the graph of $x^2 + (y - 2)^2 = 0$ consists of just one point.

Write the equation of the line satisfying the condition.

19. Parallel to the y-axis with the x-intercept 7.
20. Parallel to the x-axis with the y-intercept -4.

40. Functions

If x and y are variables, and it is said that *"y is a function of x,"* this brings to mind the existence of some rule assigning values of y corresponding to given values of x. We shall make this terminology precise.

DEFINITION III. *Let D be a given set of numbers. Suppose that, for each number x in D, some rule specifies **just one** corresponding number y, and let R be the set of all of these values of y. Then,*

$$\left\{ \begin{array}{l} this\ \textbf{correspondence}\ between\ the\ numbers\ of\ D\ and \\ those\ of\ R\ is\ called\ a\ \textbf{function},\ F,\ from\ D\ to\ R, \end{array} \right\}\ or \qquad (1)$$

$$\left\{ \begin{array}{l} the\ \textbf{whole set of ordered pairs} \\ (x, y)\ is\ called\ a\ \textbf{function},\ F. \end{array} \right\} \qquad (2)$$

The *correspondence* in (1) determines the *ordered pairs* in (2); conversely, *these pairs* create the *correspondence*. Hence, mere personal preference is involved in deciding which of (1) and (2) is to be emphasized at any time. In Definition III, each value of y is called a *value of the function*. The set D of values of x is referred to as the **domain** (of definition) of F, and R is called the **range** (of values) of F. From (2), we may refer to F as *a set of ordered pairs* (x, y). In view of (1), we may speak of F as *a correspondence between the domain D and the range R*, or as *a mapping of D on R*. We call x the **independent variable** and y the **dependent variable.** We may refer to F as *"a function of x,"* to indicate that x is to be used as a symbol for the independent variable. We call F a *function of a single variable* because D consists of *single numbers*.

Illustration 1. Let D be the set of all x such that $1 \leqq x \leqq 3$, and let $y = 2x + 3$. If $x = 1$ then $y = 5$; if $x = 2$ then $y = 7$; etc. Thus, with x in D, the values of y make up the interval R, $5 \leqq y \leqq 9$, on OY in Figure 28,

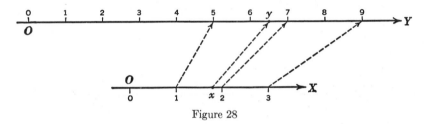

Figure 28

where the correspondence between x and y is indicated by representative arrows. This *correspondence* is a function, F, mapping D on R; we say that F is *defined as a function of x* by the equation $y = 2x + 3$.

Any formula in a variable x, specifying a single value for each value of x, defines a function whose values are given by substitution in the formula. However, a function may be defined merely by its tabulated values, or other means, without use of a formula. If a function is defined by a formula, the function frequently is named on the basis of the nature of its formula. Thus, in previous mathematics, the student has dealt extensively with algebraic functions and, less extensively, with trigonometric, logarithmic, and exponential functions. These types are called the **elementary functions** of mathematical analysis. We shall not study trigonometric functions.

Illustration 2. In Definition III, if $y = k$, a constant, for all values of x, we say that F is a **constant function.**

DEFINITION IV. *In an xy-plane, the* **graph of a function** *of a single variable, x, is the set of all points whose coordinates (x, y) form pairs of corresponding values of x and the function.*

On the basis of Definition IV, we are led to the following procedure to graph a function defined by a formula in a variable x: *place y equal to the formula and graph the resulting equation.* Usually, in graphing a function in a coordinate plane, we use the horizontal axis for plotting values of the independent variable.

Illustration 3. To graph the function whose value is $(x^2 - 2x - 1)$ at any value of the variable x, we let $y = x^2 - 2x - 1$ and graph this equation. The graph is the parabola in Figure 27 on page 75.

Illustration 4. Let D be $\{0, 1, 2, 3, 4, 5, 6, 7, 8, 9, 10, 11, 12, 13\}$. Let F be the function such that, for any x in D, the value, y, of F is the largest integral multiple of 2 which is at most equal to x. Thus, if $x = 0$ then $y = 0$; if $x = 5$ then $y = 4$, etc. The range, R, of F is $\{0, 2, 4, 6, 8, 10, 12\}$. In Figure 29,

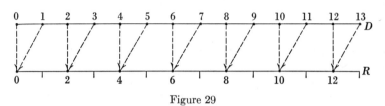

Figure 29

the correspondence between D and R is shown by arrows. F consists of fourteen pairs $(0, 0)$, $(1, 0)$, $(2, 2)$, $(3, 2)$, $\cdots$, $(11, 10)$, $(12, 12)$, $(13, 12)$. A graph of F would consist of fourteen points.

In the description of a function F, the letters used for the independent and dependent variables are of no importance. Thus, suppose that F is defined by stating that, for every number x in the domain, the value, y, of F is $y = 3x - 5$. The same function is defined by saying that, for every number u in the domain, the value, r, of F is $r = 3u - 5$.

★*Note 1.* In Definition III, since *just one* value of y corresponds to each value of x, sometimes it is said that a function, as thus defined, is *single-valued.*

★*Note 2.* In Definition III, if we change the word *number* to *element*, the definition describes a function F whose domain D is a set of *elements, of any specified variety*, and whose range is a second set of *elements*. Thus, D might consist of a *set of people*, and y, with range R, might be the *color of the eyes of the person x of D*. Functions of this nature are important but, in this book, except when otherwise indicated, the domain and range of any function will consist of *numbers*, as specified in Definition III.

Let F be a function with the domain D. Then, it frequently is convenient to represent the *value* of F corresponding to the number x in D by the symbol "$F(x)$," read "F of x" or "F at x." Thus,

$$\left\{\begin{array}{l} F(x) \text{ represents the } \textbf{value } \textit{of } F \textit{ cor-} \\ \textit{responding to any number } x \textit{ in } D. \end{array}\right\} \tag{3}$$

We then say that $F(x)$ is a symbol in functional notation. We use symbols like F, G, H, f, g, h, etc., to represent functions. In $F(x)$, we call x the **argument.**

Illustration 5. If we write $F(x) = 3x^2 + x - 5$, this assigns F as a symbol for the function, and gives a formula, $3x^2 + x - 5$, for the *values* of F. Thus, the values of F at $x = -1$ and $x = 2 + h$ are

$$F(-1) = 3 - 1 - 5 = -3; \quad F(2 + h) = 3(2 + h)^2 + (2 + h) - 5.$$

Illustration 6. If $f(x) = 5x^2 + 2$ and $g(y) = 4/y$, then

$$[f(3)]^2 = [5(9) + 2]^2 = 47^2 = 2209; \quad f(x)g(x) = (5x^2 + 2)\left(\frac{4}{x}\right) = 20x + \frac{8}{x};$$

$$f(g(y)) = 5(g(y))^2 + 2 = 5\left(\frac{4}{y}\right)^2 + 2 = \frac{80}{y^2} + 2;$$

In functional notation, Definition IV yields the following conclusion.

$$\left\{\begin{array}{l} \textit{The } \textbf{graph of a function } \textit{\textbf{F}, with the independent variable} \\ x, \textit{ in an xy-plane, is the } \textbf{graph of the equation } \textit{\textbf{y}} = \textit{\textbf{F(x)}}. \end{array}\right\} \quad (4)$$

Illustration 7. If $F(x) = 2x^2 + 5$, the graph of F is the graph of the equation $y = 2x^2 + 5$. The following table of values was computed by assigning values to x and computing y. The graph, through the corresponding points, is the parabola in Figure 30.

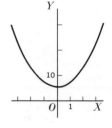

Figure 30

$x =$	-3	-1	0	1	3
$y =$	23	7	5	7	23

Suppose that the functions f and g have a common domain, D. Then, for f and g, we define their *sum function,** H, *product function,** K, and *quotient function,** Q, for f divided by g, as those functions with the following values:

$$H(x) = f(x) + g(x); \quad K(x) = f(x)g(x); \quad Q(x) = \frac{f(x)}{g(x)}.$$

The domain for both H and K is the common domain D for f and g. The domain for Q consists of all numbers x in D such that $g(x) \neq 0$. If c is any constant, the product function cf is defined as that function W for which $W(x) = cf(x)$. Above, we might write $H = f + g$, $K = f \cdot g$, $Q = f/g$, and $W = cf$. It must be remembered that these statements are abbreviations for the definitions of the functions H, K, Q, and W, and are *not* equalities involving numbers.

Illustration 8. Let $f(x) = x^2 + 1$ and $g(x) = 2x - 5$. Then, for f and g, their sum, H, product, K, and quotient, Q, for f/g, have the values

$$H(x) = (x^2 + 1) + (2x - 5); \quad K(x) = (x^2 + 1)(2x - 5); \quad Q(x) = \frac{x^2 + 1}{2x - 5}.$$

The function f^2 has the values $\qquad f^2(x) = [f(x)]^2 = (x^2 + 1)^2.$

* The word *function* frequently will be omitted in such a case.

Let x and y be variables which are free to assume any ordered pair of values (x, y) in a certain set, D, of pairs of numbers. We may represent D as a corresponding set of points (x, y) in an xy-plane. Suppose that, to each point (x, y) in D, there corresponds just one number z, and let R be the set of all values thus obtained for z. Then,

$$\left\{ \begin{array}{c} \textit{this correspondence between pairs in } D \textit{ and numbers} \\ \textit{in } R \textit{ is called a function, } F, \textit{ from } D \textit{ to } R, \end{array} \right\} \textit{or} \qquad (5)$$

$$\left\{ \begin{array}{c} \textit{the whole set of ordered triples of numbers} \\ (x, y, z) \textit{ is called a function, } F. \end{array} \right\} \qquad (6)$$

In (5) and (6), F is said to be a function of two independent variables, x and y, because D consists of *pairs of numbers*, (x, y). We refer to D as the **domain** of F, and to R as the **range** of F. We write $z = F(x, y)$, meaning that $F(x, y)$, as well as z, represents the value of F at the point (x, y) in the domain of F. Similarly, we may have a function of three or more variables. Thus, $F(x, y, w)$ would represent the value of a function F of three independent variables at the point (x, y, w) in the domain of F.

Illustration 9. If $F(x, y) = 3x^2y + 8x + 5y^2$, then
$$F(2, -3) = -36 + 16 + 45 = 25.$$

Note 3. Hereafter, unless otherwise stated, in any reference to a *function* we shall mean a *function of a single variable*.

Note 4. To define the graph of a function, f, of *two variables*, with function values $f(x, y)$, we would let $z = f(x, y)$, and graph this equation in three variables in an xyz-coordinate system in space of *three* dimensions.

EXERCISE 16

State the range R of the function F and write the complete set of ordered pairs of numbers which form F. Construct a graph of F in an xy-plane. Also, prepare a diagram like Figure 28 on page 77 to show how F maps its domain on the range.

1. F has the domain $\{-4, -3, -2, -1, 0, 1, 2, 3, 4\}$ and the value of F for any number x in the domain is x^2.
2. The domain, D, of F consists of the integers $\{1, 2, 3, \cdots, 15\}$. The value of F corresponding to any number x in D is the largest integral multiple of 3 which is less than or equal to x.

Graph the function whose values, for any number x, are given by the formula.

3. $3x - 2$.   4. $-2x + 5$.   5. $x - 7$.   6. 12.
7. $(x^2 + 6x - 5)$, with $x = -3$ used in the table of values.
8. $(4x - x^2 + 3)$, with $x = 2$ used in the table of values.

If $f(x) = 2x + 3$, find the value of the symbol.

9. $f(2)$.   10. $f(-3)$.   11. $f(-2)$.   12. $f(\tfrac{1}{2})$.   13. $|f(-4)|^2$.

If $g(z) = 2z^4 - 3z^2$, find the value of the symbol.

14. $g(-3)$.　　　**15.** $3g(5)$.　　　**16.** $g(-\tfrac{1}{2})$.　　　**17.** $g(2c)$.　　　**18.** $g(\sqrt{x+y})$.

If $F(x, y) = 3y^2 + 2x - xy$, find the value of the symbol.

19. $F(3, 2)$.　　　**20.** $F(-1, 3)$.　　　**21.** $F(a, b)$.　　　**22.** $F(c, d^2)$.

23. If $h(u) = 2u + 3$ and $g(v) = v^3 - 2$, find $h(2)g(3)$; $h(3)$; $h(2)/g(-1)$; $h(g(x))$; $3h(x) + g(x)$; $g(h(x))$.

24. If $f(x) = x^2 + 2x - 1$, find $f(h)$; $f(3h)$; $f(x+2)$; $f(x+h)$; $f(4x)$.

25. If $H(x) = x^3$, find $H(2+k)$; $H(2x)$; $H(x-3)$.

26. Let $f(x) = 2x + 3$ and $g(x) = x + 5$. (a) If H, K, and Q are, respectively, the sum function and the product function for f and g, and the quotient function for f divided by g, find $H(3)$; $K(-1)$; $Q(2)$. (b) Describe the domain of Q. (c) If M represents f^2, find $M(3)$.

Unless otherwise implied, the domain of any variable x consists of all real numbers for which given number symbols are defined. Graph the function whose values are defined.

27. $f(x) = \sqrt{4 - x^2}$.　　　**28.** $f(x) = |x|$.　　　**29.** $f(x) = [x]$.*

30. $f(x) = |x - 3|$.　　　**31.** $f(x) = |4 + x|$.　　　**32.** $f(x) = x/|x|$.

41. Relations and functions defined by equations

Suppose that x and y are variables, and that T is any *nonempty set* of ordered pairs of numbers (x, y). Then, we shall refer to T as a **relation** in (or, between) x and y, and may speak of x and y as *related variables*. In particular, any consistent equation in x and y defines a relation, S, in x and y, where S is the set of all solutions (x, y) of the equation; then, we shall say that x and y are related by the equation.† Also, from (2) on page 76, *any function, F, is a relation* between the independent variable x and the dependent variable y, with the special characteristic that *just one value of y corresponds to each value of x.* In contrast, *a relation T between x and y is a function* with x as the independent variable *when and only when the special characteristic just mentioned is true.* Thus, some relations are *not* functions.

Illustration 1. The following table of corresponding values of x and y describes a relation, T, in x and y. We see that T is *not* a function with x *as the independent variable* because there are *two* pairs $(1, 2)$ and $(1, -4)$ with

$x =$	1	1	2	3	2
$y =$	2	-4	1	2	3

$x = 1$. Also, T is *not* a function with y *as the independent variable* because there are *two* pairs $(1, 2)$ and $(3, 2)$ with $y = 2$. A graph of T in the xy-plane would consist of just five points.

* $[x]$ represents the *greatest integer at most equal to x*.
† On page 95, we shall meet relations defined by inequalities.

Consider an equation in two variables (x, y),

$$h(x, y) = 0, \tag{1}$$

whose solution set is S. Assume that there exists a function, f, with values $y = f(x)$, and domain D so that, for each number x in D, the pair (x, y) is a solution of (1), and thus is an element in S. That is, we have

$$h(x, y) = 0 \text{ when } y = f(x), \quad or \quad h(x, f(x)) = 0, \tag{2}$$

when x is in D. Then, we shall refer to f as a **solution function** of (1) *for y as a function of x*. If S contains *just one* solution (x_0, y_0) for any assigned value $x = x_0$, then S *itself is a solution function* for y as a function of x, and we may say that (1) **defines y as a function of x.** If any solution function f, with $y = f(x)$, is considered as a set of ordered pairs of numbers, then f *is a subset of S*. If (1) is sufficiently simple, by solving (1) for y in terms of x we may be able to obtain the values $y = f(x)$ of one or more solution functions, f, giving all solutions in S. On reversing the preceding roles of x and y, we may refer to a function g, with $x = g(y)$, which is a *solution function* of (2) for x as a function of y, so that $h(g(y), y) = 0$. And, S *itself is a solution function*, for x as a function of y, in case there is just one solution (x_0, y_0) in S for each permissible number $y = y_0$. Then, we say that (2) **defines x as a function of y.**

Illustration 2. From $3x - 5y = 15$, we obtain

$$y = \tfrac{3}{5}x - 3, \quad \text{and similarly,} \quad x = \tfrac{5}{3}y + 5.$$

Hence, the equation $3x - 5y = 15$ defines y as a function of x, and also x as a function of y. The graph of either of these functions in an xy-plane is identical with the graph of $3x - 5y = 15$.

In Illustration 2, we observed a special case of the fact that, if (1) defines y as a function of x (or, x as a function of y), *the graph of this function in an xy-plane is identical with the graph of* (1). This is true because the set of pairs of values (x, y) forming the *function* is the same as the *solution set* of the corresponding equation.

Illustration 3. From $x^2 + y^2 = 25$, we obtain $y^2 = 25 - x^2$. Thus, y is a square root of $(25 - x^2)$, and hence

$$y = +\sqrt{25 - x^2} \quad or \quad y = -\sqrt{25 - x^2}. \tag{3}$$

$y = +\sqrt{25 - x^2}$	$y =$	0	4	4.6	5	4.6	4	0
	$x =$	-5	-3	-2	0	2	3	5
$y = -\sqrt{25 - x^2}$	$y =$	0	-4	-4.6	-5	-4.6	-4	0
	$x =$	-5	-3	-2	0	2	3	5

Let $f(x) = \sqrt{25 - x^2}$ and $g(x) = -\sqrt{25 - x^2}$. Then, f and g are solution functions of the equation $x^2 + y^2 = 25$ for y as a function of x. To obtain a table of values of x and y, we substitute values of x in (3) and compute y, with the aid of Table I. The domain of x, for real values of y, is the set of numbers satisfying $|x| \leq 5$. From the table, the graph of $y = f(x)$ is the *upper semicircle*, and of $y = g(x)$ is the *lower semicircle* in Figure 31. The *whole circle* is the graph of $x^2 + y^2 = 25$. The graph of $y = f(x)$ passes through point $(3, 4)$.

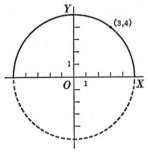

Figure 31

EXERCISE 17

By solving for y in terms of x, obtain a formula for the values of the function of x defined by the equation. Also, by solving for x in terms of y, obtain a formula for the values of the function of y defined by the equation. Then, graph the equation.

1. $4x + 3y = 12$.   2. $2x + y = 7$.   3. $3x - 6y = 8$.

4. Solve for y in terms of x to obtain a formula for the values of the function of x defined by $2y + 2x^2 - 4x = 5$. Then, graph the function, with $x = 1$ used in the table of values.

Draw a graph of the relation, T, between the variables x and y defined by the table of pairs (x, y). Is T a function (a) with x as the independent variable or (b) with y as the independent variable? Why?

5.

$x =$	3	2	0	3	-1
$y =$	1	4	-2	-2	3

6.

$x =$	0	1	2	3	6
$y =$	-3	2	1	-3	4

7. Repeat Problem 4 for the equation $2y + 2x^2 = 12x - 3$, with $x = 3$ used in the table of values for the graph.

8. Solve for x in terms of y to obtain a formula for the values of the function of y defined by the equation $2x + 4 - 6y = 3y^2$. Then, graph the function, with $y = -1$ used in the table of values, and with the x-axis horizontal in the coordinate system.

9. Obtain formulas for the values of two functions of x defined by the equation $4x^2 + y^2 = 16$. Then, graph each of these functions in an xy-plane where the same unit distance for the number scale is used on each coordinate axis. The graph in this case is a curve called an **ellipse**; this type of curve will be discussed later.

42. Equations for a line in an xy-plane

In the study of loci of a given type in analytic geometry, it is desirable to derive standard equations for the typical locus, corresponding to special features of its situation. At present, we illustrate this procedure for lines.

Illustration 1. If the x-intercept of a vertical line l is a, the equation of l is $x = a$. If the y-intercept of a horizontal line l is b, the equation of l is $y = b$. Thus we have the following standard forms.

Line parallel to OX: $y = b$. **Line parallel to OY: $x = a$.**

Two-point form. *The line l through two distinct points $P_1 : (x_1, y_1)$ and $P_2 : (x_2, y_2)$, not on a vertical line, has the equation*

$$y - y_1 = \frac{y_2 - y_1}{x_2 - x_1} (x - x_1). \tag{1}$$

Proof. 1. By substitution, $(x = x_1, y = y_1)$ and $(x = x_2, y = y_2)$ satisfy (1), so that P_1 and P_2 are on the graph of (1).

2. By page 71, segment P_1P_2 and l have the slope $(y_2 - y_1)/(x_2 - x_1)$.

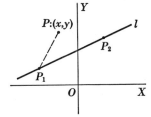

Figure 32

3. Let $P : (x, y)$ be *any* point in the plane distinct from P_1 and P_2, as in Figure 32. By Theorem IV on page 72, P is on l, or P_1, P_2, and P are *collinear*, *if and only if* line segment P_1P has a slope which is equal to the slope of segment P_1P_2. Then $x \neq x_1$ and the slope of P_1P is $(y - y_1)/(x - x_1)$. Hence, P is on l if and only if

$$\frac{y - y_1}{x - x_1} = \frac{y_2 - y_1}{x_2 - x_1}, \quad \text{or} \quad y - y_1 = \frac{y_2 - y_1}{x_2 - x_1} (x - x_1). \tag{2}$$

Therefore (1) is the equation of l, because (1) is *not true* if $P : (x, y)$ is *not* on l, and *is true* if P is P_1, P_2, or any other point on l.

In (1), we may refer to $(y_2 - y_1)/(x_2 - x_1)$ as *the slope, m, of l.* Then, (1) gives the following result.

Point-slope form. *The line through $P_1 : (x_1, y_1)$ with slope m has the equation*

$$y - y_1 = m(x - x_1). \tag{3}$$

Because of conditions A and B on page 76, a result such as (3) applies in two senses: *First,* the specified line has (3) as its equation. *Second,* the graph of any equation of the form (3) is *a line of the indicated character.*

Illustration 2. By (3), the graph of $y - 1 = 2(x - 3)$ is a line with slope 2 through $P_1 : (3, 1)$.

Illustration 3. The equation of the line through $(2, 3)$ and $(-3, 5)$ is obtained from (1) with $(2, 3)$ as P_1 and $(-3, 5)$ as P_2 (or vice versa):

$$y - 3 = \frac{5 - 3}{-3 - 2} (x - 2) \quad \text{or} \quad 5y + 2x = 19.$$

Illustration 4. An equation of the line with slope 3 through $(2, -5)$ is obtained from (3) with $m = 3$, $x_1 = 2$, and $y_1 = -5$:

$$y + 5 = 3(x - 2) \qquad or \qquad y - 3x = -11.$$

If $x_1 = x_2$, equation (1) does not apply, and $P_1 P_2$ is vertical; then, without (1), the equation of $P_1 P_2$ is $x = x_1$.

Illustration 5. The line through $(3, -5)$ and $(3, 8)$ is $x = 3$.

Note 1. To find a line will mean *to find an equation of the line.*

EXAMPLE 1. Find the line through $(2, -3)$ with the y-intercept -1.

Solution. The line l goes through $(0, -1)$ on the y-axis. From (1) with $P_1 : (2, -3)$ and $P_2 : (0, -1)$, the line l has the equation

$$y + 3 = \frac{-1 + 3}{0 - 2} (x - 2) \qquad or \qquad y + x + 1 = 0.$$

The intercept form. *If $a \neq 0$ and $b \neq 0$, the line with x-intercept a and y-intercept b has the equation*

$$\frac{x}{a} + \frac{y}{b} = 1. \tag{4}$$

Proof. Points $A : (a, 0)$ and $B : (0, b)$ are on the specified line. From the two-point form, the equation of AB is

$$y - 0 = \frac{b - 0}{0 - a} (x - a) = -\frac{b}{a} (x - a); \qquad or \qquad \frac{b}{a} x + y = b. \tag{5}$$

On dividing both sides in (5) by b we obtain (4).

Illustration 6. The equation of the line with x-intercept 3 and y-intercept -5 is obtained from (4):

$$\frac{x}{3} + \frac{y}{-5} = 1 \qquad or \qquad 5x - 3y = 15.$$

Slope-intercept form. *The line with slope m and y-intercept b in an xy-plane has the equation*

$$y = mx + b. \tag{6}$$

Proof. Point $B : (0, b)$ is on the line. From (3), an equation of the line through B with slope m is

$$y - b = m(x - 0) \qquad or \qquad y = mx + b. \tag{7}$$

Illustration 7. The line with slope -3 and y-intercept 5 is $y = -3x + 5$.

In an equation $Ax + By + C = 0$, where $B \neq 0$, we can always change the equation to the form (6) *on solving for y in terms of x*, and then *by inspection* obtain the slope and y-intercept of the graph of the given equation.

Illustration 8. By inspection, and comparison with (6), we see that the graph of $y = 3x - 7$ is a line with slope 3 and y-intercept -7.

Illustration 9. To obtain the slope-intercept form of $3x + 2y - 8 = 0$, solve for y in terms of x:

$$2y = -3x + 8 \qquad or \qquad y = -\tfrac{3}{2}x + 4.$$

Hence, $3x + 2y - 8 = 0$ is a line with slope $-\tfrac{3}{2}$ and y-intercept 4.

Illustration 10. If a line l in an xy-plane has the inclination $120°$ and y-intercept -8, the slope of l is $m = \tan 120° = -\sqrt{3}$, and the equation of l is

$$y = -\sqrt{3}x - 8.$$

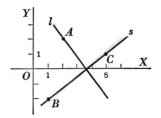

Figure 33

EXAMPLE 2. Find the equation of the line l through the point $A:(2, 2)$ perpendicular to the line s through $B:(1, -2)$ and $C:(5, 1)$.

Solution. In Figure 33, the slope of s is $\tfrac{3}{4}$. Since l is perpendicular to s, the slope m of l is the *negative reciprocal* of $\tfrac{3}{4}$, or $m = -\tfrac{4}{3}$. Hence, the equation of l is

$$y - 2 = -\tfrac{4}{3}(x - 2) \qquad or \qquad 4x + 3y = 14.$$

A function P is called a **polynomial function** of degree n in certain variables, say x and y, if $P(x, y)$ is a polynomial* of degree n in the variables. An equation in the variables, say x and y, is called a **polynomial equation** of degree n if the equation is of the form $f(x, y) = g(x, y)$ where $f(x, y)$ and $g(x, y)$ are polynomials, and $[f(x, y) - g(x, y)]$ is of degree n in the variables. We sometimes drop the word *polynomial* in the preceding terminology and refer simply to a *function* of degree n, or an *equation* of degree n. The values of any polynomial function P of degree n in x are given by a polynomial of the form

$$P(x) = a_0 + a_1 x + a_2 x^2 + \cdots + a_n x^n, \tag{8}$$

where $a_0, a_1, \cdots, a_n$ are constants and $a_n \neq 0$. If $n = 0$, then $P(x) = a_0$, where† $a_0 \neq 0$. Polynomial functions (or, equations) of degrees 1, 2, 3, and 4 are called, respectively, *linear, quadratic, cubic,* and *quartic* functions (or, equations) in the variables. With the degree $n > 4$, usually we do not use a special name, but merely state the degree.

If f is a constant function, so that $f(x) = b$, a constant, at all values of x, the graph of f in an xy-plane is the line $y = b$, or $y = 0 \cdot x + b$, whose slope is zero and y-intercept is b. If f is a *linear function* of a single variable, x, then $f(x)$ is of the form

$$f(x) = mx + b, \qquad where \qquad m \neq 0, \tag{9}$$

---

* Recall the definition of a polynomial on page 20.

† The constant function P, where $P(x) = 0$ at all values of x, is not referred to as a polynomial of degree *zero*, but sometimes is called the *zero polynomial*.

and the graph of f in an xy-plane is the line $y = mx + b$, with slope $m \neq 0$ and y-intercept b. Thus, from (6) on page 85 and the preceding remarks, we arrive at the following conclusion.

$$\left\{ \begin{array}{l} \textit{If } f(x) = mx + b, \textit{ the graph of the linear or constant function} \\ f \textit{ in an } xy\textit{-plane is the line with slope } m \textit{ and } y\textit{-intercept } b. \end{array} \right.$$

EXERCISE 18

Write the equation of the line satisfying the conditions.

1. Horizontal; y-intercept -5.   2. Vertical; x-intercept 3.
3. Slope 3; y-intercept 2.   4. Slope -2; y-intercept -3.
5. x-intercept 2; y-intercept 3.   6. x-intercept -1; y-intercept 4.
7. Slope $-\frac{2}{3}$; y-intercept 4.   8. Slope $\frac{13}{5}$; y-intercept -2.
9. Inclination $30°$; y-intercept 2.   10. Inclination $135°$; y-intercept 4.
11. *Inclination $\frac{1}{4}\pi$; y-intercept 3.   12. Inclination $\frac{1}{3}\pi$; y-intercept 3.

Write the equation of the line through the given points; or through the given point with slope m, inclination ψ, x-intercept a, or y-intercept b; or satisfying other data as given in the problem.

13. $(2, -4)$; $m = 5$.   14. $(1, 3)$; $m = -2$.   15. $(2, 0)$; $m = -\frac{1}{4}$.
16. $(-1, 3)$; $m = 0$.   17. $(5, -2)$; $\psi = \frac{1}{2}\pi$.   18. $(0, 0)$; $m = \frac{2}{3}$.
19. $(1, 5)$; $(3, 7)$.   20. $(0, 3)$; $(-1, 3)$.   21. $(-2, 3)$; $(1, 4)$.
22. $(3, -2)$; $(5, 0)$.   23. $(-1, 3)$; $(-1, 7)$.   24. $(3, 5)$; $\psi = 135°$.
25. $(-1, 3)$; $b = -3$.   26. $a = 6$; $b = -2$.   27. $b = 6$; $\psi = \frac{2}{3}\pi$.
28. $\psi = 45°$; $b = -3$.   29. $\psi = \frac{3}{4}\pi$; $b = 5$.   30. $(-1, 3)$; $\psi = \frac{1}{2}\pi$.

Write the equations of the lines through C which are, respectively, parallel to AB, and perpendicular to AB, in a coordinate plane having equal units on the axes. Check in a figure.

31. $A:(2, 5)$; $B:(1, 3)$; $C:(-2, 7)$.   32. $A:(1, -2)$; $B:(4, 7)$; $C:(5, 9)$.

Prove that the points lie on a line and find its equation.

33. $(2, 3)$; $(3, 5)$; $(1, 1)$.   34. $(1, -6)$; $(-3, -5)$; $(-7, -4)$.

Write the line in the slope-intercept form to find the slope and y-intercept, and then graph the line.

35. $2x + 3y = 6$.   36. $3x + 4y = -2$.   37. $5x = 12y + 6$.
38. $3x - 5y = 15$.   39. $6x + 10 = 5y$.   40. $x = 4y - 5$.

Graph the linear function whose values are given by the polynomial.

41. $3x - 5$.   42. $3 - 2x$.   43. $-6x$.   44. $-x - 4$.

* Recall that, when the measure of an angle is given simply as a *number*, without any indication of the *angular unit*, it is assumed to be 1 radian. Thus, "$\frac{1}{4}\pi$" in Problem 11 means "$\frac{1}{4}\pi$ radians." For discussion of radian measure, see page 384. Also, see page 386 for trigonometric functions of convenient angles.

43. General equation of the first degree in two variables

Any equation of the first degree in two variables x and y can be written in the equivalent form $Ax + By + C = 0$, where A and B are not both zero, which we call the *general equation* in x and y.

THEOREM VI. *The graph of any linear equation in x and y is a line.*

Proof. 1. If $B \neq 0$, we can solve $Ax + By + C = 0$ for y:

$$y = -\frac{A}{B}x - \frac{C}{B}. \tag{1}$$

This is the equation of a line with slope $-A/B$ and y-intercept $-C/B$.

2. If $B = 0$, then $A \neq 0$ and $Ax + By + C = 0$ becomes $Ax = -C$, from which we obtain $x = -C/A$. This is the equation of a vertical line. Hence, in *all* cases the locus of the equation $Ax + By + C = 0$ is a *line*.

THEOREM VII. *(Converse of Theorem VI.) Any line in the xy-plane has an equation linear in x and y.*

Proof. If a line l is vertical, with x-intercept a, the equation of l is $x = a$, which is linear in x and y. If l is not vertical, it has a slope m and y-intercept b. Then, the equation of l is $y = mx + b$. Hence, any line has an equation linear in x and y.

Note 1. The names *linear function* and *linear equation* may be associated with the fact that the corresponding graphs are straight lines. The nonlinear equation

$$(x^2 + 5)(x + 2y) = 0, \quad or \quad x^3 + 2x^2y + 5x + 10y = 0, \tag{2}$$

is satisfied if and only if $\quad x^2 + 5 = 0 \quad or \quad x + 2y = 0.$

But, $x^2 + 5 \neq 0$ for any real x. Hence, (2) is satisfied by a real pair (x, y) if and only if $x + 2y = 0$, whose graph is a line. Similarly, *nonlinear equations may be written for any given line,* although usually this is not done.

Hereafter, in referring to any equation for a line, we shall mean a *linear equation.* For brevity, we may refer to *"the line $Ax + By + C = 0$"* instead of to *"the line which is the graph of $Ax + By + C = 0$."*

EXAMPLE 1. Find the line l through $(-2, 3)$ perpendicular to the line $3x - 4y = 5$, in an xy-plane having equal units on the axes.

Solution. 1. Change $3x - 4y = 5$ to the slope-intercept form:

$$4y = 3x - 5; \quad y = \tfrac{3}{4}x - \tfrac{5}{4}; \quad hence, \ slope \ is \ \tfrac{3}{4}.$$

2. The slope of l is the negative reciprocal of $\tfrac{3}{4}$, or $-\tfrac{4}{3}$. Hence, by the point-slope form, the equation of l is

$$y - 3 = -\tfrac{4}{3}(x + 2), \quad or \quad 3y + 4x = 1.$$

44. Parallel or coincident lines

Note 1. Occasionally, we shall use the notation *"line $l:\{Ax + By + C = 0\}$"* to mean *"line l whose equation is $Ax + By + C = 0$."**

Consider two lines l_1 and l_2 and their slope-intercept forms:†

$$l_1:[A_1x + B_1y + C_1 = 0]; \quad l_2:[A_2x + B_2y + C_2 = 0]; \ or \tag{1}$$

$$l_1:\left[y = -\frac{A_1}{B_1}x - \frac{C_1}{B_1}\right]; \quad l_2:\left[y = -\frac{A_2}{B_2}x - \frac{C_2}{B_2}\right]. \tag{2}$$

We observe the following facts by checking slopes and intercepts in (2).

Lines l_1 and l_2 are parallel if and only if $\qquad \dfrac{A_1}{B_1} = \dfrac{A_2}{B_2}.$ $\qquad$ (3)

Lines l_1 and l_2 coincide if and only if $\quad \dfrac{A_1}{B_1} = \dfrac{A_2}{B_2} \quad$ *and* $\quad \dfrac{C_1}{B_1} = \dfrac{C_2}{B_2}.$ (4)

If, for convenience, we disregard certain simple special cases where some denominator below is zero, from (4) we obtain

$$\frac{A_1}{A_2} = \frac{B_1}{B_2} = \frac{C_1}{C_2}. \tag{5}$$

Let k be the common value of the fractions in (5). Then, from (5), l_1 **and** l_2 **of (1) coincide if and only if there exists a constant $k \neq 0$ such that**

$$A_1 = kA_2, \qquad B_1 = kB_2, \qquad C_1 = kC_2, \tag{6}$$

or such that *the equation of l_1 can be obtained by multiplying by k on both sides of the equation of l_2.* The preceding results hold for all lines l_1 and l_2, although we disregarded a few special cases, such as $A_2 = 0$ or $C_2 = 0$.

Illustration 1. $3x + 4y = 5$ is parallel to $6x + 8y + 3 = 0$ because $3:4 = 6:8$. The lines have equal slopes, $-\frac{3}{4}$ and $-\frac{6}{8}$.

Illustration 2. Lines $3x - 2y = 5$ and $-6x + 4y = -10$ coincide because we obtain the second equation on multiplying both sides of the first by -2.

Note 2. When two ordered sets of three numbers each, such as (A_1, B_1, C_1) and (A_2, B_2, C_2), are related as in (6), it is said that the two sets of numbers are *proportional.* Thus, l_1 and l_2 of (1) *coincide if and only if the coefficients in the equations for l_1 and l_2 are proportional.* Instead of (5), we sometimes write

$$A_1:B_1:C_1 = A_2:B_2:C_2,$$

which may be read *"A_1 is to B_1 is to C_1 as A_2 is to B_2 is to C_2."*

---

* This notation can be thought of as a convenient abbreviation of the current more complicated set builder notation. With l representing the set of points (x, y) on l, we would write,
in the notation of page 58, $l = \{(x, y) \mid Ax + By + C = 0\}$.
† Assume that $B_1 \neq 0$ and $B_2 \neq 0$. Special cases thus omitted are easily treated separately.

EXERCISE 19

Find the line through the given point parallel to, and perpendicular to, the given line.

1. $(2, -4); 3x - y = 6.$
2. $(6, 3); 2x - 6y - 9 = 0.$
3. $(0, 5); 3y - 4x + 7 = 0.$
4. $(a, b); hx + ky = 4, hk \neq 0.$
5. $(0, 0); y = 7.$
6. $(2, 4); x = -5.$

7. Prove that the lines intersect to form a parallelogram:

$$2x - 3y = 5; \quad 4x + 5y = 1; \quad 6y - 4x = 3; \quad 3 - 8x - 10y = 0.$$

8. Write $y = mx + b$ in the intercept form if $mb \neq 0.$
9. If $Ax + By + C = 0$ is a vertical line, prove that $B = 0.$
10. Under what conditions on A, B, and C will the line $Ax + By + C = 0$ pass through the origin; have no x-intercept; have no y-intercept?

Find the constant h if the lines are (a) parallel; (b) perpendicular.

11. $\begin{cases} 3x + 5y = 7, \\ hx + 2y = 4. \end{cases}$
12. $\begin{cases} 2x - 3y = 4, \\ hx - 2y = 5. \end{cases}$
13. $\begin{cases} 3x + 4y = 7, \\ 6x + hy = 5. \end{cases}$

Find g and h if the two lines coincide.

14. $\begin{cases} 3x - 5y = 2; \\ hx + 10y = g. \end{cases}$
15. $\begin{cases} 2x + hy = 3; \\ gx + 3y = 6. \end{cases}$
16. $\begin{cases} hx - 3y = 2; \\ 2x + gy = 8. \end{cases}$

17. If $AB \neq 0$ find the intercepts of the line $Ax + By + C = 0.$

Graph the equation.

18. $|x| + |y| = 4.$
19. $|x| - |y| = 5.$
20. $[x] = [y].$*
21. $|x + 2y| = 3.$
22. $|3x - 4y| = 12.$

45. Systems of linear equations in two variables

Let f, g, h, and k be functions of the independent variables x and y, and consider the system of equations, or the compound numerical statement,

$$f(x, y) = g(x, y) \quad and \quad h(x, y) = k(x, y). \tag{1}$$

First, recall Definition VIII and other terminology of Section 28 on page 44, when the content is recast with a *statement* such as (1) replacing an *equation* as met in Section 28. Thus, a *solution* of (1) is an ordered pair of numbers (x, y) which satisfies both equations in (1). In solving a system (1), we sometimes say that the equations are being solved *simultaneously*. If (1) has at least one solution, then (1) is said to be *consistent*, and otherwise is said to be *inconsistent*. System (1) is said to be *equivalent* to another system of two equations if the two systems have the same solution set. Similar terminology applies to a system consisting of a given number of equations in any number of variables. In the present chapter, our attention will be centered on (1) where each equation is linear in the variables.

* Recall that $[u]$ represents the greatest integer at most equal to u.

To solve a system of two equations in the variables x and y graphically, we *graph the two equations on the same coordinate system.* Then, the real solutions of the system are the pairs of coordinates (x, y) of the points of intersection, if any, of the graphs. The graphs do not intersect when and only when (*a*) all solutions of the system are non-real, or (*b*) the system has no solution, real or non-real.

EXAMPLE 1. Solve graphically:

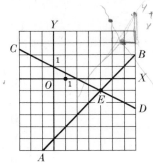

Figure 34

$$\begin{cases} x - y = 5, \text{ and} & (2) \\ x + 2y = 2. & (3) \end{cases}$$

Solution. 1. In Figure 34, AB is the graph of (2) and CD is the graph of (3). Hence, the point of intersection, E, of AB and CD is the only point whose coordinates satisfy both equations.

2. E has the coordinates $(4, -1)$. Hence, the pair $(x = 4, y = -1)$ is the only solution of the system. These values check in (2) and (3). As a rule, a graphical solution gives only approximate results. However, the graphical method furnishes a useful background for any exact algebraic solution.

Usually a system of two linear equations in two variables has just one solution and the graphs of the equations intersect in just one point, as was the case in Example 1, but the following special cases occur.

The graphs of the equations are distinct parallel lines if and only if the system has no solution, and thus the equations are **inconsistent.**

The graphs of the equations are the same line if and only if each solution of either equation is also a solution of the other equation, and hence the system has infinitely many solutions. In this case the equations are **consistent** *and also are said to be* **dependent** *equations.*

EXAMPLE 2. Solve graphically:

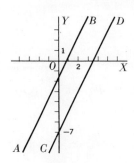

Figure 35

$$\begin{cases} 6x - 3y = 5, \text{ and} & (4) \\ 2x - y = 7. & (5) \end{cases}$$

Solution. 1. The graph of (4) is AB, and the graph of (5) is CD in Figure 35. (The graphs *appear* to be parallel, but *this must be proved.*)

2. In the slope-intercept form, equation (4) becomes $y = 2x - \frac{5}{3}$, and (5) becomes $y = 2x - 7$. Both graphs have slope 2, and hence are *parallel*, but *not identical.* Therefore, the system has no solution, or (4) and (5) are *inconsistent.*

The student will recall the following method for solving a system of two linear equations in two variables algebraically, by "addition or subtraction" of equivalent equations. We shall consider justification of this method after applying it.

A. *In each equation, multiply both members by a properly chosen number so as to obtain two equations in which the coefficients of one of the variables are equal. Then, subtract corresponding sides of the new equations so as to obtain an equation involving just one of the variables.*

B. *Solve the equation just obtained for the variable in it. Then, substitute the result in one of the given equations to obtain the corresponding value of the other variable, to form a solution of the given system.*

EXAMPLE 3. Solve for x and y:

$$\begin{cases} 4x + 5y = 6, \text{ and} & (6) \\ 2x + 3y = 4. & (7) \end{cases}$$

Solution. 1. Multiply in (6) by 3: $\qquad 12x + 15y = 18.$ $\qquad\qquad$ (8)

2. Multiply in (7) by 5: $\qquad\qquad 10x + 15y = 20.$ $\qquad\qquad$ (9)

3. Subtract, (9) from (8): $\qquad\quad 2x = -2; \quad x = -1.$ $\qquad\qquad$ (10)

4. On substituting $x = -1$ in (7) we obtain

$$3y = 4 + 2 \quad or \quad y = 2.$$

5. The solution of the system is $(x = -1, y = 2)$.

Comment. With the assumption (to be proved on page 93) that a new system consisting of [(10) *and* (7)] is equivalent to [(6) *and* (7)], we are *certain* that the values $(x = -1, y = 2)$ form *a solution* which is the *only solution* of [(6) *and* (7)]. This statement is true because (10) gives the single possible value of x, and $y = 2$ is then obtained in Step 4 as a single corresponding value for y. This gives $(-1, 2)$ as a pair which, by the substitution of $x = -1$ in (7), is known to satisfy both (10) and (7). Hence, the method in Example 3 not only obtains a *possible* solution but actually *verifies* it by substitution as it is obtained. Thus, we have no logical need for verifying by substitution that $(-1, 2)$ satisfies (6) as well as (7).

EXAMPLE 4. Solve for x and y:

$$\begin{cases} ax + by = e, \text{ and} & (11) \\ cx + dy = f. & (12) \end{cases}$$

Solution. 1. Multiply by d in (11): $\qquad adx + bdy = de.$ $\qquad\qquad$ (13)

Multiply by b in (12): $\qquad\qquad bcx + bdy = bf.$ $\qquad\qquad$ (14)

Subtract, (14) from (13): $\qquad\quad x(ad - bc) = de - bf.$ $\qquad\qquad$ (15)

Assume that $ad - bc \neq 0$, and divide by $ad - bc$ in (15):

$$x = \frac{de - bf}{ad - bc}. \qquad\qquad (16)$$

2. By similar steps, $\qquad\qquad y = \frac{af - ce}{ad - bc}. \qquad\qquad (17)$

The procedure [A, B] of page 92 is justified as follows.

THEOREM VIII. *Let r and s be any numbers not zero. Then, system* (1)* *on page* 90 *is equivalent to the system*

$$\begin{cases} f(x, y) = g(x, y), \text{ and} & (18) \\ rf(x, y) + sh(x, y) = rg(x, y) + sk(x, y). & (19) \end{cases}$$

Comment. In A on page 92, we chose r and s so that (19) would not involve one of x and y. In (18) and (19), the functions f, g, h, and k are not necessarily linear.

Proof. 1. From Theorem III on page 45, system (1) is equivalent to

$$\begin{cases} rf(x, y) = rg(x, y), \text{ and} & (20) \\ sh(x, y) = sk(x, y). & (21) \end{cases}$$

Assume that a particular pair of numbers (x, y) is a solution of (1) on page 90, and hence of [(20), (21)]. Then, on adding corresponding sides of (20) and (21), it is seen that (x, y) satisfies (19). Therefore, (x, y) satisfies both equations of [(18), (19)], since (18) is taken unchanged from (1). Or, any solution of (1) is a solution of [(18), (19)].

2. Now, suppose that a particular pair of numbers (x, y) is a solution of [(18), (19)]. Then, (x, y) satisfies (20). On subtracting each side of (20) from the corresponding side of (19), we obtain (21), and hence $h(x, y) = k(x, y)$. Therefore, any solution (x, y) of [(18), (19)] satisfies both equations in (1).

3. Thus, each solution of (1) is a solution of [(18), (19)], and each solution of [(18), (19)] is a solution of (1). Therefore, (1) is equivalent to [(18), (19)].

Observe that an equation such as (19) may replace any one of the given equations in (1), to obtain an equivalent system. Now, consider the special case where the equations in (1) are *linear*. With Theorem VIII as a basis, it is seen that any solution obtained as in Example 3 must be a solution of the given system. This solution *does not require testing* by substitution, as mentioned in the Comment following Example 3, unless we wish to check the previous details of computation. Moreover, if our process of solution should yield an equation (19) such as, for instance, $10 = 0$, this would prove that the given system has no solution, or is inconsistent. If an equation (19) of the form $0 = 0$ is obtained, this will prove that every solution of just one of the given linear equations, say (18) as above, is a solution of the other given equation. In this case, the equations in (1) are equivalent; we have called them dependent previously in this section. If the equations in (1) are not both linear, it is likely that any possible solution (x, y) obtained by use of an equivalent system would have to be verified by substitution in (1) before claiming that (x, y) actually is a solution.

* Although Theorem VIII is stated for the case of just two variables, the result applies, with negligible changes in notation, in case more than two variables are involved.

EXERCISE 20

Solve the system graphically. Also, solve the system algebraically. The word "and" is understood to apply after the first equation in each system.

1. $\begin{cases} x - y = 1, \\ y + 2x = -3. \end{cases}$
2. $\begin{cases} y + x = 2, \\ 2y - x = -5. \end{cases}$
3. $\begin{cases} y - 2x = 1, \\ 3y + 4x = 23. \end{cases}$

4. $\begin{cases} 2y - 3x = 0, \\ 4y + 3x = -18. \end{cases}$
5. $\begin{cases} 3x + 8 = 0, \\ 6x + 7y = 5. \end{cases}$
6. $\begin{cases} 5y - 3 = 0, \\ 10y + 3x = 4. \end{cases}$

7. $\begin{cases} 2y - 5x = 10, \\ 2y - 2x = 3. \end{cases}$
8. $\begin{cases} 2x - 3y = 0, \\ 5x + 7y = 0. \end{cases}$
9. $\begin{cases} 3x + 5y = 2, \\ 2x - 3y = -5. \end{cases}$

10. $\begin{cases} x + 2y = 4, \\ 3x - y = 6. \end{cases}$
11. $\begin{cases} 2x - y = 3, \\ 2y - 4x = 5. \end{cases}$
12. $\begin{cases} 3 = 2x - 3y, \\ 4x - 6 = 6y. \end{cases}$

13. $\begin{cases} x + y = 1, \\ 2x + 2y = 7. \end{cases}$
14. $\begin{cases} 3x - 4y = 5, \\ 6x - 8y = 3. \end{cases}$
15. $\begin{cases} x - 5y = 2, \\ 10y - 2x + 4 = 0. \end{cases}$

Note 1. Hereafter, to *solve* a system of equations will mean to solve *algebraically* unless otherwise stated.

Clear of fractions, if necessary, and solve the system.

16. $\begin{cases} \frac{3}{2}x = 2 + \frac{5}{4}y, \\ \frac{1}{2}x = \frac{3}{2} - \frac{5}{3}y. \end{cases}$
17. $\begin{cases} \frac{9}{2}x - 4y = -3, \\ \frac{4}{3}x - \frac{1}{2}y = \frac{7}{6}. \end{cases}$

18. $\begin{cases} 5y + 3x = 3.45, \\ 4y - \frac{5}{2}x + .67 = 0. \end{cases}$
19. $\begin{cases} \frac{3}{2}y - 5x = 5, \\ 7x - \frac{5}{2}y + 9 = 0. \end{cases}$

20. $\begin{cases} \dfrac{u - 4}{u - 1} = \dfrac{w + 2}{w + 1}, \\ \\ \dfrac{u - 5}{u - 6} = \dfrac{w + 5}{w + 4}. \end{cases}$
21. $\begin{cases} \dfrac{y - 2x + 2}{x + 3y + 3} + \dfrac{1}{5} = 0, \\ \\ \dfrac{3x + y + 2}{y + 4x + 9} - \dfrac{7}{11} = 0. \end{cases}$

Solve for x and y, or for v and w. All other letters represent constants.

22. $\begin{cases} 3ax + 2y = 2, \\ ax + 2y = 1. \end{cases}$
23. $\begin{cases} av + b^2w = 2, \\ b^2v + aw = 2. \end{cases}$
24. $\begin{cases} 6hx + y = 2h, \\ 2kx - 3y = k. \end{cases}$

25. $\begin{cases} 2av - 2w = 2 + b, \\ av + 2w = 1 - b. \end{cases}$
26. $\begin{cases} cx - dy = c^2 + d^2, \\ x + y = 2c. \end{cases}$

27. $\begin{cases} v + 2bw = a^2 + b^2, \\ v - bw = a^2 - b^2. \end{cases}$
28. $\begin{cases} 2ax + 3by = ab, \\ x - 3by = 3ab + 2b. \end{cases}$

Note 2. If all of a set of lines pass through a point, they are called **concurrent lines.** Three lines are concurrent if and only if their equations are consistent. To investigate their consistency, solve any two of them simultaneously and test the solution, if any, in the third equation.

Find the intersection of the lines or prove them not concurrent.

29. $\begin{cases} 7x - 2y = 8; \\ 5x + 2 = 4y; \\ 5x - y = 7. \end{cases}$
30. $\begin{cases} 2x - 3y = 8; \\ 3x - y = 5; \\ 2x + 5y = -8. \end{cases}$
31. $\begin{cases} x + y = 6; \\ 2x - 3y = 11; \\ 2x + 7y = 1. \end{cases}$

46. Inequalities in two variables

Let f and g be functions of two independent variables, (x, y). Then, the graph of an inequality $f(x, y) < g(x, y)$, or of $f(x, y) \leqq g(x, y)$, or of a system of such inequalities, in an xy-plane, is defined as *the set of all points whose coordinates* (x, y) *satisfy the given numerical statement.* That is, the graph of the statement is the graph of its solution set. It is reasonable to anticipate that an inequality in two variables usually will have infinitely many solutions. As a rule, this solution set would be hard to describe analytically in such a way that solutions could be computed as desired. Hence, it proves convenient in many cases to describe the solution set by obtaining its graph.

Illustration 1. Let $f(x, y) = x^2 + y^2 - 4$. Then, $f(x, y) = 0$ becomes

$$x^2 + y^2 - 4 = 0, \quad or \quad x^2 + y^2 = 4. \tag{1}$$

The student may verify, as in Illustration 3 on page 82, that the graph of (1) is a circle, C, of radius 2 with center at the origin, as in Figure 36. Now, consider the inequality $f(x, y) > 0$. Let $P_0 : (x_0, y_0)$ be any point where $f(x_0, y_0) > 0$. Suppose that $P_1 : (x_1, y_1)$ is a second point which can be joined to P_0 by a *continuous curve,* D, as in Figure 36, *which does not cross* C. If a variable point $Q : (x, y)$ moves on D from P_0 to P_1, the function value $f(x, y)$ changes continuously* from $f(x_0, y_0)$, which we have assumed is *positive,* to $f(x_1, y_1)$ at P_1, and D *does not meet* C. Hence, $f(x_1, y_1)$ is positive, because $f(x, y)$ could not change continuously from $f(x_0, y_0) > 0$ to a *negative* value without passing through the value zero, which occurs only when (x, y) is on C.

In particular, let P_0 be the point $(1, 0)$, which is inside the circle; then $f(1, 0) = -3$. Hence, by reasoning as above, we conclude that $f(x, y) < 0$ at all points $P : (x, y)$ *inside* the circle in Figure 36. Similarly, with $P_0 : (3, 0)$, we find $f(3, 0) = 5$; hence, $f(x, y) > 0$ at all points $P : (x, y)$ *outside* the circle in Figure 36. Thus, the circle appears as the *boundary, where* $f(x, y) = 0$, between the graphs of the solution sets for $f(x, y) < 0$ and $f(x, y) > 0$. A continuity argument of the type just employed will justify the following procedure in usual applications.

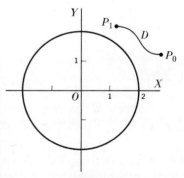

Figure 36

SUMMARY. *To graph* $f(x, y) < 0$ *and* $f(x, y) > 0$ *in an* xy-*plane, first draw the graph,* C, *of* $f(x, y) = 0$. *Select a point inside each of the regions into which* (*we assume*) C *divides the plane. Then, the value of* $f(x, y)$ *at the chosen point in any region determines the nature, positive or negative, of* $f(x, y)$ *at all points in the region.*

* We interpret *"continuously"* to mean *"smoothly, and without jumps,"* in a colloquial sense, which is interpreted in a clear analytic fashion in more advanced mathematics.

The Summary remains valid if we have $f(x, y) = F(x)$, not involving y, or if $f(x, y) = G(y)$, not involving x.

Illustration 2. The inequality $x - 2 < 0$, or $x < 2$, has a *one-dimensional* graph on a number scale, consisting of all points on the scale to the left of the point representing 2. Also, we may let $f(x, y) = x - 2$, and investigate the graph of $f(x, y) < 0$ in an xy-plane. The graph of $x - 2 = 0$ in an xy-plane is the vertical line with x-intercept 2. This line divides the plane into two half-planes. At $P_0 : (3, 0)$, we obtain $f(3, 0) = 3 - 2 = 1$. Hence, $f(x, y) > 0$ at all points $P : (x, y)$ to the right of the line $x = 2$. Similarly, we find $f(x, y) < 0$ at all points $P : (x, y)$ to the left of the line $x = 2$; thus, this *half-plane* is the graph of the set of solutions (x, y) for $x - 2 < 0$.

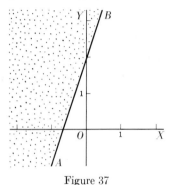

Figure 37

Illustration 3. To obtain the graph of

$$y - 3x - 2 > 0, \qquad (2)$$

we first draw the line $y - 3x - 2 = 0$, shown as AB in Figure 37. With

$$f(x, y) = y - 3x - 2,$$

we obtain $f(-2, 0) = 4 > 0$. Since $(-2, 0)$ is to the left of AB, we conclude that $f(x, y) > 0$, or (2), is satisfied at all points $P : (x, y)$ in the dotted half-plane in Figure 37.

EXAMPLE 1.   Obtain the graph of the system

$$\begin{cases} 2x + 3y - 6 < 0, \ and & (3) \\ y - x - 1 < 0. & (4) \end{cases}$$

Solution.   1. Let the solution set of (3) be G, and of (4) be H. Then, (x, y) is a solution of [(3) *and* (4)] if and only if (x, y) is in *both G and H.* Thus, the solution set, W, for [(3) *and* (4)] is given by $W = G \cap H$.

2. Let G_1, H_1, and W_1 be the graphs of G, H, and W, respectively, in Figure 38. Then, $W_1 = G_1 \cap H_1$. The student should verify that, in Figure 38, line AB is the graph of the equation $2x + 3y - 6 = 0$; CD is the graph of $y - x - 1 = 0$; G_1 is the half-plane which is dotted; H_1 is the half-plane which is ruled horizontally. W_1 is that part of the plane which is dotted and ruled (excluding points on the lines AB and CD).

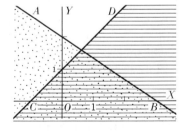

Figure 38

Note 1. The content of this section is basic for consideration of linear programming on page 356, and also finds frequent use in many other parts of mathematics.

EXERCISE 21

Graph the inequality or system of inequalities in an xy-plane.

1. $y - x - 2 < 0$.   2. $2x - 3y - 6 > 0$.   3. $x - 3 < 0$.

4. $y - 2 > 0$.   5. $4x + 3y < -12$.   6. $2x + y > 4$.

7. $2x - 3 > 0$.   8. $y < x$.   9. $y + 2 > 0$.

10. $\begin{cases} y - x - 1 < 0, \text{ and} \\ x + y - 3 > 0. \end{cases}$ 11. $\begin{cases} 2y - x - 6 < 0, \text{ and} \\ y - 2x - 1 > 0. \end{cases}$

12. $\begin{cases} y - x < 2, \text{ and} \\ x + 2y - 3 \geqq 0. \end{cases}$ 13. $\begin{cases} 3x + 2y + 2 > 0, \text{ and} \\ y - 2x + 3 \leqq 0. \end{cases}$

14. $\begin{cases} x > 2, \\ 4y + x > 8, \text{ and} \\ y - x < 1. \end{cases}$ 15. $\begin{cases} y + x < 2, \\ 3y - x < 4, \text{ and} \\ y + 3 > 0. \end{cases}$

16. $\begin{cases} 2x + 3y > 6, \\ x + 2y > 0, \text{ and} \\ x - y - 5 < 0. \end{cases}$ 17. $\begin{cases} 2y - 3x < 6, \\ x - 3y - 6 \geqq 0, \text{ and} \\ x + 8 > 2y. \end{cases}$

47. The language of variation

In applied mathematics, and also in some purely mathematical situations, we occasionally find use for a convenient vocabulary for describing some of the most simple functions.

Direct variation. *Let y be a function of x. Then, we say that*

$$\left. \begin{array}{l} y \text{ is proportional to } x, \text{ or} \\ y \text{ varies directly as } x, \text{ or} \\ y \text{ is directly proportional to } x, \text{ or} \\ y \text{ varies as } x, \end{array} \right\} \tag{1}$$

in case there exists a constant $k \neq 0$ such that, for every value of x, the corresponding value of y is given by $\boldsymbol{y} = \boldsymbol{kx}$.

In $y = kx$, we call k the **constant of proportionality**, or the **constant of variation.** From $y = kx$, we obtain $k = y/x$. Or, if y is proportional to x, *the ratio of corresponding values of y and x is a constant.* Conversely, if this ratio is a constant, then y is proportional to x, because the equation $k = y/x$ leads to $y = kx$. In these remarks, we assumed that $x \neq 0$.

Illustration 1. The circumference C of a circle varies directly as the radius r, because $C = 2\pi r$, where the constant of proportionality is 2π. In $C = 2\pi r$, C and r are *measures* in terms of the *same unit of length.* If r were a measure in feet and C a measure in inches, the statement that "C *varies directly as* r" still would be true, but then $C = 24\pi r$, where the constant of proportionality is 24π. This illustrates the fact that, when x and y are measures in assigned units, statements (1) can be made, when true, *without knowledge of the units,* whereas the value of k in $y = kx$ cannot be learned until the units are specified.

Illustration 2. If y is proportional to x^2, then $y = kx^2$.

Inverse variation. *Let y be a function of x. Then, we say that*

$$y \text{ varies inversely as } x, \text{ or } y \text{ is inversely proportional to } x, \qquad (2)$$

in case there exists a constant $k \neq 0$ such that, for every value of x, the corresponding value of y is given by $\boldsymbol{y = \dfrac{k}{x}}$.

From $y = k/x$, we obtain $xy = k$, or *the product of corresponding values of x and y is a constant.* If y varies inversely as x, then likewise x varies inversely as y, because the equation $xy = k$ leads to both of the equations

$$y = \frac{k}{x} \quad and \quad x = \frac{k}{y}.$$

Illustration 3. The time t necessary for a train to go a given distance s at constant speed varies inversely as the speed r of the train because $t = s/r$. The constant of proportionality here is s.

Joint variation. *Let z be a function of x and y. Then, we say that*

$$\left. \begin{array}{l} z \text{ varies jointly as } x \text{ and } y, \text{ or} \\ z \text{ is directly proportional to } x \text{ and } y, \text{ or} \\ z \text{ is proportional to } x \text{ and } y, \text{ or} \\ z \text{ varies as } x \text{ and } y, \end{array} \right\} \qquad (3)$$

in case z is proportional to the product xy, or $\boldsymbol{z = kxy,}$ where $k \neq 0$ is a constant of proportionality.

Illustration 4. Any of the types of variation may be combined. For instance, to say that z varies *directly* as x and y and *inversely* as w^3 means that

$$z = kxy/w^3.$$

Suppose that certain variables are related by a variation equation, with an unknown constant of proportionality, k. Then, if one set of corresponding values of the variables is given, we can find k.

EXAMPLE 1. If y is proportional to x and w^2, and if $y = 36$ when $x = 2$ and $w = 3$, find y when $x = 3$ and $w = 4$.

Solution. 1. We are given that $y = kw^2x$, where k is unknown.

2. To find k, substitute $(y = 36, x = 2, w = 3)$ in $y = kw^2x$:

$$36 = k(3^2)(2); \quad 36 = 18k \quad or \quad k = 2. \qquad (4)$$

3. From Step 1, $$y = 2w^2x. \qquad (5)$$

4. Substitute $(x = 3, w = 4)$ in (5):

$$y = 2 \cdot 16 \cdot 3 = 96.$$

EXERCISE 22

Introduce letters if necessary and express the relation by an equation.

1. W varies directly as u and inversely as v^3.
2. K is proportional to x^2 and y, and inversely proportional to z^3.
3. R varies jointly as $\sqrt{u}$, v, and $z^{\frac{3}{2}}$.
4. Z varies inversely as x^2, y^3, and $w^{\frac{1}{3}}$.
5. $(z - 3)$ is proportional to $(x + 5)$.
6. The area of a triangle is proportional to its base.
7. The volume of a sphere is proportional to the cube of its radius.
8. The volume of a specified quantity of a gas varies inversely as the pressure applied to it, if the temperature remains unchanged.
9. The weight of a body above the surface of the earth varies inversely as the square of the distance of the body from the earth's center.
10. The maximum safe load of a horizontal beam of a given material, supported at the ends, varies directly as the breadth and the square of the depth, and inversely as the distance between the supports.

By employing the data, obtain an equation relating the variables, with an explicit value for any associated constant which arises.

11. H is proportional to x^3, and $H = 20$ if $x = 2$.
12. W is inversely proportional to $\sqrt{y}$, and $W = 10$ if $y = 9$.

Find the specified number by use of an equation of variation.

13. If w is proportional to u, and if $w = 5$ when $u = 4$, find w when $u = 8$.
14. If v is inversely proportional to x and y, and if $v = 20$ when $x = 2$ and $y = 8$, find v when $x = 4$ and $y = 10$.
15. The distance fallen by a body, starting from rest in a vacuum near the earth's surface, is proportional to the square of the time spent in falling. If a body falls 256 feet in 4 seconds, how far will it fall in 11 seconds?
16. The force of a wind blowing on a certain surface varies directly as the area of the surface and the square of the speed of the wind. If the speed is 30 miles per hour, the force is 4 pounds per square foot of area. Find the force on 100 square feet when the speed is 50 miles per hour.
17. The kinetic energy E of a moving mass is proportional to the mass and the square of the speed. If $E = 2500$ foot-pounds when a body of mass 64 pounds is moving at a speed of 50 feet per second, find E when a body of mass 40 pounds has a speed of 200 feet per second.
18. See Problem 10. If the maximum safe load is 2000 pounds for a beam 5 inches wide and 10 inches deep, with supports 12 feet apart, find the maximum load for a beam which is 4 inches wide and 8 inches deep, with supports 10 feet apart.
19. Under given conditions with artificial light, the time of exposure necessary to photograph an object varies as the square of its distance from the light, and inversely as its candle power. If the exposure is .01 second when the light is 6 feet away, find the distance for the light if its candle power is doubled and the exposure is .02 second.

EXERCISE 23

Review of Chapter 3

Find the distance between the points in an xy-plane having equal scale units on the axes.

1. $(3, -5)$; $(-2, 4)$.   2. $(-3, 0)$; $(2, -6)$.   3. $(-1, -4)$; $(-6, -8)$.

4–6. Find the slope of the line through the points in Problems 1–3, respectively.

Prove that lines AB and CD are parallel, or perpendicular, or possess neither of these characteristics.

7. $A:(-1, 2)$; $B:(3, 5)$; $C:(2, -3)$; $D:(10, 3)$.

8. $A:(2, 5)$; $B:(-3, 4)$; $C:(-1, 4)$; $D:(-2, 9)$.

9. $A:(-1, 2)$; $B:(3, 0)$; $C:(-2, -3)$; $D:(4, -8)$.

10. $A:(2, 3)$; $B:(-4, 3)$; $C:(-2, 4)$; $D:(-2, 7)$.

11. Find x if the points are collinear: $(-2, 3)$; $(5, -4)$; $(x, 6)$.

Write an equation for the line satisfying the conditions.

12. Slope -2; through $(2, -5)$.   13. Slope 4; through $(-2, 4)$.

14. Slope 5; y-intercept 6.   15. Slope -2; y-intercept -2.

16. Through AB in Problem 7.   17. Through BC in Problem 9.

Find the slope and y-intercept of the given line l. Also, write an equation for the line perpendicular to l through point A.

18. $3x - 2y = 7$; $A:(-4, 2)$.   19. $4x + 5y = 20$; $A:(2, -5)$.

20. The domain of the function f is $D = \{-2, 3, 4, 6\}$. For any number x in D, the value of f is x^3. Obtain the graph of f in an xy-plane.

21. If $f(x) = -3x + 2x^2$, find $f(-2); f(0); f(3); f(2y); f(g(x))$, where $g(x) = 2x + 3$.

Obtain a formula for the values of at least one function of x defined by the equation.

22. $4x - 3y = 8$.   23. $3y - x^2 + x = 5$.   24. $x^2 - 4y^2 = 16$.

25. Find the value of the constant h if the lines $2x - 5y = 6$ and $hx + 3y = 4$ are (a) parallel; (b) perpendicular.

Solve the system graphically and algebraically. If the equations are dependent or inconsistent, prove this fact without the graph. "And" is understood after the first equation.

26. $\begin{cases} 2x - 3y = -7, \\ x + 4y = 2. \end{cases}$ 27. $\begin{cases} 3x - 5y = 7, \\ 10y - 6x = 9. \end{cases}$ 28. $\begin{cases} 2x - 3y = 4, \\ 6y - 4x = -8. \end{cases}$

Graph the inequality or system of inequalities in an xy-plane, even when just one variable occurs.

29. $2x - 5y - 6 \leq 0$.   30. $-x + 2y > 0$.

31. $4x - 9 > 0$.   32. $2x + 5 \leq 0$.   33. $7 - 2y \leq 0$.

34. $\begin{cases} 3x - 2y + 6 \geq 0, \\ x + y + 1 \geq 0, \text{ and} \\ 2x - 5 \leq 0. \end{cases}$ 35. $\begin{cases} x + y - 1 > 0, \\ x + 4y - 4 \leq 0, \text{ and} \\ x - y - 2 \leq 0. \end{cases}$

Chapter 4 Quadratic Functions and Equations in One Variable

48. Polynomial functions of degree two

On page 86, we stated that a function F of a single variable is said to be a polynomial function of degree 2, or is called a **quadratic function,** in case

$$F(x) = ax^2 + bx + c, \quad where \quad a \neq 0, \tag{1}$$

and a, b, and c are constants. On page 373, it will be proved that the graph of a quadratic function is a curve called a **parabola,** which will be defined by a certain geometric property on page 156. At present, we define a parabola as *a curve obtained as the graph of a quadratic function.*

EXAMPLE 1. Graph the function f if $f(x) = x^2 - 2x - 3$.

Solution. Let $y = x^2 - 2x - 3$. We assign values to x and compute y, as in the following table. The parabola through these points, in Figure 39, is the graph of f. The lowest point, V, of the parabola is called its **vertex.** At V, $y = -4$. This ordinate is the *smallest,* or *minimum* value of f, and hence V is referred to as the *minimum point* of the graph. The vertical line through V is called the *axis* of the parabola. In Figure 39, the equation of this axis is $x = 1$. The curve in Figure 39 is said to be *concave upward* (open upward) because, if we conceive of traveling on the curve from left to right, the curve bends counterclockwise.

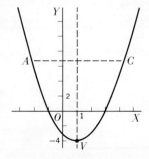

Figure 39

x	-3	-2	0	1	2	4	5
y	12	5	-3	-4	-3	5	12

101

Illustration 1. The graph of $y = -x^2 + 2x + 3$ would be a parabola concave downward, and its vertex V would be called the **maximum point** of the curve. The value of y at V would be called the **maximum value** of the function $(-x^2 + 2x + 3)$.* We shall show how to locate the maximum or minimum point of the graph of a quadratic function below.

Recall that $(x + c)^2 = x^2 + 2cx + c^2$. Hence, if we wish to add a term to $(x^2 + kx)$ so that the result will be a *perfect square* (that is, *to complete a square*), we proceed as follows: *divide the coefficient of x by 2; then add the square of the result.* In arriving at the preceding statement, we thought of $k = 2c$.

Illustration 2. To complete a square with $(x^2 + 7x)$, we add $(\frac{7}{2})^2$ or $\frac{49}{4}$:

$$x^2 + 7x + \tfrac{49}{4} = (x + \tfrac{7}{2})^2.$$

THEOREM I. *Let the quadratic function F be defined by* $F(x) = ax^2 + bx + c$, *where* $a \neq 0$. *If* $a > 0$, *then F has a* **least value**, *called the* **minimum value** *of F; if* $a < 0$, *then F has a* **greatest value**, *called the* **maximum value** *of F. The maximum or minimum, as the case may be, is attained when* $x = -b/2a$.

Proof. 1. We have
$$F(x) = a\left(x^2 + \frac{b}{a}\,x\right) + c. \qquad (2)$$

2. To complete a square within the parentheses on the right in (2), we add $(\frac{1}{2}b/a)^2$. To compensate for this, we subtract the product of $(\frac{1}{2}b/a)^2$ and a outside the parentheses on the right in (2). Thus, we obtain

$$F(x) = a\left(x^2 + \frac{b}{a}\,x + \frac{b^2}{4a^2}\right) + \left(c - \frac{b^2}{4a}\right),\; or$$

$$F(x) = a\left[x - \left(-\frac{b}{2a}\right)\right]^2 + \frac{4ac - b^2}{4a}. \qquad (3)$$

3. Suppose that $a > 0$. Then, at all values of x, the first term on the right in (3) is *positive* or *zero*, and hence

$(a > 0)$ $$F(x) \geqq \frac{4ac - b^2}{4a}. \qquad (4)$$

If $a < 0$, the first term on the right in (3) is *negative* or *zero*, and hence

$(a < 0)$ $$F(x) \leqq \frac{4ac - b^2}{4a}. \qquad (5)$$

4. In (3), F attains the value $(4ac - b^2)/4a$ only when the first term on the right is zero, or $x = -b/2a$. Thus, from (4) when $a > 0$, F has a *least value*, $(4ac - b^2)/4a$ attained only when $x = -b/2a$. Similarly, if $a < 0$, F attains its *greatest value* only when $x = -b/2a$.

* On a few occasions, to avoid circumlocution, we may use the classical abbreviation "a *function f(x)*" to mean "a *function f where x will be used for the independent variable.*" If such an abbreviation is used, the word *function* must *precede* "*f(x)*" so that there will be no possibility of confusing the *function f* and its *arbitrary value f(x)*.

A curve, D, is said to be **symmetric** *to a line* l, called an **axis of symmetry,** if, for every point A on D, there is a point C on D so that chord* AC of D is perpendicular to l and is bisected by l. We shall prove that the parabola in Figure 39 on page 101 is symmetric to the line through V.

Corollary 1. *The graph of* $y = F(x)$ *is symmetric to the line* $x = -b/2a$.

Proof. To prove the corollary, we desire to show that y has the same value when $x = (-b/2a) + k$ as when $x = (-b/2a) - k$, for any number k. If either of these values of x is substituted in (3), the right-hand side becomes

$$ak^2 + \frac{4ac - b^2}{4a}.$$

Hence, Corollary 1 has been established. The line $x = -b/2a$ just considered is called the **axis** of the parabola which is the graph of F.

SUMMARY. *Concerning the graph of a quadratic function* F, *where*

$$\underline{F(x) = ax^2 + bx + c, \quad with \quad a \neq 0,}$$

or, the graph of an equation $\underline{y = ax^2 + bx + c.}$

1. *The graph is a parabola, with its axis perpendicular to the x-axis, where the parabola is* <u>concave **upward** or **downward** according as **a** is **positive** or **negative.**</u>

2. *At the parabola's vertex,* $\underline{x = -b/2a.}$ $\underline{This}$ *value of* x *gives the function its* <u>minimum</u> *or its* <u>maximum</u> *value according as* <u>**a** is **positive** or **negative.**</u> *The equation of the axis of the parabola is* $x = -b/2a.$

Illustration 3. In Figure 39 on page 101, at V, $x = -(-2)/2 = 1$.

The roles of x and y in the preceding Summary may be interchanged. In doing this, with the understanding that the x-axis remains horizontal, we obtain facts about the graph of an equation

$$\underline{x = ay^2 + by + c,} \tag{6}$$

which expresses x as a quadratic function of y. The student should rewrite the Summary with changes to apply with (6).

Illustration 4. The graph of the equation

$$x = 3y^2 - 12y + 7$$

<u>is a parabola which is concave to the right.</u> At the vertex, $y = -(-12)/6 = 2$, so that the vertex is $V:(x = -5, y = 2)$. The parabola's axis is the horizontal line $y = 2$. The graph is shown in Figure 40.

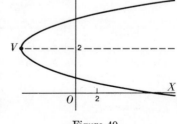

Figure 40

---

* A *chord* is a line segment joining two points of the curve. In Figure 39 on page 101, the chord AC of the parabola is bisected by its axis.

EXERCISE 24

For each quadratic function, (a) find the coordinates of the vertex of its graph and the equation of its axis; (b) graph the function in an xy-plane; (c) state the maximum or minimum value of the function.

1. x^2.
2. $x^2 - 4x + 7$.
3. $-3x^2 - 6x + 5$.
4. $4x^2 + 5$.
5. $-x^2$.
6. $x^2 + 6x + 5$.
7. $-2x^2 + 8x + 3$.
8. $8x - 2x^2$.

In an xy-plane where the x-axis is horizontal, graph the given equation, which expresses x as a quadratic function of y. Employ the Summary on page 103, with the roles of x and y interchanged. State the maximum or the minimum value of x.

9. $x = 4y^2 + 2$.
10. $x = 2y^2 + 8y - 6$.
11. $x = -y^2 + 6y - 8$.

Solve for x or for y, whichever occurs only to the first degree; then graph the resulting quadratic function, of x or y, with the x-axis horizontal in either case.

12. $2x^2 - 8x + 9 - 2y = 0$.
13. $3x - 12y^2 + 36y - 17 = 0$.

Solve by introducing a single variable x, and then finding the maximum or the minimum of a quadratic function of x.

14. Divide 40 into two parts whose product is a maximum.
15. Find the dimensions of the rectangular field of maximum area which can be enclosed with 400 feet of fence.
16. Find two numbers whose sum is 15, if the sum of the squares of the numbers is a minimum.

49. Quadratic equations in one variable

Any quadratic equation in a variable x is equivalent to an equation

$$ax^2 + bx + c = 0, \qquad (1)$$

where a, b, and c are constants and $a \neq 0$. We may refer to (1) as the *general quadratic equation in x.*

To solve a quadratic equation in x where no term, such as bx in (1), of the first degree appears, we solve for x^2 and then extract square roots.

EXAMPLE 1. Solve: $\qquad\qquad 7y^2 = 18 + 3y^2$.

Solution. 1. $\qquad\qquad 7y^2 - 3y^2 = 18; \quad 4y^2 = 18; \quad y^2 = \frac{9}{2}$.

2. Hence, the values of y satisfying the equation are the square roots of $\frac{9}{2}$. If decimal forms of the roots are desired, Table I is available for obtaining approximate values, to three decimal places. Thus,

$$y = \pm\sqrt{\frac{9}{2}} = \pm\sqrt{\frac{9 \cdot 2}{2 \cdot 2}} = \pm\frac{3}{2}\sqrt{2} = \pm\frac{3}{2}(1.414) = \pm 2.121.$$

EXAMPLE 2. Solve: $\qquad\qquad 2y^2 + 35 = -5y^2$. $\qquad (2)$

Solution. $7y^2 = -35; \quad y^2 = -5.$ $\qquad$ Hence, $y = \pm\sqrt{-5} = \pm i\sqrt{5}$.

In solving each of Examples 1–2, we used the fact that, if A^2 and B represent real numbers with $A^2 = B$, and involve one or more variables, then A is equal to one or the other of the square roots of B. That is, we reach the following conclusion.

When the square roots of both sides of an equation $A^2 = B$ are taken in a process of solution, we obtain an equivalent statement by writing

$$A = +\sqrt{B} \quad or \quad A = -\sqrt{B}. \tag{3}$$

From (3) on page 12, recall that the product of two real* numbers is zero if and only if one of the numbers is zero. That is, $bc = 0$ if and only if ($b = 0$ or $c = 0$). The preceding fact is the basis for the solution of various types of equations by use of factoring.

To solve a polynomial equation† of any degree in a variable x by use of factoring, when such a solution is possible, we proceed as follows.

1. *Transpose terms to write the equation in an equivalent form $f(x) = 0$.*

2. *Factor‡ $f(x)$ if possible. Then, place each factor equal to zero and solve the resulting equations. The solution set for $f(x) = 0$ is the union of the solution sets for the new equations.*

EXAMPLE 3.   Solve: $\qquad\qquad 6 - 5x - 6x^2 = 0.$ $\qquad\qquad$ (4)

Solution.   1. Multiply both sides by -1:

$$6x^2 + 5x - 6 = 0.$$

2. Factor: $\qquad\qquad (3x - 2)(2x + 3) = 0.$ $\qquad\qquad$ (5)

3. Hence, (5) is true if and only if

$$3x - 2 = 0 \quad or \quad 2x + 3 = 0.$$

4. If $3x - 2 = 0$, then $x = \frac{2}{3}$. If $2x + 3 = 0$, then $x = -\frac{3}{2}$. Hence, the solutions of (4) are $\frac{2}{3}$ and $-\frac{3}{2}$.

EXAMPLE 4.   Solve: $\qquad\qquad 4x^2 + 20x + 25 = 0.$

Solution.   1. Factor: $(2x + 5)^2 = 0;$ $\quad or \quad$ $(2x + 5)(2x + 5) = 0.$

2. If $2x + 5 = 0$, then $x = -\frac{5}{2}$. Since each factor gives the same value for x, we agree to say that the equation has *two equal roots*.

From page 46, recall that, in solving an equation in a variable x, if both sides are divided by $g(x)$ where g is some function of x, this operation may cause us to lose solutions, as in Illustration 6 on page 46. Hence, this type of operation should be avoided.

---

* The fact will be proved for any complex numbers in Corollary 1 on page 193.
† And, sometimes, equations which are not polynomial equations. Thus, some trigonometric equations can be solved by the stated procedure.
‡ The meaning of a *"factor"* will depend on the nature of $f(x)$.

EXAMPLE 5. Solve: $$5x^2 = 8x.$$

Solution. 1. Subtract $8x$: $\qquad 5x^2 - 8x = 0, \quad or \quad x(5x - 8) = 0.$

2. Hence, $x = 0$ or $5x - 8 = 0$. The solutions are 0 and $\frac{8}{5}$.

Incorrect solution. Divide both sides of $5x^2 = 8x$ by x, to obtain $5x = 8$. Then, incorrectly, we find $x = \frac{8}{5}$ as the only solution. In this incorrect solution, the root 0 was lost on dividing by x.

50. The quadratic formula

Any quadratic equation can be solved by completing a square with the terms involving x, after the equation has been written with all such terms on one side of the equation.

EXAMPLE 1. Solve the following equation by completing a square:

$$3x^2 - 2x + 4 = 0. \tag{1}$$

Solution. 1. Divide by 3: $\qquad x^2 - \frac{2}{3}x = -\frac{4}{3}. \tag{2}$

Since $\frac{1}{2}(\frac{2}{3}) = \frac{1}{3}$, add $(\frac{1}{3})^2$ or $\frac{1}{9}$ to both sides:

$$x^2 - \frac{2}{3}x + \left(\frac{1}{3}\right)^2 = -\frac{4}{3} + \frac{1}{9}, \quad or \quad \left(x - \frac{1}{3}\right)^2 = -\frac{11}{9}. \tag{3}$$

2. Extract square roots:

$$x - \frac{1}{3} = \pm\sqrt{-\frac{11}{9}}, \quad or \quad x = \frac{1}{3} \pm \frac{i\sqrt{11}}{3}. \tag{4}$$

The general quadratic equation

$$ax^2 + bx + c = 0, \tag{5}$$

where $a \neq 0$, can be solved by the method of *completing a square*. In (5), we allow a, b, and c to be any real numbers with $a \neq 0$, but we search for solutions which may be any *complex numbers*. Each operation in the following method leads to an equation equivalent to the preceding equation, as discussed in Theorem III on page 45. Hence, (5) is equivalent to (7) as obtained below. Therefore, no verification of the solutions (9) by substitution in (5) is necessary.

Solution of (5). Subtract c: $\qquad ax^2 + bx = -c.$

Divide by a: $\qquad x^2 + \frac{b}{a}x = -\frac{c}{a}. \tag{6}$

Complete a square on the left by adding $(b/2a)^2$ to both sides of (6):

$$x^2 + \frac{b}{a}x + \left(\frac{b}{2a}\right)^2 = \frac{b^2}{4a^2} - \frac{c}{a}, \quad or \quad \left(x + \frac{b}{2a}\right)^2 = \frac{b^2 - 4ac}{4a^2}. \tag{7}$$

Equation (7) is true if and only if $(x + b/2a)$ is a square root of the right-hand side. Hence, (7) is equivalent to

$$x + \frac{b}{2a} = +\frac{\sqrt{b^2 - 4ac}}{2a} \quad or \quad x + \frac{b}{2a} = -\frac{\sqrt{b^2 - 4ac}}{2a}. \quad (8)$$

On subtracting $b/2a$ from both sides of each equation in (8), we obtain the following solutions of (5), where we read "$\pm$" as "*plus or minus.*"

$$x = \frac{-b \pm \sqrt{b^2 - 4ac}}{2a}. \quad (9)$$

use when you can't factor

Thus, if a, b, and c are any real numbers, with $a \neq 0$, we have proved that (5) is equivalent to (9), and has just the two solutions exhibited by (9). We call (9) the **quadratic formula.** To employ (9) for a given equation, first clear the equation of fractions, by multiplying both sides by the LCD of any fractions involved. Then, write the equation in the standard form (5), and substitute the values of a, b, and c in (9).

Illustration 1. To solve $2x^2 - 4x + 5 = 0$, use $a = 2$, $b = -4$, $c = 5$:

$$x = \frac{4 \pm \sqrt{16 - 40}}{4} = \frac{4 \pm \sqrt{-24}}{4} = \frac{4 \pm 2i\sqrt{6}}{4} = \frac{2 \pm i\sqrt{6}}{2}.$$

Illustration 2. The solutions of $3x^2 - 6x - 2 = 0$ are

$$x = \frac{-(-6) \pm \sqrt{(-6)^2 - 4 \cdot 3 \cdot (-2)}}{6} = \frac{6 \pm 2\sqrt{15}}{6} = \frac{3 \pm 3.873}{3},$$

or $x = 2.291$ and $x = -.291$. Table I was used.

Note 1. To solve a quadratic equation in x involving just explicit numerals in the coefficients, solution by factoring should be employed only when polynomial factors with real coefficients are reasonably obvious. When this is not the case, even if such factors should exist, it saves time to solve by use of the quadratic formula. The method of completing a square should be used only enough to establish confidence in it as a means for deriving the quadratic formula.

EXERCISE 25

Solve for x, y, or z. All other letters represent positive constants.

1. $4x^2 = -25$.   2. $3x^2 = 2$.   3. $7x^2 = 5$.   4. $10x^2 = 3$.
5. $9z^2 = a$.   6. $4y^2 = b$.   7. $2ax^2 = b$.   8. $3bx^2 = 5$.
9. $4x^2 + 49 = 0$.   10. $45x^2 + 36 = 0$.   11. $63 + 14z^2 = 0$.

Solve for w, x, y, or z by factoring.

12. $x^2 - 3x = 10$.   13. $y^2 - 5y = 14$.   14. $x^2 + x = 12$.
15. $x^2 + 3x = 28$.   16. $21x = 14x^2$.   17. $9x^2 - 144 = 0$.
18. $3x^2 - 7x = 0$.   19. $6x^2 = 15x$.   20. $5x^2 - 9x = 0$.
21. $16x^2 = 24x - 9$.   22. $25y^2 = 20y - 4$.   23. $x^2 + 6x = -9$.

24. $4y^2 + 4y = -1$.　　25. $3x^2 + 2 = -7x$.　　26. $2x^2 + 7x = -6$.

27. $2ax^2 + bx = 0$.　　28. $3bw^2 = 2aw$.　　29. $x^2 - ax = 6a^2$.

30. $3x^2 - bx = 2b^2$.　　31. $4x^2 - ax = 3a^2$.　　32. $x^2 + 4a^2 = 4ax$.

33. $3c^2z^2 - bcz = 2b^2$.　　34. $3a^2w^2 - 7aw = 6$.　　35. $9a^2 + x^2 = 6ax$.

36. $(x - 3)(x + 2) = 14$.　　　　37. $(2x + 1)(x - 3) = 9$.

Solve for x by completing a square, as in solving (1), page 106.

38. $x^2 + 3x - 4 = 0$.　　39. $x^2 - 2x = 24$.　　40. $x^2 + 2 = 4x$.

41. $2x^2 - 5 = x$.　　42. $4x^2 + 12x + 9 = 0$.　　43. $3x^2 - 5 = 14x$.

Solve for x, y, or z by the quadratic formula.

44. $2x^2 - 10 = x$.　　45. $6x^2 - x = 12$.　　46. $3x^2 + x = 4$.

47. $9x^2 + 4 = 12x$.　　48. $8x - 4x^2 = 9$.　　49. $3y + 1 = -6y^2$.

50. $1 = 12x - 9x^2$.　　51. $81z^2 + 4 = 0$.　　52. $25y^2 + 9 = 0$.

53. $2y^2 - 2y = 3$.　　54. $9x^2 + 7 = 6x$.　　55. $8x^2 + 7 = -8x$.

56. $15x^2 - x = 28$.　　57. $4x^2 + 4x = -19$.　　58. $27 + 6z = -2z^2$.

59. $12x^2 + 8x = 15$.　　60. $10x^2 + x = 21$.　　61. $16x^2 = 24x + 19$.

62. $6x^2 + 7dx = 5d^2$.　　　　63. $ky + 3k^2 - 2y^2 = 0$.

64. $ax^2 + 2dx - 3c = 0$.　　　　65. $2bx^2 + cx - 3a = 0$.

66. $4x^2 - 4ax + a^2 - 3b^2 = 0$.　　67. $2kx^2 - 5x + 3k = 0$.

Solve for x, y, or z by the most convenient method.

68. $28 - y^2 = -3y$.　　69. $3x - x^2 = -40$.　　70. $9x^2 + 16 = 24x$.

71. $14x^2 + x = 3$.　　72. $9x^2 - 16 = 6x$.　　73. $3x^2 + 3 = 4x$.

74. $6 - 10x^2 = 11x$.　　75. $8x = 19 + 16x^2$.　　76. $6x^2 = 13x - 28$.

77. $az^2 + \frac{1}{3}b^3 = \frac{1}{3}a^3 + bz^2$.　　78. $abx^2 + c^2 = b^2 + acx^2$.

79. Solve for y in terms of x:　　$6y^2 - 8xy = 9y - 3x - 2x^2$.

80. Solve for x in terms of y:　　$x^2 - 3x + 2xy + 7y = 3y^2 + 4$.

81. Solve:　$|x(x + 3)| = 4$.　　82. Solve:　$|x(3 - x)| = 2$.

51. Graphical solution of a quadratic equation in x

Consider any function, f, of a single variable, x, not necessarily a quadratic function of x. At any point in an xy-plane where the graph of f meets the x-axis, we have $f(x) = 0$. This remark leads to the following method for obtaining approximate real roots of $f(x) = 0$.

SUMMARY. *Graphical method to obtain the real roots, if any, of an equation in one variable, x.*

1. *Transpose terms, to write the equation in the form $f(x) = 0$.*

2. *Graph the function f; that is, graph the equation $y = f(x)$.*

3. *The x-intercepts of the graph are the real roots of $f(x) = 0$.*

In graphing a quadratic function, we have no license to alter it by multiplication by any constant $k \neq 0$, because such an operation would multiply the values of the function by k. However, before solving a quadratic equation in x graphically, we may, if desired, clear of fractions; divide out any common constant factor of the two sides of the equation; arrange to have the coefficient of x^2 positive in the final form.

If the roots of $f(x) = 0$ are not real, this would be indicated graphically by the fact that the graph of f would not meet the x-axis.

In order to solve a quadratic equation $\qquad ax^2 + bx + c = 0 \qquad$ (1)

graphically, that is, to obtain its real roots, if any, or to show that the roots are not real, we graph the following related equation in two variables (x, y):

$$y = ax^2 + bx + c. \qquad (2)$$

I. *The parabola (2) cuts the x-axis in two points if and only if (1) has unequal real roots.* $\quad$ x = 2 , x = -3

II. *The parabola touches the x-axis in just one point, or is tangent to the x-axis, if and only if the roots of (1) are real and equal.* $\quad$ x = 2 , x = 2

III. *The parabola does not meet the x-axis when and only when the roots of (1) are not real.* $\quad$ x = λ

Illustration 1. To solve $x^2 - 2x - 8 = 0$ graphically, we graph the equation $y = x^2 - 2x - 8$, by the method of page 103. The graph is the parabola (I) in Figure 41, which shows that the roots of the given equation are $x = 4$ and $x = -2$. Similarly, we solve $x^2 - 2x + 1 = 0$ by use of (II) in Figure 41; the equation is seen to have equal roots $x = 1$, since the parabola is tangent to the x-axis where $x = 1$. To solve $x^2 - 2x + 5 = 0$ graphically, we draw the graph of $y = x^2 - 2x + 5$, which is (III) in Figure 41; this curve does not meet the x-axis, and hence $x^2 - 2x + 5 = 0$ does not have real roots.

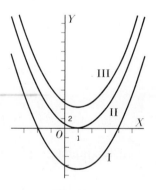

Figure 41

52. Character of the roots

Let r and s represent the roots of $ax^2 + bx + c = 0$, where the constants a, b, and c are real numbers and $a \neq 0$. Then, we may let

$$r = \frac{-b + \sqrt{b^2 - 4ac}}{2a} \, ; \qquad s = \frac{-b - \sqrt{b^2 - 4ac}}{2a} . \qquad (1)$$

If $b^2 - 4ac = 0$, then $r = s = -b/2a$. If $b^2 - 4ac > 0$, then $\sqrt{b^2 - 4ac}$ is *real* and *not zero*; hence, r and s are *real* and *unequal*, because one root involves $+\sqrt{b^2 - 4ac}$ and the other involves $-\sqrt{b^2 - 4ac}$. If $b^2 - 4ac < 0$, then the radical in (1) is imaginary and the roots are of the form

$$r = H + Ki \quad and \quad s = H - Ki, \tag{2}$$

where H and K are real and $K \neq 0$.*

DEFINITION I. *Let h, k, m, and n be any real numbers. Then, to state that $(h + ki)$ and $(m + ni)$ are* **conjugate complex numbers** *means that $h = m$ and $k = -n$.*

Illustration 1. $(3 + 2i)$ and $(3 - 2i)$ are conjugate complex numbers. The conjugate of a real number a is a because the conjugate of $(a + 0i)$ is $(a + 0i)$.

From (2), we observe that, if $b^2 - 4ac < 0$, the roots in (1) are *conjugates*, and also are *unequal* complex numbers which are not real.

Various facts mentioned in this section about the roots in (1), and corresponding graphical facts, are summarized below.

THE ROOTS OF $ax^2 + bx + c = 0$	THE VALUE OF $b^2 - 4ac$	THE GRAPH OF $ax^2 + bx + c$
real and unequal	$b^2 - 4ac > 0$	*cuts x-axis in two points*
real and equal	$b^2 - 4ac = 0$	*is tangent to x-axis*
not real and unequal	$b^2 - 4ac < 0$	*does not touch x-axis*

If a, b, and c are *rational numbers*, the roots r and s are *rational* if and only if $\sqrt{b^2 - 4ac}$ is real and is a *rational number*, or *the roots are* **rational** *if and only if* $(b^2 - 4ac)$ *is a* **perfect square.**

We shall call $b^2 - 4ac$ the **discriminant** of the *quadratic equation* $ax^2 + bx + c = 0$, or of the *quadratic function* $ax^2 + bx + c$. As soon as we know the value of $b^2 - 4ac$, we can tell the general character of the roots of the equation without solving it, and the general nature of the graph of the function without graphing it. Before computing the discriminant of a quadratic equation, simplify it by clearing of fractions and combining terms.

ILLUSTRATIONS OF THE USE OF THE DISCRIMINANT

EQUATION	DISCRIMINANT	HENCE, THE ROOTS ARE
$4x^2 - 3x + 5 = 0$	$(-3)^2 - 4 \cdot 4 \cdot 5 = -71$	*not real; unequal*
$4x^2 - 4x + 1 = 0$	$(-4)^2 - 4 \cdot 4 = 0$	*real; equal; rational*
$4x^2 - 3x - 5 = 0$	$(-3)^2 + 4 \cdot 4 \cdot 5 = 89$	*real; unequal; irrational*
$x^2 - 2x - 3 = 0$	$(-2)^2 - 4(-3) = 16 = 4^2$	*real; unequal; rational*

* The terminology of Section 20 on page 33 should be reviewed at this point.

EXAMPLE 1. State what you can learn about the graph of the quadratic function $-3x^2 + 5x - 6$ *without* graphing.

Solution. 1. The discriminant of the function is $25 - 72 = -47$. -less than 0

2. Hence, the graph would not touch the x-axis. We notice that the coefficient of x^2 is negative. Thus, the graph is a parabola with its axis perpendicular to the x-axis, concave downward. Since the graph does not touch the x-axis, the parabola lies entirely below the x-axis.

EXAMPLE 2. Find the values of k for which the following equation in x has equal roots: $kx^2 + 2x^2 - 3kx + k = 0$.

Solution. 1. Group in standard form: $(k + 2)x^2 - 3kx + k = 0$. Hence, the standard coefficients are $a = k + 2$, $b = -3k$, and $c = k$.

2. When the roots are equal, the discriminant $b^2 - 4ac$ is zero:

$discriminant = (-3k)^2 - 4(k + 2)(k) = 0;$ or $5k^2 - 8k = 0.$

3. Hence, $k(5k - 8) = 0;$ $k = 0$ or $k = \frac{8}{5}.$

Illustration 2. The roots of $x^2 + 4x + 5 = 0$ are

$$x = \frac{-4 \pm \sqrt{16 - 20}}{2} = -2 \pm i, \text{ conjugate complex numbers.}$$

53. Factored form of a quadratic polynomial in x

We have seen that, sometimes, a quadratic equation $f(x) = 0$ can be solved by first factoring $f(x)$. Now, we shall observe that this process can be reversed, to obtain factors of $f(x)$ by first solving $f(x) = 0$.

THEOREM II. *If r and s are the roots of $ax^2 + bx + c = 0$, then*

the sum of the roots is equal to $-\frac{b}{a}$, $\qquad r + s = -\frac{b}{a};$ (1)

the product of the roots is equal to $\frac{c}{a}$, $\qquad rs = \frac{c}{a}.$ (2)

Proof. From $r = \dfrac{-b + \sqrt{b^2 - 4ac}}{2a}$ and $s = \dfrac{-b - \sqrt{b^2 - 4ac}}{2a},$

we obtain $r + s = \dfrac{-2b}{2a} = -\dfrac{b}{a};$

$rs = \dfrac{-b + \sqrt{b^2 - 4ac}}{2a} \cdot \dfrac{-b - \sqrt{b^2 - 4ac}}{2a};$

$rs = \dfrac{(-b)^2 - (b^2 - 4ac)}{4a^2} = \dfrac{4ac}{4a^2} = \dfrac{c}{a}.$

THEOREM III. *If r and s are the roots of* $ax^2 + bx + c = 0$, *then*

$$ax^2 + bx + c = a(x - r)(x - s). \qquad (3)$$

Proof.
$$ax^2 + bx + c = a\left(x^2 + \frac{b}{a}x + \frac{c}{a}\right)$$

[from (1) and (2)]
$$= a[x^2 - (r + s)x + rs] = a(x - r)(x - s).$$

By use of (3), we can form a quadratic equation having specified roots, with the constant a in (3) chosen to suit our convenience.

Illustration 1. A quadratic equation whose roots are 5 and -3 is

$$(x + 3)(x - 5) = 0, \quad or \quad x^2 - 2x - 15 = 0. \quad [a = 1 \text{ in } (3)]$$

Illustration 2. A quadratic equation whose roots are $\frac{1}{2}(2 \pm 3i)$ is

$$a[x - \tfrac{1}{2}(2 + 3i)][x - \tfrac{1}{2}(2 - 3i)] = 0.$$

To eliminate fractions, we place $a = 4 = 2 \cdot 2$, and finally use $i^2 = -1$:

$$2\left(x - \frac{2 + 3i}{2}\right) \cdot 2\left(x - \frac{2 - 3i}{2}\right) = (2x - 2 - 3i)(2x - 2 + 3i) = 0;$$

$$[(2x - 2) - 3i][(2x - 2) + 3i] = 0, \quad or \quad (2x - 2)^2 - 9i^2 = 0;$$

$$4x^2 - 8x + 4 + 9 = 0, \quad or \quad 4x^2 - 8x + 13 = 0.$$

EXAMPLE 1. Factor $6x^2 - 23x + 20$ by first solving an equation.

Solution.   1. Solve $6x^2 - 23x + 20 = 0$ by the quadratic formula:

$$x = \frac{23 \pm \sqrt{49}}{12} = \frac{23 \pm 7}{12}; \quad x = \frac{5}{2} \quad or \quad x = \frac{4}{3}.$$

2. From (3), $6x^2 - 23x + 20 = 6(x - \tfrac{5}{2})(x - \tfrac{4}{3}) = (2x - 5)(3x - 4)$.

The linear factors in (3) involve rational, irrational, or imaginary numbers according as the roots r and s have corresponding characters. In particular:

If a, b, and c are rational numbers, with a $\neq$ 0, $ax^2 + bx + c$ can be expressed as a product of linear factors with rational coefficients when and only when the discriminant $b^2 - 4ac$ is a perfect square.

EXERCISE 26

Compute the discriminant and tell the character of the roots without solving the equation. Then, solve the equation graphically.

1. $y^2 - 2y + 10 = 0$.   2. $9x^2 + 12x + 4 = 0$.   3. $25x^2 + 1 = -10x$.
4. $x^2 + 2x - 2 = 0$.   5. $4x^2 + 4x = 3$.   6. $1 = 2x - 2x^2$.
7. $3x^2 - 5x + 7 = 0$.   8. $5x^2 + 1 = 2x$.   9. $3 + 5x^2 = 0$.

By use of the discriminant, find the values of the constant k for which the equation in the variable x will have equal roots.

10. $4x^2 - 3kx + 1 = 0.$ **11.** $x^2 - kx^2 - 5kx - 3k = 0.$

12. $kx^2 + 3kx + 5 = 0.$ **13.** $kx + x^2 + kx^2 - 2x = 4.$

Find the values of the constant k for which the graph of the function of x will be tangent to the x-axis.

14. $5x^2 - 2kx + k.$ **15.** $x^2 - 3x - k - kx.$

With x as the variable, find the sum and the product of the roots without solving the equation.

16. $2 - 5x = 2x^2.$ **17.** $4 - 3x = 7x^2.$ **18.** $13 - 2x^2 = 0.$

19. $cx^2 - dx = h.$ **20.** $ax^2 = 2x + b.$ **21.** $3x^2 = cx - a.$

Form a quadratic equation with integral coefficients having the given roots.

22. $-2; 5.$ **23.** $\pm\frac{3}{4}i.$ **24.** $\frac{5}{6}; \frac{5}{6}.$ **25.** $\pm\sqrt{-20}.$

26. $-3 \pm i.$ **27.** $3 \pm 5i.$ **28.** $-\frac{2}{3} \pm \frac{2}{3}i.$ **29.** $2 \pm 3\sqrt{2}.$

Find the value of the constant h under the given condition about the solutions for the variable x.

30. The sum of the roots is 2: $2x^2 - hx^2 + 4x + 5h = 0.$

31. The product of the roots is -4: $2hx^2 + 3x^2 + 4x - 5h = 0.$

32. The product of the roots is 8: $3x^2 + 5x + 3h - 5 = 0.$

Factor, after solving a related equation by the quadratic formula.

33. $12x^2 + x - 35.$ **34.** $27x^2 - 57x - 40.$ **35.** $12x^2 - 61x + 60.$

Without factoring, or solving any equation, determine whether or not the polynomial has linear factors with rational coefficients.

36. $12x^2 - 7x - 10.$ **37.** $9x^2 + 6x + 7.$ **38.** $12x^2 - 11x - 36.$

Prove the following theorems about roots of $ax^2 + bx + c = 0$, where $a \neq 0$.

39. If one root is the negative of the other, then $b = 0$.

40. If $b = 0$, then one root is the negative of the other.

Note 1. Recall that any theorem may be abbreviated as **"H implies C,"** where H represents the *hypothesis*, and C represents the *conclusion*. Then, the converse of this theorem is abbreviated by **"C implies H,"** where the roles of H and C were interchanged. A statement such as "*H implies C, and conversely,*" is equivalent to the *two* theorems

$$H \text{ implies } C, \quad \text{and} \quad C \text{ implies } H. \tag{1}$$

When (1) is true, the assertions or statements H and C are called *equivalent*, and each theorem in (1) is the *converse* of the other theorem. The theorems in Problems 39 and 40 are converses; both would be included if the words "*and conversely*" were added to the statement of Problem 39.

41. If $b = 0$ and $c = 0$, then both roots are zero, *and conversely*.

42. If $ac < 0$, then one root is positive and one is negative, *and conversely*.

43. If $ac < 0$, the roots are real and unequal. Is the converse true?

54. Equations in quadratic form

An equation is said to be in the *quadratic form* in a certain function of x in case, after substitution of a new variable, y, for the arbitrary value of this function, the equation becomes a quadratic in y.

EXAMPLE 1.   Solve:
$$x^4 - 5x^2 + 6 = 0. \tag{1}$$

Solution. The equation is in the quadratic form in x^2 because, if we let $x^2 = y$, then $x^4 = y^2$. Without using y, by factoring, (1) becomes
$$(x^2 - 3)(x^2 - 2) = 0. \tag{2}$$

Then, $x^2 = 3$ or $x^2 = 2$. The solutions are $\underline{x = \pm\sqrt{3} \quad \text{and} \quad x = \pm\sqrt{2}.}$

EXAMPLE 2.   Solve:
$$2x^{-4} - x^{-2} - 3 = 0. \tag{3}$$

Solution.   1. Let $y = x^{-2}$. Then, $y^2 = x^{-4}$ and (3) becomes
$$2y^2 - y - 3 = 0, \quad \text{or} \quad (2y - 3)(y + 1) = 0. \tag{4}$$

Hence, the solutions of (4) are $y = -1$ and $y = \frac{3}{2}$.

2. If $y = -1$, then $x^{-2} = -1$; $\dfrac{1}{x^2} = -1$; $x^2 = -1$, *or* $x = \pm i$.

3. If $y = \dfrac{3}{2}$, then $x^{-2} = \dfrac{3}{2}$; $\dfrac{1}{x^2} = \dfrac{3}{2}$; $x^2 = \dfrac{2}{3}$; $x = \pm\dfrac{1}{3}\sqrt{6}$.

EXAMPLE 3.   Solve:
$$(x^2 + 3x)^2 - 3x^2 - 9x - 4 = 0. \tag{5}$$

Incomplete solution.   1. Group terms:
$$(x^2 + 3x)^2 - 3(x^2 + 3x) - 4 = 0.$$

2. Let $y = x^2 + 3x$. Then, $y^2 - 3y - 4 = 0$; the solutions here are $y = 4$ and $y = -1$. Finally, we would obtain the four roots of (5) by solving
$$x^2 + 3x = 4 \quad \text{and} \quad x^2 + 3x = -1.$$

In solving an equation of the form $x^k = A$ where k is a positive integer greater than 2, we agree at present that we desire only *real* solutions *unless otherwise specified*. The real solutions, if any, of $x^k = A$ are the real kth roots of A, as discussed on page 35. The student should review page 27.

EXAMPLE 4.   Obtain *all* roots by use of factoring: $\underline{8x^3 + 125 = 0.}$

Solution.   1. Factor: $(2x + 5)(4x^2 - 10x + 25) = 0.$

2. Hence, $2x + 5 = 0$, *or* $4x^2 - 10x + 25 = 0.$

3. The solutions are
$$x = -\tfrac{5}{2} \quad \text{and} \quad x = \tfrac{1}{8}(10 \pm \sqrt{100 - 400}) = \tfrac{5}{4} \pm \tfrac{5}{4}i\sqrt{3}.$$

EXAMPLE 5.   Find the four 4th roots of 625.

Solution.   1. If x is any 4th root of 625, then $x^4 = 625$.

2. Solve for x:
$$x^4 - 625 = 0;$$
$$(x^2 - 25)(x^2 + 25) = 0; \qquad x^2 = 25 \quad or \quad x^2 = -25.$$

Hence, $x = \pm 5$ and $x = \pm 5i$ are the desired 4th roots of 625.   Incidentally, we have proved that 625 has *just four* 4th roots.

In this section, the student has met further illustrations of the truth of the theorem that *a polynomial equation of degree n in a single variable x has exactly n roots* (we admit the possibility that some of the roots may be equal). Also, we have seen illustrations of the related fact that, if n is a positive integer, every number $H \neq 0$ has exactly n distinct nth roots, some or all of which may be non-real (to be proved on page 196).

55. Irrational equations

Let $M = N$ represent any equation.   On squaring both sides, we obtain $M^2 = N^2$, which is equivalent to the statement $(M = N$ *or* $M = -N)$. Hence, the solutions of the equation $M^2 = N^2$ consist of all solutions of $M = N$ together with those of $M = -N$.

If an operation on an equation in x produces a new equation which is satisfied by values of x which are not roots of the given equation, we name such values (as on page 47) **extraneous roots.**   From the preceding discussion, we observe that, if both members of an equation are *squared*, extraneous roots *may* be introduced.   The statement just made is true also if both members are raised to any integral power.

An *irrational equation* is one in which the variables occur under radical signs or in expressions with fractional exponents.

EXAMPLE 1.   Solve for x in the following equations (a) and (b).

(a) $2x - 2 = \sqrt{2x^2 + 4}.$	(b) $2x - 2 = -\sqrt{2x^2 + 4}.$
Solution. 1. Square both sides: $4x^2 - 8x + 4 = 2x^2 + 4.$ 2. $2x^2 - 8x = 0; 2x(x-4) = 0;$ $\qquad x = 0 \quad or \quad x = 4.$ *Test.* Substitute $x = 0$ in (a): Does $0 - 2 = \sqrt{4}$? Or, does $\qquad -2 = 2$? **No.** Substitute $x = 4$ in (a): Does $8 - 2 = \sqrt{36}$? **Yes.** $x = 0$ is *not*, and $x = 4$ *is* a root.	*Solution.* 1. Square both sides: $4x^2 - 8x + 4 = 2x^2 + 4.$ 2. $2x^2 - 8x = 0; 2x(x-4) = 0;$ $\qquad x = 0 \quad or \quad x = 4.$ *Test.* Substitute $x = 0$ in (b): Does $0 - 2 = -\sqrt{4}$? **Yes.** Substitute $x = 4$ in (b): Does $8 - 2 = -\sqrt{36}$? Or, does $\qquad 6 = -6$? **No.** $x = 4$ is *not*, and $x = 0$ *is* a root.

Comment. The necessity for the testing in Example 1 is emphasized by the fact that, although (*a*) and (*b*) are different, all distinction between them is lost after the squaring operation.

Before squaring (or, raising to any integral power) on both sides of an equation, we first transpose terms to exhibit the most complicated radical alone on one side, and continue similarly at succeeding stages.

EXAMPLE 2. Solve: $\qquad (x - 2)^{\frac{1}{2}} - \sqrt{2x + 5} = 3.$

Partial solution. 1. $\qquad \sqrt{x - 2} = 3 + \sqrt{2x + 5}.$

2. Square: $\qquad x - 2 = 9 + 6\sqrt{2x + 5} + 2x + 5;$

$$6\sqrt{2x + 5} = -x - 16; \quad etc.$$

EXERCISE 27

Solve for x or y. Factor, or change to a quadratic in a new variable.

1. $y^4 - 2y^2 - 3 = 0.$ 2. $z^4 + z^2 = 12.$ 3. $x^4 - 16 = 0.$
4. $16z^4 - 81 = 0.$ 5. $8y^6 + 7y^3 = 1.$ 6. $x^6 + 27 = 28x^3.$
7. $36x^{-4} = 13x^{-2} - 1.$ 8. $4 - 29y^{-2} + 25y^{-4} = 0.$
9. $9x^{-4} + 5x^{-2} - 4 = 0.$ 10. $6y^{-4} - 7y^{-2} - 5 = 0.$
11. $27y^6 - 35y^3 + 8 = 0.$ 12. $(x^2 + 2x)^2 - 2(x^2 + 2x) = 3.$

Find all roots.

13. $x^3 = 8.$ 14. $8x^3 + 27 = 0.$ 15. $81x^4 = 16.$ 16. $625x^4 = 81.$

Solve for x or z.

17. $\sqrt{2 - 3x} = 4.$ 18. $\sqrt{x + 4} = -1.$ 19. $\sqrt[3]{3 + 4z} = 3.$
20. $\sqrt[4]{2z + 5} = 1.$ 21. $\sqrt{3x} + 3 = 2x.$ 22. $5x^2 + x\sqrt{3} = 0.$
23. $\sqrt{x + 5} - 1 = \sqrt{x}.$ 24. $\sqrt{3x + 1} = \sqrt{x} - 1.$
25. $\sqrt{2x - 2} - \sqrt{4x + 3} = 2.$ 26. $\sqrt{7 - 4x} - \sqrt{3 - 2x} = 1.$
27. $\sqrt{3 + 3x} + 3\sqrt{x - 1} = 6.$ 28. $\sqrt{3 + 2x} - (3 - 2x)^{\frac{1}{2}} = \sqrt{2x}.$
29. $\sqrt{3 - x} + \sqrt{3 + 3x} = 2\sqrt{3x - 2}.$ 30. $\sqrt{3x + 2a} = 3\sqrt{x} - \sqrt{2a}.$

Find all real roots. If the equation is in quadratic form, solve by changing to a quadratic in a new variable.

31. $4x^{\frac{2}{3}} + 7x^{\frac{1}{3}} = 2.$ 32. $2z = 7z^{\frac{1}{2}} - 3.$ 33. $3x + 2\sqrt{x} = 1.$

56. Graphical solution of a quadratic inequality in *x*

We cannot anticipate obtaining a formula or formulas for the infinite number of solutions which usually will exist for an inequality equivalent to $f(x) > 0$, or $f(x) < 0$, where f is some given function. However, we may proceed as follows to exhibit the solutions graphically.

SUMMARY. *Graphical solution of an inequality in one variable, x.*

1. *Write the inequality in an equivalent form,* $f(x) < 0$, *or* $f(x) > 0$.
2. *Graph the function f; that is, graph the equation* $y = f(x)$.
3. *The solutions of* $f(x) < 0$ *consist of those values of x where the graph of f is below the x-axis; the solutions of* $f(x) > 0$ *consist of those values of x where the graph is above the x-axis.*

Note 1. In graphing f as mentioned in the Summary, it is useful to carry out a preliminary solution of $f(x) = 0$, where possible, to determine the x-intercepts of the graph of $y = f(x)$ exactly, and thus the exact intervals of solutions of the inequalities.

EXAMPLE 1.   Solve graphically: $\qquad 7x + 4 - 2x^2 < 0.$ $\qquad$ (1)

Solution.   1. Transpose terms, to give x^2 a positive coefficient:

$$0 < 2x^2 - 7x - 4.$$ $\qquad$ (2)

Let $f(x) = 2x^2 - 7x - 4$. Then, (2) becomes $0 < f(x)$.

2. Solve $f(x) = 0$ to find the x-intercepts of the graph of $y = f(x)$:

$$2x^2 - 7x - 4 = 0; \quad (2x + 1)(x - 4) = 0; \quad (3)$$

$$x = -\tfrac{1}{2} \quad and \quad x = 4.$$

3. The graph of $y = f(x)$ in Figure 42 was drawn by use of $x = -\tfrac{1}{2}$, $x = 4$, and other values. The graph is above the x-axis, or $f(x) > 0$

$$if \quad x > 4 \quad or \quad x < -\tfrac{1}{2}.$$ $\qquad$ (4)

Let A represent the set of all numbers x to the *right* of $x = 4$ on the number scale, and B represent the set of all numbers to the *left* of $x = -\tfrac{1}{2}$. Then, from (4), the solution set, S, of (2) consists of all numbers in A *or* B; that is, $S = A \cup B$. *Or,*

Figure 42

$$S = \{x \mid x < -\tfrac{1}{2} \quad or \quad x > 4\}.$$

Illustration 1.   To solve $f(x) < 0$, where f is defined in Example 1, notice that the graph of $y = f(x)$ in Figure 42 is *below* the x-axis when $-\tfrac{1}{2} < x < 4$. Hence, the solution set, U, of $f(x) < 0$ consists of all numbers x on the open interval with endpoints $-\tfrac{1}{2}$ and 4, or $U = \{x \mid -\tfrac{1}{2} < x < 4\}$.

An inequality such as (2) can be solved without graphing if sufficient skill is developed for detecting the sign of a product of factors of the form $(x - a)$. For this purpose we emphasize that

$$x - a < 0 \quad when \quad x < a;$$ $\qquad$ (5)

$$x - a > 0 \quad when \quad x > a.$$ $\qquad$ (6)

EXAMPLE 2. Solve (1) without graphing.

Solution. 1. From (2) and (3), we find that (1) is equivalent to

$$0 < 2(x + \tfrac{1}{2})(x - 4) \quad \text{or} \quad 0 < [x - (-\tfrac{1}{2})](x - 4). \tag{7}$$

2. In Figure 43, the points $x = -\tfrac{1}{2}$ and $x = 4$ divide the number scale

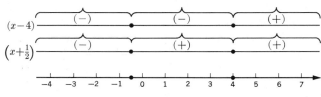

Figure 43

into *three* intervals (two of them infinite). If $x < -\tfrac{1}{2}$, from (5) and Figure 43, we find that both factors on the right in (7) are *negative*, so that (1) is true. If $-\tfrac{1}{2} < x < 4$, then $x - 4 < 0$ and $x - (-\tfrac{1}{2}) > 0$, so that (7) is not true. If $x > 4$, then both factors are positive, so that (7) is true. Thus, the values of x satisfying (7) are those specified in (4).

EXERCISE 28

Solve the inequality graphically or by general reasoning.

1. $5x - 7 < 0$.
2. $9 - 2x > 0$.
3. $x^2 - 4 > 0$.
4. $25 - x^2 < 0$.
5. $x^2 + 6 < 5x$.
6. $6x < 8 + x^2$.
7. $x^2 + 7 < 3x$.
8. $3x < 2x^2 + 2$.
9. $3 < 2x^2 + 5x$.
10. $x^2 + 6 < 0$.
11. $5x - 3x^2 < 0$.
12. $2x^2 + 7x < 0$.
13. $x^2 + 2 \leq 4x$.
14. $2x^2 + 11 \geq 10x$.
15. $3x^2 + 5 < x$.

Solve by inspection, without graphing. Check by graphing.

16. $x^2 < 49$.
17. $4x^2 \geq 25$.
18. $4x^2 < a^2$, if $a > 0$.

For what values of x is the radical real?

19. $\sqrt{x^2 - 9}$.
20. $\sqrt{16 - x^2}$.
21. $\sqrt{x^2 - 5x + 4}$.

Solve the system of inequalities graphically.

22. $\begin{cases} x^2 - 8x + 12 < 0, \text{ and} \\ x^2 + 28 < 11x. \end{cases}$

23. $\begin{cases} 2x + 3 > x^2, \text{ and} \\ x < 2. \end{cases}$

24. $\begin{cases} x^2 > 9, \text{ and} \\ x^2 + 10 < 7x. \end{cases}$

25. $\begin{cases} 2x^2 + 7x > 15, \text{ and} \\ x^2 < 4. \end{cases}$

26. $|x + 1| < 2$, and $2x^2 + 9x < 5$.

Chapter 5 Sequences and Series

57. Sequences

A **sequence**, S, is a *function* whose domain, D, is a set of positive integers. Unless otherwise stated, we shall infer that D consists of either (a) *all positive integers* $n \leq k$, where k is a fixed integer, or (b) *all positive integers*. In case (a), S is called a **finite sequence**; its values are $S(1), S(2), \cdots, S(k)$. In case (b), we call S an **infinite sequence**; the set of values of S, or its *range*, consists of the numbers

$$S(1), S(2), S(3), \cdots, S(n), \cdots, \tag{1}$$

where $S(n)$ is listed to fix the notation, and the final dots $\cdots$, read *"and so forth,"* indicate that unwritten values of S extend endlessly to the right. Instead of (1), we usually write the range of S as follows:

$$S_1, S_2, S_3, \cdots, S_n, \cdots, \tag{2}$$

where we employ subscripts, instead of customary functional notation, to indicate that the domain of the independent variable, n, consists of *integers*. We shall think of the values of S arranged, as in (2), with the subscripts in increasing order. Then, we call S_1 the 1st term, S_2 the 2d term, $\cdots$, S_n the nth term or the **general term** of the sequence. A sequence S is defined if a formula in terms of n is given for S_n. In this chapter, unless otherwise stated, any sequence to which we refer will be a finite sequence. If the domain of n has been specified for a sequence where the general term S_n is indicated, we may describe (2) as "the sequence $\{S_n\}$," instead of listing the terms as in (1) or (2).

Illustration 1. If $S_n = 3n + 5$, and $n = 1, 2, \cdots, 10$, then the sequence $\{S_n\}$ has the 10 terms

$$S_1, S_2, \cdots, S_{10}, \quad or \quad 8, 11, 14, 17, \cdots, 35.$$

119

58. Arithmetic progressions

An **arithmetic progression** (abbreviated **A.P.**) is a sequence of numbers, called terms, each of which, after the first, is obtained from the preceding one by adding to it a fixed number, called the **common difference** of the progression. Unless otherwise stated, any A.P. will be assumed to have just a finite number of terms.

Illustration 1. In the arithmetic progression 9, 6, 3, 0, -3, $\cdots$, the common difference is -3. The 6th term would be -6.

Let b be the 1st term and d be the common difference in an A.P.* Then, the 2d term is $b + d$; the 3d term is $b + 2d$; the 4th term is $b + 3d$. In each of these terms, the coefficient of d is 1 less than the number of the term. The nth term is the $(n - 1)$th after the 1st term and is obtained after d has been added $(n - 1)$ times. Hence, if l represents the nth term,

$$l = b + (n - 1)d. \tag{1}$$

Let S be the sum of the A.P. involved in (1). The first term is b; the common difference is d; the last term is l; the next to the last term is $l - d$, etc. On writing the sum of the n terms, forward and backward, we obtain

$$S = b + (b + d) + (b + 2d) + \cdots + (l - 2d) + (l - d) + l; \tag{2}$$
$$S = l + (l - d) + (l - 2d) + \cdots + (b + 2d) + (b + d) + b. \tag{3}$$

In (2), the three dots "$\cdots$" may be read "*and so forth up to.*" On adding corresponding sides of (2) and (3), we obtain

$$2S = (b + l) + (b + l) + (b + l) + \cdots + (b + l) + (b + l) + (b + l),$$

where there are n terms $(b + l)$. Hence, $2S = n(b + l)$ or

$$S = \frac{n}{2}(b + l). \tag{4}$$

Note 1. The sum of a sequence of numbers is called a *series*. If the sequence consists of just a finite number of numbers, their sum is called a *finite series*. In equation (4), we obtained a formula for the sum of a finite arithmetic series.

EXAMPLE 1. Find the sum of the A.P. $8 + 5 + 2 + \cdots$ *to twelve terms.*

Solution. First obtain l from (1) with $b = 8$, $d = -3$, and $n = 12$:

$$l = 8 + 11(-3) = -25; \quad \textit{from (4),} \quad S = 6(8 - 25) = -102.$$

On substituting $l = b + (n - 1)d$ in (4), we obtain

$$S = \frac{n}{2}[2b + (n - 1)d]. \tag{5}$$

---

* Hereafter in this text, unless otherwise specified, any *number* referred to will be a *real number.*

We call b, d, l, n, and S the **elements** of the general A.P. The elements are related by (1), (4), and (5).

EXAMPLE 2. Find d and S in an A.P. where $b = 2$, $l = 402$, and $n = 26$.

Solution. 1. From (4), $S = 13(404) = 5252$.

2. From (1), $402 = 2 + 25d$; hence, $d = 16$.

EXERCISE 29

Does the sequence form an arithmetic progression?

1. 3, 7, 11, 15.   2. 15, 17, 20, 22.   3. 23, 20, 17.   4. 35, 32, 30, 28.

Find the value of k for which the sequence forms an A.P.

5. 3, 8, k.   6. 25, 21, k.   7. 15, k, 13.   8. k, 17, 23.

Hint. If b, h, and w form an A.P., then $h - b = w - h$.

Find the specified term of the A.P. by use of a formula.

9. Given terms: 4, 7, 10; find the 50th term.

10. Given terms: -5, -8, -11; find the 29th term.

11. Given terms: 3, $3\frac{1}{4}$, $3\frac{1}{2}$; find the 83d term.

Find the last term and the sum of the A.P. by use of formulas.

12. 8, 13, 18, $\cdots$ to 15 *terms.*   13. 13, 8, 3, $\cdots$ to 17 *terms.*
14. 3, 5, 7, $\cdots$ to 41 *terms.*   15. 2.06, 2.02, 1.98, $\cdots$ to 33 *terms.*
16. 9, 6, 3, $\cdots$ to 28 *terms.*   17. 5, $4\frac{1}{2}$, 4, $\cdots$ to 81 *terms.*

Certain of b, d, l, n, and S are given. Find the other elements.

18. $b = 10$, $l = 410$, $n = 26$.   19. $b = 27$, $l = 11$, $d = -\frac{1}{4}$.
20. $b = 4$, $l = 72$, $n = 18$.   21. $b = 50$, $l = 0$, $d = -\frac{5}{2}$.

22. Find the 45th term in an A.P. where the 3d term is 7 and $d = \frac{1}{3}$.

23. Find the sum of all even integers from 10 to 380 inclusive.

24. Find the sum of all odd integers from 15 to 361 inclusive.

25. Find the sum of all positive integral multiples of 5 less than 498.

Note 1. The 1st term, b, and the last term, l, in an A.P. are called its *extremes*, and the other terms are called *arithmetic means* between b and l. An order *to insert k arithmetic means* between b and l implies that we are to find a sequence of k numbers which, when inserted between b and l, complete an A.P. with b and l as the extremes.

Insert the specified number of arithmetic means.

26. Five, between 13 and -11.   27. Four, between 23 and 16.

Hint for Problem 26. The means will complete an A.P. of 7 terms with $b = 13$ and $l = -11$. First find d from $l = b + (n - 1)d$; then compute the intermediate terms between b and l.

28. Seven, between 4 and 8.   29. Eight, between $\frac{3}{4}$ and $6\frac{3}{4}$.

Note 2. When a *single* arithmetic mean is inserted between two numbers, it is called **THE** *arithmetic mean* of the numbers. Thus, if A is the arithmetic mean of b and c, we have the arithmetic progression b, A, c, and then $A - b = c - A$; hence, $2A = b + c$. Therefore,

$$A = \tfrac{1}{2}(b + c). \tag{1}$$

Find the arithmetic mean of the numbers.

30. 8, 46.   **31.** 16, 54.   **32.** −20, −59.   **33.** −16, 20.   **34.** x, y.

35. A man invests \$800 at the beginning of each year for 15 years at 4% simple interest. Find the accumulated value of his investments at the end of 15 years if no interest has been withdrawn.

36. The bottom rung of a ladder is 26 inches long and each other rung is one half inch shorter than the rung below it. If the ladder has 20 rungs, how many feet of wood were used in making the rungs?

37. In a pile of logs, each layer contains one more log than the layer above, and the top layer contains just one log. If there are 105 logs in the pile, how many layers are there?

38. If an object falls from rest in a vacuum near sea level, then, approximately, the distance fallen in the 1st second is 16 feet, and in each succeeding second the object falls 32 feet farther than in the preceding second. How far does the object fall in 20 seconds?

39. A contractor has agreed to pay a penalty if he uses more than a specified length of time to finish a certain job. The penalties for excess time are \$25 for the 1st day and, thereafter, \$5 more for each day than for the preceding day. If he pays a total penalty of \$4050, how many excess days did he need to finish the work?

40. A mountain climber ascends 1000 feet in the first hour, and 100 feet less in each succeeding hour than in the preceding hour. When will he be 5400 feet above his starting point?

Find the total money paid by the debtor in discharging his debt.

41. *Debtor borrows* \$6000. Pays, at the end of each year for 12 years, \$500 of the principal and simple interest at 4% on all principal left unpaid during the year.

42. *Debtor borrows* \$15,000. Pays, at the end of each year for 15 years, \$1000 of the principal and simple interest at 5% on all principal left unpaid during the year.

59. Geometric progressions

A **geometric progression** (abbreviated **G.P.**) is a sequence of numbers called *terms*, each of which, after the first, is obtained by *multiplying* the preceding term by a fixed number called the **common ratio.** The common ratio is equal to the *ratio of any term, after the first, to the one preceding it.* Unless otherwise stated, any G.P. will be assumed to have just a finite number of terms.

Illustration 1. In the G.P. $(16, -8, +4, -2, \cdots)$, the common ratio is $-\tfrac{1}{2}$; the 5th term would be $(-\tfrac{1}{2})(-2) = +1$.

To determine whether or not a sequence of numbers forms a G.P., we *divide* each number by the one which precedes it. All of these ratios are equal if the terms form a G.P. In particular, if (a, b, c) form a G.P., then $b/a = c/b$.

Illustration 2. If $(a, 10, 50)$ form a G.P., then $\dfrac{10}{a} = \dfrac{50}{10}$, or $a = 2$.

If the terms of a G.P. are *reversed*, the terms will form a G.P. whose common ratio is the *reciprocal* of the ratio for the given G.P.

Illustration 3. In the G.P. $(4, 8, 16, 32)$, the common ratio is 2. When the terms are reversed, we have $(32, 16, 8, 4)$, where the ratio is $\frac{1}{2}$.

Illustration 4. The G.P. (a, ar, ar^2, ar^3) has the common ratio r, whereas the G.P. (ar^3, ar^2, ar, a) has the common ratio ar^2/ar^3 or $1/r$.

Let a be the 1st term and r be the common ratio in a G.P. Then, the 2d term is ar; the 3d term is ar^2. In each of these terms, the exponent of r is 1 less than the number of the term. Similarly, the 8th term is ar^7. The nth term is the $(n-1)$th after the 1st and hence is found by multiplying a by $(n-1)$ factors r, or by r^{n-1}. Hence, if l represents the nth term,

$$l = ar^{n-1}. \tag{1}$$

Illustration 5. If $a = 3$ and $r = 2$, the 7th term is $3(2^6) = 192$.

Let S be the sum of the first n terms of the G.P. considered in (1). The terms are $(a, ar, ar^2, \cdots, ar^{n-2}, ar^{n-1})$, where ar^{n-2} is the $(n-1)$th term. Hence,

$$S = a + ar + ar^2 + \cdots + ar^{n-2} + ar^{n-1}; \tag{2}$$
$$Sr = ar + ar^2 + ar^3 + \cdots + ar^{n-1} + ar^n; \tag{3}$$

in (3) we multiplied both sides of (2) by r. On subtracting each side of equation (3) from the corresponding side of (2), we obtain

$$S - Sr = a - ar^n, \tag{4}$$

because each term, except ar^n, on the right in (3) cancels a corresponding term in (2). From (4), we find $S(1 - r) = a - ar^n$, or

$$S = \frac{a - ar^n}{1 - r}. \tag{5}$$

Since $l = ar^{n-1}$, then $rl = ar^n$. Hence, from (5),

$$S = \frac{a - rl}{1 - r}, \tag{6}$$

which is particularly useful when l is given. From (5),

$$S = a\frac{1 - r^n}{1 - r}. \tag{7}$$

EXAMPLE 1.   Find the sum of the G.P.   2, 6, 18, $\cdots$ *to six terms.*

Solution. $n = 6; a = 2; r = 3$.   From (5),

$$S = \frac{2 - 2 \cdot 3^6}{1 - 3} = \frac{2 - 1458}{-2} = 728.$$

When a sufficient number of the elements (a, r, n, l, S) are given, we find the others by use of (1), (5), and (6).

EXAMPLE 2.   If $S = 750, r = 2$, and $l = 400$, find n and a.

Solution.   1. From (6), $750 = \dfrac{a - 800}{1 - 2}$;   *hence,* $a = 50$.

2. From $l = ar^{n-1}$,

$$400 = 50(2^{n-1}); \quad 2^{n-1} = \frac{400}{50} = 8;$$

$$2^{n-1} = 2^3; \quad hence, \quad n - 1 = 3, \quad or \quad n = 4.$$

The 1st term, a, and last term, l, of a G.P. are called its *extremes*. The other terms are called *geometric means* between a and l. To insert k geometric means between a and l, means to find a sequence of k numbers which, when placed between a and l, give a G.P. with a and l as the extremes. We shall ask only for real-valued means.

EXAMPLE 3.   Insert two geometric means between 6 and 16/9.

Solution. After the means are inserted, they will complete a G.P. of 4 terms with $a = 6$ and $l = 16/9$. We shall find the ratio r and then the desired terms of the G.P. From $l = ar^{n-1}$ with $n = 4$,

$$\tfrac{16}{9} = 6r^3; \quad r^3 = \tfrac{8}{27}; \quad r = \sqrt[3]{\tfrac{8}{27}} = \tfrac{2}{3}.$$

The G.P. is $(6, 4, \tfrac{8}{3}, \tfrac{16}{9})$. The geometric means are 4 and $\tfrac{8}{3}$.

EXERCISE 30

Write the first four terms of the G.P. for the data.

1. $a = 3, r = 5$.   **2.** $a = 2, r = -3$.   **3.** $a = 64, r = -\tfrac{1}{2}$.

If the terms form a G.P., write two more terms for it.

4. 3, 12, 48.   **5.** 15, $-\tfrac{15}{2}$, $\tfrac{15}{4}$.   **6.** 81, -27, 9.   **7.** 0, 1, 3, 9.

8. a, au, au^2.   **9.** $(1.03)^4, (1.03)^7, (1.03)^{10}$.

10. $\sqrt{1.02}, 1.02, (1.02)^{\frac{3}{2}}$.   **11.** $(1.01)^{-8}, (1.01)^{-6}, (1.01)^{-4}$.

Find x if the numbers form a G.P.

12. 3, 18, x.   **13.** x, 7, 28.   **14.** 9, x, 81.   **15.** x, -6, 30.

By use of a formula, find the specified term of the G.P. without finding intermediate terms.

16. 6th term of 2, 6, 18.

17. 9th term of 3, −6, 12.

18. 8th term of 28, 14, 7.

19. 8th term of 7, $-\frac{7}{2}, \frac{7}{4}$.

Find the last term and the sum of the G.P. by use of formulas.

20. 4, −12, 36, *to 6 terms.*

21. 18, −1.8, .18, *to 9 terms.*

22. $\frac{1}{64}, -\frac{1}{32}, \frac{1}{16}$, *to 8 terms.*

23. 2, 2a, 2a², *to 10 terms.*

Find the sum of the G.P. by a formula, without finding other terms.

24. $32 + 16 + 8 + \cdots + \frac{1}{64}$.

25. $4 + 12 + 36 + \cdots + 4(729)$.

Find the missing elements of the G.P.

26. $r = 10, a = .0001, l = 1000$.

27. $a = 5, l = -1215, S = -910$.

28. $a = 512, r = \frac{1}{2}, l = 1$.

29. $a = 972, r = \frac{1}{3}, l = \frac{4}{3}$.

Find the specified term of the G.P. without finding its first term.

30. The 10th term, if the 7th term is 4 and $r = 3$.

31. The 14th term, if the 9th term is 250 and $r = .1$.

Insert the specified number of geometric means.

32. Six, between 1 and 128.

33. Three, between $\frac{1}{16}$ and 10,000.

34. Six, between .3 and 3,000,000.

35. Four, between $\frac{2}{3}$ and 162.

If x and y are both positive or both negative, and if a single geometric mean G of the same sign is inserted between x and y, then G is called **THE** *geometric mean of x and y; thus, (x, G, y) form a G.P. Find the geometric mean of the numbers.*

36. $\frac{1}{9}$, 81.

37. $\frac{1}{4}$, 36.

38. x, y.

39. −4, −25.

Find an expression for the sum by use of a progression formula, and simplify the exponents. Use (6) on page 123, when convenient.

40. $1 + (1.02) + (1.02)^2 + \cdots + (1.02)^{44}$.

41. $1 + (1.04) + (1.04)^2 + \cdots + (1.04)^{63}$.

42. $(1.03)^3 + (1.03)^4 + (1.03)^5 + \cdots + (1.03)^{21}$.

43. $(1.02)^5 + (1.02)^8 + (1.02)^{11} + \cdots + (1.02)^{50}$.

44. $(1.05)^{-18} + (1.05)^{-16} + (1.05)^{-14} + \cdots + (1.05)^{-2}$.

60. Applications of progressions

When a sequence of terms is suspected of forming an A.P., compute the values of the first few terms to verify the existence of a common difference. If the sequence is suspected of forming a G.P., write the first few terms, *without computation*, in a form which will *exhibit any factor which enters to successive powers.*

In a problem where it is inferred that a progression enters, first we must decide whether an A.P. or a G.P. occurs. Then, we should specify the values of corresponding elements of the progression. Finally, formulas for progressions should be employed to obtain the unknown elements, which yield the solution of the problem.

EXAMPLE 1. A ball is dropped from a height of 100 feet. On each rebound, the ball rises to one half of the height from which it last fell. What distance has the ball traveled up to the instant it hits the ground for the 12th time?

Partial solution. The first few distances traveled are as follows:

1st *fall,* 100′; 1st *rise and* 2d *fall,* $2(\frac{1}{2})(100')$; 2d *rise and* 3d *fall,* $\frac{1}{2}(100')$.

The total distance, in feet, is equal to 100 plus the sum of the G.P.

$$100, \tfrac{1}{2}(100), \tfrac{1}{4}(100), \cdots, \text{to eleven terms.}$$

MISCELLANEOUS EXERCISE 31

Solve by use of formulas for progressions.

1. A man piles 150 logs in layers so that the top layer contains 3 logs and each lower layer has one more log than the layer above. How many logs are at the bottom?
2. The path of each swing, after the first, of a pendulum bob is .9 as long as the preceding swing. If the first swing is 25 inches long, how far does the bob travel on the first 5 swings?
3. In a lottery, the 1st ticket drawn will pay the holder 10¢ and each succeeding ticket twice as much as the preceding one. Find the total amount paid on the first 12 tickets drawn.
4. If none of your ancestors appears in more than one line of descent, how many ancestors have you had in the generations since the discovery of America in 1492 by Columbus? Assume that each generation covers approximately 33 years.
5. Total prize money of $1480 is to be divided among 8 contestants so that the lowest will receive $10 and each other a fixed amount more than the preceding person. What prize money goes to the leader?
6. A contractor agreed that, if his job was not done by a certain date, he would pay $100 for the 1st day of delay and, for each succeeding day, $5 more than for the preceding day. How many penalty days did he use, if his penalty was $1080?
7. An investment in an oil acreage paid a man, in each year after the 1st year, three times as much as in the preceding year. If the investment paid $45,375 in the first five years, how much did it pay in the 1st year and in the 5th year?
8. The following problem appeared in a book by the Hindu mathematician BHĀSKARA about A.D. 1150. "In an expedition to seize his enemy's elephants, a king marched 2 yojanas the first day. Say, intelligent calculator, with what increasing size of daily march did he proceed, since he reached his foe's city, a distance of 80 yojanas, in a week?"
9. Find an expression for the sum of the first n positive odd integers.
10. Prove that the squares of the terms of a G.P. also form a G.P. Then, state a more general theorem of the same nature.
11. Obtain an expression for $(x + x^2 + x^3 + \cdots + x^{50})$.

12. Prove that the reciprocals of the terms of a G.P. form a G.P.

13. If $y = 3x + 7$, find the sum of the values of y corresponding to the successive integral values $x = 1, 2, 3, \cdots, 40$.

14. If $y = ax + b$, prove that the successive values of y, corresponding to the successive integral values of x, form an A.P.

15. Suppose that $r \neq 1$, $a \neq 0$, and $n_1, n_2, \cdots, n_k$ is a sequence of k integers. Prove that, if $a, ar^{n_1}, ar^{n_2}, \cdots, ar^{n_k}$ is a G.P., then $0, n_1, n_2, \cdots, n_k$ is an A.P.

Note 1. If P is the value of a quantity *now*, and if its value increases at the rate i (a decimal) per year, then the new value at the end of one year is $(P + Pi)$, or $P(1 + i)$. That is, *the value at the end of any year is* $(1 + i)$ *times the value at the end of the preceding year.* The values at the ends of the years form a G.P. whose common ratio is $(1 + i)$. If F is the value at the end of n years, then

$$F = P(1 + i)^n. \qquad (1)$$

This formula is referred to as the **compound interest law** because, if a principal P dollars is invested now at the rate i, compounded annually, the amount F dollars at the end of n years will be $P(1 + i)^n$. In all of the following problems, it will be assumed that any *rate* is *constant*. In texts on the mathematics of investment, convenient tables are available for use with (1).

Find compact expressions for the results in Problems 16 *and* 17.

16. If 200 units of a commodity are consumed in a first year, and if the annual rate of increase in consumption is 5%, (a) what amount is consumed in the 8th year; (b) in the first 15 years?

17. A corporation will sell $2,000,000 worth of products this year, and sales are expected to increase at the rate of 5% per year. Find the total anticipated sales in the first 10 years.

18. The population of a city increased from 256,000 to 625,000 in 4 years. Find the rate of increase per year.

19. A piece of property was purchased 3 years ago for $8,100 and its value now is $19,200. Find the annual rate at which the value increased.

20. The value of a certain quantity *decreases* at the rate w (a decimal) per year. If H is the value now, and K is the value at the end of n years, prove that $K = H(1 - w)^n$. This formula is the basis for computing depreciation charges in business under the so-called *constant-percentage* method. Also, the formula is called the *law of compound discount* in the mathematics of investment.

21. An airplane was purchased for $33,750 and its value three years later was $10,000. Find the rate per year at which the value depreciated.

Note 2. A sequence of numbers is said to form a *harmonic* progression* if their reciprocals form an *arithmetic progression*. *To insert k harmonic means between two numbers, first insert k arithmetic means between the reciprocals of the numbers;* the reciprocals of the arithmetic means are the harmonic means.

* Suppose that a set of strings of the same diameter and substance are stretched to uniform tension. If the lengths of the strings form a harmonic progression, a harmonious sound results if two or more strings are caused to vibrate at one time. This fact accounts for the name *harmonic progression.*

Insert the specified number of harmonic means.

22. Four, between $\frac{1}{3}$ and $\frac{1}{13}$.

23. Five, between $\frac{1}{2}$ and $\frac{1}{26}$.

24. Four, between $\frac{5}{3}$ and $\frac{5}{11}$.

25. Four, between $\frac{3}{7}$ and $\frac{3}{17}$.

If (c, H, d) form a harmonic progression, then H is called **THE** *harmonic mean of c and d. Find the harmonic mean of the numbers.*

26. $\frac{1}{2}, \frac{1}{18}$.　　**27.** 4, 8.　　**28.** $-6, 5$.　　**29.** 6, 12.　　**30.** x and y.

Note 3. Suppose that $x > 0$, $y > 0$, and $x \neq y$. Then, from Problem 34 on page 122, Problem 38 on page 125, and Problem 30 above, respectively, the arithmetic, geometric, and harmonic means of x and y are M_A, M_G, and M_H as follows:

$$M_A = \frac{x+y}{2}; \quad M_G = \sqrt{xy}; \quad M_H = \frac{2xy}{x+y}.$$

From Problems 23 and 25 on page 57, observe that $M_H < M_G < M_A$.

61. Limit of an infinite sequence

In Sections 58 and 59, we considered finite sequences of numbers. In Section 57 on page 119, we defined an infinite sequence $\{S_n\}$ as a set of terms

$$S_1, S_2, S_3, \cdots, S_n, \cdots, \tag{1}$$

where the domain for n is all positive integers. In (1), we have referred to S_n as the nth term or as the *general term*. In the present section, if we refer to a sequence $\{S_n\}$, we shall mean an infinite sequence.

Note 1. If n is a positive integer, the symbol $n!$, which is read *"n factorial,"* represents the product of *all positive integers from 1 to n inclusive*. That is, by definition,

$$n! = 1 \cdot 2 \cdot 3 \cdot 4 \cdots n.$$

Separately, we define $0! = 1$. Thus,

$$3! = 1 \cdot 2 \cdot 3 = 6; \quad 5! = 1 \cdot 2 \cdot 3 \cdot 4 \cdot 5 = 120; \text{ etc.}$$

Illustration 1. If $S_n = (2n)!$, the sequence $\{S_n\}$ has the terms $2!, 4!, 6!, \cdots$, or $2, 24, 720, \cdots$.

Suppose that a few consecutive terms at the beginning of a sequence are given, and that we are requested to find a formula for its nth term, S_n. Then, if we obtain S_n so that it agrees with the *given terms*, this result will be considered satisfactory.

Illustration 2. If $(1!, -3!, 5!, \cdots)$ is described as a *sequence*, we conclude that $S_n = (-1)^{n+1}(2n-1)!$. To check, we compute

$$S_1 = (-1)^2(1!) = 1!; \quad S_2 = (-1)^3(3!) = -3!; \quad S_3 = (-1)^4(5!) = 5!.$$

In dealing with an infinite sequence $\{S_n\}$, frequently it is important to investigate the behavior of S_n as n *grows large without bound*.

Illustration 3. Consider the sequence

$$\frac{3}{2}, \frac{7}{4}, \frac{15}{8}, \frac{31}{16}, \ldots, \qquad where \qquad S_n = 2 - \frac{1}{2^n}. \tag{2}$$

If *n increases,* then $1/2^n$ *decreases,* and will be as *near zero as we please if n is sufficiently large.* Thus, if $n = 65$,

$$\frac{1}{2^{n-1}} = \frac{1}{2^{64}} = \frac{1}{18,446,744,073,709,551,616},$$

which is an extremely close approximation to zero. Hence, in (2), S_n will be as near $(2 - 0)$, or 2, as we please *for all values of n which are sufficiently large.* The first few terms of sequence (2) are represented on the number scale in Figure 44. On the scale, the variable point S_n from (2) moves to the right as

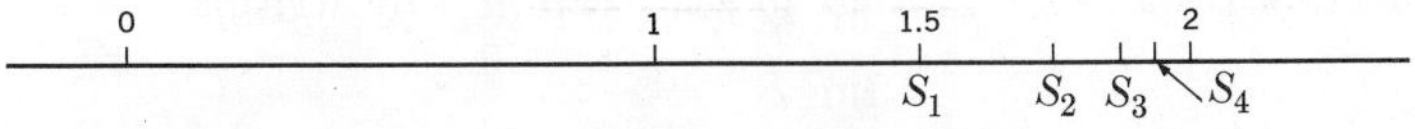

Figure 44

n increases, and S_n will be as close as we please to 2 on the scale if *n* is sufficiently large. In terminology to be introduced below, we may summarize the facts just mentioned about S_n by stating that "S_n *approaches* 2 *as a limit when n grows large without bound.*" More briefly, we say that

"*the limit of S_n as n becomes infinite is 2.*" (3)

In symbols, to be read as above, (3) is abbreviated by

$$\lim_{n \to \infty} S_n = 2, \qquad or \qquad \lim_{n \to \infty} S_n = 2. \tag{4}$$

An example of the following terminology has just been met.

DEFINITION I. *To state that the **limit** of S_n as n becomes infinite is L means that $|S_n - L|$ is as small as we please for all values of n which are sufficiently large. To abbreviate*

"*the limit of S_n as n becomes infinite is L,*" (5)

we write $$\lim_{n \to \infty} S_n = L. \tag{6}$$

Statement (5), or (6), means that S_n *will be as close to L as we please for all values of n which are sufficiently large.* The symbol "$n \to \infty$" alone may be read either "*n becomes infinite*" or "*n approaches infinity,*" where "$\to$" is read "*approaches.*" Then, instead of (5) or (6), we may write

$$S_n \to L \qquad as \qquad n \to \infty. \tag{7}$$

When (6) is true, we say that the sequence $\{S_n\}$ **converges,** or has a **limit,** or that the sequence *converges to L.* If a sequence does *not* converge, then it is said to **diverge.**

Illustration 4. Suppose that $S_n = k$, a constant, for all values of n. Then, $\lim_{n \to \infty} S_n = k$.

Illustration 5. If $S_n = (-1)^n$, the sequence is -1, 1, -1, 1, $\cdots$, where -1 and $+1$ occur alternately. Hence, S_n does *not* approach any number L as $n \to \infty$. Thus, the sequence *diverges*.

We cannot construe Definition I as *preventing* S_n from being equal to its limit L, or as *requiring* S_n to equal L for any value of n. Thus, in Illustration 3, S_n is *never* equal to its limit for any value of n; in Illustration 4, S_n is equal to its limit for *all values of n*.

Illustration 6. If $S_n = n/2$, the sequence is $\frac{1}{2}$, 1, $\frac{3}{2}$, 2, $\cdots$. If n increases without bound, then S_n likewise increases without bound.

We phrase a result such as that in Illustration 6 by writing

$$\lim_{n \to \infty} S_n = +\infty, \tag{8}$$

or $S_n \to +\infty$ as $n \to \infty$, which we read "S_n *becomes positively infinite as n becomes infinite.*" Sometimes, in such a case, we say that S_n has an *infinite limit as $n \to \infty$*. In contrast, then, a limit S as described in Definition I is called a *finite limit*. Similarly, as in (8), if S_n is *negative* when n is large, and if $|S_n| \to +\infty$ as $n \to \infty$, we write $S_n \to -\infty$ as $n \to \infty$, and say that S_n *becomes negatively infinite as $n \to \infty$*.

Note 2. Definition I may be restated as follows:

To say that $S_n \to L$ as $n \to \infty$ means that, if any number $d > 0$ is specified, there is a corresponding place in the sequence $\{S_n\}$ such that, for all terms beyond this place we have $|S_n - L| < d$.

We shall use the following theorem, where the results are intuitively evident. The proof of the theorem is met in more advanced mathematics.

THEOREM I. *Let $\{S_n\}$ and $\{T_n\}$ be sequences which have limits L and M, respectively, and let k be any constant. Then,*

$$\lim_{n \to \infty} (S_n + T_n) = \lim_{n \to \infty} S_n + \lim_{n \to \infty} T_n = L + M; \tag{9}$$

$$\lim_{n \to \infty} S_n T_n = (\lim_{n \to \infty} S_n)(\lim_{n \to \infty} T_n) = LM; \tag{10}$$

$$\lim_{n \to \infty} k S_n = k(\lim_{n \to \infty} S_n) = kL; \tag{11}$$

if $M \neq 0$,

$$\lim_{n \to \infty} \frac{S_n}{T_n} = \frac{\lim_{n \to \infty} S_n}{\lim_{n \to \infty} T_n} = \frac{L}{M}. \tag{12}$$

The results in (9) and (10) extend to the sum and the product of the general terms of three or more sequences. Thus, we may rephrase (9) and (10) as follows, where it is assumed that the given sequences are convergent.

The limits of the sum and the product of the general terms of a given number of sequences are equal to the sum and the product, respectively, of the limits of the given sequences.

Illustration 7. If k is any positive integer, then $n^k \to +\infty$ as $n \to \infty$. Hence, if h is any constant,

$$\lim_{n\to\infty} \frac{h}{n^k} = 0, \tag{13}$$

because the numerator in (13) remains fixed while $n^k \to +\infty$.

Suppose that $S_n = P_n/Q_n$, where P_n and Q_n are polynomials in n. To investigate $\lim_{n\to\infty} S_n$, we first *divide the numerator and denominator of S_n by* the **highest power of n in the denominator.** Then, we try to evaluate $\lim_{n\to\infty} S_n$ by use of (12). Sometimes, (13) is of assistance.

EXAMPLE 1. If $S_n = \dfrac{3n^2 + 2n - 3}{7n^2 + 5n - 4}$, obtain $\lim_{n\to\infty} S_n$.

Solution. Divide the numerator and denominator of S_n by n^2, and use Theorem I:

$$\lim_{n\to\infty} S_n = \lim_{n\to\infty} \frac{3 + \dfrac{2}{n} - \dfrac{3}{n^2}}{7 + \dfrac{5}{n} - \dfrac{4}{n^2}} = \frac{\lim\limits_{n\to\infty} 3 + \lim\limits_{n\to\infty} \dfrac{2}{n} - \lim\limits_{n\to\infty} \dfrac{3}{n^2}}{\lim\limits_{n\to\infty} 7 + \lim\limits_{n\to\infty} \dfrac{5}{n} - \lim\limits_{n\to\infty} \dfrac{4}{n^2}} = \frac{3 + 0 + 0}{7 + 0 + 0} = \frac{3}{7}.$$

EXAMPLE 2. If $S_n = \dfrac{3n^2 + 5}{2n + 7}$, investigate $\lim_{n\to\infty} S_n$.

Solution. Divide the numerator and denominator of S_n by n. Then,

$$S_n = \frac{3n + \dfrac{5}{n}}{2 + \dfrac{7}{n}}. \tag{14}$$

As $n \to \infty$, the numerator in (14) becomes positively infinite, the denominator approaches 2, and thus the fraction grows large without bound. That is, $S_n \to +\infty$ as $n \to \infty$.

62. Summation notation

In dealing with a finite sequence $u_1, u_2, \cdots, u_n$, we have agreed to refer to $(u_1 + u_2 + \cdots + u_n)$ as a *series*, where we now amplify the name to *"finite series"* because, in Section 63, we shall introduce the concept of an *"infinite series."* In the present section, *series* will continue to mean a *finite series*. In the consideration of series (*finite*, and later *infinite*), an abbreviated symbolism called the *"summation notation,"* or the *"sigma notation,"* is practically indispensable. We introduce capital Greek sigma, Σ, called the *sign of summation,* to abbreviate sums of *notationally similar terms.* Thus, we write

$$u_1 + u_2 + \cdots + u_n = \sum_{i=1}^{n} u_i. \tag{1}$$

We also use "$\sum_{i=1}^{n} u_i$" instead of the right-hand side of (1). We read "$\sum_{i=1}^{n} u_i$" as *"the sum of u_i from $i = 1$ to $i = n$."* In $\sum_{i=1}^{n} u_i$, we refer to i as the *index,* or *variable of summation,* and call u_i the **general term** of the sum.

Illustration 1. $\sum_{j=1}^{6} v_j = v_1 + v_2 + v_3 + v_4 + v_5 + v_6 = \sum_{i=1}^{6} v_i.$

$\sum_{x=1}^{n} x^2 = 1^2 + 2^2 + 3^2 + \cdots + n^2.$

From Illustration 1, we infer that the *letter* used for the *variable of summation* is immaterial. Hence, this variable sometimes is called a *dummy variable.*

Illustration 2. $\sum_{i=1}^{3} 5x_i = 5x_1 + 5x_2 + 5x_3 = 5(x_1 + x_2 + x_3) = 5 \sum_{i=1}^{3} x_i$

$\sum_{n=1}^{4} (u_n + 6) = (u_1 + 6) + (u_2 + 6) + (u_3 + 6) + (u_4 + 6)$

$$= (u_1 + u_2 + u_3 + u_4) + 4(6) = \sum_{n=1}^{4} u_n + 24.$$

Similarly, we obtain the following results, where c is a constant.

$$\sum_{i=1}^{n} cu_i = c\sum_{i=1}^{n} u_i; \quad \sum_{k=1}^{n} (u_k + c) = nc + \sum_{k=1}^{n} u_k. \tag{2}$$

Illustration 3. The sum of a G.P. of 12 terms, with 1st term 3 and common ratio 2, is abbreviated as follows:

$$3 + 3(2) + \cdots + 3(2^{11}) = \sum_{n=1}^{12} 3(2^{n-1}). \tag{3}$$

Similarly, $\qquad a + ar + \cdots + ar^{n-1} = \sum_{h=1}^{n} ar^{h-1}. \tag{4}$

Illustration 4. The sum of an A.P. of 10 terms, where the 1st term is 4 and common difference is 5, is abbreviated as follows, where we use formulas from page 120:

$$4 + 9 + 14 + \cdots + [4 + 9(5)] = \sum_{k=1}^{10} [4 + 5(k - 1)]$$

$$= \tfrac{10}{2}[4 + (4 + 9 \cdot 5)] = \tfrac{10}{2}(53) = 265.$$

The sum of an A.P. of n terms, with 1st term b and common difference d is abbreviated as follows:

$$b + (b + d) + \cdots + [b + (n - 1)d] = \sum_{k=1}^{n} [b + (k - 1)d].$$

Thus, from (5) on page 120,

$$\sum_{k=1}^{n} [b + (k - 1)d] = \tfrac{1}{2}n[2b + (n - 1)d].$$

EXERCISE 32

Evaluate the limit.

1. $\lim\limits_{n\to\infty} \dfrac{3n+2}{5-4n}$.

2. $\lim\limits_{n\to\infty} \dfrac{2n+n^2}{n+3n^2}$.

3. $\lim\limits_{n\to\infty} \dfrac{n+5n^2}{6+2n^3}$.

4. $\lim\limits_{n\to\infty} \dfrac{6-3n+4n^3}{2n+n^2-6n^3}$.

5. $\lim\limits_{n\to\infty} \dfrac{2+5n+4n^2}{3+2n}$.

6. $\lim\limits_{n\to\infty} \dfrac{1-2n-6n^2}{2+4n}$.

7. $\lim\limits_{n\to\infty} \left[2 + (-1)^n \dfrac{1}{2^n} \right]$.

8. $\lim\limits_{n\to\infty} \dfrac{(n-1)!}{n!}$.

9. $\lim\limits_{n\to\infty} \dfrac{(2n+1)n!}{(n+1)!}$.

By inspection, obtain a formula for the nth term of the sequence.

10. $3, 5, 7, \cdots$.

11. $2, -4, 6, \cdots$.

12. $2!, 4!, 6!, \cdots$.

13. $\frac{2}{1}, -\frac{4}{3}, \frac{8}{5}, \cdots$.

Plot the terms on a number scale. If the sequence appears to converge, write a formula for the nth term and evaluate the limit of the sequence.

14. $\frac{1}{2}, \frac{2}{3}, \frac{3}{4}, \frac{4}{5}, \cdots$.

15. $\frac{2}{1}, -\frac{3}{2}, \frac{4}{3}, -\frac{5}{4}, \cdots$.

16. $1, -\frac{1}{2}, \frac{1}{4}, -\frac{1}{8}, \cdots$.

17. $2, 4, 6, 8, \cdots$.

Expand the sum. Find its value if possible.

18. $\sum\limits_{n=1}^{4} n^2$.

19. $\sum\limits_{k=1}^{5} k$.

20. $\sum\limits_{j=1}^{6} 3j$.

21. $\sum\limits_{i=1}^{5} \frac{1}{2}i$.

22. $\sum\limits_{i=1}^{12} x_i$.

23. $\sum\limits_{k=1}^{5} x_k y_k$.

24. $\sum\limits_{h=1}^{4} x_h^2$.

25. $\sum\limits_{n=1}^{6} cx_n$.

26. $\sum\limits_{h=1}^{5} 3(2^h)$.

27. If $(x_1, x_2, x_3, x_4, x_5)$ are $(2, 3, 6, 5, 9)$, find

$$\sum_{i=1}^{5} x_i; \quad \sum_{n=1}^{5} (x_n - 4); \quad \sum_{j=1}^{5} (x_j - 2)^2.$$

28. Express in decimal form, where the x's are as in Problem 27:

$$\sum_{k=1}^{6} \frac{5}{10^k}; \quad \sum_{n=1}^{5} \frac{x_n}{10^n}.$$

Evaluate the sum by use of a formula for progressions.

29. $\sum\limits_{k=1}^{5} [3 + 4(k-1)]$.

30. $\sum\limits_{n=1}^{12} [2 - 3(n-1)]$.

31. $\sum\limits_{n=1}^{15} br^{n-1}$.

Write a symbol for the sum by use of summation notation.

32. $4 + 7 + 10 + \cdots + [4 + 3(n-1)]$.

33. $3 + 2(3) + 2^2(3) + \cdots + 2^8(3)$.

34. $2 - 2(5) + 2(5^2) - 2(5^3) + \cdots + 2(-5)^{h-1}$.

63. Certain infinite series

Let $u_1, u_2, \cdots, u_n, \cdots$ be an infinite sequence, abbreviated by $\{u_n\}$, where we call u_n the **general term** or the nth term of the sequence. Then, the symbol

$$u_1 + u_2 + \cdots + u_n + \cdots \qquad (1)$$

will be called an **infinite series.** We abbreviate (1) by writing $\sum_{n=1}^{\infty} u_n$, which is read *"the sum of u_n from $n = 1$ to infinity."* However, this phraseology does not assign any value to (1), because no meaning has been attached to the sum of infinitely many numbers. We propose introducing the concept of a *value* for *certain* infinite series.

Let S_n represent the sum of the first n terms in (1). Thus

$$S_1 = u_1, \quad S_2 = u_1 + u_2, \text{ etc.,} \quad S_n = u_1 + u_2 + \cdots + u_n = \sum_{k=1}^{n} u_k. \qquad (2)$$

In (2), we shall call S_n the nth **partial sum.** Thus, corresponding to any infinite series (1), we have defined an infinite sequence $\{S_n\}$ of partial sums.

DEFINITION II. *To say that an infinite series* **converges,** *or that* **it is convergent,** *means that the sum of the first n terms has a limit as $n \to \infty$, and then this limit is called the* **sum** *of the series.*

That is, to say that a series $\sum_{n=1}^{\infty} u_n$ converges, means that *the sequence of partial sums $\{S_n\}$ converges.* If $\sigma = \lim_{n \to \infty} S_n$, then σ is the sum of the series, or its *value*, and we say that the series *converges to σ.* Then, we use "$\sum_{n=1}^{\infty} u_n$" not only as a symbol for the series, but also for its sum, and write

$$\sum_{n=1}^{\infty} u_n = \sigma = \lim_{n \to \infty} S_n. \qquad (3)$$

Notice that the sum of an infinite series is *not a sum in the ordinary sense*, but is *the limit of an ordinary sum of n terms as $n \to \infty$.*

DEFINITION III. *If an infinite series does not converge, it is said to* **diverge,** *or to be* **divergent.**

Illustration 1. Consider the infinite (or, endless) G.P.

$$a, ar, ar^2, \cdots, ar^{n-1}, \cdots, \qquad (4)$$

and the corresponding infinite geometric series

$$a + ar + ar^2 + \cdots + ar^{n-1} + \cdots, \qquad or \qquad \sum_{n=1}^{\infty} ar^{n-1}, \qquad (5)$$

for which $\qquad S_n = a + ar + \cdots + ar^{n-1}.$

From (5) on page 123, $\qquad S_n = \dfrac{a - ar^n}{1 - r} = \dfrac{a}{1 - r} - \dfrac{ar^n}{1 - r}. \qquad (6)$

Illustration 2. Let us investigate the infinite G.P.

$$1, \frac{1}{2}, \frac{1}{4}, \cdots, \frac{1}{2^{n-1}}, \cdots, \; where \tag{7}$$

$$r = \frac{1}{2}; \quad the \; nth \; term \; is \; \frac{1}{2^{n-1}}; \quad 1 - r = \frac{1}{2}; \quad ar^n = \frac{1}{2^n}.$$

The infinite series corresponding to (7) is

$$1 + \frac{1}{2} + \frac{1}{4} + \cdots + \frac{1}{2^{n-1}} + \cdots = \sum_{n=1}^{\infty} \frac{1}{2^{n-1}}. \tag{8}$$

By use of (6) with $a = 1$ and $r = \frac{1}{2}$, the sum, S_n, for (8) is

$$1 + \frac{1}{2} + \cdots + \frac{1}{2^{n-1}} = S_n = 2 - \frac{1}{2^{n-1}}. \tag{9}$$

In Illustration 3 on page 129, in slightly different notation which is of no importance, we saw that

$$\lim_{n \to \infty} S_n = 2 - \lim_{n \to \infty} \frac{1}{2^{n-1}} = 2 - 0 = 2. \tag{10}$$

Hence, by Definition II, the infinite geometric series in (8) converges, and its sum is 2. Then, we may write

$$\sum_{n=1}^{\infty} \frac{1}{2^{n-1}} = 2. \tag{11}$$

Statement (11), with (10) as a background, means that, if we add the first n terms on the left in (11), *the sum will be as close to 2 as we please if n is sufficiently large.*

THEOREM II. *If $|r| < 1$, the infinite geometric series*

$$a + ar + ar^2 + \cdots + ar^{n-1} + \cdots, \quad or \quad \sum_{n=1}^{\infty} ar^{n-1},$$

*converges, and has the sum **a/(1 − r)**. That is,*

$$(if \; |r| < 1) \qquad \sum_{n=1}^{\infty} ar^{n-1} = \frac{a}{1-r}. \tag{12}$$

Proof. The sum, S_n, of the first n terms for the infinite series $\sum_{n=1}^{\infty} ar^{n-1}$ is given in (6). We accept the fact that, if $|r| < 1$, then $\lim_{n \to \infty} r^n = 0$, and hence $ar^n \to 0$ as $n \to \infty$. Therefore, from (6),

$$\lim_{n \to \infty} S_n = \frac{a}{1-r} - \frac{\lim_{n \to \infty} ar^n}{1-r} = \frac{a}{1-r} - 0 = \frac{a}{1-r}.$$

Hence, by Definition II, the geometric series $\sum_{n=1}^{\infty} ar^{n-1}$ converges if $|r| < 1$, and has the *sum $a/(1-r)$.*

Illustration 3. In the case of the infinite G.P.

$$2, 2(.1), 2(.1)^2, \cdots, 2(.1)^{n-1}, \cdots,$$

by use of (12), we obtain $\quad \sum_{n=1}^{\infty} 2(.1)^{n-1} = \dfrac{2}{1-.1} = \dfrac{2}{.9} = \dfrac{20}{9}.$

Illustration 4. Consider the infinite A.P. with first term 1, and common difference 1:

$$1, 2, 3, \cdots, n, \cdots. \tag{13}$$

We obtain the corresponding infinite arithmetic series

$$1 + 2 + 3 + \cdots + n + \cdots = \sum_{n=1}^{\infty} n. \tag{14}$$

For (14), $\qquad S_n = 1 + 2 + \cdots + n = \tfrac{1}{2}n(n+1). \tag{15}$

Hence, $\lim_{n\to\infty} S_n = +\infty$, because $\tfrac{1}{2}n(n+1)$ grows *large without bound as n grows large without bound.* Thus, by Definition II, series (14) does *not* converge, and hence, by Definition III, we state that the series *diverges.*

Illustration 5. For the infinite series,

$$1 - 1 + 1 - \cdots + (-1)^{n+1} + \cdots = \sum_{n=1}^{\infty} (-1)^{n+1}, \tag{16}$$

we find that $S_1 = 1$, $S_2 = 0$, $S_3 = 1$, etc., $S_n = 1$ if n is *odd* and $S_n = 0$ if n is *even*. Hence, there is *no number* σ such that $\lim_{n\to\infty} S_n = \sigma$. Thus, series (16) *diverges.*

THEOREM III. *If* $\sum_{n=1}^{\infty} u_n$ *converges, then* $\lim_{n\to\infty} u_n = 0$. *That is, a* **necessary condition** *for the convergence of* $\sum_{n=1}^{\infty} u_n$ *is that* $u_n \to 0$ *as* $n \to \infty$.

Proof. 1. Let σ be the sum of the convergent series $\sum_{n=1}^{\infty} u_n$. Then, $\lim_{n\to\infty} S_n = \sigma$.

2. Since $\qquad S_{n-1} = u_1 + u_2 + \cdots + u_{n-1},$ *and*

$$S_n = u_1 + u_2 + \cdots + u_{n-1} + u_n,$$

it is seen that $\qquad u_n = S_n - S_{n-1}.$

Hence, $\qquad \lim_{n\to\infty} u_n = \lim_{n\to\infty} S_n - \lim_{n\to\infty} S_{n-1} = \sigma - \sigma = 0.$

Corollary 1. *In an infinite series* $\sum_{n=1}^{\infty} u_n$, *if it is* **not** *true that "$u_n \to 0$ as $n \to \infty$," then the series diverges.*

Proof. (*Indirect method.*) Our hypothesis is that we do *not* have "$u_n \to 0$ as $n \to \infty$." Now, assume that $\sum_{n=1}^{\infty} u_n$ *converges.* Then by Theorem III, it *must* be true that "$u_n \to 0$ as $n \to \infty$." *But, by our hypothesis,* the preceding condition is *not true.* Hence, we have reached a *contradiction* to our assumption that $\sum_{n=1}^{\infty} u_n$ *converges.* Therefore, the series must *diverge.*

Corollary 2. *If $a \neq 0$ and $|r| \geq 1$, the infinite geometric series $\sum_{n=1}^{\infty} ar^{n-1}$ diverges.*

Proof. The nth term is $u_n = ar^{n-1}$. If $|r| > 1$, we accept the fact that $|r^{n-1}| \to +\infty$ as $n \to \infty$. If $|r| = 1$, then $|r^{n-1}| = 1$ for all values of n. Hence, if $|r| \geq 1$, we do *not* have "$|r^{n-1}| \to 0$ as $n \to \infty$," and do *not* have "$|ar^{n-1}| \to 0$ as $n \to \infty$." Therefore, by Corollary 1, $\sum_{n=1}^{\infty} ar^{n-1}$ *diverges* if $|r| \geq 1$.

Illustration 6. In the infinite geometric series

$$1 + 2 + 4 + \cdots + 2^{n-1} + \cdots, \tag{17}$$

$r = 2$ and therefore the series *diverges*. This can be appreciated otherwise by noticing that the sum, S_n, of the first n terms in (17) *grows large without bound* as n grows large without bound, or $S_n \to +\infty$ as $n \to \infty$.

In previous experience, the student has accepted endless decimals on an intuitional basis. Now, we proceed to *define* an endless decimal, below, as *the sum of an infinite series.* As a background, we assume that real numbers, both rational and irrational, have been introduced without reference to the notion of an endless decimal.

We introduce any nonnegative* endless decimal as a symbol, N, of the form

$$N = H.a_1 a_2 \cdots a_k \cdots. \tag{18}$$

In (18), each term of the infinite sequence of numbers $\{a_k\}$ in the decimal places of N is one of the digits $(0, 1, 2, \cdots, 9)$, and H is a nonnegative integer. If N is a terminating decimal (as defined on page 4), then N is assigned a value as a rational number, as usual. In all other cases, N is not yet assigned a value as a number. For any endless decimal N, for every k we define a corresponding k-place terminating decimal r_k, which is a rational number,

$$r_k = H.a_1 a_2 \cdots a_k; \ or,$$

$$r_k = H + \frac{a_1}{10} + \frac{a_2}{10^2} + \cdots + \frac{a_k}{10^k}. \tag{19}$$

DEFINITION IV. *An endless decimal $H.a_1 a_2 \cdots a_k \cdots$ is defined as the sum of the following infinite series on the right, provided that it converges:*

$$H.a_1 a_2 \cdots a_k \cdots = H + \frac{a_1}{10} + \frac{a_2}{10^2} + \frac{a_3}{10^3} + \cdots + \frac{a_k}{10^k} + \cdots, \ or$$

$$H.a_1 a_2 \cdots a_k \cdots = H + \sum_{n=1}^{\infty} \frac{a_n}{10^n}. \tag{20}$$

In (20), the sum of H and the first k terms of the infinite series is

$$H + \frac{a_1}{10} + \frac{a_2}{10^2} + \cdots + \frac{a_k}{10^k} = H.a_1 a_2 \cdots a_k = r_k.$$

* Any negative endless decimal would involve details as for (18), with minus signs inserted at appropriate places.

By Definition II, to state that the infinite series in (20) *converges* means that the sequence $\{r_k\}$ has a limit as $k \to \infty$. In such a case, by Definition IV, the value of $H.a_1a_2 \cdots a_k \cdots$ is defined as follows:

$$H.a_1a_2 \cdots a_k \cdots = \lim_{k \to \infty} r_k. \tag{21}$$

On the basis of (20), it can be proved that *every endless decimal is a real number*. The corresponding proof of the convergence of (20) for every sequence of digits $\{a_k\}$ in the decimal places of (18) would involve a firm foundation for the irrational numbers, and various theorems concerning limits of sequences, all of which is above the level of this text. However, by use of (12), we may prove the convergence of (20) for every *repeating decimal*, as in the following example. It is found that *any repeating decimal, as described in Definition* IV, *is a rational number*. Suggestions for a proof of this general fact are given in a problem of a later exercise. Otherwise, we shall restrict our attention to particular repeating decimals.

EXAMPLE 1. Prove that (20) converges, and that its sum is a rational number, for the repeating decimal $.5\dot{8}\dot{1}$.

Solution. 1. By (20) of Definition IV,

$$.5818181 \cdots = .5 + .081 + .000'81 + .000'00'81 + \cdots, \tag{22}$$

in case the series on the right converges. In (22), for later convenience, we grouped together the two terms of (20) corresponding to each repetition of "81." Thus, $(.08 + .001)$ is replaced by simply $.081$.

2. In (22), notice that the terms to the right of $.5$ form an infinite geometric series with 1st term $.081$ and common ratio $.01$. Hence, by use of (12),

$$.081 + .000'81 + .000'00'81 + \cdots = \frac{.081}{1 - .01} = \frac{.081}{.99}.$$

Therefore, from (22),
$$.5\dot{8}\dot{1} = \frac{5}{10} + \frac{81}{990} = \frac{64}{110} = \frac{32}{55}.$$

In Note 4 of the Appendix, a method is illustrated for proving that every rational number is the value of a unique repeating decimal. Since every repeating decimal is a rational number, we arrive at the conclusion that there is a one-to-one* correspondence between the set of rational numbers and the set of repeating decimals. Then, it can be proved that there is a one-to-one correspondence between the set of irrational numbers and the set of nonrepeating endless decimals. We do not have a basis for justifying the preceding remarks.

---

* To rule out the possibility of two different decimals being the same rational number, it is usually agreed that any decimal with the digit 9 repeated endlessly on the right should not be used. In Problem 25 on page 139, the student will show that the repeated 9's may be replaced by repeated zeros, if the digit preceding the 9's in the decimal is increased by 1.

EXERCISE 33

Find the sum of the infinite geometric series:

1. $5 + \frac{5}{3} + \frac{5}{9} + \cdots$.

2. $16 + 4 + 1 + \frac{1}{4} + \cdots$.

3. $15 + \frac{15}{2} + \frac{15}{4} + \cdots$.

4. $6 - 3 + \frac{3}{2} - \frac{3}{4} + \cdots$.

Find a rational number m/n which is equal to the infinite repeating decimal.

5. $.\dot{2}$.　　6. $.\dot{5}$.　　7. $.\dot{6}$.　　8. $.\dot{8}$.　　9. $.\dot{1}\dot{6}$.　　10. $.8\dot{3}$.

11. $.0\dot{9}$.　　12. $.\dot{2}\dot{7}$.　　13. $.\dot{2}\dot{1}$.　　14. $.2\dot{3}$.　　15. $3.\dot{1}$.　　16. $2.\dot{6}$.

17. $.3\dot{6}$.　　18. $.2\dot{3}\dot{4}$.　　19. $10.0\dot{6}$.　　20. $242.\dot{4}.-\frac{8,000}{33}$

21. $1\dot{6}.\dot{2}$.　　22. $.\dot{1}4285\dot{7}$.　　23. $26.\dot{0}$.　　24. $.\dot{0}7692\dot{3}$.

25. Prove that the repeating decimal $.\dot{9} = 1$. This result justifies the remarks in the footnote on page 138.

Write the first few terms of the infinite series. Then, calculate the sum of the series, if it converges.

26. $\sum_{n=1}^{\infty} (.01)^n$.

27. $\sum_{n=1}^{\infty} 3(.1)^{n-1}$.

28. $\sum_{k=1}^{\infty} 2(-3)^{n-1}$.

29. $\sum_{n=1}^{\infty} (-1)^{n-1}(\frac{1}{4})^{n-1}$.

30. $\sum_{n=1}^{\infty} (-1)^{n-1}[4(2^{n-1})]$.

31. $\sum_{n=1}^{\infty} (-1)^{n-1}(2)(\frac{1}{3})^{n-1}$.

★*Prove that the series diverges, by use of Corollary 1 on page 136.*

32. The infinite arithmetic series $\sum_{n=1}^{\infty} [3 + 5(n-1)]$.

33. The infinite arithmetic series $\sum_{n=1}^{\infty} [b + (n-1)d]$, where $d \neq 0$.

34. $\sum_{n=1}^{\infty} \frac{5n}{3n+2}$.

35. $\sum_{n=1}^{\infty} \frac{2n^2}{n+3}$.

36. $\sum_{n=1}^{\infty} \frac{4n-3}{2n+1}$.

64. Positive integral power of a binomial

By multiplication, we obtain the following results:

$$(x + y)^1 = x + y;$$
$$(x + y)^2 = x^2 + 2xy + y^2;$$
$$(x + y)^3 = x^3 + 3x^2y + 3xy^2 + y^3;$$
$$(x + y)^4 = x^4 + 4x^3y + 6x^2y^2 + 4xy^3 + y^4;$$
$$(x + y)^5 = x^5 + 5x^4y + 10x^3y^2 + 10x^2y^3 + 5xy^4 + y^5.$$

We see that, if $n = 1, 2, 3, 4,$ or 5, *the expansion of $(x + y)^n$ contains* **$(n + 1)$ terms** *with the following five properties:*

I.　*In any term the sum of the exponents of x and y is n.*

II.　*The first term is x^n, and in each other term the exponent of x is 1 less than in the preceding term.*

III.　*The second term is $nx^{n-1}y$, and in each succeeding term the exponent of y is 1 more than in the preceding term.*

IV. *If the coefficient of any term is multiplied by the exponent of x in that term and if the product is divided by the number of that term, the quotient obtained is the coefficient of the next term.*

V. *The coefficients of terms equidistant from the ends are the same.*

Illustration 1. In the expansion of $(x + y)^5$, the fourth term is $10x^2y^3$; by Property IV, we obtain $(10 \cdot 2) \div 4$, or 5, as the next coefficient. The coefficient of the second term is equal to that of the next to the last term, etc.

We shall assume that Properties I to V are true if n is any positive integer, although we merely have verified their truth when $n = 1, 2, 3, 4,$ and 5. The theorem which justifies this assumption is called the **binomial theorem,** which will be proved on page 300.

EXAMPLE 1. Expand $(c + w)^7$.

Solution. 1. By use of Properties I, II, and III, we obtain

$$(c + w)^7 = c^7 + 7c^6w + \quad c^5w^2 + \quad c^4w^3 + \quad c^3w^4 + \quad c^2w^5 + \quad cw^6 + w^7,$$

where spaces are left for the unknown coefficients.

2. By Property IV, the coefficient of the third term is $(7 \cdot 6) \div 2$, or 21; that of the fourth term is $(21 \cdot 5) \div 3$, or 35.

3. By Property V, we obtain the other coefficients; hence,

$$(c + w)^7 = c^7 + 7c^6w + 21c^5w^2 + 35c^4w^3 + 35c^3w^4 + 21c^2w^5 + 7cw^6 + w^7.$$

EXAMPLE 2. Expand $\left(2a - \dfrac{w}{3}\right)^6$.

Solution. 1. $\left(2a - \dfrac{w}{3}\right)^6 = \left[(2a) + \left(-\dfrac{w}{3}\right)\right]^6$.

2. We use Properties I to V with $x = 2a$ and $y = -w/3$:

$$\left(2a - \frac{w}{3}\right)^6 = (2a)^6 + 6(2a)^5\left(-\frac{w}{3}\right) + 15(2a)^4\left(-\frac{w}{3}\right)^2 + 20(2a)^3\left(-\frac{w}{3}\right)^3$$

$$+ 15(2a)^2\left(-\frac{w}{3}\right)^4 + 6(2a)\left(-\frac{w}{3}\right)^5 + \left(-\frac{w}{3}\right)^6$$

$$= 64a^6 - 64a^5w + \frac{80}{3}a^4w^2 - \frac{160}{27}a^3w^3 + \frac{20}{27}a^2w^4 - \frac{4}{81}aw^5 + \frac{w^6}{729}.$$

By use of properties (I)–(IV), we obtain

$$\left. \begin{aligned} (x + y)^n &= x^n + nx^{n-1}y + \frac{n(n-1)}{2!}x^{n-2}y^2 + \cdots \\ &+ \frac{n(n-1)\cdots(n-r+1)}{r!}x^{n-r}y^r + \cdots + y^n. \end{aligned} \right\} \tag{1}$$

The general term involving $x^{n-r}y^r$ in (1) can be verified by successive applications of Property IV. We shall prove that this general term is correct, and we shall use it, on page 301. We refer to (1) as the **binomial formula**. In summation notation, (1) becomes

$$(x + y)^n = x^n + \sum_{r=1}^{n} \frac{n(n-1)\cdots(n-r+1)}{r!} x^{n-r}y^r.$$

Note 1. The following array is called *Pascal's Triangle.* The rows give the coefficients in the successive positive integral powers of $(x + y)$. To form any row after the second, we first place 1 at the left; the 2d number is the sum of the 1st and 2d numbers in the preceding row; the 3d number in the new row is the sum of the 2d and 3d numbers in the preceding row; etc. This triangle was known to Chinese mathematicians in the early fourteenth century. A proof that this device gives the binomial coefficients will be met on page 302. The student may desire to use Pascal's triangle rather than Properties I–V in expanding some of the powers in the next exercise, when the exponents are not too large.

```
              1
           1     1
        1     2     1
     1     3     3     1
  1     4     6     4     1
1     5    10    10     5     1
   .     .     .     .     .
```

EXERCISE 34

Expand each power by use of Properties I to V on pages 139–140.

1. $(a + b)^5$. 2. $(c - d)^6$. 3. $(x - y)^8$. 4. $(c + 3)^5$.
5. $(2 + a)^4$. 6. $(x - 2a)^7$. 7. $(3b - y)^6$. 8. $(2c + 3d)^3$.
9. $(a + b^2)^3$. 10. $(c^3 - 3d)^4$. 11. $(a^2 - b^2)^6$. 12. $(c - x^3)^5$.
13. $(x - \frac{1}{2})^5$. 14. $(1 - a)^8$. 15. $(\sqrt{x} - \sqrt{y})^6$. 16. $(x^{\frac{1}{4}} + a)^5$.
17. $(-a + y^{-2})^4$. 18. $(z^{-3} - x)^5$. 19. $(x^{\frac{1}{2}} - 2a^{-1})^4$.

Find only the first three terms of the expansion. All letters used in exponents represent positive integers.

20. $(a + 12)^{15}$. 21. $(c - 3)^{25}$. 22. $(a^2 + b^3)^{20}$. 23. $(1 + 2a)^{10}$.
24. $(1 - .1)^{22}$. 25. $(1 + .2)^{12}$. 26. $(1 - \sqrt{2})^{12}$. 27. $(1 - 3x^3)^{18}$.
28. $(2x - a^2)^{30}$. 29. $(x^{\frac{1}{2}} + b)^{14}$. 30. $(a^{-1} + 3)^{26}$. 31. $(x - a^{-2})^{11}$.
32. $(x - y)^n$. 33. $(a + x)^k$. 34. $(x^2 - y)^m$. 35. $(w^2 + z)^h$.

Compute the power correct to three decimal places by using only as many terms as necessary in a binomial expansion.

36. $(1.01)^8$. 37. $(1.02)^9$. 38. $(1.03)^{11}$. 39. $(1.01)^{20}$.

Hint. $(1.01)^8 = (1 + .01)^8 = 1 + 8(.01) + 28(.01)^2 + \cdots$.

EXERCISE 35

Review of Chapters 4 and 5

(a) Graph the function f. (b) State the coordinates of the vertex of the graph, and the equation of its axis of symmetry. (c) Solve $f(x) = 0$ graphically. (d) Describe the solution set of $f(x) < 0$, and of $f(x) \geqq 0$.

1. $f(x) = 2x^2 - 8x + 5$.   **2.** $f(x) = 3 - 2x - x^2$.

3. $f(x) = 4x^2 - 28x + 49$.   **4.** $f(x) = 4x^2 + 12x + 15$.

Graph the equation in an xy-plane where the x-axis is horizontal. State the coordinates of the vertex of the graph.

5. $y = x^2 - 4x$.   **6.** $x = y^2 + 6y - 5$.   **7.** $2x - y^2 + 4y = 6$.

Solve for x, or y, by the most convenient method. Obtain a partial check by computing the discriminant.

8. $2x^2 + 15 = 3x$.   **9.** $6x^2 + 5x = 6$.   **10.** $10x^2 = 41x + 77$.

11. $3x^2 = 20 - 2x$.   **12.** $8y^2 - 2y = 15$.   **13.** $2y^2 + 6y + 17 = 0$.

14. Solve for y, if h is a constant: $2hy^2 + 6y + 5hy = -15$.

Without solving, find the nature of the roots of the equation.

15. $3x^2 - 5x = 7$.   **16.** $2x^2 + 7x = -9$.   **17.** $6x^2 + 11x - 35 = 0$.

18. Factor $(6x^2 + 11x - 35)$ by first solving an equation.

19. Solve $4x^2 - 12x + 7 = 0$ by the method of completing a square.

20. If $f(x) = 4x^2 + 20x + 32$, state all facts which can be learned, without graphing, about the graph of f by use of its discriminant.

Find the specified term, and the sum up to and including that term, for the A.P. with the given terms.

21. 19, 15, 11; the 48th term.   **22.** 4, $4\frac{1}{2}$, 5; the 94th term.

Find the last term and the sum of the A.P. by use of formulas.

23. 27, 22, 17, $\cdots$ to 16 terms.   **24.** 2.6, 2.8, 3.0, $\cdots$ to 48 terms.

25. Find the 63d term in an A.P. where the 7th term is 23 and $d = -.3$.

26. Find the arithmetic mean of 13 and 27.

27. Find the 10th term of a G.P., without finding its first term, if the 7th term is 4 and common ratio is 3.

28. Find the 7th term of the G.P. with the terms $(5, -\frac{15}{2}, \cdots)$.

Find the missing constants among (a, r, l, n, S) for the G.P.

29. $S = 215; r = -2; l = 320$.   **30.** $a = 2; r = 3; l = 1458$.

31. Insert three geometric means between 2 and 162.

32. Insert five arithmetic means between -6 and $\frac{3}{2}$.

33. Find the positive geometric mean of 5 and 125.

34. Find integers m and n such that $1.2\dot{3}\dot{5} = m/n$.

35. Expand $(2b - y^2)^6$.

36. Find the first four terms in descending powers of x in the expansion of $(x - 2a^2)^{15}$.

Find the value of the constant k to satisfy the given condition.

37. The roots of $9x^2 - 2kx + 1 = 0$ are equal.

38. The graph of $y = 4x^2 - 12x + k$ is tangent to the x-axis.

39. The product of the roots of the equation $2x^2 - 8x + 3k = 0$ is 4.

40. The sum of the roots of the equation $3kx^2 - 2x = 8$ is 2.

41. Solve the equation $(2 - x) : 3 = (4 + 2x) : 2$.

42. Find the minimum value of $(2x^2 - 8x - 7)$. $y = \frac{-b}{2a}$ ans = -15

Find all complex numbers which are solutions of the equation.

43. $3\sqrt{2 + x} - \sqrt{4x + 1} = 3$.　　　　**44.** $2\sqrt{x + 1} - 2\sqrt{x} = 1$.

45. $3x^4 - x^2 - 10 = 0$.　　　　　　　　**46.** $y^6 + 56y^3 - 512 = 0$.

47. Find all fourth roots of 1296.

48. At the beginning of each year for 15 years, a man invests $500 at simple interest at the rate 6%. At the end of 15 years, what is the total value of his investments if no interest has been withdrawn?

49. The radiator of a truck contains 12 gallons of water. We draw off 3 gallons and replace it with alcohol, then draw off 3 gallons of the mixture and replace it by alcohol, etc., until 8 drawings and replacements have been made. How much alcohol is in the final mixture?

50. A certain factory is valued now at $40,000. We estimate that its value will depreciate by $2000 in the 1st year, and, in each succeeding year, by $50 less than in the preceding year. What will the factory be worth 16 years from now?

51. *Expand the sum and calculate it if possible.*

$$\sum_{n=1}^{6} n^2; \quad \sum_{n=1}^{4} (x_n - 6); \quad \sum_{h=1}^{n} [3 + 2(h - 1)]; \quad \sum_{n=1}^{\infty} 5\left(\frac{1}{3}\right)^{n-1}$$

★**52.** Prove that any endless repeating decimal is a rational number.

　　Hint. Let N be the decimal. Suppose that

$$N = H.a_1 \cdots a_h \dot{a}_{h+1} \cdots \dot{a}_{h+w}$$

where $\dot{a}_{h+1} \cdots \dot{a}_{h+w}$ repeats endlessly to the right. Express N as the sum of $H.a_1 \cdots a_h$ and the sum of an infinite geometric series.

Chapter **6** Quadratic Equations in Two Variables

65. Some basic principles in graphing

A polynomial function of degree 2 in two variables, (x, y), is referred to as a *quadratic function of x and y.* In the present chapter, we shall be concerned mainly with functions of this type, and numerical statements involving them. First, we shall consider graphs of certain types of equations of the form $f(x, y) = 0$ where f is a quadratic function of x and y. Any equation of this variety is of the form

$$Ax^2 + Bxy + Cy^2 + Dx + Ey + F = 0, \qquad (1)$$

where A, B, C, D, E, and F are constants and at least one of (A, B, C) is not zero. Any point, line, or curve which we shall mention in this chapter is assumed to lie in some given plane.

We recall that the product of two or more numbers is zero if and only if one or more of the factors is zero. This result may be useful in graphing an equation.

Illustration 1. The equation

$$(2x - y + 3)(x + y - 7) = 0 \qquad (2)$$

is satisfied if and only if

$$2x - y + 3 = 0 \quad or \quad x + y - 7 = 0.$$

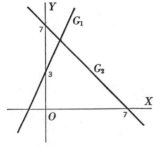

Figure 45

Hence, a point (x, y) satisfies (2), or is on the graph, G, of (2) if and only if (x, y) is on the graph, G_1, of $2x - y + 3 = 0$ or on the graph, G_2, of $x + y - 7 = 0$. Thus, G consists of the *two lines* G_1 and G_2 in Figure 45. Or, G is the *union* of the sets of points on G_1 and G_2; in symbols, $G = G_1 \cup G_2$.

144

Suppose now that a polynomial $f(x, y)$, of any degree, is expressed as a product of polynomial factors. Then, as illustrated in (2), the graph, G, of $f(x, y) = 0$ consists of the graphs of the new equations obtained by placing each of the specified factors equal to zero. In set terminology, G is the *union* of the graphs of the new equations.

Illustration 2. In order to graph
$$4x^2 - 4xy + y^2 = 9, \qquad (3)$$
we first arrange to have one member zero, and then factor:
$$(2x - y)^2 - 9 = 0 \quad or \quad (2x - y - 3)(2x - y + 3) = 0. \qquad (4)$$
Equation (3) is satisfied if and only if
$$2x - y - 3 = 0 \quad or \quad 2x - y + 3 = 0. \qquad (5)$$
The graph of (3) consists of the two lines which are the graphs of the linear equations in (5).

Illustration 3. To graph $4x^2 = 9y^2$, we first obtain $2x = \pm\sqrt{9y^2}$;
$$x = \tfrac{3}{2}y \quad or \quad x = -\tfrac{3}{2}y. \qquad (6)$$
Hence, the graph of $4x^2 = 9y^2$ consists of the *two lines* which are the graphs of the equations in (6). We could have written, first, $4x^2 - 9y^2 = 0$ and
$$(2x - 3y)(2x + 3y) = 0.$$
This also leads to (6).

Two points P and Q are said to be symmetric *with respect to a line l* if l is the perpendicular bisector of the segment PQ, as in Figure 46.*

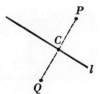

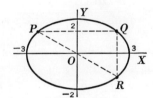

Figure 46   Figure 47

DEFINITION I. *A curve D is symmetric with respect to a line l as an **axis of** **symmetry** in case, for each point P on D, there is a point Q on D which is symmetric to P with respect to l.*

Illustration 4. A circle is symmetric with respect to any diameter. The ellipse in Figure 47 has OX and OY as axes of symmetry; P and Q are symmetric with respect to OY, and Q and R are symmetric to OX.

---

* This notion, and the corresponding concept of *symmetry for a curve*, as in Definition I below, were met on page 103 in the discussion of a parabola, but need re-emphasis here.

Two points P and Q are symmetric *with respect to a point* C in case C is the midpoint of the segment PQ, as in Figure 46 on page 145.

DEFINITION II. *A curve* D *is symmetric with respect to a point* C, *called a* center of symmetry, *in case, for each point* P *on* D, *there is a point* Q *on* D *which is symmetric to* P *with respect to* C.

Illustration 5. From Definition II, for the curve D, every chord PQ through C is bisected by C. In Figure 47 on page 145, the origin is a center of symmetry for the ellipse; P and R are symmetric with respect to the origin.

Illustration 6. The following facts are exhibited in Figure 48.

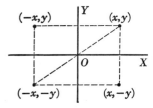

I. (x, y) *and* $(x, -y)$ *are symmetric with respect to the x-axis.*

II. (x, y) *and* $(-x, y)$ *are symmetric with respect to the y-axis.*

III. (x, y) *and* $(-x, -y)$ *are symmetric with respect to the origin.*

Figure 48

As a rule, a reference to *symmetry* will mean symmetry of the *preceding types.* Each of the following tests involves showing that, if a point (x, y) satisfies the equation, the symmetric point of I, II, or III above also satisfies it.

SUMMARY. *The graph of* $f(x, y) = 0$ *has the indicated symmetry if and only if an equivalent equation is obtained by the specified change.*

1. **Symmetry to x-axis :** *replace* y *by* $-y$.

2. **Symmetry to y-axis :** *replace* x *by* $-x$.

3. **Symmetry to the origin :** *replace* x *by* $-x$ *and* y *by* $-y$.

Illustration 7. To test the graph of $xy = 8$ for symmetry, replace x by $-x$ and obtain $-xy = 8$, *not equivalent to* $xy = 8$. Hence, its graph is *not* symmetric to OY and, similarly, is *not* symmetric to OX. If we replace x by $-x$ and y by $-y$ we obtain $(-x)(-y) = 8$ or $xy = 8$, the original equation. Hence, if (x, y) is on its graph, the point $(-x, -y)$ also is on the graph, and it is symmetric to the origin. The graph of $xy = 8$ is given in Figure 49 and is called a **hyperbola.**

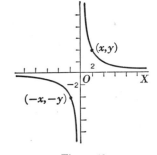

Figure 49

In graphing an equation $f(x, y) = 0$, we exclude any value of x or y for which the other variable is *not real* or *undefined.* To determine excluded values, we inspect $f(x, y)$ itself, and also any expression obtained in solving $f(x, y) = 0$ for x or for y, if this operation is convenient. After such exclusions, the remaining values for x, or y, are taken as the *domain* for the variable. If no real values (x, y) satisfy the equation, its locus is said to be *imaginary*.

EXAMPLE 1.   Graph the equation $\qquad 4x^2 + 9y^2 = 36.$ $\qquad$ (7)

Solution. 1. *Types of symmetry.*   Since $(-x)^2 = x^2$ and $(-y)^2 = y^2$, equation (7) is unaltered if we replace x by $-x$, or y by $-y$, or both x by $-x$ and y by $-y$. Hence, the graph is symmetric to OX, OY, and the *origin*.

2. *Domains for x and y.*   On solving (7) for x, we obtain

$$x^2 = \frac{36 - 9y^2}{4} \quad or \quad x = \pm\tfrac{3}{2}\sqrt{4 - y^2}. \qquad (8)$$

Similarly, from (7), $\qquad\qquad\qquad y = \pm\tfrac{2}{3}\sqrt{9 - x^2}.$ $\qquad\qquad$ (9)

From (8), x would have an imaginary value if $|y| > 2$; thus, the domain for y is $|y| \leq 2$. From (9), the domain for x is $|x| \leq 3$.

3. *The intercepts.*   By using $x = 0$ in (7), we find $y = \pm 2$, which are the y-intercepts. With $y = 0$ in (7), we find the x-intercepts, $x = \pm 3$.

4. With $x = \pm 2$, in (9), we obtain $y = \pm 1.5$. The solutions (x, y) thus found for (7) are in the following table, from which the graph of (7) was obtained in Figure 50. The graph is a curve called an **ellipse,** which will be defined as a certain geometrical locus on page 159.

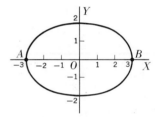

$x =$	-3	-2	0	2	3
$y =$	0	± 1.5	± 2	± 1.5	0

Figure 50

Comment.   Recall the discussion on page 82 about functions defined by equations. Let $f(x) = \tfrac{2}{3}\sqrt{9 - x^2}$ and $g(x) = -\tfrac{2}{3}\sqrt{9 - x^2}$. Then, in (9), we see that f and g are solution functions of (7) for y as a function of x. The graph of $y = f(x)$ is the upper half, and of $y = g(x)$ is the lower half of the ellipse in Figure 50 which is the graph of (7). Similarly, in (8), we observe formulas defining two solution functions of (7) for x as a function of y. The graphs of these functions, separately, are the right-hand and left-hand halves of the ellipse in Figure 50.

In Example 1, we illustrated the fact that the graph of an equation in x and y is symmetric to OX if y is involved just with *even* exponents. Also, if the graph is symmetric to both OX and OY, then the graph *also has the origin as a center of symmetry.* The converse of the last statement is not true, as seen in Figure 49 on page 146, where the origin is a center of symmetry but neither OX nor OY is an axis of symmetry. If we now think of OX and OY as *any two perpendicular axes of symmetry,* we have the following result.

{ *If a plane curve has two perpendicular axes of symmetry, the intersection of these axes is a center of symmetry for the curve.* }

Note 1. Recall the following terminology about intervals of numbers. If b is a constant, the set of all numbers $x > b$ is called an *infinite interval* of the number scale. Similarly, "*all* $x < b$," "*all* $x \leq b$," "*all* $x \geq b$," and "*all real numbers* x" define infinite intervals. The domain of a variable is said to be *infinite* if the domain includes an infinite interval.

A set of points, in a plane or in space, is said to have *infinite extent*, or *to extend to infinity*, if the distance from a fixed point to a point P of the set can be made to exceed any number, however large, by properly selecting P. A variable point $P\colon (x, y)$ is said *to recede to infinity* on a curve in the xy-plane if the distance from the origin to P grows large without bound as x, or y, grows large without bound.

Illustration 8. In Illustration 7, the domains of both x and y are infinite. If $P\colon (x, y)$ varies on either branch of the curve so that $|x|$, or $|y|$, grows large without bound, then P recedes to infinity and approaches a coordinate axis.

We shall call a line l an **asymptote** of a curve if the shortest distance between l and a point P on the curve approaches zero if P recedes to infinity on some branch of the curve. Thus, each of the coordinate axes is an asymptote for the hyperbola in Figure 49 on page 146.

EXERCISE 36

Graph the equation by use of factoring.

1. $(2x - y + 4)(x + y) = 0.$
2. $(3x - 4 + y)(x - y) = 0.$
3. $(x + 2)(x + y - 1) = 0.$
4. $(y - 3)(2x - y - 1) = 0.$
5. $x^2 - 4y^2 = 0.$
6. $4y^2 - 9x^2 = 0.$
7. $4x^2 = 25y^2.$
8. $(x - 3)(x - 5) = 0.$
9. $(x - 3)(y + 5) = 0.$
10. $(x - 1)^2 = 0.$
11. $2x^2 - x = 1.$
12. $3y^2 + 5y = 2.$
13. $x^2 + 6y^2 = 5xy.$

For each point, give the symmetric points with respect to the coordinate axes and the origin, and plot all points.

14. $(2, 3).$
15. $(-3, 5).$
16. $(-2, -3).$
17. $(0, -4).$
18. $(a, b).$

For each equation, without graphing, test for the symmetry of its graph with respect to the coordinate axes and the origin.

19. $4x^2 - 9y^2 = 0.$
20. $9x^2 + 4y^2 = 36.$
21. $x^2 - y^2 = 9.$
22. $xy = 6.$
23. $xy = -5.$
24. $y^2 = -8x.$

Graph each equation which has a real locus.

25. $y^2 = 4.$
26. $x^2 = -9.$
27. $y^2 = 0.$
28. $x^2 + 4y^2 = 0.$
29. $4x^2 + y^2 = -2.$
30. $(y - 3)^2 = 0.$
31. $xy = -6.$
32. $x^2 = y.$
33. $(x - 2y)^2 = 4.$
34. $x^2 + y^2 = 16,$ (a) using *equal* scale units on the two axes; (b) using a scale unit on OX which is just *one-half as long as the scale unit on OY*.
35. $4x^2 + y^2 = 16,$ with directions (a) and (b) as in Problem 34.

36. In an xy-plane where the scale units on the axes are equal, a line l bisects the angle in quadrant I between the axes. What point is symmetric to $P:(x, y)$ with respect to l? Test the graph of each of the equations in Problems 31, 32, and 33 for this type of symmetry.

Graph the equation.

37. $|2x - y| = 2$.   **38.** $|-x - 3y| = 5$.   **39.** $|x^2 - 2| = 7$.

66. Equations for a circle

In this section, we stipulate that *equal units* are to be used on the axes. Then, the distance formula (2) of page 68 is available.

Suppose that a locus in an xy-plane is defined geometrically. Then, to obtain an equation for the locus, we apply its definition to obtain an equation satisfied by the coordinates of P if and only if P is on the locus.

Consider the circle T with center $C:(h, k)$ and radius r, in Figure 51. If $P:(x, y)$ is any point in the plane, from page 68 we obtain

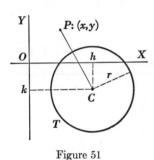

Figure 51

$$|\overline{CP}| = \sqrt{(x - h)^2 + (y - k)^2}.$$

If $|\overline{CP}| = r$, or $(\overline{CP})^2 = r^2$, then P *is on* T. If $(\overline{CP})^2 \neq r^2$, P *is not on* T. Hence, we obtain the equation of T by writing $(\overline{CP})^2 = r^2$, or

$$(x - h)^2 + (y - k)^2 = r^2. \tag{1}$$

We call (1) the **center-radius form** for the equation of a circle. If the center is $(0, 0)$, then (1) becomes

$$x^2 + y^2 = r^2. \tag{2}$$

Illustration 1. The equation of the circle with center $(2, -3)$ and radius 5 is $(x - 2)^2 + (y + 3)^2 = 25$.

In (1) or (2), we permit $r = 0$. Such a circle is just a point, a *point-circle*. If $r = 0$ in (1), the only solution is $(x = h, y = k)$.

When we expand the center-radius form (1), we obtain

$$x^2 + y^2 - 2hx - 2ky + (h^2 + k^2 - r^2) = 0. \tag{3}$$

In (3), let $\qquad D = -2h; \quad E = -2k; \quad F = h^2 + k^2 - r^2.$

Then, from (3), $\qquad x^2 + y^2 + Dx + Ey + F = 0. \tag{4}$

Thus, every circle has an equation of type (4). Conversely, for any values of the constants D, E, and F, (4) can be changed to the center-radius form and therefore represents a circle, real or imaginary. We call (4) the **general form** for the equation of a circle. To obtain the center and radius of a circle whose equation is given in this form, group the terms in x and, separately, those in y, and *complete a square in each set of terms;* then rewrite in the center-radius form.

EXAMPLE 1. Obtain the center and radius of

$$x^2 + y^2 - 4x + 6y - 12 = 0. \tag{5}$$

Solution. 1. Add 4 and 9 to complete squares:

$$(x^2 - 4x + 4) + (y^2 + 6y + 9) = 12 + 4 + 9 = 25; \textit{ or}$$
$$(x - 2)^2 + (y + 3)^2 = 5^2. \tag{6}$$

2. From (6), the center is $(2, -3)$ and radius is 5.

Illustration 2. The equation $(x - 1)^2 + (y - 3)^2 = -25$ has no graph, because the left-hand side is positive or zero for all values of x and y, while the right-hand side is negative. Such an equation may be said to represent an *imaginary circle.*

If $a \neq 0$, any equation of the form

$$ax^2 + ay^2 + bx + cy + d = 0 \tag{7}$$

can be changed to the general form (4) by dividing both sides in (7) by a. Hence, we reach the following conclusion.

If an equation of the second degree in x and y is of the form (7), *where the coefficients of x^2 and y^2 are equal and there is no term involving xy, the graph of the equation is a circle, real or imaginary, in an xy-plane where the units on the axes are* **equal.**

Note 1. A formal discussion of tangents to curves is met in calculus. In this text, from elementary geometry, we accept the notion of a tangent to a circle, and assume the well-known fact that *the tangent is perpendicular to the radius* of the circle drawn to the point of tangency.

EXAMPLE 2. Obtain an equation for the circle with center at $(5, 7)$ which is tangent to the line $y = 3$.

Solution. The student should sketch a figure exhibiting the data. The radius, r, of the circle is the perpendicular distance between $(5, 7)$ and the line $y = 3$. Hence, $r = 4$. Then, from (1), an equation for the circle is

$$(x - 5)^2 + (y - 7)^2 = 16.$$

EXERCISE 37

In this exercise, it is understood that **equal scale units** *are used on the axes in the coordinate plane.*

Write an equation of the circle with center C and radius r.

1. $C: (3, 4); r = 2.$ 2. $C: (-2, 5); r = 3.$ 3. $C: (3, -2); r = 4.$
4. $C: (-2, -4); r = 3.$ 5. $C: (0, 0); r = 4.$ 6. $C: (0, 3); r = 3.$
7. $C: (-2, 0); r = 2.$ 8. $C: (a, 0); r = a.$ 9. $C: (0, b); r = b.$

If the graph is a real circle, find its center and radius.

10. $x^2 + 2x + y^2 - 4y = 4.$

11. $x^2 - 6x + y^2 - 4y = 3.$

12. $x^2 + y^2 + 4x + 2y = -1.$

13. $x^2 + y^2 + 6x + 3 = 4y.$

14. $x^2 + y^2 + 8y + 19 = 0.$

15. $x^2 + y^2 - 6x - 11 = 0.$

16. $x^2 + y^2 + 6x + 9 = 4y.$

17. $x^2 + y^2 + 6x + 13 = 4y.$

18. $x^2 + y^2 + 5x + \frac{9}{4} = 6y.$

19. $x^2 + y^2 + 3y + 3 = x.$

Obtain the equations of the circles satisfying the conditions.

20. Center $(3, 0)$; tangent to the y-axis.

21. Tangent to the y-axis at $(0, -3)$; radius 4.

22. Tangent to the line $y = 4$; center $(2, 7)$.

23. Tangent to the line $x = -3$; center $(-5, 4)$.

67. The conic sections

At the center of a circle T, erect a line m perpendicular to the plane in which T lies. Select any point V on m, not in the plane of T, as seen in Figure 52 below. From any point Q on T, draw a line l through V. Then, the locus of all points swept out by l, as Q moves around T, is a surface of infinite extent called a (*complete*) *right circular cone*, whose *vertex* is V and *axis* is m. Each position of l is called a *ruling* of the cone. Its *vertex*, V, divides the cone into two parts called *nappes*. In Figure 54, each nappe is cut off above and below V by a plane perpendicular to the cone's axis.

If a plane cuts the cone, the curve of intersection is called a **conic section,** or simply a *conic*. First, suppose that the plane does not pass through V. Then, if the plane cuts just one nappe and is not parallel to a ruling (Figure 54), the conic section AB is called an **ellipse;** the ellipse is a *circle* if the plane is perpendicular to the axis of the cone. If the plane cuts just one nappe and is parallel to a ruling (Figure 54), the conic CDE is called a **parabola,** which has infinite extent. If the plane cuts both nappes in any fashion (Figure 53), the

Figure 52

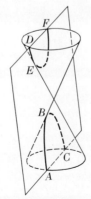

Figure 53

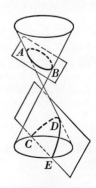

Figure 54

conic, *ABC* and *DEF*, is called a **hyperbola,** which has a separate piece or *branch* of infinite extent on each nappe.

If a cone is cut by a plane through *V*, the only point of intersection may be *V*, so that the conic section is *just this point.* Or, the plane may touch the cone merely along one ruling, in which case the conic is *just this line.* Or, the plane may cut the cone along two rulings, so that the conic consists of these *two lines* intersecting at *V*. Such sections through *V* are called **degenerate conics.** We may think of a conic which is a single point as a limiting case of an ellipse or circle, and of two intersecting lines as a limiting case of a hyperbola.

In the future, unless otherwise specified, we shall include under the name *conic sections* all curves mentioned in lists I and II below. Notice that two parallel lines are mentioned in II. This is done for later convenience, although two parallel lines cannot be obtained as a plane section of a cone.

I. **The nondegenerate conics :** *parabola; ellipse, including a circle as a special case; hyperbola.* Curves

II. **The degenerate conics :** *a single point; two lines in the same plane, where the lines may intersect in just one point, or may be coincident, or may be parallel but not coincident.* straight lines

In Sections 68–71,* the following facts will be proved about conics, and about equations for various conics when they are suitably located in an *xy*-plane where the units for the coordinates may be either equal or unequal.

An **ellipse, hyperbola,** or **degenerate conic** has **two perpendicular axes of symmetry,** and hence a **center** of symmetry which is the intersection of the axes of symmetry. These conics are called the **central conics.**

A **hyperbola** has two **asymptotes,** which pass through its center.

A **parabola** has one **axis of symmetry.** The point in which this axis meets the parabola is called its **vertex.**

$$\left\{ \begin{array}{l} An \text{ \textbf{ellipse, hyperbola,} or \textbf{degenerate conic}} \text{ with } OX \text{ and } OY \text{ as axes of} \\ \text{symmetry has an equation of the form } \mathbf{A}x^2 + \mathbf{C}y^2 = \mathbf{G,} \text{ where } A \text{ and } C \\ \text{are \textbf{not both zero.} Conversely, the graph of any equation of this form} \\ \text{with } A \text{ and } C \text{ not both zero is a conic of the specified type or is} \\ \text{imaginary, with the following possibilities when the graph is real:} \end{array} \right\} \quad (1)$$

$$\left. \begin{array}{l} A \text{ and } C \text{ of \textbf{opposite signs} and } G \neq 0: \text{ a \textbf{hyperbola,}} \\ \text{with } \mathbf{A}x^2 + \mathbf{C}y^2 = \mathbf{0} \text{ as an equation for the \textbf{asymptotes.}} \end{array} \right\} \quad (2)$$

$$\{A, C, \text{ and } G \text{ \textbf{all positive} or \textbf{all negative}: an \textbf{ellipse.}}\} \quad (3)$$

$$\left\{ \begin{array}{l} G = 0, \text{ or } G \neq 0 \text{ and } A = 0 \text{ or } C = 0: \\ \text{a \textbf{degenerate conic.}} \end{array} \right\} \quad (4)$$

* If the teacher has time to present Sections 68–71, the remainder of the present section and Exercise 38 may be *held in reserve as a future review* of Sections 68–71. If desired, the class may proceed immediately to Section 72 after finishing Exercise 38.

To graph an ellipse of type (3), obtain the x-intercepts and the y-intercepts. By use of this slender data (four points), with practice, the student should be able to draw a good ellipse, sufficiently accurate for most applications in this text or in calculus. To obtain a more accurate graph, four more points on the graph could be obtained by substituting a value for x (or, for y) in the given equation and computing the values for y (or, for x), and by symmetry.

Illustration 1. For the ellipse of Figure 50 on page 147, given by (7) on page 147, the table of coordinates (x, y) illustrates the preceding paragraph. In Figure 50, the line segment AB, or its length 6 units, on one axis of symmetry is called the *major axis* of the ellipse, and the segment from -2 to $+2$ on the y-axis is called the *minor axis* of the ellipse, because of the relative lengths of these line segments. With a choice of unequal units on the coordinate axes, the graph still would be an ellipse, but we could arrange to have it elongated vertically so that the major axis would become a segment of the y-axis. Hence, no great importance should be associated with the *major axis* and *minor axis*, because their locations depend on the arbitrary choices of scale units on the coordinate axes.

To graph a hyperbola quickly, with an equation as in (2), first find the x-intercepts, if they exist, or the y-intercepts, if they exist (one set of intercepts will *not* exist). Next, write *the equation for the asymptotes*, and draw them through the origin. Then, sketch each branch of the hyperbola through an intercept point to approach the asymptotes smoothly. Usually, a hyperbola drawn carefully in this simple fashion will be satisfactory in applications.

EXAMPLE 1. Graph: $\qquad\qquad 16y^2 - 9x^2 = 144.$ $\qquad\qquad$ (5)

Solution. 1. By (2), the graph of (5) is a hyperbola. Place $x = 0$, to obtain $16y^2 = 144$, or $y = \pm 3$. Hence, the y-intercepts, in Figure 55, are ± 3.

2. Place $y = 0$, to obtain $-9x^2 = 144$, or $x^2 = -16$. Thus, if $y = 0$ then $x = \pm\sqrt{-16}$, or $x = \pm 4i$. Hence, the graph has *no* x-intercepts, and we say that they are *imaginary*.

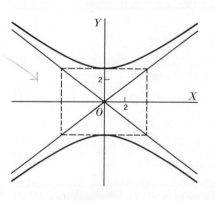

Figure 55

3. From (2), an equation for the asymptotes of the hyperbola is

$$16y^2 - 9x^2 = 0, \; or$$

$$(4y - 3x)(4y + 3x) = 0. \qquad (6)$$

The graph of (6) consists of the two lines

$$4y - 3x = 0 \quad and \quad 4y + 3x = 0.$$

To graph $4y - 3x = 0$, we use the points $(0, 0)$ and $(x = 4, y = 3)$. To graph $4y + 3x = 0$, we use points $(0, 0)$ and $(x = 4, y = -3)$. The asymptotes in Figure 55 are the lines through the origin and the corners of the broken-line rectangle. The coordinates of its corners are found by placing $y = \pm 3$ in (6) and computing corresponding values of x, which are $x = \pm 4$. A good approximation to each branch of the hyperbola in Figure 55 is obtained by sketching the branch through a y-intercept, 3 or -3, to approach an asymptote on each side. The student may desire to obtain a few more points for the graph by substituting for x or for y in (5). Thus, if $x = \pm 4$ in (5),

$$16y^2 - 144 = 144, \quad or \quad 16y^2 = 288; \quad y^2 = 18, \quad or \quad y = \pm 3\sqrt{2} = \pm 4.2.$$

From Section 68, and then with the aid of Note 5 in the Appendix, it can be learned that a "*parabola,*" as met on page 101, is a *parabola*, defined as a *conic section* and illustrated by curve CDE in Figure 54 on page 151. Hence, for ready reference, we repeat items from page 103 in slightly altered form:

$$\left. \begin{array}{l} \textit{If a quadratic polynomial } f(x, y) \textit{ is } \textbf{linear in } \textbf{y,} \textit{ the graph of} \\ f(x, y) = 0 \textit{ is a } \textbf{parabola} \textit{ whose axis is } \textbf{perpendicular to the x-axis.} \\ \textit{This parabola is found as on page 103 by first solving } f(x, y) = 0 \\ \textit{for } y, \textit{ to obtain } y = F(x), \textit{ where } F \textit{ is a quadratic function of } x. \end{array} \right\} \quad (7)$$

$$\left. \begin{array}{l} \textit{If a quadratic polynomial } f(x, y) \textit{ is } \textbf{linear in } \textbf{x,} \textit{ the graph of} \\ f(x, y) = 0 \textit{ is a } \textbf{parabola} \textit{ whose axis is } \textbf{perpendicular to the y-axis.} \\ \textit{This parabola is found by first solving } f(x, y) = 0 \textit{ for } x, \textit{ to ob-} \\ \textit{tain } x = F(y), \textit{ where } F \textit{ is a quadratic function of } y, \textit{ and then} \\ \textit{using the Summary on page 103 with the roles of x and y interchanged.} \end{array} \right\} \quad (8)$$

EXAMPLE 2.   Graph the quadratic equation

$$2x - 14 - 6y^2 + 24y = 0. \tag{9}$$

Solution.   1. Since (9) is linear in x, the graph of (9) is a parabola, as specified in (8). On solving (9) for x, we obtain

$$x = 3y^2 - 12y + 7. \tag{10}$$

2. By reference to the Summary on page 103, we see that the graph of (9) is a parabola whose axis is perpendicular to the y-axis, and has the equation $y = -(-12)/(2 \cdot 3) = 2$.   At the vertex, $y = 2$ and hence $x = -5$, from (10). The graph is in Figure 40 on page 103.

Illustration 2.   The student should verify that the graph of

$$2y - 2x^2 + 4x + 6 = 0$$

is the parabola $y = x^2 - 2x - 3$ in Figure 39, page 101.

In Exercise 41, it will be proved that the graph of any equation $axy = b$, where $a \neq 0$ and $b \neq 0$, is a **hyperbola** *with the coordinate axes as its asymptotes.* To graph an equation $axy = b$, the student should compute a few points on the curve by substituting for x (or for y) in the equation, and computing y (or x).

Illustration 3. The graph of $3xy = 24$, or $xy = 8$, is the hyperbola in Figure 49 on page 146.

Note 1. The student should recall equation (7) on page 150, and the method for finding the center and radius for any circle represented by such an equation.

EXERCISE 38*
Miscellaneous Graphing of Conic Sections

Name the graph of the equation before drawing the graph. Then, obtain a good graph relatively quickly, by selecting strategically located points such as the vertex of any parabola, and the intercepts of any curve. Draw the asymptotes for any hyperbola. Usually, choose equal scale units on the coordinate axes. Draw any circle with compasses.

1. $x^2 + y^2 = 49$.
2. $4x^2 + y^2 = 16$.
3. $4x^2 - y^2 = 0$.
4. $4x^2 - y^2 = 16$.
5. $4y^2 - 25x^2 = 100$.
6. $4x^2 + 9y^2 = 0$.
7. $3x^2 + 5y^2 = -8$.
8. $5x^2 = 0$.
9. $5x^2 + 5y^2 - 30 = 0$.
10. $2x^2 + 9 = 0$.
11. $9x^2 + 16y^2 = 144$.
12. $xy - 10 = 0$.
13. $2xy + 7 = 0$.
14. $y = 4x^2$.
15. $x = -6y^2$.
16. $y - x^2 - 6x + 2 = 0$.
17. $y^2 - x - 4y + 7 = 0$.
18. $x^2 - 4x + y^2 + 6y = 12$.
19. $9x^2 - 2y^2 - 3xy = 0$.

20. Graph $4x^2 + 9y^2 = 36$, (a) with equal scale units on the coordinate axes; (b) with the y-unit three times as long as the x-unit.

★*Exhibit the solutions of the inequality, or system of inequalities, graphically. Use the method of page 95.*

21. $x^2 - 4y < 0$.
22. $y^2 - 2x > 0$.
23. $4x^2 + 25y^2 < 100$.
24. $4x^2 - 49y^2 - 196 > 0$.
25. $4y^2 - x^2 - 4 < 0$.
26. $\begin{cases} x^2 + 4y^2 < 16, \text{ and} \\ 4x^2 + y^2 - 4 \geq 0. \end{cases}$
27. $\begin{cases} x^2 > 12y, \text{ and} \\ x^2 + 9y^2 - 9 < 0. \end{cases}$

★28. Suppose that the domains of x and y are restricted to be just integers, with $|x| \leq 5$ and $|y| \leq 2$. Then, list all solutions of the inequality $x^2 - y^2 > 9$.

★68. Simple standard equations for a parabola

In this section, and in Sections 69 and 70, we shall deal with loci in a Euclidean plane. Hence, in this plane, we have a designated unit for length, which we shall assume is taken as the scale unit on each of the axes for an xy-system of coordinates. Then, agreement (1) on page 68 applies.

For our present purposes, if we refer to a *conic section*, we shall mean only an ellipse, a hyperbola, or a parabola (and thus shall *not* be considering the degenerate conics). We proceed to define them anew by means of characteristic properties. Proof of the equivalence of these new definitions and the definition of the conics as sections of a cone is beyond the scope of this text.

* See footnote on page 152.

DEFINITION III. *A* **parabola** *is the locus of a point P whose undirected distance from a fixed point F, called the* **focus,** *is equal to the undirected distance of P from a fixed line D, called the* **directrix,** *which does not go through F.*

EXAMPLE 1. Find the equation of the parabola with focus $F:(-3, 0)$ and directrix $D:[x = 3]$.

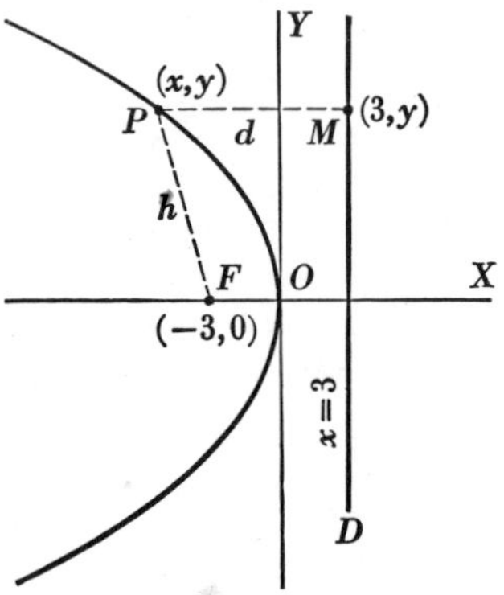

Solution. 1. In Figure 56, let $P:(x, y)$ be any point not on D, and let MP be perpendicular to D from P. Then M is the point $(3, y)$.

2. Let h be the length of PF; then

$$h = \sqrt{(x + 3)^2 + y^2}.$$

3. From (4) on page 51, $\overline{PM} = 3 - x$. Let $d = |\overline{PM}|$; then $d^2 = (3 - x)^2$.

4. P is on the parabola if and only if $h = d$. Since h and d are positive, the equation $h = d$ is equivalent to $h^2 = d^2$, which becomes

$$(3 - x)^2 = (x + 3)^2 + y^2 \qquad or \qquad y^2 = -12x, \tag{1}$$

which is an equation for the specified parabola.

Figure 56

Derivation of a standard equation for a parabola

1. Refer to Figure 57. Let p be the distance from the directrix D to the focus F, where $p > 0$. Designate the x-axis as the line through F perpendicular to D, with the origin midway between F and D, and F in the positive direction from O. Then, F is the point $(\frac{1}{2}p, 0)$ and D is the line $x = -\frac{1}{2}p$.

2. Let $P:(x, y)$ be any point in the plane, and let the undirected distance of P from F be h, and from D be d. In Figure 57, M is the point $(-\frac{1}{2}p, y)$. Hence, from (4) on page 51, $\overline{MP} = x - (-\frac{1}{2}p)$;

$$h = |\overline{PF}| = \sqrt{\left(x - \frac{p}{2}\right)^2 + y^2};$$

$$d = |\overline{MP}| = \left|x + \frac{p}{2}\right|. \tag{2}$$

3. The equation of the parabola is $h = d$, which is equivalent to

$$h^2 = d^2 \quad or \quad \left(x - \frac{p}{2}\right)^2 + y^2 = \left(x + \frac{p}{2}\right)^2.$$

On expanding and simplifying, we obtain

$$y^2 = 2px, \tag{3}$$

whose graph is shown in Figure 57.

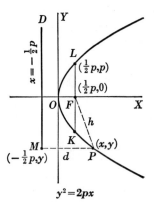

$y^2 = 2px$

Figure 57

Discussion of $y^2 = 2px$. The graph is symmetric to the x-axis because y occurs only with an *even* exponent. Thus, the line perpendicular to the directrix through the focus is an axis of symmetry, called the **axis of the parabola.** The intersection of this axis and the parabola is called its **vertex,** the origin in Figure 57. Since $y = \pm\sqrt{2px}$, negative values of x are excluded; or, the domain for x is all numbers $x \geq 0$. In calculus, it is proved that the tangent to the parabola at its vertex is perpendicular to the axis of the parabola. The chord KL of the parabola perpendicular to its axis at the focus is called the **focal chord,** or **latus rectum** of the parabola. When $x = \frac{1}{2}p$, at F, we find that $y^2 = p^2$ or $y = \pm p$. Hence, K and L are the points $(\frac{1}{2}p, \pm p)$ and $|\overline{KL}| = 2p$. The parabola is *concave* to the right (*open* to the right). In our primary applications, the location of the focus, directrix, and latus rectum will be of negligible interest. Hence, our essential information for graphing (3) is as follows:

$$y^2 = 2px,\ p > 0: \quad (axis,\ y = 0;\ vertex,\ (0, 0);\ concave\ to\ right). \quad (4)$$

Similarly, we obtain the following additional standard equations for a parabola having p as the distance between the focus F and directrix D. We refer to (4), (5), (6), and (7) as *standard forms* for a parabola with its *vertex at the origin* and *axis along a coordinate axis.*

$$y^2 = -2px,\ p > 0: \quad (axis,\ y = 0;\ vertex,\ (0, 0);\ concave\ to\ left). \quad (5)$$
$$x^2 = 2py,\ p > 0: \quad (axis,\ x = 0;\ vertex,\ (0, 0);\ concave\ upward). \quad (6)$$
$$x^2 = -2py,\ p > 0: \quad (axis,\ x = 0;\ vertex,\ (0, 0);\ concave\ downward). \quad (7)$$

The corresponding *standard positions* are in Figures 57, 58, 59, and 60.

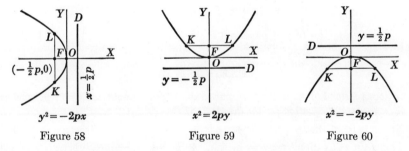

$y^2 = -2px$	$x^2 = 2py$	$x^2 = -2py$
Figure 58	Figure 59	Figure 60

Note 1. For (5), the focus is $F: (-\frac{1}{2}p, 0)$ and directrix is the line $x = \frac{1}{2}p$. For (6), the focus is $F: (0, \frac{1}{2}p)$ and directrix is the line $y = -\frac{1}{2}p$. Etc. for (7).

Illustration 1. To graph $x^2 = -12y$, which is of type (7), we locate the vertex $(0, 0)$ and the axis, the line $x = 0$, as in Figure 60. By using $y = -3$ we obtain $x = \pm 6$, and the two points $(\pm 6, -3)$ on the curve. Other points could be found similarly.

Illustration 2. To change $3x^2 = 7y$ to a standard form, divide by 3 to obtain $x^2 = \frac{7}{3}y$. Hence, $3x^2 = 7y$ is of type (6), with the vertex of the graph at $(0, 0)$ and the line $x = 0$ as the axis.

The method of Illustration 2 shows that each equation of type (8) or (9) below is equivalent to one of the standard forms (4)–(7). These remarks justify the following conclusions.

Any **parabola** *whose vertex is the origin and whose axis of symmetry is a coordinate axis has an equation as follows. Conversely, the graph of any equation of this nature is a parabola of the specified type:*

$$(\text{With } A \neq 0, C \neq 0, D \neq 0, \text{ and } E \neq 0)$$

Parabola *with OY as the axis:* $\qquad\qquad$ $Ax^2 + Ey = 0.$ $\qquad\qquad$ (8)

Parabola *with OX as the axis:* $\qquad\qquad$ $Cy^2 + Dx = 0.$ $\qquad\qquad$ (9)

EXAMPLE 2. By use of a standard form, find the equation of a parabola whose axis is a coordinate axis, and vertex is $(0, 0)$, if the parabola passes through the point $(12, -6)$.

Solution. 1. On account of the location of $(12, -6)$, we decide that two parabolas can be found as specified. One parabola will have the standard form $x^2 = ky$ and appearance as in Figure 60 on page 157. The other parabola will have the standard form $y^2 = hx$ and appearance as in Figure 57 on page 156.

2. *The case of $x^2 = ky$.* On substituting $(x = 12, y = -6)$, we obtain

$$144 = -6k, \quad or \quad k = -24.$$

Hence, the equation of the parabola is $x^2 = -24y$.

3. *The case of $y^2 = hx$.* On substituting $(x = 12, y = -6)$, we obtain

$$36 = 12h, \quad or \quad h = 3.$$

Hence, the equation of the parabola is $y^2 = 3x$.

EXERCISE 39

By the locus method of Example 1 on page 156, obtain the equation of the parabola with the given focus and equation for the directrix.

1. Focus $(4, 0)$; directrix, $x = -4$. $\qquad$ 2. Focus $(0, -3)$; directrix, $y = 3$.
3. Focus $(0, -2)$; directrix, $y = 6$. $\qquad$ 4. Focus $(0, -\frac{1}{2}p)$; directrix, $y = \frac{1}{2}p$.

Plot the parabola by use of its vertex and a few points symmetric to the parabola's axis.

5. $y^2 = -12x.$ $\qquad$ 6. $y^2 = 8x.$ $\qquad$ 7. $x^2 = 8y.$ $\qquad$ 8. $x^2 = -8y.$
9. $y^2 = -8x.$ $\qquad$ 10. $y^2 = -6x.$ $\qquad$ 11. $x^2 = 4y.$ $\qquad$ 12. $x^2 = -6y.$
13. $y^2 = 2x.$ $\qquad$ 14. $2x^2 = 9y.$ $\qquad$ 15. $3y^2 = -10x.$ $\quad$ 16. $y^2 = -x.$
17. $x^2 + y = 0.$ $\qquad\qquad$ 18. $4x^2 + y = 0.$ $\qquad\qquad$ 19. $2y^2 - 7x = 0.$

By use of a standard form, find the equation of a parabola whose axis is a coordinate axis and whose vertex is $(0, 0)$, if the parabola passes through the given point.

20. $(\frac{2}{3}, -2).$ $\qquad$ 21. $(-6, -6).$ $\qquad$ 22. $(-16, -8).$ $\qquad$ 23. $(-6, 18).$

24. A parabola has the line $x + y + 3 = 0$ as directrix, and the focus $F : (-4, -5)$. By a geometric construction, find the vertex and axis of the parabola. Construct enough points on it to draw it, by use of lines perpendicular to the axis, and arcs of circles with F as a center. State a clear rule for constructing the parabola.

★69. Ellipse defined by focal radii

DEFINITION IV. *An* **ellipse** *is the locus of a point for which the sum of the undirected distances to two fixed points F and F', called the* **foci,** *is a constant greater than the distance between F and F', which may coincide (to give a circle).*

If a point P is on any conic with a focus, let the undirected distance from a focus to P be called a **focal radius** of P.

EXAMPLE 1. Find the equation of the ellipse with foci $F : (4, 0)$ and $F' : (-4, 0)$, if the sum of the focal radii for any point on the ellipse is 10.

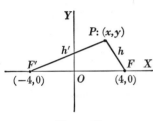

Figure 61

Solution. 1. Let $P : (x, y)$ be any point in the plane. If the lengths of PF and PF' in Figure 61 are h and h', respectively, then P is on the ellipse if and only if $h + h' = 10$. By the distance formula (2) of page 68,

$$h = \sqrt{(x - 4)^2 + y^2}, \; and$$

$$h' = \sqrt{(x + 4)^2 + y^2}.$$

Hence, an equation for the ellipse is

$$\sqrt{(x - 4)^2 + y^2} + \sqrt{(x + 4)^2 + y^2} = 10, \; or \tag{1}$$

$$\sqrt{(x - 4)^2 + y^2} = 10 - \sqrt{(x + 4)^2 + y^2}. \tag{2}$$

Square and simplify:
$$5\sqrt{(x + 4)^2 + y^2} = 25 + 4x. \tag{3}$$

Square and simplify:
$$9x^2 + 25y^2 = 225. \tag{4}$$

2. If (1) is satisfied by $P : (x, y)$, then (3) is satisfied, and then (4), because the squares of equal numbers are equal. Conversely, as proved below, if $P : (x, y)$ satisfies (4), then (1) also is satisfied. Hence, (4) is our final equation for the ellipse. The graph of (4) is in Figure 63 on page 160, with $\overline{OF} = 4$.

★*Comment.* The solution set for (4) is the *union* of the solution sets for the four equations obtained by using all possible combinations of the ambiguous signs $\pm$ in $[\pm h \pm h' = 10]$. This is true because (a) if (x, y) satisfies any one of these equations, the squaring operations above would yield a true statement in (4); (b) by two successive extractions of square roots (reversing steps), if (x, y) satisfies (4) then (x, y) satisfies *at least one* of the four equations just mentioned. However, the only possible combination of signs is $+h + h' = 10$, because h, h', and 8 are the lengths of the sides of triangle PFF' in Figure 61, and therefore $|h - h'| < 8$. Hence, (4) is equivalent to the *single* equation $h + h' = 10$, in (1). Such reasoning will be omitted hereafter.

Derivation of a standard equation for an ellipse

1. Let the distance between the foci F and F' be $2c$, let the line through F and F' be the x-axis, and place the origin at the midpoint of $F'F$, as in Figure 62. Then, the foci are $(\pm c, 0)$. Let the constant of Definition IV on page 159 be $2a$, where $a > c$.

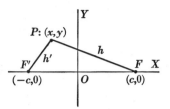

Figure 62

2. If $P:(x, y)$ is any point, let h and h' be the lengths of PF and PF', as in Figure 62. We obtain h and h' by use of the distance formula (2) on page 68. P is on the ellipse if and only if $h + h' = 2a$, or an equation for the ellipse is

$$\sqrt{(x - c)^2 + y^2} + \sqrt{(x + c)^2 + y^2} = 2a, \text{ or} \qquad (5)$$

$$\sqrt{(x - c)^2 + y^2} = 2a - \sqrt{(x + c)^2 + y^2}. \qquad (6)$$

3. On squaring both sides of (6) and collecting like terms, we obtain

$$4a\sqrt{(x + c)^2 + y^2} = 4cx + 4a^2. \qquad (7)$$

After dividing both sides by 4 in (7) and squaring both sides, we obtain

$$(a^2 - c^2)x^2 + a^2y^2 = a^2(a^2 - c^2). \qquad (8)$$

Define a positive number $b \leq a$ as follows:

$$b^2 = a^2 - c^2. \qquad (9)$$

Then, (8) becomes $b^2x^2 + a^2y^2 = a^2b^2$, or

$$[foci \; (\pm c, 0), \; c^2 = a^2 - b^2] \qquad \frac{x^2}{a^2} + \frac{y^2}{b^2} = 1. \qquad (10)$$

The graph of the standard equation (10) is in Figure 63.

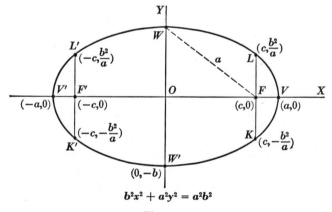

$$b^2x^2 + a^2y^2 = a^2b^2$$

Figure 63

Discussion of (10). Since x and y occur only with *even* exponents in (10), its graph is symmetric to OX and to OY, and hence also has *the origin as a center of symmetry*, called the *center* of the ellipse. Its x-intercepts are $\pm a$; the y-intercepts are $\pm b$. From (10),

$$y = \pm \frac{b}{a}\sqrt{a^2 - x^2} \quad and \quad x = \pm \frac{a}{b}\sqrt{b^2 - y^2}.$$

Thus, to give real values for y, the domain for x is $|x| \le a$; for y, the domain is $|y| \le b$. Since $b \le a$, in Figure 63 we call $V'V$, with length $2a$, the **major axis**; we call $W'W$, with length $2b$, the **minor axis** of the ellipse. Points V and V' are called the **vertices** of the ellipse. Each of the chords KL and $K'L'$ through a focus perpendicular to the major axis is called a **focal chord,** or **latus rectum** of the ellipse. By substituting $x = c$ in (10) we find that $y = b^2/a$ at L. The focal chords and their lengths will be of no importance in our applications in this text.

Similarly, with the roles of x and y in (10) interchanged, we may obtain

[*foci* $(0, \pm c)$, $c^2 = a^2 - b^2$]
$$\frac{y^2}{a^2} + \frac{x^2}{b^2} = 1 \qquad (11)$$

as the equation of an ellipse with its foci on the y-axis, as in Figure 64. We refer to (10) and (11) as *standard forms,* and call the corresponding locations of the ellipse, in Figures 63 and 64, *standard positions* for an ellipse with its axes along the coordinate axes.

Illustration 1. To graph the equation $25x^2 + 9y^2 = 225$, we divide both sides by 225 to change to the standard form

$$\frac{x^2}{9} + \frac{y^2}{25} = 1. \qquad (12)$$

Since $25 > 9$, the ellipse (12) is of type (11), with the foci on OY. The vertices are $(0, \pm 5)$. The endpoints of the minor axis are $(\pm 3, 0)$. From (11),

$$c^2 = 25 - 9 = 16;$$

the foci are $(0, \pm 4)$. If $y = \pm 4$, from (12) we obtain $x = \pm\frac{9}{5}$; the endpoints of the focal chords are $(\pm\frac{9}{5}, 4)$ and $(\pm\frac{9}{5}, -4)$. The graph of (12) is in Figure 64.

To combine results (10) and (11), we note first that, if the constants A, C, and G are all of one sign, then $Ax^2 + Cy^2 = G$ is equivalent to an equation of form (10) or (11), as was the case with (12). Conversely, (10) and (11) are of the form $Ax^2 + Cy^2 = G$, as just described. Hence,

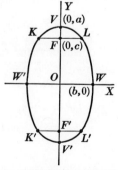

Figure 64

$$\left\{\begin{array}{l}\textit{any } \textbf{ellipse } \textit{with } OX \textit{ and } OY \textit{ as axes of symmetry has an equa-}\\ \textit{tion of the following form; conversely, the graph of each}\\ \textit{equation of this form is an ellipse of the preceding type:}\end{array}\right\} \qquad (13)$$

$$\left\{\begin{array}{c}\textbf{Ellipse:}\\ A, C, \textit{ and } G \textit{ of } \textbf{same sign}\end{array}\right\} \qquad \boldsymbol{Ax^2 + Cy^2 = G.} \qquad (14)$$

In our main applications of ellipses, with equations as in (10) or (11), we shall be interested in obtaining graphs *quickly, without interest in the location of the foci, or specification of the major and minor axes.* * Then, we may eliminate (11) from our thoughts and concentrate on (10) as an ellipse with OX and OY as axes of symmetry, x-intercepts $\pm a$, and y-intercepts $\pm b$, even when $a < b$. Thus, (10) may be thought of as the *intercept form* of (14). If the foci are of interest in any case, then both (10) and (11) must be kept in mind.

SUMMARY. *To graph an* **ellipse** *of type* (14), *find its x-intercepts and y-intercepts; then sketch the ellipse through its intercept points with recollection of the nature of the curve. To improve on such a graph, compute solutions* (x, y) *of* (14) *as desired.*

Illustration 2. The ellipse of type (14), or (10), with x-intercepts ± 3 and y-intercepts ± 5 has the equation

$$\frac{x^2}{9} + \frac{y^2}{25} = 1. \qquad (15)$$

Note 1. Construction of an ellipse. With a and c given, prepare a loop of string with length $(2c + 2a)$. Pass the loop around tacks placed at the foci F and F' on paper. With a pencil point, stretch the string tightly, anchored by the tacks. Then, as the point moves through all possible positions, it traces the ellipse continuously.

EXERCISE 40

By direct use of the locus method, as in Example 1 on page 159, derive an equation for the ellipse with the given foci, if the sum of the focal radii at each point of the ellipse is the given constant 2a. The scale units are equal on the coordinate axes.

1. Foci $(\pm 2, 0)$; $2a = 6$. 　　　　　2. Foci $(0, \pm 4)$; $2a = 12$.

3. Write an equation for the ellipse with axes along OX and OY, semi-major axis of length 4, and semi-minor axis of length 3, if the foci are (*i*) on OX; (*ii*) on OY. Graph each equation.

4. Repeat Problem 3 for semi-axes of lengths 17 and 8.

Graph the equation.

5. $\dfrac{x^2}{9} + y^2 = 1.$ 　　　6. $\dfrac{x^2}{4} + \dfrac{y^2}{25} = 1.$ 　　　7. $\dfrac{x^2}{25} + \dfrac{y^2}{289} = 1.$

* This will be particularly true whenever we graph (10) or (11) in an *xy*-plane where the scale units on the coordinate axes are *unequal.*

Graph the ellipse by use of its x-intercepts, y-intercepts, and four other symmetrically located points obtained after substituting just one value for x or for y in the equation.

8. $16x^2 + 25y^2 = 400.$ **9.** $4x^2 + y^2 = 16.$

10. $4x^2 + 9y^2 = 36.$ **11.** $9x^2 + 5y^2 = 45.$

12. $2x^2 + 3y^2 = 6.$ **13.** $5x^2 + 2y^2 = 10.$ **14.** $3x^2 + 4y^2 = 12.$

Write the equation of the ellipse with axes along OX and OY satisfying the conditions.

15. x-intercepts ± 6; y-intercepts ± 5.   **16.** x-intercepts ± 3; y-intercepts ± 6.

17. x-intercepts ± 2; y-intercepts ± 1.

18. Vertices $(\pm 5, 0)$; semi-minor axis of length 2.

★70. Hyperbola defined by focal radii

DEFINITION V. *A **hyperbola** is the locus of a point for which the **absolute value** of the difference of the undirected distances to two fixed points F and F', called the **foci**, is a positive constant which is less than the distance FF'.*

Derivation of a standard equation for a hyperbola

1. Let the distance between the foci F and F' be $2c$; let the line through F and F' be the x-axis, with the origin O at the mid-point of $F'F$, and F in the positive direction from O. Then the foci are $(\pm c, 0)$. Let the constant of Definition V be $2a$, where $a < c$.

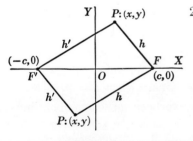

Figure 65

2. If $P:(x, y)$ is any point in the plane, let h and h' be the lengths of PF and PF', as in Figure 65, where $(h - h')$ is positive for one position of P, and negative for the other position. P is on the hyperbola if and only if $|h - h'| = 2a$; this is true if and only if the coordinates of P satisfy

$$h - h' = 2a \quad or \quad h' - h = 2a. \quad (1)$$

3. The equation $h - h' = 2a$, or $h = h' + 2a$, becomes

$$\sqrt{(x - c)^2 + y^2} = \sqrt{(x + c)^2 + y^2} + 2a. \quad (2)$$

On rationalizing in (2), as in the case of (6) on page 160 for an ellipse, we obtain

$$(c^2 - a^2)x^2 - a^2y^2 = a^2(c^2 - a^2). \quad (3)$$

If the equation $h' - h = 2a$ is discussed similarly, we again obtain (3). Thus, we conclude that (3) is equivalent to (1), or (3) is an equation for the hyperbola. Define a positive number b by the equation

$$b^2 = c^2 - a^2. \quad (4)$$

Then, (3) becomes $b^2x^2 - a^2y^2 = a^2b^2$, or

[*foci* $(\pm c, 0)$, *where* $c^2 = a^2 + b^2$]

$$\frac{x^2}{a^2} - \frac{y^2}{b^2} = 1, \tag{5}$$

whose graph consists of the two branches in Figure 66.

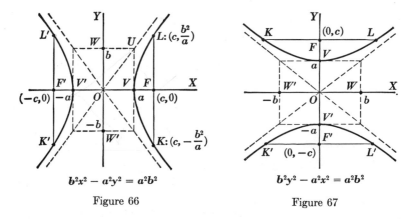

$$b^2x^2 - a^2y^2 = a^2b^2 \qquad\qquad b^2y^2 - a^2x^2 = a^2b^2$$

Figure 66   Figure 67

Discussion of (5). 1. The hyperbola has the x-axis and the y-axis as axes of symmetry and the origin as a center of symmetry, called the *center* of the hyperbola. On solving (5) for x and for y, we obtain

$$y = \pm\frac{b}{a}\sqrt{x^2 - a^2} \qquad and \qquad x = \pm\frac{a}{b}\sqrt{y^2 + b^2}. \tag{6}$$

Thus, y is imaginary if $|x| < a$, and the domain for x is $x \leq -a$ and $x \geq a$. From (6), x is defined and real for all values of y. The x-intercepts are $x = \pm a$, and there are no y-intercepts because y is imaginary when $x = 0$.

2. In Figure 66, we refer to V and V' as the **vertices** of the hyperbola and call the segment $V'V$ the **transverse axis.** We complete the **associated rectangle** having vertices $(\pm a, \pm b)$, with $W'W$ perpendicular to the transverse axis at the origin. We call $W'W$ the **conjugate axis.** The *semi-transverse* axis has length a and the *semi-conjugate* axis has length b. Without proof, we mention that the diagonals, extended, of the associated rectangle are *asymptotes* for the hyperbola. The equations of the asymptotes are $y = \pm bx/a$, or

$$\frac{x}{a} - \frac{y}{b} = 0 \qquad and \qquad \frac{x}{a} + \frac{y}{b} = 0, \tag{7}$$

which are equivalent to the single equation

$$\frac{x^2}{a^2} - \frac{y^2}{b^2} = 0, \qquad or \qquad b^2x^2 - a^2y^2 = 0. \tag{8}$$

3. Each of the chords KL and $K'L'$, perpendicular to the transverse axis at F and F', is called a **focal chord,** or **latus rectum,** of the hyperbola. With $x = c$

in (5), we find that the ordinate of L is b^2/a, or $KL = 2b^2/a$. The focal chords and their lengths will be of no importance in our applications.

In the work leading to (5), if we had let the line FF' be the y-axis, we would have obtained the hyperbola as in Figure 67, with the equation

$$[foci\ (0,\ \pm c);\ c^2 = a^2 + b^2] \qquad\qquad \frac{y^2}{a^2} - \frac{x^2}{b^2} = 1. \qquad (9)$$

We refer to (5) and (9) as *standard forms*, and call the corresponding locations of the hyperbola, in Figures 66 and 67, *standard positions* for a hyperbola with its axes along the coordinate axes.

Illustration 1. The equation

$$16x^2 - 9y^2 = 144 \qquad (10)$$

can be changed to the standard form (5) by dividing both sides by 144,

$$\frac{x^2}{9} - \frac{y^2}{16} = 1. \qquad (11)$$

Similarly, as in Illustration 1, when A and C are of *opposite signs* and $G \neq 0$, the equation $Ax^2 + Cy^2 = G$ is equivalent to form (5), or (9), and hence represents a hyperbola. *Conversely*, (5) and (9) are of the form $Ax^2 + Cy^2 = G$ as just described. Moreover, we note that (8), and the corresponding equation $b^2y^2 - a^2x^2 = 0$ for (9), can be obtained from (5), or (9), on replacing the constant term "1" by "0" on the right. Hence,

$$\left\{\begin{array}{l} any \text{ \textbf{hyperbola}} with\ OX\ and\ OY\ as\ axes\ of\ symmetry\ has\ an \\ equation\ of\ the\ following\ form\ and,\ conversely,\ the\ graph\ of \\ such\ an\ equation\ is\ a\ hyperbola\ of\ the\ preceding\ nature: \end{array}\right\} \qquad (12)$$

$$\left\{\begin{array}{c} \textbf{Hyperbola:} \\ A\ and\ C\ of\ \textbf{opposite signs};\ G \neq 0 \end{array}\right\} \qquad Ax^2 + Cy^2 = G. \qquad (13)$$

Asymptotes for (13): $\qquad\qquad Ax^2 + Cy^2 = 0.$ $\qquad (14)$

In applications of (5) and (9), we shall be interested mainly in obtaining a graph of any equation (13) without reference to (5) or (9).

SUMMARY. *To graph a* **hyperbola** $Ax^2 + Cy^2 = G$, *obtain its intercepts on that coordinate axis which intersects the curve; draw the asymptotes by graphing* (14); *sketch each branch of the hyperbola through an intercept point (a vertex) to approach the asymptotes smoothly.*

Note 1. From Figures 66 and 67, we observe that, after an equation for a hyperbola is written in the standard form (5) or (9), the coordinates of the vertices of the associated rectangle are $(\pm a, \pm b)$ in the case of (5), and $(\pm b, \pm a)$ in the case of (9).

Illustration 2. To graph $\qquad 16y^2 - 9x^2 = 144,$ (15)

first divide on both sides by 144, to obtain

$$\frac{y^2}{9} - \frac{x^2}{16} = 1.$$ (16)

When $x = 0$ in (15), or (16), we obtain $y = \pm 3$, the y-intercepts; the vertices are $(0, \pm 3)$. If $y = 0$ in (15), or (16), then $x^2 = -16$, or x is imaginary. Hence, the hyperbola has *real y-intercepts* and *no x-intercepts*, as for the hyperbola in Figure 67 on page 164. Directly from (15), the equation for the asymptotes is

$$16y^2 - 9x^2 = 0, \qquad or \qquad (4y - 3x)(4y + 3x) = 0.$$ (17)

By the method on page 144, the graph of (17) consists of the two asymptotes

$$y = \tfrac{3}{4}x \qquad and \qquad y = -\tfrac{3}{4}x.$$ (18)

Hyperbola (15) now could be sketched with each branch drawn through one of the vertices $(0, \pm 3)$, and approaching the asymptotes smoothly. The graph is shown in Figure 55 on page 153. The corners of the associated rectangle in Figure 55 are found by substituting $y = +3$ and $y = -3$ in (18), or by recalling that the corners are $(\pm 4, \pm 3)$, as seen from the standard form (16).

EXERCISE 41*

By direct use of the locus method as in Example 1 on page 159, obtain the equation of the hyperbola without using (5) or (9) of the preceding section.

1. Foci $(0, \pm 5)$; absolute value of difference of the focal radii is 6.

2. Foci $(\pm 5, 0)$; absolute value of difference of the focal radii is 8.

Obtain the real intercepts of the graph of the equation, find the equations of the asymptotes of the graph, and sketch the hyperbola. Obtain the vertices of the associated rectangle.

3. $4x^2 - 9y^2 = 144.$ **4.** $4y^2 - x^2 = 4.$ **5.** $x^2 - 9y^2 = 9.$

6. $3y^2 - 12 = x^2.$ **7.** $x^2 - y^2 = 25.$ **8.** $9x^2 + 63 = 7y^2.$

Note 1. An **equilateral** or **rectangular hyperbola** is one whose transverse and conjugate axes are equal, so that the associated rectangle is a square and the asymptotes are perpendicular. The hyperbola in Problem 7 is equilateral.

9. $225 + 9x^2 = 25y^2.$ **10.** $9x^2 - 144 = 4y^2.$

Note 2. The hyperbolas $b^2x^2 - a^2y^2 = a^2b^2$ and $a^2y^2 - b^2x^2 = a^2b^2$ are called **conjugate hyperbolas.** They have the same asymptotes.

Graph the pair of conjugate hyperbolas on one coordinate system.

11. $\begin{cases} 9x^2 - 4y^2 = 36. \\ 4y^2 - 9x^2 = 36. \end{cases}$ **12.** $\begin{cases} 4x^2 - y^2 = 16. \\ y^2 - 4x^2 = 16. \end{cases}$ **13.** $\begin{cases} x^2 - y^2 = 16. \\ y^2 - x^2 = 16. \end{cases}$

* If Exercise 38 has not yet been assigned, it could be used for review.

Note 3. In Problem 22, the student may prove that the graph of $xy = k$, where $k \neq 0$, represents an equilateral hyperbola whose asymptotes are the coordinate axes, and whose transverse axis makes an angle of 45° with OX.

Graph by use of the asymptotes and a few accurate points.

14. $xy = 4.$ **15.** $xy = -6.$ **16.** $3xy + 7 = 0.$ **17.** $2xy = 9.$

18. If a degenerate conic is simply a *point* in an xy-plane, which two perpendicular lines are axes of symmetry for the conic, and which point is the center of symmetry? Also, if this conic is the origin, write at least two equations for it.

19. If a degenerate conic consists of two parallel lines (possibly coincident), which perpendicular lines are axes of symmetry for it? Where is the center of symmetry for the conic? Also, write two types of equations for it, if it is in an xy-plane, and the x-axis or y-axis is an axis of symmetry.

20. Repeat Problem 19 if the degenerate conic consists of two lines intersecting in only one point.

Use the directions preceding Problem 1, for the data.

21. Foci $(2, 4)$ and $(8, 4)$; absolute value of difference of focal radii is 2.

22. Foci $F: (h, h)$ and $F: (-h, -h)$; absolute value of difference of focal radii is $2h$.

Comment. Suppose that $h > 0$ in Problem 22, where the result is $xy = \frac{1}{2}h^2$. The transverse axis (through the foci) bisects the angles between the coordinate axes in quadrants I and III, and thus lies on the line $y = x$. This line meets the hyperbola at the solution points for the system $(y = x \text{ and } xy = \frac{1}{2}h^2)$; these solutions give the vertices V and V' of the hyperbola,

$$V: (\tfrac{1}{2}h\sqrt{2}, \tfrac{1}{2}h\sqrt{2}) \quad and \quad V': (-\tfrac{1}{2}h\sqrt{2}, -\tfrac{1}{2}h\sqrt{2}).$$

In the notation of (5) on page 164, by use of the distance formula (2) of page 68,

$$|\overline{FF'}| = 2h\sqrt{2} = 2c; \quad |\overline{VV'}| = 2h = 2a.$$

Hence, $h = a$ and $c = h\sqrt{2}$. Then, $b^2 = c^2 - a^2 = h^2$, or $b = h = a$. Therefore, the hyperbola $xy = \frac{1}{2}h^2$ is *equilateral*, and thus its asymptotes make angles of 45° with the transverse axis. Hence, *these asymptotes are the coordinate axes.* This completes the proof of the statement about $xy = k$ in Note 3 if $k = 2h^2 > 0$. If $k < 0$, the corresponding results are true because the graph of $xy = k$ is the *reflection** of the graph of $xy = -k$ in the y-axis (proved by letting x become $-x$ in $xy = k$).

★71. Conics in an *xy*-plane with arbitrary coordinate units

In applications of coordinate systems, it frequently is convenient to use unequal scale units on the coordinate axes. However, in deriving standard equations for the nondegenerate conics, it was essential to use *equal* scale units on the coordinate axes. It is important, now, to emphasize that *the final*

---

* Imagine the xy-plane standing *vertically* with the x-axis directed upward, and the y-axis in the *surface of a flat lake.* Then, if we should observe the reflection in the water of that part of the graph of $xy = k$ in quadrant I, the reflection would coincide with the graph of $xy = -k$ in quadrant II. The student may desire to cultivate this language of "*reflection.*"

standard equations remain unchanged in form if unequal units are used on the axes.

Consider two coordinate systems superimposed on the same plane, an xy-system, which we shall call the original system, and a new $x'y'$-system. Then, each point P in the plane has two sets of coordinates, (x, y) and (x', y'). Any locus with an equation $f(x, y) = 0$ also will have a related equation $F(x', y') = 0$ in the new system. The process of obtaining (x', y') for any point $P:(x, y)$, or the new equation $F(x', y') = 0$ for any locus, is called a *transformation of coordinates.**

We now return to the viewpoint that, *unless otherwise specified*, the scale units on the coordinate axes in an xy-plane are not necessarily equal. However, as usual, there is a unit specified for measuring any distance in the Euclidean plane with which we are involved. Then, let h and k be positive constants, and define a transformation from an xy-system to a new $x'y'$-system of coordinates by

$$x' = hx \qquad and \qquad y' = ky, \ or \tag{1}$$

$$x = \frac{1}{h}x' \qquad and \qquad y = \frac{1}{k}y'. \tag{2}$$

Transformation (1), or (2), gives a new $x'y'$-system with the same origin, axes, and positive directions on the axes as in the xy-system. However, the scale unit for x' is $1/h$ times the scale unit for x, because $x' = h$ when $x = 1$ in (1); the scale unit for y' is $1/k$ times the scale unit for y. Thus, if the scale units are h *inches* (or, h times *any* specified unit for length) for x, and k *inches* for y, the scale unit is *1 inch* for both x' and y'. That is, for *any* xy-system, by (1) we can transform to a new $x'y'$-system having *equal units* on the axes, with this unit the same as the unit of length in the Euclidean plane.

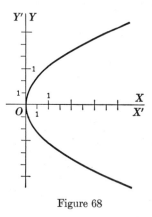

Figure 68

Illustration 1. Let the scale units be 2 inches for x and 3 inches for y, as shown proportionately in Figure 68. To obtain an $x'y'$-system with the scale unit 1 inch on both axes, we use equations (1) with $h = 2$ and $k = 3$:

$$x' = 2x \qquad and \qquad y' = 3y. \tag{3}$$

Then, from (3), $P:(x = 1, y = 1)$ is seen to become $P:(x' = 2, y' = 3); Q:(x = 2, y = -3)$ becomes $Q:(x' = 4, y' = -9)$. The graph of

$$9y^2 = 10x \tag{4}$$

has a new $x'y'$-equation, which we obtain by using $x = \frac{1}{2}x'$ and $y = \frac{1}{3}y'$ from (3) in (4):

$$9(\tfrac{1}{9}y'^2) = 10(\tfrac{1}{2}x'), \qquad or \qquad y'^2 = 5x'. \tag{5}$$

---

* For transformation of coordinates by translation of the axes, see Note 5 in the Appendix. Applications to equations of conics also are found in Note 5.

From (9) on page 158, where the scale units on the axes were assumed to be equal, the graph of (5), and hence of (4), is a *parabola* whose vertex is at O', which is O, and whose axis is the line $y' = 0$, which also is the line $y = 0$. The graph is in Figure 68. Thus, although the scale units on the axes in the xy-system are *unequal*, the remarks concerning (9) on page 158 are true for (4).

The method of Illustration 1 can be applied to each of the standard forms previously obtained for nondegenerate conics. We shall omit the verification of the preceding statement, which the student may wish to demonstrate in particular cases. The essential fact is that each of the standard equations remains unchanged in general form when transformation (1) is applied. Thus, the student may use the methods for graphing, as presented previously in this chapter, with either *equal* or *unequal* scale units on the coordinate axes. The result justifying the preceding statement is as follows.

THEOREM I. *The statements about parabolas in* (8) *and* (9) *on page* 158, *about ellipses in* (13) *and* (14) *on page* 162, *and about hyperbolas in* (12), (13), *and* (14) *on page* 165 *remain true where the scale units on the axes may be unequal.*

Illustration 2. If the equation $x^2 + y^2 = 25$ is graphed in an xy-plane having equal scale units on the axes, the graph is a circle. If the scale unit on OX is $\frac{3}{5}$ inch and on OY is 1 inch, the graph becomes an ellipse with its major axis along OY. If the scale units are interchanged, the graph is an ellipse with its major axis along OX. The student should sketch these graphs.

Note 1. With all conics assumed to be in simplest positions in the xy-plane, we have seen that the equation of any conic is equivalent to an equation of the form $f(x, y) = 0$, where f is a quadratic function. If f is *any* quadratic function of two variables, in later mathematics it is proved that the graph of $f(x, y) = 0$ is a conic, or is imaginary (no graph). When we do not require the scale units on the coordinate axes to be equal, from Illustration 2 we infer that no importance should be attached to the notions of the major or minor axes of an ellipse, or the location of the foci of any conic $f(x, y) = 0$. In general, the *shape* but not the *type* of conic which is the graph of the equation is affected by the choice of scale units on the coordinate axes.

72. Graphical solution of a system involving quadratics

We recall that a solution of a system of two equations in two variables x and y is an ordered pair of values of (x, y) which satisfies both equations. To solve such a system graphically, we graph the two equations on the same coordinate system. Then, the real solutions of the system are the pairs of coordinates (x, y) of the points of intersection, if any, of the graphs. The graphs fail to intersect when and only when (*a*) all solutions of the system involve imaginary numbers, or (*b*) the system has no solution, real or not real.

In the graphical solution of systems considered in this chapter, it will be convenient to refer to the summaries about graphing conics in Section 67, and to the Summary on page 103 concerning the graph of a quadratic function of x, or of a quadratic function of y.

Note 1. The discussion of the preceding section shows that, whenever desired, unequal scale units may be used on the coordinate axes. However, until otherwise specified, remarks in the text will be based on the assumption that equal scale units are employed on the axes. From page 150, the student should recall how to recognize that the graph of an equation is a circle, and how to find its center and radius by completing squares; after this is done, *the circle should be drawn by use of compasses.*

EXAMPLE 1. Solve graphically:

$$\begin{cases} x^2 - 2y^2 = 1, \ and & (1) \\ x^2 + 4y^2 = 25. & (2) \end{cases}$$

Solution. In Figure 69, the graph of (1) is the hyperbola, and the graph of (2) is the ellipse. Any point on the hyperbola has coordinates satisfying (1), and any point on the ellipse has coordinates satisfying (2). Hence, both equations are satisfied by the coordinates of A, B, C, and D, where the ellipse and hyperbola intersect. The pairs of coordinates are the four solutions of [(1), (2)]:

Figure 69

$A: (x = 3, y = 2);$

$B: (x = -3, y = 2);$

$C: (x = -3, y = -2);$

$D: (x = 3, y = -2).$

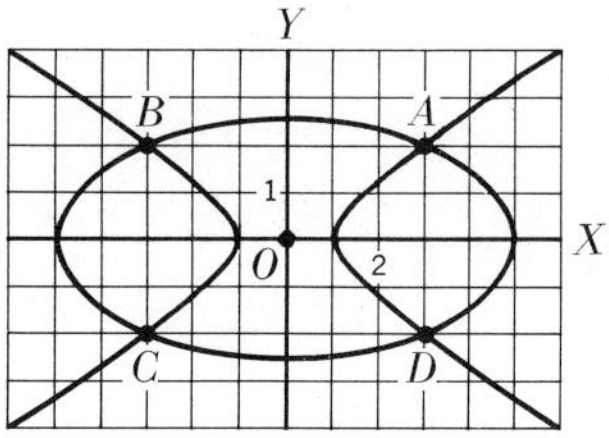

EXERCISE 42

*Solve graphically.**

1. $\begin{cases} x^2 + y^2 = 16, \\ y - 2x = 3. \end{cases}$

2. $\begin{cases} x + 2y = 3, \\ x^2 + y^2 = 9. \end{cases}$

3. $\begin{cases} x^2 - y^2 = 4, \\ x + y = 1. \end{cases}$

4. $\begin{cases} 4y^2 - x^2 = 16, \\ 3 = y - x. \end{cases}$

5. $\begin{cases} 4x^2 + y^2 = 16, \\ y^2 - 4x^2 = 4. \end{cases}$

6. $\begin{cases} 4x^2 + y^2 = 9, \\ 4x^2 + 4y^2 = 25. \end{cases}$

7. $\begin{cases} x^2 - 4y^2 = 4, \\ xy = 2. \end{cases}$

8. $\begin{cases} x^2 + y^2 = 1, \\ 4x^2 + y^2 = 9. \end{cases}$

9. $\begin{cases} x^2 + y^2 = 9, \\ x^2 - 9y^2 = 9. \end{cases}$

10. $\begin{cases} x^2 - xy - 12y^2 = 0, \\ x^2 + 4y^2 = 4. \end{cases}$

11. $\begin{cases} x = 2y^2 - 8y + 9, \\ xy = 12. \end{cases}$

12. $\begin{cases} x^2 - 10x + y^2 + 25 = 4y, \\ y + 4 = 2x. \end{cases}$

13. $\begin{cases} (x - 3y)(x + 2y - 5) = 0, \\ x^2 - 2x + y^2 - 4y = 11. \end{cases}$

14. $\begin{cases} x^2 - 14x + y^2 + 33 = 0, \\ x^2 + y^2 - 6x + 4y + 4 = 0. \end{cases}$

* The word *and* is understood to be implied after the comma for the first equation of each system, as in (1) on this page. Hereafter, frequently we shall omit "and" in such places.

73. Algebraic solution of a simple system

Hereafter, to *solve* a system of equations will mean to *solve algebraically.* If a system of two equations consists of a linear equation and a quadratic equation, in two variables, the equations will be called a *simple system.* We shall ·find that, usually, it will have either (1) two distinct real solutions, or (2) two identical real solutions, or (3) two non-real solutions. These possibilities correspond, respectively, to the following geometrical situations: the straight line, which is the graph of the linear equation, (1) may intersect the conic, which is the graph of the quadratic equation, in two distinct points; (2) may be tangent to the conic; (3) may not intersect the conic. The following substitution method for solving the system algebraically is convenient.

SUMMARY. *Solution of a system of one linear and one quadratic equation, in two variables, x and y.*

1. *Solve the linear equation for a first variable in terms of the other variable, say for y in terms of x; substitute the result in the quadratic equation, and thus eliminate the first variable.*

2. *Solve the equation (usually of degree 2) just obtained for the second variable.*

3. *For each value thus found for the second variable, obtain the corresponding value of the first variable by substitution for the second variable in the linear equation.*

EXAMPLE 1.   Solve:
$$\begin{cases} 4x^2 - 6xy + 9y^2 = 63, \text{ and} & (1) \\ 2x - 3y = -3. & (2) \end{cases}$$

Solution.   1. Solve (2) for x:
$$x = \frac{3y - 3}{2}. \qquad (3)$$

2. Substitute (3) in (1) to eliminate x:
$$4\left(\frac{3y - 3}{2}\right)^2 - 6y\left(\frac{3y - 3}{2}\right) + 9y^2 = 63. \qquad (4)$$

$y^2 - y - 6 = 0;$ $(y - 3)(y + 2) = 0;$ $y = 3$ *and* $y = -2.$

3. In (3), if $y = 3,$ then $x = 3;$ if $y = -2,$ then $x = -9/2.$

4. The solutions are $\boxed{x = 3, y = 3}$ and $\boxed{x = -\frac{9}{2}, y = -2}$.

EXERCISE 43

Solve (a) graphically and (b) algebraically.

1. $\begin{cases} x^2 + y^2 = 25, \\ x + y = 1. \end{cases}$ 2. $\begin{cases} x^2 + y^2 = 169, \\ x - y = 7. \end{cases}$ 3. $\begin{cases} y^2 - x^2 = 16, \\ 3x + 5y = 16. \end{cases}$

4. $\begin{cases} u^2 + v^2 = 25, \\ 3u - 4v = 25. \end{cases}$ 5. $\begin{cases} x^2 + 3y^2 = 6, \\ x + 2y = 4. \end{cases}$ 6. $\begin{cases} x - 2y = 3, \\ x^2 + 4y^2 = 4. \end{cases}$

Solve algebraically for (x, y) *or* (u, v).

7. $\begin{cases} 4x^2 + y^2 = 25, \\ 2x + y - 7 = 0. \end{cases}$

8. $\begin{cases} 5uv = 4v + u, \\ u + 4v = 5. \end{cases}$

9. $\begin{cases} x^2 - 4y^2 = 16, \\ 5x - 6y = 16. \end{cases}$

10. $\begin{cases} 5u - 2v = 6, \\ 4u^2 + 4u - v^2 - 4v = 12. \end{cases}$

11. $\begin{cases} 2x + 3y + 9 = 0, \\ 2xy + 9y + 4x = 3. \end{cases}$

12. $\begin{cases} 4y - 3x = 1, \\ 2x^2 - 8y^2 + 3x + 2y = 2. \end{cases}$

13. $\begin{cases} xy + x^2 + 2y = 3, \\ 3x - 2y + 2 = 0. \end{cases}$

14. $\begin{cases} 4x^2 + 9y^2 = 2a^2 + 2b^2, \\ 2x - 3y = 2a. \end{cases}$

Exhibit the solutions of the system of inequalities graphically.

15. $\begin{cases} x^2 + 9y^2 - 9 < 0, \ and \\ 4x^2 + y^2 - 4 < 0. \end{cases}$

16. $\begin{cases} 3x^2 - 4y^2 - 12 > 0, \ and \\ 2x + y - 4 < 0. \end{cases}$

74. Systems linear in the squares of two variables

In a system of two quadratic equations in two variables, x and y, suppose that each equation involves x and y only in the form x^2 and y^2. Such an equation is equivalent to $ax^2 + by^2 = c$, where a, b, and c are constants, with a and b not both zero. An equation of this variety is said to be linear in x^2 and y^2, because substitution of $u = x^2$ and $v = y^2$ would lead to an equation linear in u and v. A system of the preceding character can be solved algebraically by methods of elimination as met in the solution of linear equations.

EXAMPLE 1. Solve algebraically: $\begin{cases} x^2 + y^2 = 25, \ and & (1) \\ x^2 + 2y^2 = 34. & (2) \end{cases}$

Discussion. The graph of (1) is a circle, and of (2) is an ellipse, with the coordinate axes as axes of symmetry. Such curves may intersect in four distinct points, in which case [(1), (2)] would have four distinct real solutions. Or, the graphs might not intersect, in which case the algebraic solution would exhibit entirely non-real solutions. Or, the graphs might be tangent, at two points if any, because of symmetry with respect to the origin; in this case, there would be pairs of identical real solutions.

Solution. 1. Multiply by 2 in (1): $\qquad 2x^2 + 2y^2 = 50.$ (3)

2. Subtract, (2) from (3): $\qquad x^2 = 16; \quad x = \pm 4.$

3. Substitute $x^2 = 16$ in (1): $\quad 16 + y^2 = 25; \quad y^2 = 9; \quad y = \pm 3.$

4. Hence, if x is either $+4$ or -4, we obtain as corresponding values $y = +3$ and $y = -3$, and there are *four* solutions of the system.

$$\boxed{x = 4, y = 3} \ ; \ \boxed{x = -4, y = 3} \ ;$$

$$\boxed{x = 4, y = -3} \ ; \ \boxed{x = -4, y = -3} \ .$$

Note 1. In advanced algebra, it is proved that, usually, a system of two polynomial equations in x and y, in which one equation is of degree m and the other of degree n, has mn solutions, real or non-real, with the possibility of duplicates among the solutions. Thus, if $m = 1$ and $n = 2$, as for a simple system, we should expect 2×1 or 2 solutions. If both of the given equations are quadratic, so that $m = n = 2$, we should expect 2×2 or 4 solutions, as in Example 1.

EXERCISE 44

Solve algebraically. Also, solve graphically in Problems 1–3.

1. $\begin{cases} x^2 + y^2 = 4, \\ 9x^2 + y^2 = 9. \end{cases}$
2. $\begin{cases} 9x^2 + y^2 = 36, \\ x^2 + y^2 = 36. \end{cases}$
3. $\begin{cases} y^2 - 4x^2 = 16, \\ 9x^2 + 9y^2 = 4. \end{cases}$

4. $\begin{cases} 4x^2 + y^2 = 14, \\ 2x^2 = y^2 - 8. \end{cases}$
5. $\begin{cases} x^2 - 4y^2 = 4, \\ 2x^2 + 4y^2 = 11. \end{cases}$
6. $\begin{cases} 2u^2 + 3v^2 = 12, \\ 3u^2 - 4v^2 = 1. \end{cases}$

7. $\begin{cases} 5x^2 + 2y^2 = 6, \\ 2x^2 - 3y^2 = 10. \end{cases}$
8. $\begin{cases} 6x^2 + 5y^2 = 17, \\ 3x^2 - 4y^2 = 2. \end{cases}$
9. $\begin{cases} 3u^2 + 4v^2 = 21, \\ 9u^2 + 8v^2 = 54. \end{cases}$

10. $\begin{cases} x^2 - 3y^2 = 5, \\ 3x^2 - 5y^2 = 3. \end{cases}$
11. $\begin{cases} 3x^2 + 4y^2 = 3, \\ 5x^2 + \frac{1}{3}y^2 = \frac{11}{6}. \end{cases}$
12. $\begin{cases} 12v^2 - 5w^2 = 8, \\ 5v^2 + 9w^2 = \frac{51}{2}. \end{cases}$

75. Reduction to simpler systems

We shall say that a given system of equations in certain variables is *equivalent* to two or more other systems in case the set of their solutions consists of all solutions of the given system. In set terminology, the given system is equivalent to the new systems in case *the union of their solution sets is the solution set of the given system.* We shall discuss methods for obtaining equivalent systems of more simple types than a given system, under various conditions.

Consider a system of equations in x and y in which one equation can be written in the form $f(x, y) = 0$, where $f(x, y)$ *can be expressed as a product of linear factors.* Then, the given system is equivalent to a set of simpler systems, in each of which *one equation is obtained by placing a linear factor of $f(x, y)$ equal to zero.*

EXAMPLE 1. Solve:
$$\begin{cases} x^2 + y^2 = 14, \text{ and} & (1) \\ x^2 - 3xy + 2y^2 = 0. & (2) \end{cases}$$

Solution. 1. Factor in (2):
$$(x - 2y)(x - y) = 0. \quad (3)$$
Thus, (2) is satisfied if either
$$x - 2y = 0 \quad \text{or} \quad x - y = 0. \quad (4)$$

2. Hence, (1) and (2) are satisfied if and only if x and y satisfy one of the following simple systems.

I. $\begin{cases} x^2 + y^2 = 14, \text{ and} \\ x - y = 0. \end{cases}$
II. $\begin{cases} x^2 + y^2 = 14, \text{ and} \\ x - 2y = 0. \end{cases}$

3. On solving system I by the method of Section 73, we find two solutions:

$$(x = \sqrt{7}, y = \sqrt{7}) \qquad and \qquad (x = -\sqrt{7}, y = -\sqrt{7}).$$

From system II,

$$(x = \tfrac{2}{5}\sqrt{70}, y = \tfrac{1}{5}\sqrt{70}) \qquad and \qquad (x = -\tfrac{2}{5}\sqrt{70}, y = -\tfrac{1}{5}\sqrt{70}).$$

Comment. System [(1), (2)] *is equivalent to* systems I and II. We reduced the solution of [(1), (2)] to the solution of *two simple systems.*

A system in which *all terms involving the variables are of the second degree* sometimes can be solved by use of the equation we obtain on **eliminating the constant terms** from the original system.

EXAMPLE 2. Solve:
$$\begin{cases} x^2 + 3xy = 28, and & (5) \\ xy + 4y^2 = 8. & (6) \end{cases}$$

Incomplete solution. 1. *Eliminate the constants.*

Multiply by 2 in (5): $\qquad\qquad 2x^2 + 6xy = 56.$ $\qquad\qquad$ (7)

Multiply by 7 in (6): $\qquad\qquad 7xy + 28y^2 = 56.$ $\qquad\qquad$ (8)

Subtract, (8) from (7): $\qquad\qquad 2x^2 - xy - 28y^2 = 0, or$ $\qquad$ (9)

$$(2x + 7y)(x - 4y) = 0. \qquad\qquad (10)$$

2. By Theorem VIII on page 93, equation (9), or (10), may replace either one of the two given equations [(5), (6)], to yield an equivalent system. Thus, the system [(5), (6)] is equivalent to the system [(6), (10)], or

$$xy + 4y^2 = 8 \qquad and \qquad (2x + 7y)(x - 4y) = 0. \qquad (11)$$

3. By the method of Example 1, system (11) is equivalent to the following simple systems:

$$\textbf{I.} \quad \begin{cases} xy + 4y^2 = 8, and \\ 2x + 7y = 0. \end{cases} \qquad \textbf{II.} \quad \begin{cases} xy + 4y^2 = 8, and \\ x - 4y = 0. \end{cases}$$

We solve systems I and II separately by the method of Section 73 and find the following four solutions for [(5), (6)]:

From (I): $\boxed{x = -14, y = 4}$; $\boxed{x = 14, y = -4}$.

From (II): $\boxed{x = 4, y = 1}$; $\boxed{x = -4, y = -1}$.

Comment. In a system such as [(5), (6)], instead of eliminating constants, we could commence by using the so-called homogeneous substitution $y = wx$ to obtain two new equations in (w, x). Each of these equations can be solved easily for x^2, to permit elimination of x^2. On obtaining values for w, then corresponding values for x, and finally values of y from $y = wx$, we obtain the solutions of the given system for the variables x and y.

Sometimes, by combinations of the equations in a given system, we may obtain an equation of lower degree, or an equation which is equivalent to two or more equations of lower degree. In such a case, we may be able to reduce the solution of the given system to the solution of one or more simpler systems. The method of *ingenious devices* is the only rule which can be specified in solutions of the preceding nature.

★EXAMPLE 3. Solve:

$$\begin{cases} x^3 + y^3 = 27, \text{ and} & (12) \\ x + y = 3. & (13) \end{cases}$$

Incomplete solution. 1. Factor in (12):

$$(x + y)(x^2 - xy + y^2) = 27. \qquad (14)$$

2. Divide each side of (14) by the corresponding side of (13):

$$x^2 - xy + y^2 = 9.$$

3. Hence, (x, y) satisfies [(12), (13)] if and only if (x, y) satisfies

$$\begin{cases} x + y = 3, \text{ and} & (15) \\ x^2 - xy + y^2 = 9. & (16) \end{cases}$$

The student should complete the solution by solving [(15), (16)] by the method of Section 73.

★EXAMPLE 4. Solve:

$$\begin{cases} x^2 + xy + y^2 = 20, \text{ and} & (17) \\ xy = 5. & (18) \end{cases}$$

Incomplete solution. Add sides in (17) and (18):

$$x^2 + 2xy + y^2 = 25, \quad or \quad (x + y)^2 = 25, \text{ or} \qquad (19)$$
$$x + y = 5 \quad and \quad x + y = -5. \qquad (20)$$

Hence, (19) is equivalent to the two linear equations in (20), and system [(17), (18)] is equivalent to the following two simple systems:

$$\begin{cases} x + y = 5, \text{ and} \\ xy = 5. \end{cases} \qquad \begin{cases} x + y = -5, \text{ and} \\ xy = 5. \end{cases}$$

EXERCISE 45

Solve algebraically and graphically.

1. $\begin{cases} x^2 + y^2 = 25, \\ (3x - 4y)(4x + 3y) = 0. \end{cases}$

2. $\begin{cases} x^2 + y^2 = 169, \\ (5x - 12y)(12x + 5y) = 0. \end{cases}$

*Solve by reducing to simpler systems.**

3. $\begin{cases} 2x^2 - 3xy + y^2 = 0, \\ 2x^2 = 3xy - 4. \end{cases}$

4. $\begin{cases} 7x^2 - 3xy = 40, \\ 3x^2 + xy - 2y^2 = 0. \end{cases}$

* Or, by using the substitution $y = wx$ in a few places.

5. $\begin{cases} 2x^2 + 3xy = 14, \\ xy + 2y^2 = 4. \end{cases}$

6. $\begin{cases} 2x^2 + 5xy + 3y^2 = 5, \\ 2x^2 + xy = 2. \end{cases}$

7. $\begin{cases} u^2 + uz + 10z^2 = 22, \\ uz - 2z^2 = -6. \end{cases}$

8. $\begin{cases} x^2 + 2xy = 1, \\ 2x^2 + 8y^2 = 5. \end{cases}$

9. $\begin{cases} 26u^2 + 17uz = 30, \\ z^2 + 5uz + 6u^2 = 10. \end{cases}$

10. $\begin{cases} y^2 + 3xy = 2, \\ 9x^2 + 2y^2 = 9. \end{cases}$

11. $\begin{cases} x^2 + 3y^2 = 7, \\ x^2 - xy + 4y^2 = 10. \end{cases}$

12. $\begin{cases} u^2 + 2uv = 21, \\ 2uv + v^2 = 16. \end{cases}$

13. $\begin{cases} 3x^2 - 13xy - 10y^2 = 0, \\ (y - 2)(2x + y - 3) = 0. \end{cases}$

14. $\begin{cases} (2x - y)(2x + y)(2x - 3y) = 0, \\ (2x - 2y + 1)(x + y - 1) = 0. \end{cases}$

Hint. Find a set of equivalent linear systems.

★*Solve by any convenient method.*

15. $\begin{cases} u + v = 2, \\ u^3 + v^3 = 8. \end{cases}$

16. $\begin{cases} x - 2y = 2, \\ x^3 - 8y^3 = 98. \end{cases}$

17. $\begin{cases} x^2 + 4y^2 = 13, \\ xy = 3. \end{cases}$

18. $\begin{cases} x^2 + 2xy + 4y^2 = 7, \\ x^3 - 8y^3 = 35. \end{cases}$

19. $\begin{cases} x^2y - 4xy^2 = 12, \\ x - 4y = 4. \end{cases}$

20. $\begin{cases} x^2 - 2xy + y^2 = 1, \\ 3x - 2xy + 3 = 0. \end{cases}$

21. $\begin{cases} u^2 - 4uv + 4v^2 = 1, \\ 9u^2 + 3uv + v = 1. \end{cases}$

22. $\begin{cases} x^2 + y^2 + 2x + 2y = 18, \\ xy + x + y = 7. \end{cases}$

23. $\begin{cases} 4x^2 + 8x + 4y^2 + 8y = 17, \\ 2xy = -3. \end{cases}$

Hint. The equations are said to be **symmetrical** *in x and y* because the equations are unaltered if x and y are interchanged. In such a case, the solution can be obtained conveniently by substituting $x = u + v$ and $y = u - v$, then solving for (u, v), and finally obtaining (x, y) by use of the equations of the substitution.

24. $\begin{cases} 2x^2 = 6xy - 5z - 2, \\ x - y + z = 1, \\ 4x + 2y + z = 16. \end{cases}$

25. $\begin{cases} 9x^2 + 4y^2 + 3z^2 = 3, \\ y^2 - 6x^2 = 6z^2 - 3, \\ z^2 - y^2 - x^2 = 2. \end{cases}$

26. $\begin{cases} 3u^3 - 2v^3 = 8, \\ 4v^3 - 3u^3 = 8. \end{cases}$

27. $\begin{cases} x^{\frac{2}{3}} + 3y^{\frac{2}{3}} = 28, \\ x^{\frac{2}{3}} - x^{\frac{1}{3}}y^{\frac{1}{3}} + 4y^{\frac{2}{3}} = 40. \end{cases}$

★*Find the value of the real constant k so that the graphs of the equations are tangent. Check by graphing.*

28. $\begin{cases} y = x^2 - 4x + 9, \\ y + kx = 8. \end{cases}$

29. $\begin{cases} 3x^2 + 4y^2 = 48, \\ x + ky = 8. \end{cases}$

30. $\begin{cases} x^2 + y^2 = 9, \\ kx - y = 4. \end{cases}$

★*Find an expression for c in terms of the other constants if the graphs of the equations in the variables x and y are tangent.*

31. $\begin{cases} 4x^2 + 9y^2 = 36, \\ y = mx + c. \end{cases}$

32. $\begin{cases} y = mx + c, \\ a^2x^2 - b^2y^2 = a^2b^2. \end{cases}$

Chapter 7 Complex Numbers

★76. Complex numbers as pairs of real numbers*

Although an introduction to complex numbers appeared on page 33, we shall give a different foundation here.

We commence with the assumption that the system, R, of real numbers is at our disposal, and that we have complete knowledge of addition, multiplication, subtraction, and division in R. The key feature of the following procedure is that we shall define complex numbers in terms of *pairs of real numbers*.

DEFINITION I. *A complex number is an ordered pair of real numbers, (a, b). The complex number M defined by such a pair will be represented by $[a, b]$, and we write $M = [a, b]$, where a and b will be called the* **components** *of M.*

Let C represent the set of all complex numbers. If $M = [a, b]$ and $N = [c, d]$, then M and N are said to be the *same number*, or are called *equal*, and we write

$$\boldsymbol{M = N} \qquad \textit{if and only if} \qquad \boldsymbol{a = c \text{ and } b = d.} \tag{1}$$

We accept (1) as the meaning of the *identity of two ordered pairs* (a, b) and (c, d). Let

$$\boldsymbol{\alpha = [0, 0]} \qquad and \qquad \boldsymbol{\epsilon = [1, 0].} \tag{2}$$

We shall use $\oplus$ and $\otimes$ to indicate two binary operations on C which will be called *addition* and *multiplication*, respectively.

DEFINITION II. *If $M = [a, b]$ and $N = [c, d]$, then*

$$M \oplus N = [(a + c), (b + d)], and \tag{3}$$

$$M \otimes N = [(ac - bd), (ad + bc)], \tag{4}$$

to which we refer as the **sum** *and the* **product**, *respectively, of M and N.*

---

* If desired, Section 76 may be covered lightly, with detailed study of this chapter starting at Section 77, page 183, on the basis of the more elementary foundation for complex numbers on page 33.

Illustration 1. $[2, -3] \oplus [4, 1] = [(2 + 4), (-3 + 1)] = [6, -2]$.

$[2, -3] \otimes [4, 1] = [(8 + 3), (2 - 12)] = [11, -10]$.

Since the right-hand sides of (3) and (4) exhibit ordered pairs of real numbers, for every choice of M and N in C, it follows that *C is closed under addition and under multiplication.*

PROPOSITION I.   *Addition and multiplication in C obey Laws I–V of page 6, when these laws are rephrased for numbers in C.*

Proof.   1. Let $M = [a, b]$ and $N = [c, d]$.   With the roles of M and N reversed in (4), we obtain

$$N \otimes M = [c, d] \otimes [a, b] = [(ca - db), (cb + da)]. \tag{5}$$

Since multiplication of real numbers is commutative, $ca = ac$, $db = bd$, etc., so that the right-hand sides of (4) and (5) are the same.   Hence, we have $M \otimes N = N \otimes M$, or multiplication in C is *commutative.*   It is left for the student to prove in the next exercise that addition in C is commutative and associative.

2. Let $T = [u, v]$.   Then, to prove that multiplication in C is associative, we shall calculate

$$H = (M \otimes N) \otimes T \qquad and \qquad K = M \otimes (N \otimes T),$$

and prove that $H = K$.   From (4), applied twice,

$$\begin{aligned} H &= [(ac - bd), (ad + bc)] \otimes [u, v] \\ &= [(acu - bdu - adv - bcv), (acv - bdv + adu + bcu)]. \end{aligned} \tag{6}$$

Also, from (4), $N \otimes T = [(cu - dv), (du + cv)]$;

$$\begin{aligned} K &= [a, b] \otimes [(cu - dv), (du + cv)] \\ &= [(acu - adv - bdu - bcv), (adu + acv + bcu - bdv)]. \end{aligned} \tag{7}$$

From (6) and (7), we see that $H = K$, and hence Law II of page 6 is obeyed by multiplication in C.

3. In the next exercise, the student may prove that

$$T \otimes (M \oplus N) = (T \otimes M) \oplus (T \otimes N),$$

so that Law V of page 6 is obeyed by addition and multiplication in C.

PROPOSITION II.   *For any complex number M,*

$$\boldsymbol{M \otimes \alpha = \alpha; \qquad M \oplus \alpha = M; \qquad M \otimes \epsilon = M.} \tag{8}$$

Proof.   Let $M = [a, b]$.   By use of (2) and (4),

$$M \otimes \epsilon = [a, b] \otimes [1, 0] = [(a + 0), (b + 0)] = M.$$

The student should verify the other statements in (8).

In (8), observe that α acts in C as 0 acts in the system, R, of real numbers. We describe this by stating that α is *an* **additive identity** element for C. Also, ϵ acts in C as 1 acts in R. Hence, ϵ is called *a* **multiplicative identity** element for C.

PROPOSITION III. *For every complex number M, there exists just one corresponding number N such that*

$$M \oplus N = \alpha. \tag{9}$$

Proof. Let $M = [a, b]$ and $N = [c, d]$. Then, from (3), equation (9) is equivalent to

$$[(a + c), (b + d)] = [0, 0], \quad or \quad a + c = 0 \text{ and } b + d = 0. \tag{10}$$

For given numbers (a, b), there exists *one and only one* pair (c, d) satisfying (10), where $c = -a$ and $d = -b$. Hence, Proposition III has been proved,

with $$N = [-a, -b]. \tag{11}$$

We shall call N the **additive inverse** for M. Thus, we have proved that there exists *a unique additive inverse for every complex number.* Hereafter, with $M = [a, b]$, we shall let $N = -[a, b]$, or $N = -M$, and shall call N the **negative** of M. Thus, we have agreed to write

$$-[a, b] = [-a, -b].$$

PROPOSITION IV. *For every complex number $M \neq \alpha$, there exists just one number N such that*

$$M \otimes N = \epsilon. \tag{12}$$

Proof. 1. Let $M = [a, b]$ and $N = [c, d]$. By use of (4), equation (12) is equivalent to $$[(ac - bd), (ad + bc)] = [1, 0], or$$

$$\begin{cases} ac - bd = 1, and \\ ad + bc = 0. \end{cases} \tag{13}$$

2. Since $[a, b] \neq [0, 0]$, we have $a^2 + b^2 \neq 0$. Then, with a and b as assigned numbers in (13), on solving the system for (c, d) by one of the methods applying to a system of linear equations, we find that (13) has one and only one solution:

$$c = \frac{a}{a^2 + b^2} \quad and \quad d = \frac{-b}{a^2 + b^2}. \tag{14}$$

Thus, (12) has a unique solution for N, whose components are in (14).

Let M^{-1} be the unique solution for N in (12). We shall call M^{-1} the **multiplicative inverse** of M, or the **reciprocal** of M. From (12) and (14),

$$M \otimes M^{-1} = \epsilon \quad and \quad M^{-1} = \left[\frac{a}{a^2 + b^2}, \frac{-b}{a^2 + b^2}\right]. \tag{15}$$

Illustration 2. If $M = [2, -4]$, then $M^{-1} = [\frac{2}{20}, \frac{4}{20}] = [\frac{1}{10}, \frac{1}{5}]$.

PROPOSITION V. *The only additive identity element for C is α, and the only multiplicative identity element for C is ε.*

Proof. 1. Suppose that ϵ' is *any* multiplicative identity element for C, so that, for every M in C,

$$M \otimes \epsilon' = M. \tag{16}$$

In (16), assume that $M \neq \alpha$. Then, on multiplying each side on the left by M^{-1}, from (15) we obtain

$$M^{-1} \otimes (M \otimes \epsilon') = M^{-1} \otimes M, \quad or \quad (M^{-1} \otimes M) \otimes \epsilon' = \epsilon, \tag{17}$$

by use of the associative law for multiplication. Hence, $\epsilon \otimes \epsilon' = \epsilon$. By Proposition II, $\epsilon \otimes \epsilon' = \epsilon'$ since ϵ is *a* multiplicative identity element. Hence, we have $\epsilon' = \epsilon$, or ϵ is the *only* multiplicative identity element.

2. Suppose that α' is *any* additive identity element for C, so that, for every M in C,

$$M \oplus \alpha' = M. \tag{18}$$

Let $M = [a, b]$ and $N = [-a, -b]$, the additive inverse of M from (11). Then, on adding N to each side of (18), from (9) we obtain

$$N \oplus (M \oplus \alpha') = N \oplus M = \alpha. \tag{19}$$

By the associative law for addition, from (9) and (19) we find

$$(N \oplus M) \oplus \alpha' = \alpha, \quad or \quad \alpha \oplus \alpha' = \alpha. \tag{20}$$

Since α is *an* additive identity element, we have $\alpha \oplus \alpha' = \alpha'$. Hence, from (20), $\alpha' = \alpha$, or any additive identity element α' must be the same as α.

DEFINITION III. *Suppose that $N \neq \alpha$, and M is any complex number. Then, to **divide** M by N means to find U in C so that $M = N \otimes U$. Also, we write $U = M \div N$, or $U = \dfrac{M}{N}$, and call U the **quotient** of M divided by N.*

PROPOSITION VI. *If M and N are any complex numbers with $N \neq \alpha$, then just one number U exists such that $U = M \div N$, and*

$$\boldsymbol{U = M \otimes N^{-1}}, \quad or \quad \frac{\boldsymbol{M}}{\boldsymbol{N}} = \boldsymbol{M \otimes N^{-1}}. \tag{21}$$

Proof. 1. With $N \neq \alpha$ and M as given numbers, we desire to find U so that

$$M = N \otimes U. \tag{22}$$

2. Suppose that U satisfies (22). Then, on multiplying both sides of (22) by N^{-1}, we obtain

$$N^{-1} \otimes M = N^{-1} \otimes (N \otimes U) = (N^{-1} \otimes N) \otimes U.$$

From (15), $N^{-1} \otimes N = \epsilon$. Thus, from above,

$$N^{-1} \otimes M = \epsilon \otimes U = U.$$

Hence, *if* $U = M \div N$, *we must have* $U = M \otimes N^{-1}$, as in (21).

3. It remains to prove that U from (21) satisfies (22). On substituting for U from (21) into (22) on the right, by use of laws for multiplication we obtain

$$N \otimes (M \otimes N^{-1}) = N \otimes (N^{-1} \otimes M)$$
$$= (N \otimes N^{-1}) \otimes M = \epsilon \otimes M = M.$$

Hence, (22) is satisfied by U from (21), and Proposition VI has been proved.

If $M = [c, d]$ and $N = [a, b] \neq \alpha$, by use of (15) for N^{-1}, we verify that

$$\frac{M}{N} = M \otimes N^{-1} = [c, d] \otimes \left[\frac{a}{a^2 + b^2}, \frac{-b}{a^2 + b^2} \right], \text{ or}$$

$$\frac{[c, d]}{[a, b]} = \left[\frac{ac + bd}{a^2 + b^2}, \frac{ad - bc}{a^2 + b^2} \right]. \tag{23}$$

Illustration 3. $\qquad \dfrac{[3, 5]}{[2, -4]} = [-\tfrac{14}{20}, \tfrac{22}{20}] = [-\tfrac{7}{10}, \tfrac{11}{10}].$

Let R' be the set of all complex numbers of the form $[a, 0]$, and let

$$a' = [a, 0]. \tag{24}$$

Thus, for every real number a, we have defined *just one* corresponding complex number a'. For instance, if $a = -3$, we have $a' = [-3, 0]$.

PROPOSITION VII. *If a and b are any real numbers,*

$$[a, 0] \oplus [b, 0] = [(a + b), 0], \quad or \quad a' \oplus b' = (a + b)'. \tag{25}$$
$$[a, 0] \otimes [b, 0] = [ab, 0], \quad or \quad a' \otimes b' = (ab)'. \tag{26}$$

Proof. The equations at the left in (25) and (26) are verified easily by use of (3) and (4). The equations at the right in (25) and (26) are consequences of (24).

In (24), we established a *one-to-one correspondence* between the set of real numbers $R = \{a\}$, and the set of complex numbers $R' = \{a'\}$. Moreover, by (25), this correspondence is **"addition-preserving"**; that is, when a corresponds to a' and b to b', then $(a + b)$ corresponds to $(a' + b')$. Likewise, by (26), the correspondence between R and R' is **"multiplication-preserving."** Such a correspondence is called an **isomorphism** between R and R'. Since all of our operations for R' are defined in terms of addition and multiplication, as indicated by $\oplus$ and $\otimes$, we conclude that *we may as well use the symbol a of R in place of a' of R'* for any complex number $[a, 0]$. Then, to calculate a sum or a product of numbers in R', we would carry out the similarly named operations for the corresponding numbers of R.

Illustration 4. To obtain $M = [-3, 0] + [5, 0]$, we may first compute $(-3 + 5) = 2$; then, by (25), $M = [2, 0]$.

On account of preceding remarks, hereafter, *when desired,*

$$\text{``[a, 0]'' } \textit{will be written simply } \text{``a.''} \tag{27}$$

In particular, we may write $\epsilon = [1, 0]$ as $\epsilon = 1$. On account of the isomorphism between R and R', so that any real number a may be thought of as a new symbol for $[a, 0]$ of R', we shall say that *the system R, of real numbers, is a subset of the set C of all complex numbers.* Hereafter, let $\oplus$ and $\otimes$ be replaced by simply "+" and "×," because no ambiguity will result when just real numbers are involved. Also, hereafter, mere juxtaposition of numbers, as in algebra for real numbers, will sometimes be used to denote multiplication.

PROPOSITION VIII. *Let $i = [0, 1]$ and let a and b be any real numbers. Then,*

$$\boldsymbol{[a, b] = a + bi} \quad \textit{and} \quad \boldsymbol{i \cdot i = -1.} \tag{28}$$

Proof. 1. With $a = [a, 0]$ and $b = [b, 0]$, and with original notations finally used for all numbers in C,

$$a + bi = [a, 0] + ([b, 0] \otimes [0, 1]) = [a, 0] + [0, b] = [a, b],$$

where we used the definitions of addition and multiplication.

2. Similarly, $i \cdot i = [0, 1] \otimes [0, 1] = [(0 - 1), (0 + 0)] = [-1, 0] = -1.$

Note 1. Hereafter in this chapter, when we mention a *number,* without a qualifying statement, we shall mean a *complex number.*

PROPOSITION IX. *For any number M, the additive inverse of M is $(-1) \cdot M$. That is,*

$$\boldsymbol{-M = (-1) \cdot M.} \tag{29}$$

Proof. Let $M = [a, b]$. With $-1 = [-1, 0]$, we find

$$(-1) \cdot M = [-1, 0] \times [a, b] = [(-a + 0), (-b + 0)] = [-a, -b].$$

In (11) on page 179, we found that $[-a, -b]$ was the additive inverse of M, and then let $-M = [-a, -b]$. Hence, (29) has been proved.

DEFINITION IV. *To* **subtract** *a number N from a number M means to find W so that*

$$\boldsymbol{M = W + N.} \tag{30}$$

The student may verify that Definition IV reads the same as Definition V for subtraction of real numbers on page 10. With details similar to those for real numbers, it is found that (30) is satisfied by *just one number,*

$$\boldsymbol{W = M + (-N).} \tag{31}$$

Then, as for real numbers, we agree to write

$$\boldsymbol{M + (-N)} \quad \textit{as} \quad \boldsymbol{M - N,} \tag{32}$$

and call $(M - N)$ the **difference** of M and N.

77. Algebraic manipulation with complex numbers

Hereafter, unless otherwise implied, any literal number symbol will represent a real number except that *i* **will represent [0, 1],** in the notation of Section 76. We shall refer to the form $(a + bi)$ of (28) on page 182 as the **standard form** for a complex number. When desired, we shall use simply a to represent $(a + 0i)$, bi for $(0 + bi)$ when $b \neq 0$, and 0 for $(0 + 0i)$. We shall call *i* the **imaginary unit.** With $i \cdot i$ defined as i^2, in (28) on page 182 we saw that $i^2 = -1$. Hence, we agree to call *i* a *square root* of -1, and sometimes may write $i = \sqrt{-1}$.

We now reintroduce certain terminology from page 33. In any complex number $(a + bi)$, we refer to a as the **real part** and to b as the **imaginary part.** If $a = 0$ and $b \neq 0$, the complex number $(a + bi)$ also is called an **imaginary number,** and can be written simply bi. If $b = 0$, the complex number $(a + bi)$ also is called a *real number* and can be written simply a. The definitions of addition and multiplication in (3) and (4) on page 177, and the result for a quotient in (23) on page 181, take on the following forms in the notation of (28) on page 182.

$$(a + bi) + (c + di) = (a + c) + (b + d)i. \tag{1}$$

$$(a + bi)(c + di) = (ac - bd) + (ad + bc)i. \tag{2}$$

$$\frac{c + di}{a + bi} = \frac{ac + bd}{a^2 + b^2} + \frac{ad - bc}{a^2 + b^2}\, i. \tag{3}$$

As a special case of (2), if k is a real number:

$$k(c + di) = kc + kdi. \tag{4}$$

It is not necessary to memorize (1), (2), and (3). Thus, in (1), by the associative law for addition, we may remove parentheses on the left, to obtain

$$(a + bi) + (c + di) = a + c + bi + di = (a + c) + (b + d)i.$$

In (2), since multiplication is distributive with respect to addition, we may expand on the left as for polynomials in real numbers. Thus,

$$(a + bi)(c + di) = ac + bci + adi + bdi^2$$
$$= (ac - bd) + (bc + ad)i, \text{ since } i^2 = -1.$$

In (3), notice that

$$(a + bi)(a - bi) = a^2 - b^2i^2 = a^2 + b^2, \text{ and}$$
$$(ac + bd) + (ad - bc)i = (c + di)(a - bi).$$

Hence, (3) may be written

$$\frac{c + di}{a + bi} = \frac{(c + di)(a - bi)}{(a + bi)(a - bi)}. \tag{5}$$

It is tempting to think that (5) is a means for proving (3). Of course, this is not true. *After* (3) *has been proved, we merely notice, as above, that* (5) *is true.* If we write $a + bi = a + b\sqrt{-1}$, then multiplication of both numerator and denominator by $(a - bi)$, or $(a - b\sqrt{-1})$, can be thought of as analogous to the procedure for rationalizing a denominator in Illustration 3 on page 41.

Illustration 1. $\qquad (3 + 4i) + (-2 + 6i) = 1 + 10i$

$$(3 + 4i)(-2 + 6i) = -6 - 8i + 18i + 24i^2 = -30 + 10i.$$

$$\frac{3 + 4i}{-2 + 6i} = \frac{(3 + 4i)(-2 - 6i)}{(-2 + 6i)(-2 - 6i)} = \frac{18 - 26i}{40} = \tfrac{9}{20} - \tfrac{13}{20}i.$$

From (1) on page 177,

$$\underline{a + bi = c + di} \quad \text{means that} \quad \textbf{(}a = c \text{ and } b = d\textbf{)}. \qquad (6)$$

In particular, since $0 = 0 + 0i$,

$$a + bi = 0 \quad \text{means that} \quad \textbf{(}a = 0 \text{ and } b = 0\textbf{)}. \qquad (7)$$

Illustration 2. $\underline{\text{If } 3 + 5i = (2 - x) + (3 - y)i, \text{ then}}$

$$(3 = 2 - x \text{ and } 5 = 3 - y), \quad or \quad \underline{(x = -1 \text{ and } y = -2)}.$$

Illustration 3. Suppose that $(5 - x) + (3 - y)i = 0$, or

$$(5 - x) + (3 - y)i = 0 + 0i; \quad then \quad (x = 5 \text{ and } y = 3).$$

In (29) on page 182, we saw that $-M = (-1) \cdot M$. Hence, insertion of a minus sign at the left of a symbol for a number M gives a symbol for $(-1) \cdot M$. We know that $M = (+1) \cdot M$. Hereafter, we shall let $+M$ be an abbreviation for $(+1) \cdot M$. Hence, insertion of a plus sign at the left of a symbol for a number M gives a new symbol for the same number. In the future, we agree to think of any symbol for a number as having a sign, "+" or "−," at the left, where "+" can be inserted if desired, and is understood to be present if no sign is visible. Since addition in the system, C, of complex numbers obeys the associative law, we may represent the sum of any set of numbers by writing their symbols, without grouping, in a line with their attached signs, where "+" is supplied at the left of any symbol where no sign was visible. This procedure duplicates the routine for a sum of real numbers in (6) on page 11.

Illustration 4. The sum of $(-2 + 3i)$, $(5 - 6i)$, and $-(7 + 4i)$ is

$$(-2 + 3i) + (5 - 6i) - (7 + 4i)$$
$$= -2 + 5 - 7 + 3i - 6i - 4i = -4 - 7i.$$

By the associative law for multiplication, the product of any number of complex numbers has a unique meaning which is independent of the manner in which the numbers might be associated first into products of two or more numbers. Thus, if N, U, V, and W are any complex numbers, we may speak of their product, represented by $NUVW$, without indicating preliminary grouping, such as $(NU)(VW)$, etc. In particular, if k is a positive integer, the product of k *factors* N is well defined. Then, as in algebra for real numbers, we let

$$N^k = N \cdot N \cdots N, \quad (k \text{ factors } N).$$

Without discussion, we shall accept the fact that the following laws for exponents are obeyed in C, when h and k are positive integers:

$$N^h N^k = N^{h+k}; \quad (N^h)^k = N^{hk}; \quad (WN)^h = W^h N^h. \tag{8}$$

Illustration 5. $\quad i^4 = i \cdot i \cdot i \cdot i = i^2 i^2 = (-1)^2 = +1.$

$$i^3 = i(i^2) = -i; \quad i^{15} = i^{12} i^3 = (i^4)^3 i^3 = (+1)(-i) = -i.$$

If M and N are any unequal complex numbers which are *not real*, observe that we *do not define an inequality relationship*, such as $M < N$. That is, the relations *"less than"* and *"greater than"* are defined *only for real numbers*.

If K is any complex number, we use the same definition for a square root of K as in the case where K is a real number. Thus, if a and b are real numbers, and

$$K = (a + bi)^2, \tag{9}$$

we say that $(a + bi)$ is a square root of K. Similarly, on page 195, we shall define nth roots of K, where n is any positive integer. At present, we restrict our attention to square roots of K when K is negative; we already know that K has two square roots when K is positive.

THEOREM I. *If $P > 0$, then $-P$ has two square roots, $i\sqrt{P}$ and $-i\sqrt{P}$. In particular, -1 has the two square roots $+i$ and $-i$.*

Proof. The specified result is true because

$$(i\sqrt{P})^2 = i^2(P) = -P \quad and \quad (-i\sqrt{P})^2 = i^2(P) = -P.$$

Hereafter, if $P > 0$, we shall let $\sqrt{-P}$ denote the particular root $i\sqrt{P}$:

$$\sqrt{-P} = i\sqrt{P}. \tag{10}$$

Then, the two square roots of $-P$ are $\pm i\sqrt{P}$. With $P = 1$ in (10), we have $\sqrt{-1} = i$. To avoid a certain danger mentioned below, *whenever a symbol $\sqrt{-P}$ is met in a number expression, it is very essential to change $\sqrt{-P}$ to $i\sqrt{P}$.*

We emphasize that the result $\sqrt{ab} = \sqrt{a}\sqrt{b}$ was proved earlier in the text *just for the case where both a and b are positive.* The formula is *not* true if a and b are negative.

Illustration 6. To compute $\sqrt{-4}\sqrt{-9}$ correctly, we express each radical by use of (10) as a first step. Then,

$$\sqrt{-4}\sqrt{-9} = i\sqrt{4}(i\sqrt{9}) = 2 \cdot 3 \cdot i^2 = -6.$$

If we had employed $\sqrt{ab} = \sqrt{a}\sqrt{b}$, we would have obtained

$$\sqrt{-4}\sqrt{-9} = \sqrt{+36} = 6, \tag{11}$$

which is wrong. To prove that a specified theorem is *not true*, it is sufficient to produce one example where the hypotheses of the theorem are satisfied but the conclusion of the theorem is not true. Then, on page 58, we have referred to the example as a **counterexample.** Thus, in (11), we produced a counterexample to prove that the statement "$\sqrt{ab} = \sqrt{a}\sqrt{b}$ *if a and b are negative*" is *false.*

The **conjugate complex number** for any complex number $(a + bi)$ is defined as $(a - bi)$. Thus, the conjugate of $(a - bi)$ is $[a - (-bi)]$ or $(a + bi)$. Hence, we call $(a + bi)$ and $(a - bi)$ *conjugate complex numbers;* each is the conjugate of the other.

Illustration 7. The conjugate of $(3 + 2i)$ is $(3 - 2i)$.

A complex number $(a + bi)$ is equal to its conjugate just when $b = 0$, that is, if and only if $(a + bi)$ is a *real number.* The sum and the product of the conjugate numbers $(a + bi)$ and $(a - bi)$ are real numbers; if $b \neq 0$, the difference of the conjugate numbers is an imaginary number. In the next exercise, the student may prove the facts mentioned in this paragraph.

EXERCISE 46

Express in terms of i and simplify. Assume that a > 0 and b > 0.

1. $\sqrt{-121}$. 2. $\sqrt{-75}$. 3. $\sqrt{-81a^2}$. 4. $\sqrt{-48b^3}$. 5. $\sqrt{-\frac{25}{9}}$.

6. State the two square roots of -64; -45; $-25a^2$; $-\frac{3}{49}b^2$.

7. Specify the conjugate of $(5 - 7i)$; $-5i$; $6i$; 8; $(2 - 3\sqrt{-5})$.

Perform the indicated operation and simplify to the form a + bi.

8. i^9. 9. i^{10}. 10. i^5. 11. i^{39}. 12. $3i(8i^4)$.

13. $(2 + 3i) - (5 - 7i)$. 14. $(8 + \sqrt{-4}) - (3 - \sqrt{-25})$.

15. $2i^4(3i^3)$. 16. $(2i)^5$. 17. $(3i^3)^2$. 18. $(5i)^4$.

19. $\sqrt{-5}\sqrt{-20}$. 20. $\sqrt{-2}\sqrt{-18}$. 21. $\sqrt{-3}\sqrt{-15}$.

22. $(3 + 4i)(2 - 7i)$. 23. $(4 - i)(3 + 5i)$. 24. $(2 - 7i)(2 + 7i)$.

25. $(\sqrt{-5} + 2)(\sqrt{-5} - 2)$. 26. $(3 - 4\sqrt{-2})(3 + 4\sqrt{-2})$.

27. $\dfrac{2 + 3i}{5 + 4i}$. 28. $\dfrac{5 + i}{2 - i}$. 29. $\dfrac{3 + 2i}{4 - 3i}$. 30. $\dfrac{5}{3 + 2i}$.

31. $\dfrac{3 + \sqrt{-25}}{1 + \sqrt{-4}}$. 32. $\dfrac{7}{4 - \sqrt{-9}}$. 33. $\dfrac{36 + 5i}{3i}$. 34. $\dfrac{6 - 5i}{4i}$.

35. $\dfrac{6}{5i}$. 36. $\dfrac{-3}{2i}$. 37. $\dfrac{-5}{4i}$. 38. $\dfrac{1}{i}$. 39. $\dfrac{3}{i^3}$. 40. $\dfrac{-4}{3i^5}$.

41. $(2\sqrt{-5})^3$. 42. $(3i - 5)^2$. 43. $2i^{-5}$. 44. $3i^{-7}$.

45. $(2 + i)^3$. 46. $(3 - 2i)^3$. 47. $(2 + \sqrt{-3})^3$. 48. $(3 + 2i)^{-1}$.

Express the reciprocal of the number in the form $(a + bi)$.

49. $2 - 5i$.   **50.** $7 + i$.   **51.** $5i$.   **52.** $-4 + \sqrt{-50}$.

Solve, and notice that the roots are conjugate complex numbers.

53. $2x^2 + 6x + 5 = 0$.   **54.** $3x^2 - 4x + 7 = 0$.

Form a quadratic equation with the given numbers as roots.

55. $(3 - 5i)$ and $(3 + 5i)$.   **56.** $(c + di)$ and $(c - di)$.

Find the real numbers x and y to satisfy the equation.

57. $x + yi = 3 + 7i$.   **58.** $2i = x - yi$.   **59.** $3x + 5yi = 8$.
60. $x - 3 + iy = 6i$.   **61.** $3x - y + ix + 2iy = 4 - i$.
62. $2xi + 3x + 3yi - 4y - 7 - i = 0$.

63. If $a^2 + b^2 = 1$, find the reciprocal of $(a + bi)$.

Note 1.   If N is complex,* hereafter let us use $\overline{N}$ for the conjugate of N.

64. Verify that $\overline{(3 - 2i) + (5 + 7i)} = \overline{3 - 2i} + \overline{(5 + 7i)}$.

65. Verify that $\overline{(3 - 2i)(5 + 7i)} = \overline{(3 - 2i)} \; \overline{(5 + 7i)}$.

66. If $z = a + bi$ and $w = c + di$, where (a, b, c, d) are real, prove that

$$\overline{z + w} = \overline{z} + \overline{w}; \quad \overline{zw} = \overline{z} \cdot \overline{w}.$$

Comment.   The preceding result extends easily to the sum and product of any number of numbers.   Thus, the conjugate of the product of three numbers is the product of their conjugates, because, if u, z, and w are complex,

$$\overline{uzw} = \overline{(uz)w} = \overline{uz} \cdot \overline{w} = (\overline{u}\,\overline{z})\,\overline{w} = \overline{u}\,\overline{z}\,\overline{w}.$$

67. If u and z are complex and n is a positive integer, prove that

$$\overline{uz^3} = \overline{u}(\overline{z})^3; \quad \overline{uz^n} = \overline{u}(\overline{z})^n.$$

68. If $f(z) = a + bz + cz^2 + dz^3$, where a, b, c, and d are real, prove that

$$\overline{f(z)} = a + b\overline{z} + c\overline{z}^2 + d\overline{z}^3.$$

69. Prove that the *conjugate of the conjugate* of a complex number z is z, or $\overline{\overline{z}} = z$.

70. Prove that the conjugate of a complex number N is N if and only if N is a real number.

71. Prove that the sum and the product of $(a + bi)$ and its conjugate are real, and that their difference is imaginary if $b \neq 0$.

★*Employ the notations of page 177 in the following problems.*

72. Prove that addition in C is commutative and associative.

73. Prove that multiplication in C is distributive with respect to addition, as stated in paragraph 3 of the proof of Proposition I on page 178.

---

* Frequently, the word *number* is omitted, and just *real, imaginary,* or *complex* is used in place of *real number, imaginary number,* or *complex number,* respectively.

78. The complex plane

Let $(x + yi)$ be any complex number. Then, we shall represent it geometrically in a coordinate plane by the *point P* whose abscissa is x and ordinate is y. Or, we may think of $(x + yi)$ as represented by the **vector*** $\overrightarrow{OP}$ from the origin to the point $P:(x, y)$. This form of representation is illustrated in Figure 70.

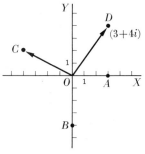

Illustration 1. In Figure 70, $(3 + 4i)$ is represented by $D:(3, 4)$ or by the vector $\overrightarrow{OD}$, as we choose. The real number 3, or $(3 + 0i)$, is represented by A. The imaginary number $-4i$, or $(0 - 4i)$, is represented by B. Point C represents the number $(-4 + 2i)$.

Figure 70

In Figure 70, all real numbers are represented by the points on the horizontal axis OX, and all imaginary numbers by the points on OY. When we use a coordinate plane in this way, we call the horizontal axis *the axis of real numbers*, the vertical axis *the axis of imaginary numbers*, and the whole plane *the complex plane*.

The vector representation of a complex number is important as well as interesting because of the following result, which states that, as vectors, complex numbers obey the so-called *parallelogram law* for vector addition.

THEOREM II. *If z_1 and z_2 are complex numbers, and $z = z_1 + z_2$, the vector $\overrightarrow{OP}$ representing z is obtained by drawing the vectors for z_1 and z_2 from the origin, completing the parallelogram with these vectors as sides, and drawing the diagonal OP of this parallelogram.*

Proof. 1. Let $z_1 = a + bi$; $z_2 = c + di$. Then $z = (a + c) + (b + d)i$. Vectors $\overrightarrow{OM}$ and $\overrightarrow{ON}$ represent z_1 and z_2, respectively, in Figure 71.

2. In Figure 71, P has the coordinates $x = \overline{OR}$ and $y = \overline{RP}$. Similarly, the coordinates of M and N are the values of corresponding directed line segments. By considering congruent triangles, for all possible positions of M and N as in Figure 71, we verify that

$$\overline{OK} = \overline{MH} = \overline{SR} \quad and \quad \overline{KN} = \overline{HP}.$$

Hence, by use of (3) on page 50,

$$\overline{OR} = \overline{OS} + \overline{SR} = \overline{OS} + \overline{OK} = a + c; \quad (1)$$

$$\overline{RP} = \overline{RH} + \overline{HP} = \overline{SM} + \overline{KN} = b + d. \quad (2)$$

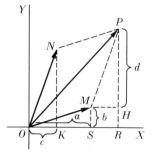

Figure 71

Therefore, from (1) and (2), $\overrightarrow{OP}$ represents z.

---

* Only the most elementary reactions to a *vector* as met previously by the student in trigonometry are used in this chapter.

Illustration 2. In Figure 72, we find

$$z = (5 + 3i) + (-3 + 2i) = 2 + 5i$$

by adding the vectors for the numbers $(5 + 3i)$ and $(-3 + 2i)$.

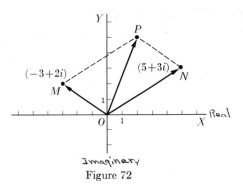

Figure 72

Note 1. To *subtract* $(c + di)$ from $(a + bi)$ geometrically, we geometrically *add* the number $(-c - di)$ to $(a + bi)$.

Note 2. Imaginary numbers were introduced in the 16th century by the Italian mathematician JERONIMO CARDANO (1501–1576), but were not thoroughly appreciated until 100 years later. The words *real* and *imaginary*, as now employed in references to numbers, were introduced by the French mathematician RENÉ DESCARTES (1596–1650), and the symbol i for $\sqrt{-1}$ by the Swiss mathematician LEONHARD EULER (1707–1783). A Norwegian surveyor, WESSEL (1797), was the first to employ the geometrical representation of complex numbers on a plane. This representation is of prime importance in advanced mathematics. The name *imaginary number* is somewhat unfortunate, because imaginary numbers are no more imaginary, in the colloquial sense, than any other numbers. The name *imaginary* arose because, when imaginary numbers first were admitted as solutions of equations, mathematicians labeled these solutions as illusory and useless.

EXERCISE 47

Represent the complex number as a point, and also as a vector.

1. $3 + 4i$.   2. $6i - 3$.   3. $-4 - 5i$.   4. $8i$.   5. $-3i$.
6. $2 - i\sqrt{2}$.   7. $3 - \sqrt{-9}$.   8. $\sqrt{-24}$.   9. $\sqrt{-25}$.   10. -7.

On one plane, plot the number, its conjugate, and its negative.

11. $4 - 5i$.   12. $-3 - 2i$.   13. 6.   14. $-5i$.   15. $2 - \sqrt{-49}$.

Separately plot each number in parentheses, or its negative, and find the sum or difference geometrically. Read the sum from the figure.

16. $(2 + 2i) + (4 + i)$.   17. $(2 + i) + (-3 + 5i)$.
18. $(-2 + i) + (-6 - 3i)$.   19. $(-3 - 4i) + (7 - 2i)$.
20. $(5 + 0i) + (0 + 4i)$.   21. $(-3 + 0i) + (0 - 6i)$.
22. $(1 + 3i) + (5 - 4i)$.   23. $(-2 + 3i) - (4 + 2i)$.
24. $(-2i) + (4)$.   25. $(3i) + (-5)$.
26. $(2i) + (-4i)$.   27. $(-2 - i) - (3 + 6i)$.
28. $(5 + 2i) - (3 - 4i)$.
29. $(5 - 2i) + (3 + 2i) + (-4 + 3i)$.

30. Let z be a complex number. State and demonstrate a construction for locating the point representing $-z$; the conjugate of z.

79. Trigonometric form

In our future discussion in this chapter, in any representation of complex numbers in an xy-plane, we shall assume that the scale units on the two axes are equal. Also, in use of trigonometric functions, we shall consider them as functions of *angles*, with the attitude of Definition I on page 383. As a rule, on account of our principal objectives, we shall use degree measure for angles.

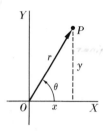

In Figure 73, let $\overrightarrow{OP}$ represent $x + yi$, let $r = |\overrightarrow{OP}|$, and let $\theta = \angle XOP$. Then, θ is in its standard position on the coordinate system, and thus the following equations are a consequence of Definition I on page 383.

$$r = \sqrt{x^2 + y^2}; \qquad \tan \theta = \frac{y}{x}; \qquad (1)$$

$$x = r \cos \theta; \qquad y = r \sin \theta; \qquad (2)$$

$$x + yi = r(\cos \theta + i \sin \theta). \qquad (3)$$

Figure 73

We call $r(\cos \theta + i \sin \theta)$ the **trigonometric** (or **polar**) form, θ the **amplitude** (or **argument**), and the positive length r the **absolute value** (or **modulus**) of $x + yi$. The amplitude may be taken as any angle with initial side OX and terminal side OP, because the values of the trigonometric functions are the same for all such coterminal angles. Hence, if θ is one amplitude, the other permissible amplitudes are $(\theta + k \cdot 360°)$, where k is any integer. Usually, we select the amplitude as an angle which is positive or $0°$ and less than $360°$. Two complex numbers are *equal* if and only if *their absolute values are equal* and *their amplitudes differ at most by an integral multiple of* $360°$.

To plot $r(\cos \theta + i \sin \theta)$, *construct $\angle XOP = \theta$, with $|\overrightarrow{OP}| = r$; then P represents the given number.*

Illustration 1. In Figure 74, the vector $\overrightarrow{OM}$ represents

$$6(\cos 60° + i \sin 60°).$$

Instead of $60°$, we could use $420°$, or $-300°$, etc., as the amplitude. Thus, $\overrightarrow{OM}$ also represents the following complex numbers:

$$6(\cos 420° + i \sin 420°);$$

$$6[\cos (-300°) + i \sin (-300°)];$$

etc.

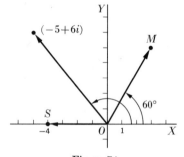

Figure 74

To change a complex number *from the trigonometric form to the form* $(x + yi)$, obtain $\cos \theta$ and $\sin \theta$ from a trigonometric table, or from memory* if θ is $0°$, $30°$, $45°$, $60°$, $90°$, or some corresponding angle greater than $90°$.

* See table of trigonometric functions of familiar angles on page 386.

Illustration 2. We may write

$$0 = 0 \cdot (\cos \theta + i \sin \theta),$$

where θ has any value. That is, the absolute value of zero is 0, and the amplitude is *any* angle whatever.

Illustration 3. $\quad 3(\cos 45° + i \sin 45°) = \frac{3}{2}\sqrt{2} + \frac{3}{2}i\sqrt{2}.$

$$6(\cos 35° + i \sin 35°) = 6(.819 + .574i) \qquad \text{(Table IV)}$$
$$= 4.914 + 3.444i.$$

The absolute value of a real number a, or $(a + 0i)$, as defined for a complex number, is $\sqrt{a^2 + 0^2}$ or $\sqrt{a^2}$, which is $+a$ if $a \geq 0$ and is $-a$ if $a < 0$; this is identical with $|a|$ as defined on page 11. Hence, *the two uses of the absolute value terminology are consistent.* Thus, it is consistent to use the symbol $|x + yi|$ to represent *the absolute value of* $(x + yi)$, that is, to represent r in the trigonometric form of $(x + yi)$:

$$|x + yi| = \sqrt{x^2 + y^2}. \qquad (4)$$

Illustration 4. $\quad |-4 + 0i| = |-4| = 4. \quad |3 + 4i| = \sqrt{25} = 5.$

SUMMARY. *To change from the form* $(x + yi)$ *to* $r(\cos \theta + i \sin \theta)$.

1. *Plot* $(x + yi)$ *as a vector* $\overrightarrow{OP}$, *and indicate* θ *by an arrow.*
2. *If* $(x + yi)$ *is real or imaginary, read* $r = |\overrightarrow{OP}|$ *from the figure, observe the value of* θ, *and write the trigonometric form.*
3. *If* θ *is not quadrantal, obtain* $r = \sqrt{x^2 + y^2}$; *find* θ *by noticing its quadrant, and also using one of the following functions of* θ:

$$\tan \theta = \frac{y}{x} ; \qquad \sin \theta = \frac{y}{r} ; \qquad \cos \theta = \frac{x}{r} \cdot \qquad (5)$$

Illustration 5. To express the real number -4 in trigonometric form, we plot $(-4 + 0i)$, as vector $\overrightarrow{OS}$ in Figure 74 on page 190. The amplitude is $\theta = 180°$. The absolute value is $r = |\overrightarrow{OS}| = 4$. Hence,

$$-4 = -4 + 0i = 4(\cos 180° + i \sin 180°),$$

which can be checked by using $\cos 180° = -1$ and $\sin 180° = 0$.

EXAMPLE 1. Find the trigonometric form of $(-5 + 6i)$.

Solution. 1. $r = \sqrt{61}$ and θ is in quadrant II (Figure 74 on page 190).

2. $\tan \theta = -\frac{6}{5} = -1.200$. In Table IV, we seek an acute angle α such that $\tan \alpha = 1.200$; by interpolation we obtain $\alpha = 50.2°$. Hence,

$$\theta = 180° - 50.2° = 129.8°;$$
$$-5 + 6i = \sqrt{61}(\cos 129.8° + i \sin 129.8°).$$

EXERCISE 48

Plot the number.   Then, express it in the form $x + yi$. pq 386

1. $3(\cos 30° + i \sin 30°)$.
2. $4(\cos 210° + i \sin 210°)$.
3. $2(\cos 360° + i \sin 360°)$.
4. $5(\cos 90° + i \sin 90°)$.
5. $3(\cos 300° + i \sin 300°)$.
6. $7(\cos 135° + i \sin 135°)$.
7. $4(\cos 225° + i \sin 225°)$.
8. $3(\cos 60° + i \sin 60°)$.
9. $5(\cos 270° + i \sin 270°)$.
10. $6(\cos 180° + i \sin 180°)$.
11. $4(\cos 123° + i \sin 123°)$.
12. $10(\cos 328° + i \sin 328°)$.
13. $\cos(-135°) + i \sin(-135°)$.
14. $2[\cos(-45°) + i \sin(-45°)]$.
    Hint. From page 385, $\cos(-\theta) = \cos\theta$; $\sin(-\theta) = -\sin\theta$.

Change the given number to its trigonometric form.

15. $3i$.   16. $-2i$.   17. -8.   18. 6.   19. $2 + 2i$.
20. $3 - 3i$.   21. $-8 + 8i$.   22. $\sqrt{3} + i$.   23. $i - \sqrt{3}$.
24. $-2 - 2i\sqrt{3}$.   25. $-4 + 4i\sqrt{3}$.   26. $3\sqrt{3} - 3i$.   27. $-5 - 5i$.
28. $3 + 4i$.   29. $-12 + 5i$.   30. $5 - 12i$.   31. $4 + 3i$.
32. $\cos 60° - i \sin 60°$.   33. $5(\cos 120° - i \sin 120°)$.

34. Change the number and its conjugate to trigonometric form: $(1 + i)$.
35. If $N = r(\cos\theta + i \sin\theta)$, find $\overline{N}$ and N^{-1} in trigonometric form.
36. Compute $|5 - 12i|$; $|7 + 24i|$; $|h - ki|$.

80. Products and quotients in trigonometric form

THEOREM III.   *An amplitude for a product of complex numbers is the sum of their amplitudes, and the absolute value of the product is the product of the absolute values of the factors.*

Proof.   Consider a product of just two complex numbers:

$r_1(\cos\theta_1 + i \sin\theta_1) \cdot r_2(\cos\theta_2 + i \sin\theta_2)$

$\quad = r_1 r_2(\cos\theta_1 \cos\theta_2 + i \sin\theta_1 \cos\theta_2 + i \cos\theta_1 \sin\theta_2 + i^2 \sin\theta_1 \sin\theta_2)$

$\quad = r_1 r_2[(\cos\theta_1 \cos\theta_2 - \sin\theta_1 \sin\theta_2) + i(\sin\theta_1 \cos\theta_2 + \cos\theta_1 \sin\theta_2)]$.

Hence, from the addition formulas III and IV of page 385,

$$r_1(\cos\theta_1 + i \sin\theta_1) \cdot r_2(\cos\theta_2 + i \sin\theta_2)$$
$$= r_1 r_2[\cos(\theta_1 + \theta_2) + i \sin(\theta_1 + \theta_2)]. \qquad (1)$$

We extend (1) to a product of any number of factors by successive applications of (1).   Thus, we use (1) twice below:

$$r_1(\cos\theta_1 + i \sin\theta_1) \cdot r_2(\cos\theta_2 + i \sin\theta_2) \cdot r_3(\cos\theta_3 + i \sin\theta_3)$$
$$= r_1 r_2[\cos(\theta_1 + \theta_2) + i \sin(\theta_1 + \theta_2)] \cdot r_3(\cos\theta_3 + i \sin\theta_3)$$
$$= r_1 r_2 r_3[\cos(\theta_1 + \theta_2 + \theta_3) + i \sin(\theta_1 + \theta_2 + \theta_3)]. \qquad (2)$$

Illustration 1. $3(\cos 40° + i \sin 40°) \cdot 5(\cos 170° + i \sin 170°)$
$$= 15(\cos 210° + i \sin 210°).$$

Corollary 1. *A product of complex numbers is equal to zero if and only if at least one factor is zero.*

Proof. The product is zero if and only if its absolute value is zero. This absolute value is the product of the absolute values of all factors. The product of these real numbers is zero if and only if *at least one factor is zero*, which means that at least one of the original complex numbers has *zero as its absolute value*, which proves the corollary.

A complex number is zero if and only if its absolute value is zero. Thus, in considering a fraction with the denominator $s(\cos \beta + i \sin \beta)$, an assumption that it is *not zero* is equivalent to the condition $s \neq 0$. We accept this fact in the following result.

THEOREM IV. *The absolute value of the quotient of two complex numbers, where the divisor is not 0, is the quotient of their absolute values, and an amplitude for the quotient of the complex numbers is the amplitude of the dividend minus the amplitude of the divisor.*

Proof. 1. Consider $[r(\cos \alpha + i \sin \alpha)]/[s(\cos \beta + i \sin \beta)]$ where s is not zero, and multiply both numerator and denominator of the given fraction by $(\cos \beta - i \sin \beta)$:

$$\frac{r(\cos \alpha + i \sin \alpha)}{s(\cos \beta + i \sin \beta)} = \frac{r}{s} \cdot \frac{(\cos \alpha + i \sin \alpha)(\cos \beta - i \sin \beta)}{(\cos \beta + i \sin \beta)(\cos \beta - i \sin \beta)}$$

$$= \frac{r}{s} \cdot \frac{(\cos \alpha + i \sin \alpha)[\cos (-\beta) + i \sin (-\beta)]}{\cos^2 \beta + \sin^2 \beta}, \tag{3}$$

because $\cos (-\beta) = \cos \beta$ and $\sin (-\beta) = -\sin \beta$.

2. In (3), apply Theorem III and recall that $\sin^2 \beta + \cos^2 \beta = 1$:

$$\frac{r(\cos \alpha + i \sin \alpha)}{s(\cos \beta + i \sin \beta)} = \frac{r}{s} \cdot [\cos (\alpha - \beta) + i \sin (\alpha - \beta)]. \tag{4}$$

Illustration 2. $\dfrac{15(\cos 350° + i \sin 350°)}{5(\cos 240° + i \sin 240°)} = 3(\cos 110° + i \sin 110°).$

THEOREM V. **(De Moivre's theorem.)** *If n is any positive integer, then*

$$[r(\cos \theta + i \sin \theta)]^n = r^n(\cos n\theta + i \sin n\theta). \tag{5}$$

Proof. The left-hand side in equation (5) indicates the product of n factors $r(\cos \theta + i \sin \theta)$. Hence, the absolute value of the nth power is the product of n factors r, or r^n, and an amplitude is the sum of n amplitudes θ, or $n\theta$. Hence, (5) is true.

Illustration 3. To aid in appreciation of the preceding proof, consider the case of (5) when $n = 3$. From (2) with θ_1, θ_2, and θ_3 replaced by θ, and r_1, r_2, and r_3 replaced by r,

$[r(\cos \theta + i \sin \theta)]^3$

$$= r(\cos \theta + i \sin \theta) \cdot r(\cos \theta + i \sin \theta) \cdot r(\cos \theta + i \sin \theta)$$
$$= r \cdot r \cdot r \cdot [\cos (\theta + \theta + \theta) + i \sin (\theta + \theta + \theta)]$$
$$= r^3(\cos 3\theta + i \sin 3\theta).$$

EXAMPLE 1. Find $(1 - i)^4$ by use of De Moivre's theorem.

Solution. 1. Express $(1 - i)$ in trigonometric form:

$r = \sqrt{2};$ $\tan \theta = -1$, *with θ in quadrant* IV, *so that* $\theta = 315°$.

2. Hence, we obtain

$$(1 - i)^4 = [\sqrt{2}(\cos 315° + i \sin 315°)]^4$$
$$= (\sqrt{2})^4(\cos 1260° + i \sin 1260°) = 4(\cos 180° + i \sin 180°) = -4.$$

In the preceding details, we noticed that $1260° = 3 \cdot 360° + 180°$ and used the periodicity of the sine and cosine functions.

EXERCISE 49

Give the result in trigonometric form, except when the final sine and cosine are known without using tables; in that case, express the result in the form $(x + yi)$. Compute any power by use of De Moivre's theorem.

1. $3(\cos 18° + i \sin 18°) \cdot 4(\cos 42° + i \sin 42°)$.
2. $6(\cos 25° + i \sin 25°) \cdot 3(\cos 125° + i \sin 125°)$.
3. $2(\cos 85° + i \sin 85°) \cdot 6(\cos 310° + i \sin 310°)$.
4. $4(\cos 140° + i \sin 140°) \cdot 5(\cos 275° + i \sin 275°)$.
5. $[2(\cos 15° + i \sin 15°)]^3$.   6. $[3(\cos 60° + i \sin 60°)]^4$.
7. $[2(\cos 45° + i \sin 45°)]^6$.   8. $[5(\cos 250° + i \sin 250°)]^3$.
9. $(2 + 2i)^4$.   10. $(-3 - 3i)^5$.   11. $(-1 + i\sqrt{3})^5$.   12. $(i + \sqrt{3})^6$.
13. $(-\sqrt{3} - i)^4$.   14. $(1 - i\sqrt{3})^3$.   15. $(-4 + 4i)^3$.   16. $(3 + 4i)^3$.

17. $\dfrac{6(\cos 140° + i \sin 140°)}{2(\cos 30° + i \sin 30°)}$.   18. $\dfrac{5(\cos 250° + i \sin 250°)}{20(\cos 310° + i \sin 310°)}$.

19. $\dfrac{15(\cos 150° + i \sin 150°)}{1 + i}$.   20. $\dfrac{25(\cos 250° + i \sin 250°)}{5\sqrt{2} - 5i\sqrt{2}}$.

21. $\dfrac{2 - 2i\sqrt{3}}{3(\cos 150° + i \sin 150°)}$.   22. $\dfrac{15(\cos 150° + i \sin 150°)}{5(\cos 30° - i \sin 30°)}$.

★23. If $z = r(\cos \theta + i \sin \theta)$, where $r \neq 0$, and if n is a positive integer, prove that $z^{-n} = r^{-n}[\cos (-n\theta) + i \sin (-n\theta)]$, so that *De Moivre's theorem holds if the exponent is a negative integer.*

★24. In the complex plane with the origin at O, let U be the unit point on the real axis and let P and Q represent $r(\cos \alpha + i \sin \alpha)$ and $s(\cos \beta + i \sin \beta)$, respectively. Construct $\triangle UOP$ and $\angle QOM = \alpha$; complete $\triangle QOM$ similar to $\triangle UOP$. (Give the figure for α and β acute, for convenience.) Prove that M represents the product of the given complex numbers.

81. The nth roots of a complex number

In this section, n always represents a *positive integer*. Then, to say that a complex number R is an nth root of a complex number z means that $z = R^n$.

EXAMPLE 1.   Find the cube roots of $8(\cos 150° + i \sin 150°)$.

Solution.   1. Let $r(\cos \alpha + i \sin \alpha)$ be any cube root. Then,

$$8(\cos 150° + i \sin 150°) = [r(\cos \alpha + i \sin \alpha)]^3.$$

Or, by De Moivre's theorem,

$$8(\cos 150° + i \sin 150°) = r^3(\cos 3\alpha + i \sin 3\alpha). \tag{1}$$

2. If two complex numbers are equal, their absolute values are *equal* and their amplitudes *differ at most by some integral multiple of* 360°. Hence, from (1), the values of r and α which give cube roots satisfy

$$r^3 = 8, \quad or \quad r = 2;$$
$$3\alpha = 150° + k \cdot 360°, or$$
$$\alpha = 50° + k \cdot 120°, \tag{2}$$

where k is any integer. On placing $k = 0$, 1, and 2 in (2), we obtain 50°, 170°, and 290° as the values of α. These give the following cube roots:

$$2(\cos 50° + i \sin 50°);$$
$$2(\cos 170° + i \sin 170°);$$
$$2(\cos 290° + i \sin 290°).$$

Comment.   If $k = 3$ in (2), then $\alpha = 50° + 360°$, equivalent to the amplitude 50°. If $k = -1$, then

$$\alpha = 50° - 120° = -70° = 290° - 360°,$$

equivalent to 290°. Similarly, if k has any integral value in (2), the value found for α is equivalent to one of (50°, 170°, 290°). Hence, the roots obtained in Step 2 are the *only* cube roots. The cube roots are represented by P, Q, and S in Figure 75. These points lie on a circle whose radius is 2, because 2 is the modulus of each of the roots. Moreover, P, Q, and S divide the circumference into *three equal parts* because the amplitudes of the roots are 50°, 170°, and 290°, where adjacent angles differ by 120°.

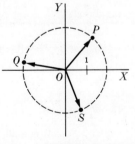

Figure 75

THEOREM VI. *If n is any positive integer, and $R > 0$, any complex number $R(\cos \theta + i \sin \theta)$ has just n distinct nth roots.*

Proof. 1. Suppose that $0 \leq \theta < 360°$. Let $r(\cos \alpha + i \sin \alpha)$ be any nth root. Then, by De Moivre's theorem,

$$R(\cos \theta + i \sin \theta) = [r(\cos \alpha + i \sin \alpha)]^n = r^n(\cos n\alpha + i \sin n\alpha). \quad (3)$$

2. From (3), $r^n = R$, or $r = \sqrt[n]{R}$, and $n\alpha = \theta + k \cdot 360°$, or

$$\alpha = \frac{\theta}{n} + k \cdot \frac{360°}{n}, \quad (4)$$

where k is any integer. On placing $k = 0, 1, 2, \cdots, (n - 1)$ in (4), we obtain the following n distinct values for α, all less than $360°$:

$$\frac{\theta}{n} \; ; \; \left(\frac{\theta}{n} + \frac{360°}{n} \right) \; ; \; \left(\frac{\theta}{n} + 2 \frac{360°}{n} \right) \; ; \; \cdots \; ; \; \left[\frac{\theta}{n} + (n - 1) \frac{360°}{n} \right]. \quad (5)$$

Corresponding to (5), we obtain the following n distinct nth roots:

$$\sqrt[n]{R} \left(\cos \frac{\theta}{n} + i \sin \frac{\theta}{n} \right) \; ; \; \sqrt[n]{R} \left[\cos \left(\frac{\theta}{n} + \frac{360°}{n} \right) + i \sin \left(\frac{\theta}{n} + \frac{360°}{n} \right) \right] \; ; \; etc.$$

3. If k has any integral value other than $0, 1, 2, \cdots, (n - 1)$ in (4), we obtain a value of α differing from some amplitude in (5) by an integral multiple of $360°$. Hence, in (5) we have the only distinct amplitudes which give nth roots. Thus, $R(\cos \theta + i \sin \theta)$ has *exactly* n distinct nth roots.

SUMMARY. *The nth roots of $R(\cos \theta + i \sin \theta)$ are obtained by placing $k = 0, 1, 2, \cdots, (n - 1)$ in the formula*

$$\sqrt[n]{R} \left[\cos \left(\frac{\theta}{n} + k \cdot \frac{360°}{n} \right) + i \sin \left(\frac{\theta}{n} + k \cdot \frac{360°}{n} \right) \right]. \quad (6)$$

To obtain the nth roots of a complex number given in the form $(a + bi)$, that is, to solve $z^n = a + bi$ for z, express $(a + bi)$ in trigonometric form and then use (6).

Illustration 1. The 4th roots of $16(\cos 80° + i \sin 80°)$ are

$$2(\cos 20° + i \sin 20°), \qquad 2(\cos 110° + i \sin 110°),$$
$$2(\cos 200° + i \sin 200°), \qquad 2(\cos 290° + i \sin 290°).$$

Illustration 2. To find the 5th roots of -32, or to solve $z^5 = -32$, first write -32 in trigonometric form:

$$-32 = 32(\cos 180° + i \sin 180°).$$

Hence, the five values of z which satisfy $z^5 = -32$ are

$$2(\cos 36° + i \sin 36°), \qquad 2(\cos 108° + i \sin 108°),$$
$$2(\cos 180° + i \sin 180°), \; or \; -2, \; etc.$$

Note 1. ABRAHAM DE MOIVRE (1667–1754) was a French mathematician who was compelled to leave France for religious reasons. He settled in London, where he earned a precarious living by miscellaneous mathematical work, partly by solving problems associated with games of chance. He is particularly noted for his work entitled *The Doctrine of Chances*, which was published in 1718 and dedicated to SIR ISAAC NEWTON.

★*Note 2.* Let m and n be integers, with $n > 0$ and m/n in lowest terms. We defined $a^{m/n}$ on page 37 as the principal nth root of a^m in case a is real and a^m has a *real* nth root. Also, we have defined $\sqrt{-P}$ or $(-P)^{\frac{1}{2}}$ as $i\sqrt{P}$ if $P > 0$. Otherwise, *no meaning has been given to* $a^{m/n}$. Now, if $z = R(\cos\theta + i\sin\theta)$, define $z^{m/n}$ as an *n-valued symbol* to represent *any one of the nth roots of z^m*. Then, by De Moivre's theorem, $z^m = R^m(\cos m\theta + i\sin m\theta)$. Hence, all values of $z^{m/n}$ are given by (6) with θ replaced by $m\theta$. In particular, with $k = 0$ in (6), we obtain

$$z^{m/n} = R^{m/n}\left(\cos\frac{m\theta}{n} + i\sin\frac{m\theta}{n}\right), \qquad (7)$$

which is the same as obtained from (5) on page 193 in De Moivre's theorem with n replaced by m/n. That is, this theorem holds for *rational exponents* in the sense that the theorem gives *one of the values of* $z^{m/n}$, as in (7). In (6), with $k = 0$, we have one value of $z^{1/n}$.

EXERCISE 50

Leave any result in trigonometric form, unless its amplitude is an angle for which the values of the trigonometric functions are known without tables; in the latter case, give the result in the form $(a + bi)$. In each problem, find all of the specified roots, and plot them as vectors in a plane.

1. 4th roots of $81(\cos 160° + i\sin 160°)$.
2. Cube roots of $125(\cos 60° + i\sin 60°)$.
3. Cube roots of $27(\cos 228° + i\sin 228°)$.
4. 5th roots of $32(\cos 210° + i\sin 210°)$.
5. Square roots of $9i$.　　　　　6. Square roots of $-25i$.
7. Cube roots of 27.　　8. Cube roots of -1.　　9. 5th roots of $32i$.
10. Cube roots of i.　　11. 4th roots of 81.　　12. 4th roots of -16.
13. 4th roots of $(8\sqrt{2} - 8i\sqrt{2})$.　　14. Square roots of $(-2 + 2i\sqrt{3})$.
15. 4th roots of $(8 - 8i\sqrt{3})$.　　16. Cube roots of $(-4\sqrt{2} - 4i\sqrt{2})$.
17. 4th roots of $(-8\sqrt{3} + 8i)$.　　18. Square roots of $(7 - 24i)$.

For the equation, find all roots in trigonometric forms, or otherwise.

19. $z^4 = 16$.　　20. $z^5 = 243$.　　21. $z^6 - 64 = 0$.　　22. $z^4 + 81i = 0$.

Chapter 8 Theory of Equations

82. Polynomials and equations of degree n in one variable

From page 86, recall that, if f is a polynomial function of degree n in a single variable, x, then

$$f(x) = a_0 + a_1x + a_2x^2 + \cdots + a_nx^n, \tag{1}$$

where $n \geqq 0$ and $(a_0, a_1, \cdots, a_n)$ are constants with $a_n \neq 0$. A polynomial equation in x of degree n is an equation which is equivalent to

$$a_0 + a_1x + a_2x^2 + \cdots + a_nx^n = 0, \tag{2}$$

where $n \geqq 1$ and $a_n \neq 0$. We may call (2) *the general equation of degree n*. We have agreed to refer to polynomial functions of degrees 1, 2, 3, and 4 as linear, quadratic, cubic, and quartic functions, respectively. Equations of degrees 1, 2, 3, and 4 in x are called linear, quadratic, cubic, and quartic equations, respectively. In this chapter, any functional symbol such as $f(x)$, $g(x)$, $H(x)$, etc., will represent a polynomial in x, unless otherwise stated. In any theorem and its proof, the numbers may be any complex numbers, unless exceptions are mentioned. Also, in any polynomial (1), we shall assume that $n \neq 0$ unless $n = 0$ is included explicitly.

83. Certain fundamental theorems

THEOREM I. (The remainder theorem.) *If r is a constant, and if a polynomial $f(x)$ is divided by $(x - r)$ until a constant remainder is obtained, then this remainder is equal to $f(r)$.*

Proof. After $f(x)$ is divided by $(x - r)$, let $q(x)$ represent the partial quotient, and let R be the constant remainder. Then, since

$$dividend \equiv (divisor) \cdot (quotient) + remainder,$$
$$f(x) \equiv (x - r)q(x) + R. \tag{1}$$

Since (1) is true for all values of x, we may use $x = r$ in (1). Hence,

$$f(r) = 0 \cdot q(r) + R \quad \text{or} \quad R = f(r).$$

Illustration 1. The following division of $(5x^2 - 3x + 7)$ by $(x - 2)$ illustrates the remainder theorem.

$$
\begin{array}{r}
5x + 7 = q(x) \\
x - 2 \, \overline{\big)\, 5x^2 - 3x + 7} \\
\underline{5x^2 - 10x} \\
7x + 7 \\
\underline{7x - 14} \\
21 = R
\end{array}
$$

By substitution, if
$f(x) = 5x^2 - 3x + 7$, *then*
$f(2) = 5(4) - 3(2) + 7$, *or*
$f(2) = 21$, *which checks.*

Illustration 2. If $f(x) = 5x^3 - 11x^2 - 14x - 10$, and if $f(x)$ is divided by $(x + 2)$, where $x + 2 = x - (-2)$, then the constant remainder is

$$f(-2) = 5(-2)^3 - 11(-2)^2 - 14(-2) - 10 = -66.$$

Note 1. To say that r is a *root* of an equation $f(x) = 0$ *means that* $f(r) = 0$. Thus, if $f(x) = x^2 - x - 2$, we find that 2 is a root of $f(x) = 0$, or $x^2 - x - 2 = 0$, because $f(2) = 4 - 2 - 2 = 0$.

THEOREM II. (The factor theorem.) *If $f(r) = 0$ then $(x - r)$ is a factor of $f(x)$. That is, if r is a root of $f(x) = 0$, then $(x - r)$ is a factor of $f(x)$.*

Proof. In (1), $R = f(r)$; hence, by our hypothesis, $R = 0$ and the division of $f(x)$ by $(x - r)$ is exact. Or, from (1),

$$f(x) \equiv (x - r)q(x),$$

which states that $(x - r)$ is a factor of $f(x)$.

THEOREM III. (Converse of the factor theorem.) *If $(x - r)$ is a factor of $f(x)$, then $f(r) = 0$, or r is a solution of the equation $f(x) = 0$.*

Proof. If $f(x)$ is divided by $(x - r)$, the division is exact and yields a polynomial $q(x)$ as a quotient, so that $f(x) \equiv (x - r)q(x)$. Thus, we have $f(r) = 0 \cdot q(r) = 0$, and hence r is a solution of the equation $f(x) = 0$.

EXAMPLE 1. Is $(x + 3)$ a factor of $3x^3 - 2x + 5$?

Solution. 1. Let $f(x) = 3x^3 - 2x + 5$, and notice that

$$x + 3 = x - (-3); \quad f(-3) = 3(-27) + 6 + 5 = -70 \neq 0.$$

2. Hence, by the preceding theorem, $(x + 3)$ is *not* a factor of $f(x)$.

Let $f(x)$ be a given polynomial and let r be a constant. Then, to say that r is a **zero** of the function f, or of $f(x)$, means that $f(r) = 0$, and hence $x = r$ satisfies $f(x) = 0$. Thus, *the zeros of f are the roots of the equation $f(x) = 0$.*

EXERCISE 51

Divide until the remainder is a constant. Also, compute the indicated value of $f(x)$ by substitution, to verify a preceding theorem.

1. $f(x) = 3x^2 + 14x + 8$; divide by $(x - 3)$ and also compute $f(3)$; divide by $(x + 2)$ and also compute $f(-2)$.

2. $f(x) = 2x^2 - 7x + 5$; divide by $(x - 4)$ and also compute $f(4)$.

Divide by long division and verify the remainder theorem.

3. $(2x^3 + 4x^2 + 8) \div (x - 2)$. 　　　4. $(3x^3 + 5x + 9) \div (x + 3)$.

Answer the question by computing a value of f and applying the factor theorem or its converse. If the answer is yes, find another factor by long division.

5. If $f(x) = x^3 + 3x^2 - 5x + 2$, is $(x - 2)$ a factor of $f(x)$? ⁿᵒ
6. If $f(x) = 2x^3 - 5x^2 - 6x + 9$, is $(x - 3)$ a factor of $f(x)$?
7. If $f(x) = 2x^3 + 6x^2 - x + 12$, is $(x + 2)$ a factor of $f(x)$?
8. Is $(x - 3)$ a factor of $x^3 - 27$; of $x^3 + 27$?
9. Is $(x + 2)$ a factor of $x^5 - 32$; of $x^5 + 32$?
10. Is $(x + u)$ a factor of $x^4 - u^4$; of $x^4 + u^4$?

Find the values of k for which $(x - 2)$ is a factor of $f(x)$.

11. $f(x) = 3x^2 + 4kx - 5$. 　　　12. $f(x) = k^2x^2 + 2kx - 3$.

Find the zeros of the function f.

13. $f(x) = x^2 - 3x - 10$. 　　　14. $f(x) = 2x^2 + 3x - 5$.

84. Synthetic division

A telescopic method for division, with detached coefficients, is available for abbreviating the division of a polynomial $f(x)$ by a binomial $(x - r)$. The method is referred to as *synthetic division*, illustrated as follows.

Illustration 1. Let us divide $(5x^3 - 11x^2 - 14x - 10)$ by $x - 3$, in the usual form I below:

I.　　　　　　　　　　　**II.**

$$
\begin{array}{l}
5x^2 + 4x - 2 = quotient \\
\hline
5x^3 - 11x^2 - 14x - 10 \;\big|\; x - 3 \\
\bigstar 5x^3 - 15x^2 \\
\hline
\quad\quad 4x^2 - 14x \bigstar \\
\quad\quad \bigstar 4x^2 - 12x \\
\hline
\quad\quad\quad\quad - 2x - 10 \bigstar \\
\quad\quad\quad\quad \bigstar - 2x + 6 \\
\hline
\quad\quad\quad Remainder = -16
\end{array}
$$

II.

$5x^2$	$+ 4x$	$- 2 = quotient$	
$5x^3$	$-11x^2$	$-14x$	-10 $\;\big|\; x - 3$
	$-15x^2$	$-12x$	$+ 6$
	$4x^2$	$- 2x$	-16

III.

5	-11	-14	-10	1	-3
	-15	-12	$+ 6$		
5	4	$- 2$	-16		

In $(x - 3)$, the coefficient of x is 1; hence, at each stage in the division, the coefficient of the highest power of x in the remainder is the next coefficient in the quotient. We obtain form II by omitting each "★" term in form I and then condensing form I into three lines. We obtain form III from form II by writing only the coefficient in place of each term; we introduce "5" into the third line so that all coefficients of the quotient appear in that line, and then omit writing the quotient. Form III suggests form IV, which illustrates synthetic division. In form IV, we use "+3" instead of "−3" as a multiplier so that we may *add* instead of *subtract* in the third row.

IV.

5	−11	−14	−10	+3
	+15	+12	− 6	
5	+ 4	− 2	−16	

$$Quotient = 5x^2 + 4x - 2. \qquad Remainder = -16.$$

The following Summary is seen to be a verbal description of the usual details involved in obtaining the coefficients of the quotient, and the remainder, when $f(x)$ is divided by $(x - r)$.

SUMMARY. *Routine for synthetic division of $f(x)$ by $(x - r)$.*

1. *Arrange $f(x)$ in descending powers of x, supplying each missing power with zero as a coefficient. Then, arrange the following details in three lines.*

2. *In the first line, write the coefficients $a_n, a_{n-1}, \cdots, a_1, a_0$ of $f(x)$ in this order. Write a_n in the first place in the third line.*

3. *Multiply a_n by r, add the product ra_n to a_{n-1}, and write the sum in the third line; multiply this sum by r, add the product to the next coefficient, and write the sum in the third line; etc., to the last coefficient of $f(x)$.*

4. *The last number in the third line is the remainder, and the other numbers in the third line are the coefficients of the powers of x in the quotient, arranged in descending powers of x.*

EXAMPLE 1. Divide $(2x^4 - 12x^2 - 5)$ by $(x + 3)$, or $[x - (-3)]$.

Solution.

2	0	−12	0	− 5	−3
	−6	+18	−18	+54	
2	−6	+ 6	−18	+49	

$$Quotient = 2x^3 - 6x^2 + 6x - 18. \qquad Remainder = 49.$$

$$\frac{2x^4 - 12x^2 - 5}{x + 3} = 2x^3 - 6x^2 + 6x - 18 + \frac{49}{x + 3}. \qquad (1)$$

In Example 1, by Theorem I, $+49$ is the value of $2x^4 - 12x^2 - 5$ when $x = -3$. This illustrates the following important use of synthetic division.

$$\left\{\begin{array}{l} \textit{To find the value of a polynomial } f(x) \textit{ when } x = r, \textit{ divide} \\ f(x) \textit{ by } (x - r) \textit{ by synthetic division; the remainder is } f(r). \end{array}\right\} \qquad (2)$$

EXAMPLE 2. If $f(x) = 3x^3 + 2x - 3$, find $f(-2)$.

Solution. Divide by $[x - (-2)]$ or $(x + 2)$:

$$
\begin{array}{r|rrr|r}
3 & 0 & 2 & -3 & \underline{}-2 \\
  & -6 & 12 & -28 & \\
\hline
3 & -6 & 14 & -31 = f(-2). \\
\end{array}
$$

EXERCISE 52

Divide by long division and also by synthetic division. Check the remainder by finding a value of the dividend by direct substitution of a value for x.

1. $(2x^3 - 2x + 7) \div (x - 2)$. **2.** $(3x^3 + 4x - 5) \div (x + 2)$.

By synthetic division, find the quotient and the remainder, and summarize as in (1) on page 201.

3. $(4x^2 + 3 - 2x) \div (x - 3)$. **4.** $(3x - 7 + 2x^2) \div (x + 4)$.
5. $(3x^3 - x^2 + 2x - 7) \div (x - 2)$. **6.** $(-2x^3 - 4x^2 + 3x - 5) \div (x - 3)$.
7. $(2x^3 - 5x^2 + 7) \div (x + 2)$. **8.** $(-3x^3 + 2x - 75) \div (x + 3)$.
9. $(2x^3 + 5x^2 - 4x - 5) \div (x + \tfrac{1}{2})$.

Solve by synthetic division.

10. If $f(x) = 2x^3 - 2x^2 - x - 5$, find $f(3)$; $f(-1)$.
11. If $f(x) = 3x^4 - 2x^3 + x^2 - x + 7$, find $f(2)$; $f(-3)$.
12. If $f(x) = -2x^4 + 5x^3 - 2x^2 - 7x + 5$, find $f(3)$; $f(-2)$.
13. If $f(x) = x^3 + 3x^2 - x + 3$, find exactly $f(.7)$; $f(-.4)$; $f(1.2)$.
14. If $g(z) = z^3 - 4z + 8$, find exactly $g(\tfrac{1}{3})$; $g(.2)$; $g(-1.1)$.
15. Find $(x^4 - 12x^3 + 46x^2 - 60x + 9) \div (x - 3)^2$, by dividing twice.

16. Prove that $(x - 1)$ is a factor of $(x^7 - 1)$, without synthetic division, by use of the factor theorem. Then, find the other factor by synthetic division.
17. Prove that $(x + c)$ is a factor of $(x^6 - c^6)$, and proceed as in Problem 16.
★**18.** Prove Properties A, B, C, and D of Section 16, page 28, by use of theorems on page 199. Then, find any implied second factors by use of synthetic division.

85. Graphs of polynomial functions of one variable

The graph of a polynomial function f is the graph of the equation $y = f(x)$. In obtaining the graph, synthetic division may be used in computing values of $f(x)$. Whenever we refer to the graph of a polynomial function f, we assume that the coefficients in $f(x)$ are *real* numbers.

Illustration 1. If $f(x) = x^3 - 12x + 3$, a graph of f is given in Figure 76 on page 203. The following values of $f(x)$ were computed and the graph of

WHEN x =	-4	-3	-2	-1	0	1	2	3	4
THEN $f(x)$ =	-13	$+12$	$+19$	$+14$	$+3$	-8	-13	-6	$+19$

the equation $y = f(x)$ was drawn through the corresponding points. On the graph, point M (where $x = -2$) is *higher* than any neighboring point of the curve. We call M a *maximum point* of the curve. We say that f has a *relative maximum* at $x = -2$ because $f(-2)$ is greater than any other value of $f(x)$ if x *is sufficiently near* $x = -2$. Point m (where $x = 2$) is *lower* than any neighboring point of the graph, and is called a *minimum point* of the graph. We say that f has a *relative minimum* when $x = 2$.

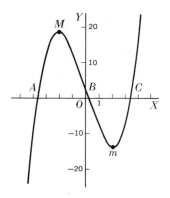

Figure 76

Note 1. Figure 76, and curves I, II, and III in Figure 77 illustrate the different types met as the graphs of cubic functions. Curve IV in Figure 77 is the graph of a certain quartic function.

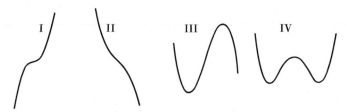

Figure 77

In calculus, it is proved that the graph of a polynomial function f of degree n is a *continuous curve, with at most* $(n - 1)$ *relative maxima and minima.* Also, the graph is proved to be a *smooth curve;* that is, it has *no sharp corners.* A polynomial function f is called a *continuous function* because of its properties which lead us to call its graph a continuous curve.

Recall that the real roots of the equation $f(x) = 0$ are the x-intercepts of the graph of the equation $y = f(x)$.

EXAMPLE 1. Solve graphically: $\qquad\qquad x^3 + 3 = 12x.$ $\qquad\qquad$ (1)

Solution. 1. Subtract $12x$: $\qquad\qquad x^3 - 12x + 3 = 0.$

2. Let $f(x) = x^3 - 12x + 3$. A graph of the equation $y = f(x)$ is given in Figure 76. At the points A, B, and C, we have $f(x) = 0$. Hence, the abscissas of these points are the real roots of (1). These roots are, approximately, -3.6, $.3$, and 3.4. Later, we shall refine the graphical method so that it will yield real roots to any desired degree of accuracy.

EXERCISE 53

Graph each polynomial function.

1. x^3.   2. $-x^3$.   3. x^4.   4. $-x^4$.
5. $x^3 + 2x^2 - 3x + 4$.   6. $-x^3 + 2x^2 - x + 1$.
7. $-x^3 - 3x^2 + 6x + 7$.   8. $x^3 - 3x^2 + 4x + 7$.
9. $x^4 + 3x^3 - 6x^2 + 16x - 5$.   10. $-x^4 + 24x^2 - 12x + 4$.

Obtain approximate values of the real roots of the equation graphically.

11. $x^3 - 4x^2 - 3x + 7 = 0$.   12. $x^3 + x^2 - 7x - 8 = 0$.
13. $x^3 + 3x^2 + 3x - 2 = 0$.   14. $2x^4 - 11x^2 + 10 = 0$.
15. $x^4 + 3x^3 + x^2 - 2x - 1 = 0$.

86. Consequences of the fundamental theorem of algebra

The following result was proved first in 1799 by the great German mathematician JOHANN KARL FRIEDRICH GAUSS (1777–1855). The proof is beyond the scope of this book.

THEOREM IV. (Fundamental theorem of algebra.) *Every polynomial equation $f(x) = 0$ of degree $n > 0$ with complex numbers as coefficients, has at least one root. Or, every polynomial $f(x)$ of degree $n > 0$ has at least one zero.*

In Theorem IV, the root (or, zero) is merely known to be a complex number, $(a + bi)$, where no statement is made concerning a and b. By use of the preceding result, we shall establish the following sequence of theorems.

THEOREM V. *If $f(x)$ is a polynomial of degree n in x, where $n > 0$, there exist n factors, linear in x, whose product is $f(x)$.*

Proof. 1. Suppose that

$$f(x) = a_0 + a_1 x + a_2 x^2 + \cdots + a_n x^n, \tag{1}$$

where $a_n \neq 0$. By Theorem IV, the polynomial $f(x)$ has at least one zero. Let r_1 be this zero; then, by the factor theorem, $f(x)$ has $(x - r_1)$ as a factor. If we let $Q_1(x) = [f(x) \div (x - r_1)]$, then $Q_1(x)$ is a polynomial whose term of highest degree is $a_n x^{n-1}$:

$$f(x) = (x - r_1)Q_1(x). \tag{2}$$

2. By Theorem IV, the polynomial $Q_1(x)$ has a zero, r_2. Therefore,

$$Q_1(x) = (x - r_2)Q_2(x),$$

where $Q_2(x)$ is a polynomial whose term of highest degree is $a_n x^{n-2}$. On using the expression for $Q_1(x)$, from (2) we obtain $f(x) = (x - r_1)(x - r_2)Q_2(x)$.

3. On continuing this process through n steps, we obtain n numbers r_1, $r_2, \cdots, r_n$, perhaps not all real or distinct, and a polynomial $Q_n(x)$ such that

$$f(x) = (x - r_1)(x - r_2) \cdots (x - r_n)Q_n(x),$$

where a_n is the coefficient of the term of highest degree in $Q_n(x)$. Moreover, the degree of $Q_n(x)$ is $(n - n)$ or zero. That is, $Q_n(x)$ is a constant and hence $Q_n(x) = a_n$. Therefore,

$$f(x) = a_n(x - r_1)(x - r_2) \cdots (x - r_n). \tag{3}$$

THEOREM VI. *Any equation $f(x) = 0$ of degree $n > 0$ has at most n distinct roots.*

Proof. 1. By Theorem V, $f(x) = a_n(x - r_1)(x - r_2) \cdots (x - r_n)$. Hence, by the converse of the factor theorem, each of $r_1, r_2, \cdots, r_n$ is a root of $f(x) = 0$. These roots may not all be distinct.

2. If r is any number different from all of $r_1, r_2, \cdots, r_n$, then

$$f(r) = a_n(r - r_1) \cdots (r - r_n) \neq 0,$$

because no factor is zero. Therefore, r is not a root of $f(x) = 0$, and hence $f(x) = 0$ has no roots other than $r_1, r_2, \cdots, r_n$.

If a root R occurs just once among $r_1, r_2, \cdots, r_n$, then R is called a **simple root**. If R occurs exactly h times or, in other words, *if $(x - R)^h$ is the highest power of $(x - R)$ which is a factor of $f(x)$*, R is called a **multiple root** of $f(x) = 0$, whose **multiplicity** is h. Roots of multiplicities 2 and 3 are called **double** and **triple roots,** respectively. The preceding theorem may be restated as follows:

Every equation of degree $n > 0$ has exactly n roots $r_1, r_2, \cdots, r_n$, where a root of multiplicity h is counted as h roots.

Corollary 1. *If two polynomials*

$$a_0 + a_1x + \cdots + a_nx^n, \text{ and}$$
$$b_0 + b_1x + \cdots + b_nx^n,$$

each of degree not greater than n, are equal for more than n distinct values of x, then the polynomials are identical term by term; that is, $a_0 = b_0, a_1 = b_1, \cdots, a_n = b_n$, and hence the polynomials are equal for all values of x.

Proof. By assumption, the equation

$$a_0 + a_1x + \cdots + a_nx^n - (b_0 + b_1x + \cdots + b_nx^n) = 0, \text{ or} \tag{4}$$
$$(a_0 - b_0) + (a_1 - b_1)x + \cdots + (a_{n-1} - b_{n-1})x^{n-1} + (a_n - b_n)x^n = 0, \tag{5}$$

has more than n distinct roots. If any one of the coefficients $(a_n - b_n)$, $(a_{n-1} - b_{n-1}), \cdots, (a_0 - b_0)$ in (5) were not zero, then (5) would be an equation of degree n or less, with *more* than n distinct roots. This fact would contradict the preceding theorem. Hence, all coefficients in (5) must be zero; that is,

$$a_0 = b_0, a_1 = b_1, \cdots, a_n = b_n.$$

From Theorem VI and (3), any equation $f(x) = 0$, of degree n, with the roots $r_1, r_2, \cdots, r_n$, can be written in the form

$$a(x - r_1)(x - r_2)(x - r_3) \cdots (x - r_n) = 0, \tag{6}$$

where $a \neq 0$, and a may be chosen arbitrarily.

EXAMPLE 1.   Form an equation with the following roots, and no others: -2, 4 as a triple root, $(3 \pm i\sqrt{2})$.

Solution.   By use of (6) with $a_0 = 1$, one equation is

$$(x + 2)(x - 4)^3[x - (3 + i\sqrt{2})][x - (3 - i\sqrt{2})] = 0, \text{ or}$$
$$(x + 2)(x - 4)^3[(x - 3) - i\sqrt{2}][(x - 3) + i\sqrt{2}] = 0, \text{ or}$$
$$(x + 2)(x - 4)^3(x^2 - 6x + 11) = 0.$$

87. Occurrence of conjugate complex roots for $f(x) = 0$

At this point, recall Problems 64–69 of page 187, dealing with the operation of taking conjugates of complex numbers.

Illustration 1.   Let $f(x) = 2x^2 - 2x + 5$ and consider the equation

$$2x^2 - 2x + 5 = 0. \tag{1}$$

If r is a root of (1), then $f(r) = 0$, or

$$f(r) = 2r^2 - 2r + 5 = 0. \tag{2}$$

Recall that $0 = 0 + 0i$ so that $\bar{0} = 0 + 0i = 0$. Also, if a is a real number, then $\bar{a} = a$. Hence, by use of Problem 66 on page 187,

$$\overline{f(r)} = 2(\bar{r})^2 - 2\bar{r} + 5 = 0. \tag{3}$$

In (3), we see that $\overline{f(r)} = f(\bar{r})$. Hence, $f(\bar{r}) = 0$. Thus, if $x = r$ satisfies (1), we conclude that $x = \bar{r}$ *also* satisfies (1). We can verify the preceding result by solving (1) by the quadratic formula, which gives

$$x = \frac{1 \pm \sqrt{-9}}{2}, \quad \text{or} \quad x = \tfrac{1}{2} + \tfrac{3}{2}i \quad \text{and} \quad x = \tfrac{1}{2} - \tfrac{3}{2}i,$$

where the two solutions are conjugate complex numbers. In this illustration, we have met a special case of the following theorem.

THEOREM VII.   *If a complex number* $(a + bi)$, *with a and b real and* $b \neq 0$, *is a root of a polynomial equation* $f(x) = 0$ *with* **real** *coefficients, then the conjugate complex number* $(a - bi)$ *also is a root of* $f(x) = 0$.

Proof.   1. For convenience, we shall write the proof for the case where $f(x)$ is of degree 3, but the method clearly will apply to an equation of any degree. Suppose that

$$f(x) = a_0 + a_1x + a_2x^2 + a_3x^3. \tag{4}$$

2. Let $z = a + bi$. By hypothesis,

$$f(z) = a_0 + a_1 z + a_2 z^2 + a_3 z^3 = 0. \tag{5}$$

Hence,

$$\overline{a_0 + a_1 z + a_2 z^2 + a_3 z^3} = 0, \text{ or}$$

$$a_0 + a_1 \bar{z} + a_2 (\bar{z})^2 + a_3 (\bar{z})^3 = 0. \tag{6}$$

3. In (6), we have $f(\bar{z}) = 0$. Therefore, the value $x = \bar{z}$ satisfies $f(x) = 0$, or $\bar{z}$ also is a root of the equation.

Illustration 2. If $f(x)$ has real coefficients and if $(3 + 2i)$ is a zero of the function f, or a root of $f(x) = 0$, then $(3 - 2i)$ also is a zero of f.

Corollary 1. *Every polynomial $f(x)$ with real coefficients can be expressed as a product of linear and quadratic factors having real coefficients.*

Proof. 1. If $r_1, r_2, \cdots, r_n$ are the zeros of f, as in (3) on page 205, then

$$f(x) = h(x - r_1)(x - r_2) \cdots (x - r_n), \tag{7}$$

where h is some real number, not zero.

2. By Theorem VII, if $f(x)$ has a factor $[x - (a + bi)]$, then $f(x)$ also has $[x - (a - bi)]$ as a factor. We notice that

$$[x - (a + bi)][x - (a - bi)] = [(x - a) - bi][(x - a) + bi]$$
$$= x^2 - 2ax + (a^2 + b^2), \tag{8}$$

which has real coefficients. Hence, all linear factors of $f(x)$ in (7) involving imaginary numbers can be combined by pairs to yield quadratic factors with real coefficients, and thus the corollary has been proved.

EXERCISE 54

Solve without multiplying the factors.

1. $(x - 3)(x + 4)(x - 8) = 0.$ 2. $(2x^2 - 5x)(x^2 + 3x + 7) = 0.$
3. $(3x^2 - 2x)(2x^2 - 5x + 9) = 0.$ 4. $(9x^2 + 25)(2x^2 - 5x - 1) = 0.$

Form an equation with integral coefficients which has the given roots.

5. $1, 1, -3, 2.$ 6. $2, 3, 3, -2.$ 7. $2, (1 \pm \sqrt{3}).$
8. $6, \frac{3}{2}, \pm 2i.$ 9. $\frac{2}{3}, \frac{2}{3}, \pm 3i.$ 10. $4, (2 \pm \sqrt{2}).$
11. $2, (3 \pm i).$ 12. $-3, (2 \pm i\sqrt{2}).$ 13. $\pm 4, -\frac{3}{2}, 2.$
14. $3, (-2 \pm \frac{1}{3}\sqrt{2}).$ 15. $\frac{3}{2}, \frac{1}{3}(2 \pm i\sqrt{3}).$ 16. $-\frac{1}{2}, (\frac{1}{4} \pm \frac{3}{4}\sqrt{2}).$
17. 2 as a triple root.   18. -3 as a root of multiplicity 4.
19. -2 as a double root and $\pm\frac{1}{2}$ as simple roots.

If $f(x)$ has real coefficients, and if $f(x) = 0$ has the given root, what other root is possessed by the equation?

20. $(3 - 7i).$ 21. $(-4 + 3i).$ 22. $(-3 - 5i).$ 23. $(8 - 4i).$

Form an equation $f(x) = 0$ with real coefficients having the given character.

24. A cubic equation, with 2 and $(1 + 2i)$ as roots.

25. A cubic equation, with -3 and $(2 - 5i)$ as roots.

26. A quartic equation, with $(2 + 3i)$ and $(3 - i\sqrt{2})$ as roots.

27. A quintic (degree 5) equation with roots 3, $-2i$, and $(4 + 3i)$.

Note 1. Recall that $\overline{a + bi} = a + bi$ if and only if $b = 0$, because $\overline{a + bi} = a - bi$. Hence, a reference to a pair of *distinct* conjugate numbers implies that they are of the form $(a + bi)$ and $(a - bi)$ where $b \neq 0$.

28. Prove that a cubic equation with real coefficients has either three real roots, or one real root and two distinct conjugate complex roots. Also, state and prove similar theorems for equations of degrees 4 and 5.

88. Inequalities involving factored polynomials

If a polynomial with real coefficients is the product of powers of linear factors with real coefficients, naturally the roots of $f(x) = 0$ can be read at sight. Also, a graph of f can be obtained very quickly with reasonable accuracy in general, and with absolute accuracy as to x-intercepts. The intercepts are essential in solving either of the inequalities $f(x) < 0$ or $f(x) > 0$. Even when $f(x)$ is not a product of powers of linear factors as just mentioned, any linear factor of $f(x)$ gives knowledge of an x-intercept of the graph of f.

Suppose that r is real and that $(x - r)^h$ is the highest power of $(x - r)$ which is a factor of a polynomial $f(x)$. Then, the following facts about the graph of the equation $y = f(x)$ should be noticed.

I. *If h is **odd**, the graph of $y = f(x)$ crosses the x-axis at $x = r$. If $h = 1$, the graph cuts the x-axis sharply at $x = r$ (see I_a in Figure 78). If h is odd, and $h > 1$, the graph, as drawn from each side of $x = r$, is tangent to the x-axis at $x = r$ (see I_b in Figure 78).*

II. *If h is **even**, the graph is on just one side of the x-axis near $x = r$, and is tangent to the x-axis at $x = r$ (see II in Figure 78).*

In Case I with h odd, the graph crosses the x-axis at $x = r$ because $(x - r)^h$ changes from being *negative* to being *positive* when x changes from $x < r$ to $x > r$, and this causes $f(x)$ to *change in sign*. Similarly, in Case II with h even, there is *no change in the sign of $f(x)$* as x changes from $x < r$ to $x > r$, because $(x - r)^h$ remains positive when $x \neq r$. The other facts mentioned in Cases I and II about the graph of $y = f(x)$ are proved in calculus.

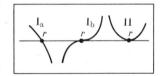

Figure 78

EXAMPLE 1. Solve the inequality:

$$(x + 4)^3(x + 1)(x - 1) < 0. \tag{1}$$

Solution. 1. Let $f(x)$ represent the left-hand member of (1). The graph of $y = f(x)$ has the x-intercepts -4 and ± 1, which are the roots of $f(x) = 0$. The graph, in Figure 79, was constructed by use of the x-intercepts and a few other points. The graph is tangent to the x-axis from either side at $x = -4$.

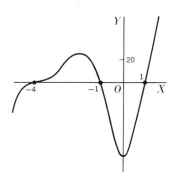

2. From Figure 79, the solution set of (1) is the union of the following intervals of numbers:

$$x < -4; \quad -1 < x < 1.$$

Figure 79

EXERCISE 55

Graph the function without expanding.

1. $x + 3$. **2.** $(x + 2)^2$. **3.** $(x - 2)^3$. **4.** $(x - 1)^4$.

Solve the inequality graphically.

5. $(x - 3)(x - 5) < 0$. **6.** $(x - 2)(x + 2)(x - 1) > 0$.

7. $(x - 2)(x + 3)(1 - x) > 0$. **8.** $(2x - 1)(x + 3)(x - 2) < 0$.

9. $(3 - x)(x - 1)^2 < 0$. **10.** $(x + 2)^2(x - 3)^3 > 0$.

11. $(x - 2)(x + 3)(x - 4)(x - 6) < 0$.

12. $(x - 2)^2(x - 3)(x + 5) \geqq 0$.

89. The roots of $f(-x) = 0$

Let $r_1, r_2, \cdots, r_n$ be the roots of the equation $f(x) = 0$. If we place $x = -X$ in $f(x) = 0$, we obtain $f(-X) = 0$, which is satisfied if and only if

$$-X = r_1, \quad -X = r_2, \quad \cdots, \quad -X = r_n, \text{ or}$$
$$X = -r_1, \quad X = -r_2, \quad \cdots, \quad X = -r_n.$$

Or, the roots of $f(-X) = 0$ are the *negatives* of the roots of $f(x) = 0$. Usually, there is no object in using the new letter X for the new variable. Thus, we have the following conclusion.

THEOREM VIII. *To obtain an equation whose roots are the negatives of those of a given equation $f(x) = 0$, replace x by $-x$ in the equation. Or, the roots of $f(-x) = 0$ are the negatives of the roots of $f(x) = 0$.*

Illustration 1. The roots of $x^2 - 5x + 6 = 0$ are 3 and 2. On replacing x by $-x$ in the given equation, we obtain

$$(-x)^2 - 5(-x) + 6 = 0, \quad or \quad x^2 + 5x + 6 = 0. \qquad (1)$$

From (1), $(x + 3)(x + 2) = 0$, which has the roots -3 and -2.

The following rule is easily established:

To obtain the equation $f(-x) = 0$ whose roots are the negatives of those of $f(x) = 0$, change the sign of the coefficient of each term of odd degree.

In any particular case, we prefer to proceed directly by use of Theorem VIII, which leads naturally to the preceding rule without memorization.

EXAMPLE 1. Obtain an equation whose roots are the negatives of the roots of

$$x^5 - 4x^4 + 3x^3 + 2x^2 - 5x - 7 = 0. \tag{2}$$

Solution. We replace x by $-x$ in (2), which gives

$$(-x)^5 - 4(-x)^4 + 3(-x)^3 + 2(-x)^2 - 5(-x) - 7 = 0, \text{ or}$$
$$-x^5 - 4x^4 - 3x^3 + 2x^2 + 5x - 7 = 0. \tag{3}$$

90. Signs of the roots

In this section, if we refer to a number as having a *plus* sign, this will mean that the number is *positive*. If it is stated that a number has a *minus* sign, this will mean that the number is *negative*. Any polynomial $f(x)$ to which we shall refer will have *real* coefficients.

Let $f(x)$ be a polynomial arranged in descending* powers of x. Then, if the coefficients of two successive terms differ in sign, there is said to be a **variation of sign.** In counting the variations, zero coefficients (due to missing powers of x) are disregarded.

Illustration 1. $(x^4 - 5x^3 + 6x^2 - 9)$ has three variations of sign.

Lemma 1. *If all roots of $g(x) = 0$ are* **negative,** *or of the form $(a + bi)$ with a and b real and $b \neq 0$, then $g(x)$ has an even number of variations of sign.*

★*Proof.* 1. Let $r_1, r_2, \cdots, r_n$ be the roots of $g(x) = 0$. Then,

$$g(x) = a_0(x - r_1)(x - r_2) \cdots (x - r_n), \tag{1}$$

where we shall take $a_0 = 1$, which does not affect variations of sign.

2. Consider the product of all factors of $g(x)$ in (1) where each corresponding zero, r_i, of g is a *real* number. If we let $r_i' = |r_i|$ for the negative zero r_i, the corresponding factor is $(x + r_i')$, where $r_i' > 0$. Hence, the product of all of the factors of $g(x)$ of the form $(x + r_i')$ is a polynomial whose *constant term is positive.*

3. Consider any pair of complex roots of $g(x) = 0$ of the form $(a + bi)$ and $(a - bi)$, where $b \neq 0$. The product of the corresponding factors of $g(x)$ is

$$[(x - a) + bi][(x - a) - bi] = x^2 - 2ax + (a^2 + b^2),$$

* Just as well, we could arrange in ascending powers of x.

where the constant term is *positive*. Hence the product of all of the linear factors of $g(x)$ involving imaginary numbers has a *positive constant term*. Then, from Step 2, the product of *all* factors of $g(x)$ gives a *positive constant term*.

4. In $g(x)$, the coefficients of the *first* and *last* terms are both positive. Hence, in going from the first to the last, there are an *even number* of variations in the signs of coefficients, from "$+$" to "$-$", etc., to "$+$."

Lemma 2. *If $g(x)$ is any polynomial, and $r > 0$, then the number of variations of sign in $(x - r)g(x)$ exceeds the number of variations in $g(x)$ by an* **odd** *number.*

Illustration 2. In $g(x) = x^3 - 3x^2 - x - 5$, there is 1 variation of sign. We find that $$(x - 2)g(x) = x^4 - 5x^3 + 5x^2 - 3x + 10,$$ which has 4 variations of sign.

★*Proof of Lemma 2.* 1. Let us abbreviate $g(x)$ and other polynomials below by writing merely the signs of terms, arranged in columns of like powers, for instance,

$$
\begin{array}{llllllllllllllllllll}
g(x) = & & + & + & + & + & - & - & - & - & - & + & + & + & + & - & - & - & - & ; & \quad (2)\\
xg(x) = & + & + & + & + & - & - & - & - & - & + & + & + & + & - & - & - & - & & ; & \quad (3)\\
-rg(x) = & & & & & - & - & - & - & + & + & + & + & - & - & - & - & - & + & + & + & . & \quad (4)\\
\hline
(x - r)g(x) = & + & \pm & \pm & \pm & - & \pm & \pm & \pm & + & \pm & \pm & \pm & - & \pm & \pm & + & . & & & & \quad (5)
\end{array}
$$

To obtain (5), we added like powers in (3) and (4).

2. The first of each group of "$+$" terms in (3) is part of a "$+$" term in (5). The first of each group of "$-$" terms in (3) is part of a "$-$" term in (5). The intermediate terms are "$\pm$" in (5) because each one is $+$, or $-$, or zero, depending on the values of r and of coefficients in $g(x)$.

3. If the *nonambiguous signs* in (5) are considered apart from the others, we observe 1 more variation of sign than in $g(x)$, because the sign at the right-hand end in (5) is opposite to the last sign in (2). Hence, there is *at least* 1 more variation of sign in (5) than in (2).

4. Consider any group in (5) from *one definite sign* to *the next definite sign*, inclusive, for instance, "$+ \pm \pm \pm -$." Since the first and last signs here are *opposite*, there are $(1 + h)$ variations of sign, where h is some *even* integer. For this group in Step 3, we counted only the single variation between the nonambiguous signs. Hence, in Step 3, we *underestimated* the number of variations in (5) by a *sum of even integers* (which might all be zero). Thus, the number of variations in (5) exceeds the number in $g(x)$ by 1 *plus an even integer.*

THEOREM IX. (**Descartes' rule of signs.**) *If $f(x)$ is a polynomial with real coefficients, the number of positive roots of the equation $f(x) = 0$ cannot exceed the number of variations of sign in $f(x)$, and, in any case, differs from the number of variations by an even integer.*

Proof. 1. Let $r_1, r_2, \cdots, r_n$ be the roots of $f(x) = 0$; then,

$$f(x) = (x - r_1)(x - r_2) \cdots (x - r_n), \tag{6}$$

where a constant factor a has been dropped for convenience. In (6), let $r_1, r_2, \cdots, r_k$ be the *positive* roots, and let $g(x)$ be the product of the factors corresponding to the other roots. Then,

$$f(x) = (x - r_1)(x - r_2) \cdots (x - r_k)g(x). \tag{7}$$

2. By Lemma 1, $g(x)$ has an *even number* of variations of sign.

3. By Lemma 2, the number of variations of sign in $(x - r_1)g(x)$ exceeds the number in $g(x)$ by $(1 + h_1)$, where h_1 is an *even integer*. The number of variations in $(x - r_2)[(x - r_1)g(x)]$ exceeds the number in $(x - r_1)g(x)$ by $(1 + h_2)$, where h_2 is an *even integer*. $\cdots$ Multiplication in sequence by the k factors $(x - r_1) \cdots (x - r_k)$ in (7) *increases* the number of variations of sign in $g(x)$ by $(k + H)$, where H is the *sum of the even integers* $h_1, h_2, \cdots$. Since $g(x)$ originally had an *even number* of variations, the number of variations in $f(x)$ is at least k, but may exceed k by an *even integer*, which proves Descartes' rule of signs.

Note 1. If $f(x) = 0$ had *zero as a root of multiplicity m*, this would produce a factor x^m in (6) but would not affect signs of coefficients, and hence Descartes' rule remains valid.

The roots of $f(-x) = 0$ are the negatives of the roots of $f(x) = 0$. Hence, the *negative* roots of $f(x) = 0$ give rise to the *positive* roots of $f(-x) = 0$. Therefore, we obtain the following result.

Corollary 1. *The number of negative roots of $f(x) = 0$ cannot exceed the number of variations of sign in $f(-x)$ and, in any case, differs from the number of variations by an even integer.*

Without actually solving an equation, we can obtain useful information about its roots by use of Descartes' rule of signs and other theorems.

EXAMPLE 1. Without solving, investigate the roots of

$$2x^4 + 5x^2 - 4x - 1 = 0. \tag{8}$$

Solution. 1. Let $f(x)$ represent the left-hand member; $f(x)$ has one variation of sign. Hence, by Descartes' rule, there *cannot be more than one positive root*. The possibility of *no* positive root does not enter, because $1 - 0 = 1$, which is *not an even integer*. Hence, there is *exactly one positive root*.

2. We obtain $f(-x) = 2x^4 + 5x^2 + 4x - 1$, which has one variation of sign. Hence, as in Step 1, (8) has *exactly one negative root*.

3. Since (8) has four roots, there are two complex roots which are not real, one positive root, and one negative root.

EXAMPLE 2. State what can be learned about the roots of the equation $2x^5 - 3x^4 + 2x - 5 = 0$ without solving it.

Solution. 1. Let $f(x)$ represent the left-hand side. Then, $f(x)$ has three variations of sign. Hence, the equation has one or three positive roots.

2. $f(-x) = -2x^5 - 3x^4 - 2x - 5$, with no variations of sign. Hence, there are *no negative roots*.

3. There are four complex roots which are not real and one positive root, or three positive roots and two unequal conjugate complex roots, because nonreal roots occur in pairs.

EXERCISE 56

Find an equation whose roots are the negatives of those of the given equation.

1. $2x^4 - 3x^3 + 4x^2 - 6x = 5.$ **2.** $4x^3 + 2x^2 - 3x = 7.$

3. $2x^3 + 5x^2 + 7x - 3 = 0.$ **4.** $4x^5 - x^3 + x^2 - 5x = 8.$

5. $5x^6 - 4x^4 - x^2 + 7 = 0.$ **6.** $3x^4 - 2x^3 - 2x + 6 = 0.$

7. $2x^5 - 3x^4 - x^3 = 3x - 1.$ **8.** $5x^5 - 3x^3 + 2x^2 - 7x = 9.$

Without solving the equation, investigate the roots by use of general theorems.

9. $2x^2 - 3x - 5 = 0.$ **10.** $2x^3 - 5x^2 + 2x = 4.$ **11.** $x^4 - 3x = 2.$

12. $x^4 + x^2 + 1 = 2x^3.$ **13.** $3x^5 - 4x^3 + 2x^2 = 3.$ **14.** $4x^4 + 3x^2 = 2.$

15. $x^4 + 5x^3 + x^2 = 6.$ **16.** $x^3 + 2x^2 = 5.$ **17.** $x^3 + 3 = 0.$

18. $x^5 + 2x^3 = 4.$ **19.** $x^3 + 3x = 4.$ **20.** $x^6 + 4 = 0.$

21. $x^7 - x^3 = 1 - x.$ **22.** $x^5 + 2x^2 - x = 3.$ **23.** $x^7 + 5 = 0.$

24. $x^6 + 3x^4 + 2x^3 = 5.$ **25.** $3x^6 - 2x^4 - 15 = 0.$

Given that all roots are real, determine their nature.

26. $x^3 + 4x^2 - 20x = 48.$ **27.** $x^6 - 6x^4 + 12x^2 - 8 = 0.$

28. $4x^3 - 12x^2 + 11x = 3.$ **29.** $x^5 - 2x^4 - 13x^3 + 39x^2 = 24x.$

91. Bounds for the real roots of $f(x) = 0$

In this section, we shall assume that the coefficients in the polynomial $f(x)$ are real numbers. Suppose that b and B are real numbers such that, if r is any real root of $f(x) = 0$, then

$$b \leqq r \leqq B. \tag{1}$$

If (1) is true, we refer to b as a **lower bound,** and to B as an **upper bound,** for the real roots of $f(x) = 0$. If b satisfies (1), and if $b_1 < b$, then b_1 also is a lower bound for the real roots. Similarly, if $B_1 > B$ and (1) is true, then B_1 also is an upper bound for the real roots. Thus, the bounds described by (1) are *not unique.* Bounds b and B, as in (1), can be found by use of the following theorem. We shall prefer to check its conclusion in each application rather than to give a proof of the general statement.

THEOREM X. *If $k > 0$, and if all numbers in the third row of the synthetic division of $f(x)$ by $(x - k)$ are of the same sign or zero, then k is an upper bound for the real roots of $f(x) = 0$.*

A lower bound for the real roots of $f(x) = 0$ can be found by first applying Theorem X to find an upper bound, β, for the real roots of the equation $f(-x) = 0$, whose roots are the negatives of those of $f(x) = 0$. Then, $-\beta$ is a lower bound for the real roots of $f(-x) = 0$.

EXAMPLE 1.   Find bounds for the real roots of

$$f(x) = x^3 + 3x^2 - 12x - 9 = 0.$$

Solution.   1. On dividing $f(x)$ by $(x - 3)$ by synthetic division, all numbers in the third line are found to be positive, and $f(3) = 9$.

$$\left. \begin{array}{r|rrr|r} 1 & 3 & -12 & -9 & 3 \\ & 3 & 18 & 18 & \\ \hline 1 & 6 & 6 & 9 \end{array} \right\} \tag{2}$$

Hence, if we should divide $f(x)$ by $(x - a)$, where a is any number *greater* than 3, we would find that $f(a) > 9$, because each number in the second row in this new division would be greater than the corresponding number in the division by $(x - 3)$. Hence, if $a > 3$, then a is not a root of $f(x) = 0$; or, 3 is an *upper* bound for the real roots of $f(x) = 0$.

2. To find a lower bound, consider

$$f(-x) = -x^3 + 3x^2 + 12x - 9 = 0, \text{ or}$$
$$x^3 - 3x^2 - 12x + 9 = 0. \tag{3}$$

We find that 6 is an upper bound for the roots of $f(-x) = 0$. Hence, -6 is *less* than any root of $f(x) = 0$, or -6 is a *lower* bound for the roots.

Comment.   The bound 3 in (2) was found after first trying 2, with lack of success. In dealing with (3), the first possible bound, 4, was not satisfactory; trial of 5 also would prove unsatisfactory; etc. Thus, a trial and error process is involved in applying Theorem X.

Note 1.   Instead of the method of the preceding solution in finding a lower bound for the roots, the student might desire to use the following result. In such a case, he should prove the theorem, or justify each application as in Illustration 1 below.

THEOREM XI.   *If $k < 0$, and if the numbers in the 3d row of the synthetic division of $f(x)$ by $(x - k)$ **alternate in sign**, then k is a lower bound for the roots of $f(x) = 0$.*

Illustration 1.   With $f(x)$ as in Example 1, synthetic division by $(x + 6)$, or $[x - (-6)]$, is as follows:

$$\left.\begin{array}{|c|c|c|c|c|}
\hline
1 & 3 & -12 & -9 & -6 \\
 & -6 & +18 & -36 & \\
\hline
1 & -3 & +6 & -45 & \\
\hline
\end{array}\right\} \quad (4)$$

Hence, if $r < -6$, then synthetic division of $f(x)$ by $(x - r)$ would give numbers of the same signs, but larger absolute values, in the 2d row of (4); thus, $f(r) < -45$, and $f(r) \neq 0$. Or, -6 is a lower bound for the roots.

EXERCISE 57

Find bounds for the real roots of the equation.

1. $x^3 + 3x^2 - 14x + 7 = 0.$
2. $4x^3 + 2x^2 - 17x + 10 = 0.$
3. $2x^4 - 3x^3 - 17x^2 = 55.$
4. $x^4 - 2x^2 - 80 = 0.$
5. $x^3 - 5x^2 - 90 = 0.$
6. $2x^5 - 8x^3 + 2x^2 = 45.$
7. $x^3 - 3x^2 = 43x - 17.$
8. $3x^4 - 12x^3 + 10x^2 = 19.$
9. $x^5 - 4x^4 - 25x = 85.$
10. $x^4 - 18x^3 + 35x = 28.$

92. Rational roots

We may obtain rational roots of a polynomial equation by a trial and error process based on the following result.

THEOREM XII. *If an equation*

$$a_0 + a_1 x + \cdots + a_{n-1}x^{n-1} + a_n x^n = 0, \quad (1)$$

with integral coefficients, and $a_n \neq 0$, has a rational root c/d, where c and d are integers and c/d is in lowest terms, then c is a factor of a_0 and d is a factor of a_n.

Proof. 1. By hypothesis, c and d are integers with no common factor except ± 1. On substituting c/d for x in (1), we obtain

$$a_0 + a_1 \frac{c}{d} + \cdots + a_{n-1}\frac{c^{n-1}}{d^{n-1}} + a_n \frac{c^n}{d^n} = 0. \quad (2)$$

2. On multiplying both sides of (2) by d^n, we find

$$a_0 d^n + a_1 c d^{n-1} + \cdots + a_{n-1}c^{n-1}d + a_n c^n = 0, \text{ or} \quad (3)$$
$$d(a_0 d^{n-1} + a_1 c d^{n-2} + \cdots + a_{n-1}c^{n-1}) = -a_n c^n. \quad (4)$$

3. In (4), all letters represent integers and d is a factor on the left. Hence, d is a factor of $a_n c^n$. But, unless $d = \pm 1$, d is *not* a factor of c^n because d is not a factor of c. Hence, d is a factor of a_n.

4. On subtracting $a_0 d^n$ from both sides in (3), we obtain

$$a_1 c d^{n-1} + \cdots + a_{n-1}c^{n-1}d + a_n c^n = -a_0 d^n. \quad (5)$$

In (5), c is a factor on the left, and hence is a factor of a_0.

Corollary 1. *Any rational root of*

$$b_0 + b_1x + b_2x^2 + \cdots + b_{n-1}x^{n-1} + x^n = 0, \tag{6}$$

with integral coefficients is an integer and is a factor of b_0.

Proof. By the theorem, if c/d is a root of (6), then d is a factor of the coefficient of x^n, and c is a factor of b_0. Since the coefficient of x^n is 1, hence $d = \pm 1$, and therefore c/d is an integer, $\pm c$, which is a factor of b_0.

In solving a polynomial equation, whenever a rational root is found, *depress the degree of the original equation $f(x) = 0$* by removing the factor of $f(x)$ corresponding to the known root. Then, continue the solution by finding the roots of the **depressed equation,** with Theorem XII possibly used again.

EXAMPLE 1.   Solve the equation:

$$f(x) = x^4 - 6x^3 + 3x^2 + 24x - 28 = 0.$$

Solution.   1. By Corollary 1, the possible rational roots are the integral divisors of -28, or ± 1, ± 2, ± 4, ± 7, ± 14, and ± 28.

2. By inspection of $f(x)$, we find $f(1) = -6$; hence, 1 is not a root. Also, $f(-1) = -42$ and -1 is not a root.

3. From synthetic division by $(x - 2)$, we find $f(2) = 0$, and

$$f(x) = (x - 2)(x^3 - 4x^2 - 5x + 14).$$

	1	−6	3	24	−28	2
		2	−8	−10	28	
	1	−4	−5	14	0	

Hence, 2 is a root. The other roots of $f(x) = 0$ are the roots of the *depressed equation* $x^3 - 4x^2 - 5x + 14 = 0$.

4. Let $Q(x) = x^3 - 4x^2 - 5x + 14$. Then, the possible rational roots of $Q(x) = 0$ are ± 1, ± 2, ± 7, ± 14. By Step 2, ± 1 are not roots. From synthetic division of $Q(x)$ by $(x + 2)$, we find $Q(-2) = 0$ and

$$Q(x) = (x + 2)(x^2 - 6x + 7).$$

	1	−4	−5	14	−2
		−2	12	−14	
	1	−6	7	0	

Hence, -2 is a root. The depressed equation is $x^2 - 6x + 7 = 0$, whose solutions, obtained by the quadratic formula, are $(3 \pm \sqrt{2})$.

EXAMPLE 2.   Find all roots of $f(x) = 3x^3 + 2x^2 - 3x - 2 = 0$.

Solution.   1. By Theorem XII, if c/d is a root, the possible values of c are ± 1 and ± 2; the possible values of d are ± 1 and ± 3. On forming all possible fractions c/d from these values, we find the following as the possible rational roots: ± 1; ± 2; $\pm \frac{1}{3}$; $\pm \frac{2}{3}$.

2. From synthetic division by $(x - 1)$, we find that $f(1) = 0$, and that

$f(x) = (x - 1)(3x^2 + 5x + 2).$

$$\begin{array}{r|rrr|r} 3 & 2 & -3 & -2 & \underline{1} \\ & & 3 & 5 & 2 \\ \hline & 3 & 5 & 2 & 0 \end{array}$$

Hence, 1 is a root; the depressed equation is $3x^2 + 5x + 2 = 0$. From this equation, we find that the other roots are -1 and $-\frac{2}{3}$.

★93. Transformation to multiply the roots

If we substitute $x = y/m$ in $f(x) = 0$, we obtain $f(y/m) = 0$, where each root is m times a root of $f(x) = 0$, because $y = mx$ in the equations.

THEOREM XIII. *To obtain a simplified form of the equation $f(y/m) = 0$, each of whose roots is m times a root of $f(x) = 0$, where*

$$f(x) = a_n x^n + a_{n-1} x^{n-1} + \cdots + a_1 x + a_0, \tag{1}$$

multiply the successive coefficients in $f(x)$, starting with a_{n-1}, by $m, m^2, m^3, \cdots, m^n$, respectively, and replace x by y.

Proof. 1. On replacing x by y/m in $f(x) = 0$, we find

$$f\left(\frac{y}{m}\right) = a_n \left(\frac{y}{m}\right)^n + a_{n-1} \left(\frac{y}{m}\right)^{n-1} + \cdots + a_1 \left(\frac{y}{m}\right) + a_0 = 0. \tag{2}$$

2. On multiplying both sides of (2) by m^n, we obtain

$$a_n y^n + a_{n-1} m y^{n-1} + \cdots + a_1 m^{n-1} y + a_0 m^n = 0,$$

as specified in Theorem XIII.

In applying Theorem XIII, each missing power of x in $f(x)$ should be considered present, with the coefficient zero. Theorem XIII furnishes a new method for finding the rational roots of an equation $f(x) = 0$ where $f(x)$ has the form (1) with integral coefficients and $a_n \neq 1$.

EXAMPLE 1. Find the rational roots of $64x^3 - 16x^2 + 12x - 3 = 0$.

Solution. 1. Divide by 64: $\qquad x^3 - \dfrac{x^2}{4} + \dfrac{3x}{16} - \dfrac{3}{64} = 0.$ $\tag{3}$

2. Transform (3) to multiply the roots by 4, chosen as the smallest integer which will cause the resulting equation to have integral coefficients, with 1 as the coefficient of the term of highest degree. We substitute $x = \frac{1}{4}y$ and,

by Theorem XIII, obtain $\qquad y^3 - y^2 + 3y - 3 = 0.$ $\tag{4}$

3. Any rational root of (4) is an integer; by the method of page 216, 1 is the only rational root. Since $x = \frac{1}{4}y$, the only rational root of (3) is $\frac{1}{4}$.

EXERCISE 58

Find all rational roots and, if their determination leads to a depressed equation which is a quadratic, find all of the roots. In case there are no rational roots, this fact must be demonstrated thoroughly.

1. $x^3 - 7x + 6 = 0$.
2. $x^3 + 3x^2 + 12 = 16x$.
3. $2x^3 - 3x^2 - 7x = 6$.
4. $x^3 - 3x - 2 = 0$.
5. $x^3 - x^2 = 8x - 12$.
6. $x^3 + 2x^2 - 9x = 4$.
7. $x^4 - 4x^3 - 5x^2 = 36 - 36x$.
8. $x^4 + 10x + 24 = 15x^2$.
9. $x^3 + x^2 - 6x = 2$.
10. $x^4 - 6x^2 + 15x = 4$.
11. $2x^3 + 5x^2 - 8x = 6$.
12. $5x^3 + 6x + 4 = 8x^2$.
13. $2x^3 + 7x^2 + 6x = 5$.
14. $4x^3 - 25x^2 + 50x = 11$.
15. $3x^3 + 2x^2 - 3x = 1$.
16. $4x^3 - 19x^2 + 32x = 15$.
17. $2x^3 + 5x^2 - 14x = 8$.
18. $3x^3 - 2x^2 = 2x - 8$.
19. $8x^3 + 18x^2 + 3x = 2$.
20. $x^4 - 3x^3 - 12x = 16$.

Find bounds for the roots and then obtain all rational roots. Make use of the bounds and general theorems in rejecting possibilities.

21. $x^3 + 4x^2 - 36x = 72$.
22. $x^4 - x^2 - 32x + 3x^3 = 87$.
23. $x^4 - 3x^3 - 16x^2 = 48x - 168$.
24. $x^3 + 18x^2 + 72x = 54$.
25. $x^4 + 4x^3 + 10x^2 - 41x = 156$.
26. $x^4 + 16x + 30 = 23x^2$.
27. $4x^4 + 3x^3 - 180x = x^2 - 45$.
28. $x^4 - 2x^3 - 21x^2 - 94x = 136$.

★*Transform the equation, to multiply the roots as specified.*

29. $3x^4 - 2x^2 + 7x - 4 = 0$; to multiply the roots by 3.
30. $x^4 - \frac{1}{8}x^3 + 2x^2 - \frac{5}{4} = 0$; to multiply the roots by -2.

★*Find all rational roots by the method of Example 1 on page 217. Make use of bounds for roots where desirable.*

31–39. Problems 11–19 of this exercise, respectively.
40. $16x^3 - 20x^2 + 9 = 12x$.
41. $4x^4 - 8x^3 - x^2 + 8x = 3$.
42. $8x^3 - 4x^2 = 30x - 28$.
43. $3x^4 + 8x^2 - x + 10 = 0$.

94. Real roots from successive enlarged graphs

Consider an equation $f(x) = 0$, where f is a real-valued function but is not necessarily a polynomial function, and where the graph of $y = f(x)$ in an xy-plane is a continuous curve (a curve without breaks). Then, various graphical methods exist for obtaining the real roots of $f(x) = 0$ to any desired degree of accuracy. The method to be presented in this section can be based either on successive enlargements and approximations to the graph of f by use of straight line segments, or on successive approximations to any given root by interpolation, as described later. In any graphical method for obtaining the real roots of $f(x) = 0$, the following result provides a desirable start, in order to minimize future computation.

THEOREM XIV. (Location theorem for real roots.) *If a and b are real numbers for which one of $f(a)$ and $f(b)$ is positive and one is negative, then the equation $f(x) = 0$ has at least one real root and, in any case, an odd number of real roots, between a and b.*

Proof. On a graph of $y = f(x)$, as in Figure 80, the points P and Q corresponding to $x = a$ and $x = b$ are on opposite sides of the x-axis. Since the graph is a continuous curve joining P and Q, the graph must cross the x-axis *at least once*, and in any case, an *odd number* of times, between P and Q. To each intersection with the x-axis, there corresponds a real root of $f(x) = 0$.

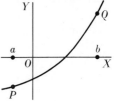

Figure 80

Note 1. We say that we have **bracketed** an unknown real number r between a and b if we prove that r *lies between a and b.*

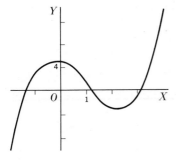

Figure 81

EXAMPLE 1. Solve the equation:

$$x^3 - 3x^2 - 2x + 5 = 0. \qquad (1)$$

Solution. 1. By the method of Section 92, we find that (1) has no rational root. Let $f(x)$ represent the left-hand member of (1). By synthetic division, we compute the values of $f(x)$ below, observe the changes in sign for $f(x)$, and conclude that there is a real root of (1) between -2 and -1; between 1 and 2; between 3 and 4. These facts check with the graph of $y = f(x)$ drawn in Figure 81 by use of the table.

WHEN x =	-2	-1	0	1	2	3	4
THEN $f(x)$ =	-11	3	5	1	-3	-1	13

2. From Figure 81, we estimate that the roots are approximately -1.3, 1.2, and 3.2.

3. **To obtain more accurately the root r_1 near 3.2:**

A. *To bracket the root r_1 between successive tenths.* By synthetic division, we compute $f(x)$ at $x = 3.2$, because 3.2 is our best estimate for r_1, and find $f(3.2) = +.65$. From Figure 81, where we think of the root r_1 as unknown but near 3.2, we see that

$$f(x) > 0 \quad if \quad x > r_1.$$

Hence, $r_1 < 3.2$, because $f(3.2) > 0$. Therefore, we compute $f(x)$ at $x = 3.1$, *rather than* at $x = 3.3$. Since $f(3.1) = -.24$, we become *certain* that r_1 lies between 3.1 and 3.2.

B. *Enlarge the graph between* $x = 3.1$ *and* $x = 3.2$, by use of the following values of $f(x)$. The graph, in Figure 82, is taken as a straight line, because we used just two points to determine it, and acted as if a small segment of the graph is well approximated by a straight line. From Figure 82, we estimate $r_1 = 3.13$.

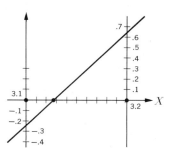

Figure 82

WHEN x =	3.1	3.2
THEN $f(x)$ =	−.24	+ .65

C. *To bracket the root* r_1 *between successive hundredths.* First, we compute $f(3.13) = +.014$. Then, after inspection of Figure 82, we decide that $r_1 < 3.13$ and hence compute $f(3.12) = -.073$. We conclude that the root r_1 lies between 3.12 and 3.13.

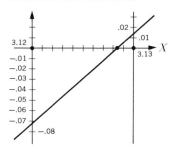

Figure 83

WHEN x =	3.12	3.13
THEN $f(x)$ =	−.073	+.014

D. By use of the preceding values, we draw a straight line approximation to the graph of $y = f(x)$ between $x = 3.12$ and $x = 3.13$ on an enlarged scale, in Figure 83, and estimate $r_1 = 3.128$. The final 8 is doubtful, but could be verified by computing $f(x)$ for values of x to successive thousandths near $x = 3.128$.

4. Similarly, we find the other roots, −1.330 and 1.202.

Note 2. The result, 3.13, obtained from Figure 82 can be found *without a figure* by use of **simple interpolation,** as used for instance with logarithm tables. In this method, we first notice that, if r is the unknown root, then $f(r) = 0$. From the following data,

WHEN x =	3.1	r	3.2
THEN $f(x)$ =	−.24	0	.65

$3.2 − 3.1 = .1; 0 − (−.24) = .24;$

$.65 − (−.24) = .89.$

we assume that, since 0 is 24/89 of the *numerical distance* from −.24 to .65, then r is *the same proportion of the way from* 3.1 *to* 3.2. Or, we assume that

$$r = 3.1 + \frac{24}{89} (.1) = 3.1 + .027 = 3.13, \text{ approximately.}$$

The preceding assumption is *exactly* equivalent to assuming that the graph of $f(x)$ between $x = 3.1$ and $x = 3.2$ is a *straight line*. This statement can be proved by drawing appropriate triangles in Figure 82 and then using properties of similar triangles.

SUMMARY.   *To find irrational roots of $f(x) = 0$ as accurately as desired.*

1. *From a graph of $y = f(x)$, estimate the value of each root to the nearest tenth. Let one of these estimates be x_1, for a particular unknown root r_1. Then, improve on the estimate as follows.*

2. *Bracket r_1 between successive tenths by computing $f(x)$ first for $x = x_1$, and then for successive tenths in the values of x, on whichever side of x_1 is appropriate, as judged by the graph which was used in Step 1.*

3. *Graph f on an enlarged scale, for values of x between the tenths of the bracket found in Step 2, with a straight line as the approximate curve. From this graph, read an estimate x_2 of the root r_1 to the nearest hundredth.*

4. *Bracket the root r_1 between successive hundredths by computing $f(x)$ at $x = x_2$, etc.; continue by the method of Step 3 to obtain r_1 as accurately as desired.*

To determine a root by the preceding method accurately to k decimal places, the root should be estimated to $(k + 1)$ places, where the last place remains in doubt.

Note 3.   If all roots of an equation of degree n,

$$a_0 + a_1x + \cdots + a_{n-1}x^{n-1} + a_nx^n = 0, \tag{2}$$

have been specified by some means, the values can be checked by the following result, to be proved on page 223:

The sum of the roots of (2) is equal to $-\dfrac{a_{n-1}}{a_n}$.

EXERCISE 59

Obtain the results accurate to two decimal places, unless otherwise specified. Find any specified root by starting with a graph over just one x-unit (use three accurate points).

1. The root of $2x^3 - 11x^2 + 15x - 1 = 0$ between 2 and 3.
2. The root of $x^3 - 10x^2 + 32x + 66 = 0$ between -2 and -1.
3. The root of $x^3 + x^2 - 10x + 4 = 0$ between 0 and 1.
4. The root of $x^4 + x^3 + x^2 - 2x = 6$ between 1 and 2.
5. The two roots of $x^3 - 7x + 7 = 0$ between 1 and 2.
   Hint. Start from a graph using $x = 1$, $x = 1.5$, and $x = 2$.
6. The two roots of $5x^3 + 6x^2 - 7x + 1 = 0$ between 0 and 1.

Find all real roots accurate to two decimal places.

7. $x^3 + 3x^2 + 3x = 10$.
8. $x^3 - 3x^2 + 3x = 14$.
9. $x^3 - 2x^2 = x - 1$.
10. $x^3 - 2x^2 = 5x - 4$.
11. $x^3 + 2x^2 = 7x - 1$.
12. $x^4 - 6x^3 + 12x^2 = 10x + 2$.
13. $4x^3 - 12x^2 + 8x = 1$.
14. $3x^4 + 5x^3 - x^2 - 4x = 1$.
15. $x^4 - 2x^3 + 3x^2 = 11x - 10$.
16. $x^3 - 2x^2 = 14x + 13$.

Find the indicated principal root.

17. $\sqrt[4]{10}$.   **18.** $\sqrt[3]{185}$.   **19.** $\sqrt[3]{-62}$.   **20.** $\sqrt[5]{-148}$.

    Hint for Problem 17. We desire the positive root of $x^4 - 10 = 0$.

The equation has no rational roots. Find the real roots.

21. $x^3 - 4.57x^2 + 6.14x = 2.139$.   **22.** $x^4 + 4x^3 + 6x^2 + 384x = 1063$.

23. An open box is to be made from a rectangular piece of cardboard, 12″ long and 8″ wide, by cutting equal squares from the corners and turning up the sides. Find the length of a side of these squares if the box is to contain 56 cubic inches.

24. It is known that the maximum safe load S in pounds for a beam of a certain material and specified length, supported at both ends, is given by $S = 15d^2x$, where x is the breadth and d is the depth, in inches. The beam is to be cut from a log 10 inches in diameter. Find x correct to one decimal place, if $S = 3500$.

★95. Coefficients in terms of the roots

    Let $f(x) = 0$ be a polynomial equation where the coefficients in $f(x)$ are any complex numbers. Then, we find that the coefficients can be expressed in terms of the roots of $f(x) = 0$.

    Illustration 1. Let r_1, r_2, and r_3 be the roots of

$$b_0 + b_1 x + b_2 x^2 + x^3 = 0. \tag{1}$$

From page 205,

$$b_0 + b_1 x + b_2 x^2 + x^3 \equiv (x - r_1)(x - r_2)(x - r_3)$$
$$\equiv x^3 - (r_1 + r_2 + r_3)x^2 + (r_1 r_2 + r_1 r_3 + r_2 r_3)x - r_1 r_2 r_3. \tag{2}$$

As a consequence of Corollary 1, page 205,

$$b_2 = -(r_1 + r_2 + r_3); \qquad b_1 = r_1 r_2 + r_1 r_3 + r_2 r_3; \qquad b_0 = -r_1 r_2 r_3. \tag{3}$$

    Similarly, we find that, if $r_1, r_2, \cdots, r_n$ are the roots of

$$b_0 + b_1 x + \cdots + b_{n-2} x^{n-2} + b_{n-1} x^{n-1} + x^n = 0, \tag{4}$$

$$\left.\begin{array}{l} b_{n-1} = -(r_1 + r_2 + \cdots + r_n), \\[4pt] b_{n-2} = r_1 r_2 + r_1 r_3 + \cdots + r_1 r_n + r_2 r_3 + \cdots + r_{n-1} r_n, \\[4pt] b_{n-3} = -(r_1 r_2 r_3 + r_1 r_2 r_4 + \cdots), \\[4pt] \cdot \quad \cdot \quad \cdot \quad \cdot \quad \cdot \quad \cdot \quad \cdot \quad \cdot \quad \cdot \\[4pt] b_0 \ \ = (-1)^n r_1 r_2 r_3 \cdots r_n. \end{array}\right\} \tag{5}$$

Or, $b_{n-1} = -(\text{the sum of all the roots}),$

            $b_{n-2} = +(\text{the sum of the products of the roots, two at a time}),$

            $b_{n-3} = -(\text{the sum of the products of the roots, three at a time}),$

            $\cdot \quad \cdot \quad \cdot \quad \cdot \quad \cdot \quad \cdot \quad \cdot \quad \cdot \quad \cdot \quad \cdot \quad \cdot$

            $b_0 \ \ = (-1)^n \cdot (\text{the product of the roots}).$

If $a_n \neq 0$, and we divide both sides of

$$a_0 + a_1 x + \cdots + a_{n-1} x^{n-1} + a_n x^n = 0 \qquad (6)$$

by a_n, we obtain

$$\frac{a_0}{a_n} + \frac{a_1}{a_n} x + \cdots + \frac{a_{n-1}}{a_n} x^{n-1} + x^n = 0.$$

Hence, from (5), if $(r_1, r_2, \cdots, r_n)$ are the roots of (6), then

$$\frac{a_{n-1}}{a_n} = -(r_1 + r_2 + \cdots + r_n);$$

$$\frac{a_{n-2}}{a_n} = +(r_1 r_2 + r_1 r_3 + \cdots); \; etc.$$

EXERCISE 60

1. By the method of Illustration 1, page 222, derive equations (5) of page 222 for the case of $x^4 + b_3 x^3 + b_2 x^2 + b_1 x + b_0 = 0$.

By use of (5) on page 222, obtain an equation with the specified roots.

2. $2, 3, -4$.   3. $\pm\sqrt{3}, 2, -3$.   4. $\pm 3i, 2, -4$.

In the following problems, x is the variable.

5. Find the third root of $x^3 + ax^2 + bx - 40 = 0$ if 2 and -5 are known to be roots.

6. Find the third root of $x^3 + hx^2 - 14x + k = 0$ if -3 and 4 are known to be roots.

7. Find the roots of $9x^3 - 30x^2 + bx + c = 0$ if one root is 2 and the other roots differ by 2.

8. Find all the roots of $x^4 - 2x^3 - 11x^2 + hx + 36 = 0$ if it has two double roots.

9. Find all the roots of $x^3 + 4x^2 + kx - 18 = 0$ if it has one simple real root and one double real root.

Solve the equation if the roots in some order form an A.P.

10. $x^3 - 3x^2 - x + h = 0$.   11. $9x^3 + 18x^2 + 11x + k = 0$.

Solve the equation if the roots in some order form a G.P.

12. $x^3 + 3x^2 - 6x + k = 0$.   13. $8x^3 + 18x^2 - 27x + k = 0$.

14. Prove that if $x^3 + qx^2 + rx + s = 0$ has one root the negative of another, then $qr = s$, and conversely.

15. If the roots of $x^3 + bx^2 + cx + d = 0$, taken in some order, form a geometric progression, prove that $c^3 = b^3 d$, and conversely.

★96. Algebraic solution

In any reference to an algebraic formula involving (or based on) a certain finite number of complex numbers, say $a, b, c, \cdots$, we shall mean a formula specifying a finite number of the operations of addition, subtraction, multiplication, division, and the extraction of roots, and no other operations on the assigned numbers. Now, consider a polynomial equation of degree n,

$$a_0 + a_1 x + a_2 x^2 + \cdots + a_n x^n = 0, \tag{1}$$

where $(a_0, a_1, \cdots, a_n)$ are arbitrary complex numbers, with $a_n \neq 0$. Then, we shall refer to (1) as the *general equation* of degree n. For any particular integer n, and any particular coefficients, if it is possible to express each of the roots of (1) by means of an algebraic formula involving the coefficients, we shall say that (1) is *solvable by radicals* (where we admit that no radicals occur in the formula when $n = 1$). The following theorems concerning solvability by radicals can be proved.

THEOREM XV. *If $0 < n \leq 4$, and if the coefficients in* (1) *are arbitrary complex numbers, then* (1) *is solvable by radicals.*

THEOREM XVI. *If $n > 4$, there exist equations of degree n which are not solvable by radicals.* *

Previously, we have proved Theorem XV for the cases $n = 1$ and $n = 2$, by obtaining formulas for the solutions of the general equations of these degrees (the quadratic formula when $n = 2$). In the next two sections, we shall prove Theorem XV for the cases $n = 3$ and $n = 4$. The proof of Theorem XVI demands methods of very advanced mathematics (in particular, the so-called theory of "*groups*"). The first proof of Theorem XVI was given in 1824 by the brilliant Norwegian mathematician† NIELS HENRIK ABEL (1802–1829), who left a tremendous record of mathematical achievement in spite of his short and largely unhappy life.

If $f(x)$ is defined by an algebraic formula in x, we call f an **algebraic function.** However, such functions are merely a subset of the larger class referred to as *algebraic functions.* Thus, let $g(x, y)$ be any polynomial in x and y, and consider solving the polynomial equation $g(x, y) = 0$ for y in terms of x; the coefficients of the powers of y in $g(x, y)$ would involve x. Suppose that f is a function of a single variable, x, with the domain, D, of f consisting of all numbers x on some interval or intervals of numbers, and let $y = f(x)$. Assume that f is continuous‡ in D and that, for each x in D, the pair $(x, y = f(x))$ is a *solution* of $g(x, y) = 0$, or $g(x, f(x)) = 0$. Then, it is said that y is an *algebraic function of x;* also, it may be said that f is a *solution function* for y in terms of x. In view of preceding remarks in this section, it is seen that, if $g(x, y)$ is a polynomial of degree greater than 4 in y alone, algebraic solution functions for y in terms of x may exist for $g(x, y) = 0$ where it is *impossible to define $f(x)$ by an algebraic formula.*

---

* See page 440, *A Survey of Modern Algebra* by GARRETT BIRKHOFF and SAUNDERS MACLANE; the Macmillan Company, publishers.

† For a fascinating biography of Abel, see *Niels Henrik Abel*, by OYESTEIN ORE; University of Minnesota Press, publishers.

‡ We continue to accept this term intuitively with the basis described on page 95.

★97. Solution of the general cubic in one variable

Any cubic equation in a single variable x can be written in the form

$$x^3 + bx^2 + cx + d = 0. \tag{1}$$

The following solution of (1) applies when b, c, and d are any complex numbers.

SOLUTION OF THE CUBIC. 1. In equation (1), let

$$x = y - \tfrac{1}{3}b. \tag{2}$$

Then, we obtain

$$y^3 + py + q = 0, \tag{3}$$

where the coefficients p and q are given by

$$p = c - \frac{b^2}{3}, \quad and \quad q = d - \frac{bc}{3} + \frac{2b^3}{27}.$$

2. We call (3) the **reduced cubic**; its advantage is that it contains no term in y^2. In (3), place

$$y = z - \frac{p}{3z}. \tag{4}$$

Then, z satisfies

$$z^3 - \frac{p^3}{27z^3} + q = 0, \quad or \quad z^6 + qz^3 - \frac{p^3}{27} = 0. \tag{5}$$

Since (5) is in the quadratic form in z^3, we solve for z^3 by use of the quadratic formula. The solutions are

$$z^3 = -\frac{q}{2} + \sqrt{R} \quad and \quad z^3 = -\frac{q}{2} - \sqrt{R}, \tag{6}$$

where

$$R = \frac{p^3}{27} + \frac{q^2}{4}.$$

In (6), R may not be a real number. In such a case, $\sqrt{R}$ is understood to represent any one of the two square roots of R.

3. The first equation in (6) has three solutions, z_1, z_2, and z_3, the cube roots of the right-hand side. Then, from (4), the values of y are

$$y_1 = z_1 - \frac{p}{3z_1}; \quad y_2 = z_2 - \frac{p}{3z_2}; \quad y_3 = z_3 - \frac{p}{3z_3}.$$

4. Therefore, from (2), the roots of (1) are

$$x_1 = z_1 - \frac{p}{3z_1} - \frac{b}{3}; \quad x_2 = z_2 - \frac{p}{3z_2} - \frac{b}{3}; \quad x_3 = z_3 - \frac{p}{3z_3} - \frac{b}{3}. \tag{7}$$

Comment. It can be proved that, if in place of (z_1, z_2, z_3) we had used the solutions (z_4, z_5, z_6) of the second equation in (6), the three values obtained for x would be the same as those in (7).

In the preceding solution, p, q, and R are rational functions of b, c, and d. Hence, z_1, z_2, and z_3 are the cube roots of a number represented by an algebraic formula in b, c, and d. Therefore, in (7) we have algebraic formulas for x_1, x_2, and x_3 in terms of the coefficients b, c, and d.

Illustration 1. To solve $x^3 + 3x^2 - 9x - 3 = 0$, we obtain $p = -12$, $q = 8$, and $R = -48$. Then, the first equation in (6) becomes

$$z^3 = -4 + 4i\sqrt{3} = 8(\cos 120° + i \sin 120°).$$

Hence, we obtain

$$z_1 = 2(\cos 40° + i \sin 40°); \qquad z_2 = 2(\cos 160° + i \sin 160°);$$

$$z_3 = 2(\cos 280° + i \sin 280°).$$

From (7),

$$x_1 = 2(\cos 40° + i \sin 40°) + \frac{12}{6(\cos 40° + i \sin 40°)} - 1;$$

$$x_1 = 2(\cos 40° + i \sin 40°) + 2(\cos 40° - i \sin 40°) - 1 = 4 \cos 40° - 1.$$

Similarly, by use of (7) we find

$$x_2 = 4 \cos 160° - 1; \quad x_3 = 4 \cos 280° - 1.$$

Then, by use of Table IV we obtain

$$x_1 = 2.06; \quad x_2 = -4.76; \quad x_3 = -.30.$$

Note 1. The essential elements of the preceding solution of the general cubic were published first in 1545 by GERONIMO CARDANO (1501–1576) in his famous treatise called *Artis magnae sive de regulis algebraicis*, *Ars Magna* for short, a cornerstone in the development of algebra. He had obtained the method under promise of secrecy from NICCOLÒ TARTAGLIA (1506–1557). The clue to the method is supposed to have been discovered independently by Tartaglia and an earlier writer, perhaps SCIPIONE DEL FERRO (1496–1526). Expressions (7) frequently are called Cardano's formulas, which is an injustice to the memory of Tartaglia. All mathematicians just mentioned were Italians. The French algebraist, FRANCIS VIETA (1540–1603), was the first to consider the general cubic, in contrast to special cubics.

★98. Solution of the general quartic in one variable

Any quartic equation in one variable can be written in the form

$$x^4 + bx^3 + cx^2 + dx + e = 0, \tag{1}$$

where b, c, d, and e represent arbitrary complex numbers. Then, the following solution applies.

SOLUTION OF THE QUARTIC. 1. From (1)

$$x^4 + bx^3 = -cx^2 - dx - e. \tag{2}$$

The left-hand side in (2) contains two terms of the expansion of $(x^2 + \frac{1}{2}bx)^2$. Hence, on adding $\frac{1}{4}b^2x^2$ to both sides in (2), we obtain

$$(x^2 + \tfrac{1}{2}bx)^2 = (\tfrac{1}{4}b^2 - c)x^2 - dx - e. \tag{3}$$

2. Now, we seek a polynomial in x which, if added to both sides of (3), will produce the square of some polynomial in x on each side. Let y be a number to be specified later. Then, the left-hand side of (3) will become a perfect square in case we add

$$y(x^2 + \tfrac{1}{2}bx) + \tfrac{1}{4}y^2. \tag{4}$$

When (4) is added on both sides of (3), we obtain

$$(x^2 + \tfrac{1}{2}bx + \tfrac{1}{2}y)^2 = (\tfrac{1}{4}b^2 - c + y)x^2 + (\tfrac{1}{2}by - d)x + (\tfrac{1}{4}y^2 - e). \tag{5}$$

The right-hand side of (5) is a quadratic polynomial in x which will be a perfect square if the discriminant is zero, that is, if

$$(\tfrac{1}{2}by - d)^2 - 4(\tfrac{1}{4}b^2 - c + y)(\tfrac{1}{4}y^2 - e) = 0, \text{ or}$$

$$y^3 - cy^2 + (bd - 4e)y - b^2e + 4ce - d^2 = 0. \tag{6}$$

We call (6) the **resolvent cubic** for (1). We can solve (6) by the method of Section 97.

3. Let S be any root of (6), and substitute $y = S$ in (5). The right-hand side becomes the square of some linear polynomial $(hx + k)$, and (5) gives

$$(x^2 + \tfrac{1}{2}bx + \tfrac{1}{2}S)^2 = (hx + k)^2. \tag{7}$$

From (7),
$$x^2 + \tfrac{1}{2}bx + \tfrac{1}{2}S = hx + k, \tag{8}$$

or
$$x^2 + \tfrac{1}{2}bx + \tfrac{1}{2}S = -(hx + k). \tag{9}$$

Each of (8) and (9) can be solved by use of the quadratic formula. The four values of x obtained on solving (8) and (9) are the roots of (1). It can be proved that, if any root of (6) other than $y = S$ were used in (7), the same four values of x would be obtained.

Note 1. By use of the formulas of Section 97, we could write a formula for the root S of the resolvent cubic which we used in (7). This formula would involve the coefficients b, c, d, e of (1). On using this formula for S, we could obtain formulas for h and k, in terms of b, c, d, e. Then, on solving (8) and (9) in terms of h, k, and S, we could obtain formulas for the four roots of (1), in terms of b, c, d, e. These formulas would be very complicated, and are of interest mainly for theoretical reasons.

Usually, the real roots of particular cubic or quartic equations are found more conveniently by some method of successive approximations rather than by use of the formulas of Sections 97–98.

Note 2. The preceding method was invented by the Italian mathematician Lodovico Ferrari (1522–1560), a pupil of Cardano, who published the method for the first time in his *Ars Magna*.

★EXERCISE 61

Solve each equation by taking the steps used in arriving at the text formulas, but do not employ them, except as directed by the instructor. In Problems 6–10, use a rational root of the resolvent cubic which gives right-hand sides with real coefficients in (8) and (9).

1. $x^3 - 6x^2 + 9x = 1$.

2. $x^3 + 3x^2 - 9x - 19 = 0$.

3. $x^3 + 18x = 6x^2 + 27$.

4. $x^3 + 3x^2 - 6x = 36$.

5. $x^3 + 15x + 17 = 9x^2$.

6. $x^4 + 2x^3 - x^2 - 10x = 8$.

7. $x^4 - 6x^3 + 10x^2 = 14 - 3x$.

8. $x^4 - 9x^2 + 2x + 8 = 2x^3$.

9. $x^4 + 11x^2 - 18x + 18 = 2x^3$.

10. $x^4 - 4x^3 + 9x^2 + 20 = 16x$.

EXERCISE 62

Review of Chapter 8

1. If $f(x) = 4x^4 - x^2 + 3x - 7$, calculate $f(3)$ and $f(-2)$ by use of synthetic division.

2. Find the value of the constant k if $(x - 3)$ is a factor of the polynomial $(3x^3 + x^2 - kx + 5)$.

3. Find $(2x^4 - 10x^3 + 7x^2 + 12x + 9) \div (x - 3)^2$ by use of synthetic division.

4. If $f(x) = x^3 + x^2 - 7x - 9$, obtain a graph of f. Then, (a) read off the real roots of $f(x) = 0$ approximately; (b) describe the solution set of $f(x) < 0$.

5. With f as in Problem 4, obtain the real roots of $f(x) = 0$ correct to two decimal places.

6. Form an equation $f(x) = 0$ of degree 4, with integers as coefficients, where two roots are $(\frac{1}{3} - 2i)$ and $(2 + 3i)$.

7. Obtain an equation whose roots are the negatives of the roots of the equation $3x^3 + 2x^2 - x + 8 = 0$.

8. Without solving the equation in Problem 7, (a) obtain an upper bound and also a lower bound for the real roots of the equation; (b) state a list of possibilities as to the reality or complex character of the roots.

9. Repeat Problem 8 for the equation $x^4 + 20x^3 - 3x^2 - 40 = 0$.

Find all rational roots of the equation, or prove that it has no rational roots. Also, find all roots if just two roots are not rational.

10. $x^4 - 15x^2 + 24 = 10x$.

11. $4x^3 + 4x^2 - 9x = 2$.

12. $8x^4 - 12x^2 + 15x - 2 = 0$.

Obtain the indicated root correct to one decimal place by solving an equation.

13. $\sqrt[3]{37}$.

14. $\sqrt[4]{53}$.

15. $\sqrt[5]{125}$.

Chapter **9** **Exponential and Logarithmic Functions**

99. The exponential function *

Let any real number, x, be represented as in (18) on page 137:

$$x = \pm H.a_1 a_2 a_3 \cdots, \tag{1}$$

where H is a nonnegative integer and each term of the infinite sequence $\{a_n\}$ is one of the numbers $(0, 1, 2, \cdots, 9)$. Let $r_k = \pm H.a_1 a_2 \cdots a_k$, which we shall call the kth *decimal approximation to* x. Then, from (21) on page 138,

$$x = \lim_{k \to \infty} r_k. \tag{2}$$

Illustration 1. In (1), if $x = \sqrt{2} = 1.4142 \cdots$, then

$$r_1 = 1.4 = \frac{14}{10}; \quad r_2 = 1.41 = \frac{141}{100}; \quad r_3 = 1.414 = \frac{1414}{1000}; \; etc.$$

The meaning of a power $a^{m/n}$ with a rational exponent was defined on page 37. Now, we shall introduce *irrational* numbers as exponents.

DEFINITION I. *Let x be a variable whose domain consists of all real numbers and, for any value of x, let r_k be the kth decimal approximation to x. Then, if* $a > 0,$ *the* **exponential function,** $E,$ *with the* **base** a *is defined by the statement that*

$$E(x) = \lim_{k \to \infty} a^{r_k}, \tag{3}$$

and we let $E(x) = a^x$. That is, by definition,

$$(a > 0, \; x = \lim_{k \to \infty} r_k) \qquad\qquad a^x = \lim_{k \to \infty} a^{r_k}. \tag{4}$$

* For an intuitive development, detailed study of this chapter could commence at page 236, with only informal discussion of Sections 99–101.

It can be proved that the limit in (4) exists when x is any real number. However, the proof of this fact is above the level of this text. With the assumption that the limit in (4) exists, we remark that, by use of a^{r_k}, we may obtain *rational powers* of a which will approximate a^x as closely as we desire.

Illustration 2. From Illustration 1, $a^{\sqrt{2}} = \lim_{k \to \infty} a^{r_k}$, where

$$a^{r_1} = a^{1.4} = a^{\frac{7}{5}}; \quad a^{r_2} = a^{1.41} = \sqrt[100]{a^{141}}; \quad a^{r_3} = a^{\frac{1414}{1000}}; \ etc. \qquad (5)$$

In (5), we have a sequence of improving approximations to that number which has been defined as $a^{\sqrt{2}}$.

Illustration 3. If $x = 1.315$ in (4), then $x = \frac{1315}{1000} = \frac{263}{200}$. From (4), with $x = 1.315000 \cdots$,

$$a^{r_1} = a^{\frac{13}{10}}; \quad a^{r_2} = a^{\frac{131}{100}}; \quad a^{r_3} = a^{\frac{263}{200}} = a^{r_4} = a^{r_5} = \cdots,$$

because $r_3 = 1.315 = r_4 = r_5 = \cdots$. Hence,

$$\lim_{k \to \infty} a^{r_k} = a^{r_3} = a^{\frac{263}{200}}.$$

This illustrates the fact that, *if x is a terminating decimal*, then (4) designates the same value for a^x as obtained from the definition of $a^{m/n}$ on page 37.

Illustration 4. In (4), suppose that $x = .666 \cdots$, or $x = .\dot{6}$, a symbol for $\frac{2}{3}$. We defined $a^{\frac{2}{3}} = \sqrt[3]{a^2}$ on page 37. Now, in (4), with $\frac{2}{3} = .\dot{6}$, we have a new definition specifying

$$a^{.\dot{6}} = \lim_{k \to \infty} a^{r_k}. \qquad (6)$$

Although $.\dot{6} = \frac{2}{3}$, let us act temporarily as if $a^{.\dot{6}}$ is a new symbol, described by (6). We wish to prove that $a^{.\dot{6}} = \sqrt[3]{a^2}$. We have $\frac{2}{3} = \sum_{n=1}^{\infty} 6(.1)^n$, and r_k is the kth partial sum of the infinite series, or

$$r_k = 6(.1) + 6(.1)^2 + \cdots + 6(.1)^k.$$

By use of (6) on page 134,

$$r_k = \frac{.6}{1 - .1} - \frac{.6(.1)^k}{1 - .1} = \frac{2}{3} - \frac{2}{3(10^k)} . \qquad (7)$$

Let $\epsilon_k = -\frac{2}{3}10^{-k}$. Then $\epsilon_k \to 0$ as $k \to \infty$ and $r_k = \frac{2}{3} + \epsilon_k$, with ϵ_k of the form m/n where m and n are integers. Hence, by a law for rational exponents,

$$a^{r_k} = a^{\frac{2}{3} + \epsilon_k} = a^{\frac{2}{3}} a^{\epsilon_k}. \qquad (8)$$

Since $\epsilon_k \to 0$ as $k \to \infty$, we shall accept the fact that $a^{\epsilon_k} \to a^0 = 1$ as $k \to \infty$. Then, by use of (8), and (11) of Theorem I on page 130,

$$\lim_{k \to \infty} a^{r_k} = \lim_{k \to \infty} a^{\frac{2}{3}} a^{\epsilon_k} = a^{\frac{2}{3}}(\lim_{k \to \infty} a^{\epsilon_k}) = a^{\frac{2}{3}} \cdot 1 = a^{\frac{2}{3}},$$

where $a^{\frac{2}{3}} = \sqrt[3]{a^2}$. Hence, the number represented by the new symbol $a^{.\dot{6}}$ in equation (6) is the same as the number defined as $a^{\frac{2}{3}}$ on page 37. Therefore, hereafter, we may write $a^{.\dot{6}} = a^{\frac{2}{3}} = \sqrt[3]{a^2}$.

Now, consider (4) when x is any rational number m/n whose decimal symbol is a repeating decimal which is not a terminating decimal. Then, on the basis of Illustration 4, without added discussion, we shall accept the fact that the limit in (4) is equal to $\sqrt[n]{a^m}$. Hence, (4) is equivalent to the definition of $a^{m/n}$ if x is rational, and extends use of a^x to the case where x is irrational.

Note 1. In Definition I, it was specified that $a > 0$. This was done in order that a^x and a^{r_k} would be real numbers for all real x and every integer k. Thus, if $a < 0$ and $x = m/n$, where m and n are integers, m/n is in lowest terms, $n \neq 0$, and n is even, then $a^{m/n}$ represents a non-real number [for instance, $(-4)^{\frac{3}{2}} = 8i$]. Also, if $x = -2$, then $a^x = 1/a^2$, which is not defined when $a = 0$. Hence, even without consideration of a^x where x is irrational, it is essential to have $a > 0$ if a^x is to be real-valued for all real x. To observe another reason for the restriction to $a > 0$, consider $a^{\sqrt{2}} = \lim_{k\to\infty} a^{r_k}$ in Illustration 2. Suppose that $a = -5$. Then, from (5),

$$a^{r_1} = (-5)^{\frac{7}{5}}; \quad a^{r_2} = (-5)^{\frac{141}{100}}; \ etc. \tag{9}$$

In (9), a^{r_1} is negative, but a^{r_2} represents a non-real number because a^{r_2} is a root of even order (the 100th root) of the negative number $(-5)^{141}$. Thus, if we allowed $a < 0$ in (4), sometimes a^{r_k} in (4) would be non-real. The difficulties just enumerated justify our restriction to $a > 0$ in a^x.

Since Definition I assigns the familiar meaning to $a^{m/n}$ when m and n are integers, we may graph the function a^x by use of a table of values employing just convenient rational values for x. With $y = a^x$ and $a = 3$, we obtain the following table. Without proof, on the basis of our acquaintance with a^n when n is an integer, we accept the facts that, when $a > 1$,

(a > 1) $\qquad\qquad \lim_{x\to-\infty} a^x = 0; \quad \lim_{x\to+\infty} a^x = +\infty. \tag{10}$

$x =$	-2	-1	0	$.5$	2	3
$y = 3^x$	$\frac{1}{9}$	$\frac{1}{3}$	1	1.7	9	27

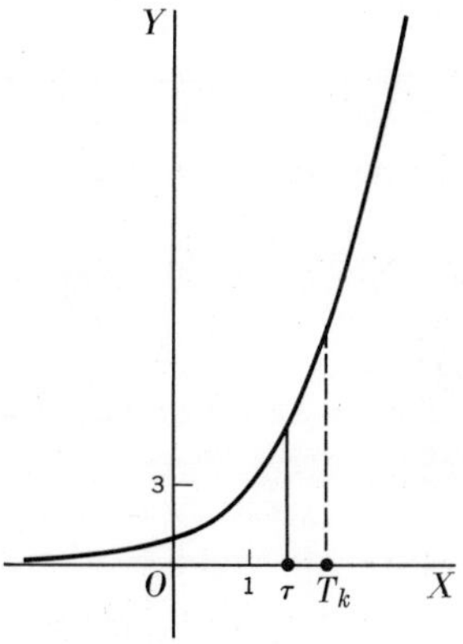

If $a > 1$, the graph of $y = a^x$ approaches the x-axis as an asymptote if $x \to -\infty$. By use of the preceding table of values, a graph of $y = a^x$ (with $a = 3$) is obtained in Figure 84. From the graph, we accept the fact that the exponential function is *continuous.* Suppose, now, that an infinite sequence of numbers $\{T_k\}$ converges to a limit τ; that is, $T_k \to \tau$ as $k \to \infty$. Then, since the function a^x is continuous, the ordinate of the graph when $x = T_k$, or a^{T_k}, approaches as a limit the ordinate when $x = \tau$, or a^τ, as in Figure 84.

$y = 3^x$

Figure 84

Thus, if $\lim_{k\to\infty} T_k = \tau$, then $\qquad\qquad \lim_{k\to\infty} a^{T_k} = a^\tau, \tag{11}$

which may be written $\qquad\qquad \lim_{k\to\infty} a^{T_k} = a^{\lim_{k\to\infty} T_k}. \tag{12}$

If $0 < a < 1$, the graph of $y = a^x$ has the x-axis as an asymptote, approached as $x \to +\infty$. A graph of $y = .5^x$ is shown in Figure 85. If $a = 1$ then $a^x = 1$ for all real x, and a^x is uninteresting.

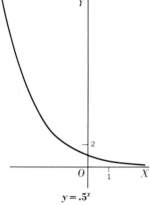

$y = .5^x$

Figure 85

DEFINITION II. *Let f be a function whose domain is* $D: \{a \leq x \leq b\}$. Then, f is called an increasing function on D in case, when x_1 and x_2 are on D,*

$$x_1 < x_2 \text{ implies that } f(x_1) < f(x_2). \quad (13)$$

Also, f is said to be a decreasing function on D if

$$x_1 < x_2 \text{ implies that } f(x_1) > f(x_2). \quad (14)$$

Illustration 5. Let $E(x) = a^x$. From Figure 84 on page 231, observe that, if **$a > 1$,** then E is an *increasing* function, or the graph of $y = a^x$ *rises* as x increases. From Figure 85, we see that E is a *decreasing* function if $a < 1$, or the graph of $y = a^x$ *falls* as x increases.

Note 2. If f is any function of a single variable, x, and $a > 0$, and if $g(x) = a^{f(x)}$, it is said that g is an *exponential function* of x. Then, if $E(x) = a^x$, it might be said that E is the most simple exponential function with base a.

100. Laws for operations with any real exponents

THEOREM I. *If x, y, and w are real numbers, and $a > 0$, then*

$$a^x a^y = a^{x+y}; \quad (1)$$

$$(a^x)^w = a^{wx}. \quad (2)$$

Proof. 1. Let r_k, s_k, and t_k be the kth decimal approximations to x, y, and w, respectively. Then,

$$r_k \to x, \quad s_k \to y, \quad \text{and} \quad t_k \to w, \quad \text{as } k \to \infty. \quad (3)$$

2. *To establish* (1). From (3) on page 229, and (10) on page 130,

$$a^x a^y = (\lim_{k \to \infty} a^{r_k})(\lim_{k \to \infty} a^{s_k}) = \lim_{k \to \infty} (a^{r_k} a^{s_k}). \quad (4)$$

Since r_k and s_k are rational numbers, a law of exponents from page 18 applies in (4), to yield

$$a^x a^y = \lim_{k \to \infty} a^{r_k + s_k} = a^{\lim_{k \to \infty} (r_k + s_k)} = a^{x+y}, \quad (5)$$

where we used (12) on page 231, and finally (9) on page 130.

3. *To establish* (2). From Definition I, $\quad (a^x)^w = (\lim_{k \to \infty} a^{r_k})^w. \quad (6)$

---

* D may be an infinite interval $-\infty < x \leq a$, or $-\infty < x < \infty$, etc.; also, D may or may not include any endpoint.

By a justifiable alteration* in (6), $\qquad\qquad (a^x)^w = \lim_{k\to\infty} a^{wr_k}.$ $\qquad$ (7)

Hence, by use of (12) on page 231,

$$(a^x)^w = a^{\lim_{k\to\infty} wr_k} = a^{w \lim_{k\to\infty} r_k} = a^{wx},$$

where we made use of (11) on page 130.

In the notation of Definition I and (4) on page 229, suppose that $y = -x$. Then $-r_k \to y$ as $k \to \infty$, and Definition I states that

$$a^y = \lim_{k\to\infty} a^{-r_k} = \lim_{k\to\infty} \frac{1}{a^{r_k}} = \frac{1}{\lim_{k\to\infty} a^{r_k}} = \frac{1}{a^x}.$$

That is, for any real number x, with $a > 0$,

$$a^{-x} = \frac{1}{a^x}.$$

Hence, by use of (1) on page 232,

$$\frac{a^x}{a^y} = a^x a^{-y} = a^{x-y}, \qquad (8)$$

so that the familiar law of exponents in division of powers of the same base applies with any real numbers as the exponents.

Later in mathematics, it is found that one of the most useful bases for exponential functions is a certain irrational number, always represented by e, where $e = 2.71828\cdots$, and is defined as follows.

$$e = \lim_{h\to 0} (1 + h)^{\frac{1}{h}} = 2.71828\cdots. \qquad (9)$$

Let $f(h) = (1 + h)^{\frac{1}{h}}$. Then, intuitional appreciation of (9) is gained by inspection of the following table. The student will be asked to construct a

h	$-.5$	$-.1$	$-.01$	$-.001$	$\cdots$	$.001$	$.01$	$.1$	$.5$	5
$f(h)$	4.000	2.868	2.732	2.718	$\cdots$	2.717	2.705	2.594	2.250	1.431

graph of $y = f(h)$ in a problem of the next exercise. We shall meet e as a *base* for logarithms later in this chapter. In statistics, the standard *normal probability curve* has the equation

$$y = \frac{1}{\sqrt{2\pi}} e^{-\frac{1}{2}x^2}.$$

In calculus, the function e^x is found to have very useful properties in differentiation and integration. Table VIII in this text for values of e^x should be used where graphs are requested for exponential functions with the base e.

---

* The proof of the plausible fact is beyond the level of this course.

EXERCISE 63

Choose scale units (probably unequal) on the coordinate axes so that a significant part of the graph will be accommodated in the available space.

Graph on the same coordinate system.

   1. $y = 10^x$ and $y = 10^{-x}$.   **2.** $y = e^x$ and $y = e^{-x}$.

Comment. Notice that each curve is the *reflection* of the other curve in the *y*-axis.

Graph the equation.

   3. $y = 2^x$.   **4.** $y = 10^{-x^2}$.   **5.** $y = e^{-x^2}$.   **6.** $y = e^{-\frac{1}{2}x^2}$.

   7. With $f(h) = (1+h)^{\frac{1}{h}}$, graph $y = f(h)$ by use of the table on page 233. The graph should show a neat hole where $h = 0$ because $f(0)$ is undefined. The graph emphasizes the fact that $\lim_{h \to 0} f(h)$ exists.

★**8.** Refer to (13) on page 232. Suppose that f is an increasing function, and that $f(x_1) < f(x_2)$. Then, prove that $x_1 < x_2$, by considering three possibilities and ruling out two of them. Similarly, for a decreasing function, prove that, if $f(x_2) < f(x_1)$, then $x_1 < x_2$.

101. Inverse functions

Suppose that $y = f(x)$, where the domain of f is a set, T, of numbers x and the range of f is a set, R, of numbers y. Then, by the definition of a function, to each x in T there corresponds a y in R so that $y = f(x)$. In general, it is *not* true that

$$\left\{ \begin{array}{l} \textit{to each number } y \textit{ in the range } R \textit{ of } f \textit{ there cor-} \\ \textit{responds } \textbf{just one } \textit{number } x \textit{ in the domain } T \textit{ of } f. \end{array} \right\} \qquad (1)$$

However, (1) *is true* if f is an *increasing* function, or a *decreasing* function, as illustrated by the graphs of $y = f(x)$ in Figures 86 and 87, for f increasing and for f decreasing, respectively. When (1) is true, we say that there is a *one-to-one*

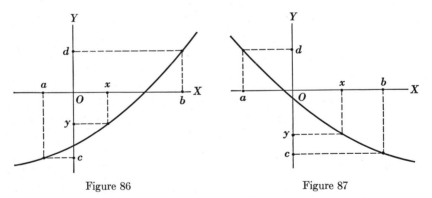

Figure 86   Figure 87

correspondence between the numbers x in the domain and y in the range of f. In such a case we meet the following terminology.

DEFINITION III. *Suppose that f is an increasing (or, a decreasing) function with the domain* $T = \{a \leq x \leq b\}$ and range* $R = \{c \leq y \leq d\}$, and let $g(y)$ represent the single number x in T which corresponds to the number y in R. Then, the function g, thus defined with domain R and range T, is called the* **inverse** *of f. Also, f is called the inverse of g, and then the pair f and g jointly are referred to as* **inverse functions.**

If f and g are inverse functions, then, as in Figures 86 and 87 on page 234,

$$(with \ a \leq x \leq b; c \leq y \leq d) \qquad y = f(x) \quad is \ equivalent \ to \quad x = g(y). \quad (2)$$

On account of (2), the graphs of $y = f(x)$ and $x = g(y)$ on the same xy-plane are identical. In (2), if the equation $y = f(x)$ can be solved for x in terms of y, we thus obtain $x = g(y)$.

Illustration 1. Let y be the function of x defined by $y = 3x + 7$. Then, $x = \frac{1}{3}y - \frac{7}{3}$. In this case, with the notation of (2), $f(x) = 3x + 7$ and $g(y) = \frac{1}{3}y - \frac{7}{3}$. The graph of either $y = f(x)$ or $x = g(y)$ in this case would be the line $y = 3x + 7$, with slope 3 and y-intercept 7.

Illustration 2. Let a function f be defined on domain $D : \{-2 \leq x \leq 2\}$ by $f(x) = x^2$, and let $y = x^2$. A graph of the equation $y = x^2$ is given in Figure 88. For each x on D, there exists *just one* y on the interval

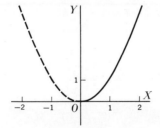

Figure 88

$R : \{0 \leq y \leq 4\}$ such that $y = x^2$. However, for each y on R, except $y = 0$, there exist exactly *two* corresponding values of x on D such that $y = x^2$. Thus, if $y = 2$ we have $x = \pm\sqrt{2}$. Hence, the equation $y = x^2$ defines y as a function of x, for x on D, but *does not define x as a function of y*, for y on R. That is, with f having the domain D and range R, there does *not* exist an inverse function having the domain R and range D. However, if we restrict x to the domain $D_1 : \{0 \leq x \leq 2\}$, the graph of $y = f(x)$ is the unbroken part of the graph in Figure 88, and there *does exist an inverse g for f*. We obtain a formula for the values of g by solving $y = x^2$, with x nonnegative; we find $x = +\sqrt{y}$. Hence, with $g(y) = +\sqrt{y}$, we note that f and g are inverse functions with x having the domain D_1 and y on R.

* Either T or R may be *open*, or *half-open;* also, T or R may be an infinite interval, such as $-\infty < x < a$, or $-\infty < x < \infty$.

102. The logarithm function

Let $E(x) = a^x$, with $a > 1$; a representative graph of $y = E(x)$ is shown in Figure 89. We have observed that E is an *increasing* function, and thus the

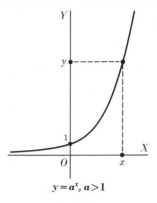

$$y = a^x, \, a > 1$$

Figure 89

graph of $y = E(x)$ has the essential characteristic of the curve in Figure 86 on page 234. Hence, as illustrated in Figure 89, to each number y in the range $R: \{0 < y < \infty\}$ of E, there corresponds *just one number x in the domain* $D: \{-\infty < x < \infty\}$ of E such that $y = E(x)$. Temporarily, let $L(y)$ represent the value of x such that $y = E(x)$. Then, the equations

$$y = E(x) \quad and \quad x = L(y) \quad are \; equivalent; \; or, \tag{1}$$

E and L are a pair of *inverse functions* defined by the equation $y = E(x)$.

Illustration 1. If $a = 10$, then $y = E(x)$ becomes $y = 10^x$. If $y = 100$, then $x = L(100) = 2$, because $100 = 10^2$. If $y = .001$, then $L(.001) = -3$ because $.001 = 10^{-3}$.

With minor changes, the preceding remarks could be repeated for the case $a < 1$; in this case, E is a *decreasing* function, as observed in Figure 85 on page 232. Hereafter, except when otherwise implied, *we shall assume that $a > 1$ in dealing with $L(y)$ of* (1).

In the setting used for (1), hereafter we shall write "**$\log_a y$**" instead of $L(y)$, which implies "**$\log_a$**" in place of merely L. We shall read "$\log_a y$" as "*the logarithm of y to the base a*," and read "$\log_a$" as "*the logarithm function to the base a.*" The symbol "$\log_a y$" is a special case of functional notation with $\log_a$ as a symbol for the function. Then, (1) yields the following statement:

$$\left\{ \begin{array}{l} With \quad 0 < y < \infty \quad and \quad -\infty < x < \infty, \\ y = a^x \quad and \quad x = \log_a y \quad are \; equivalent. \end{array} \right\} \tag{2}$$

Thus, with $E(x) = a^x$, in (2) *we have defined the logarithm function $\log_a$ as the inverse of the exponential function E.*

In the future in this chapter, the values of the logarithm function $\log_a$ rather than of the exponential function E will have the primary importance. Hence, it is desirable to interchange the roles of x and y in (2), as follows, so that x will represent the independent variable in dealing with $\log_a$.

$$\left\{ \begin{array}{l} With \quad 0 < x < \infty \quad and \quad -\infty < y < \infty, \\ x = a^y \quad and \quad y = \log_a x \quad are \; equivalent. \end{array} \right\} \tag{3}$$

On account of (3), the graph of $y = \log_a x$ is the same as the graph of $x = a^y$, on the same xy-coordinate plane.

Illustration 2. To graph $y = \log_a x$ for a particular base a, it is more convenient to write the equivalent equation $x = a^y$, and then to graph this equation. A graph of $y = \log_{10} x$ is seen in Figure 90, and was obtained by graphing $x = 10^y$.

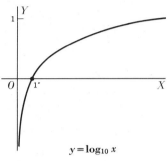

$y = \log_{10} x$

Figure 90

The equivalence in (3) justifies the following statement, which frequently is adopted as the definition of $\log_a x$ when the function is introduced in elementary mathematics.

$$\left\{ \begin{array}{l} \textit{The } \textbf{logarithm} \textit{ of a number } x > 0 \textit{ to a base } \boldsymbol{a} > 0, \textit{ where } \boldsymbol{a} \neq 1, \textit{ is} \\ \textit{the exponent of the power to which the base must be raised to obtain } x. \end{array} \right\} \tag{4}$$

If the *exponential form*, $x = a^y$, in (3) is given for particular numbers (x, y), we can write the *logarithmic form*, $y = \log_a x$, and vice versa.

Illustration 3. If $N = 4^5$, then 5 is the logarithm of N to the base 4.

Illustration 4. "$\log_2 64$" is read "*the logarithm of 64 to the base 2*":

$$since \quad 64 = 2^6, \quad \log_2 64 = 6.$$

Illustration 5. Since $\qquad \sqrt[3]{5} = 5^{\frac{1}{3}}, \quad \log_5 \sqrt[3]{5} = \frac{1}{3} = .333 \cdots .$

Illustration 6. Since $\qquad \dfrac{1}{8} = \dfrac{1}{2^3} = 2^{-3}, \quad \log_2 \dfrac{1}{8} = -3.$

Illustration 7. If $\log_b 16 = 4$, then $b^4 = 16$; $b = \sqrt[4]{16} = 2$.

Illustration 8. If $\log_a 2 = -\frac{1}{3}$, then $a^{-\frac{1}{3}} = 2$. Hence, $a = (\frac{1}{2})^3 = \frac{1}{8}$.

Illustration 9. If $\log_{10} N = -4$, then $N = 10^{-4} = .0001$.

Illustration 10. For any base a,

$$\log_a a = 1 \qquad because \qquad a^1 = a; \tag{5}$$

$$\log_a 1 = 0 \qquad because \qquad a^0 = 1. \tag{6}$$

The following facts can be checked by observation of Figure 90, or by recollection of details discussed earlier in this section.

I. *The equation $x = a^y$ defines y as a logarithmic function of x, $y = \log_a x$, so that $x = a^y$ and $y = \log_a x$ are equivalent equations.*

II. *In $\log_a x$, the domain of x consists of all positive numbers, or the interval $0 < x < \infty$; that is,* **negative numbers and zero do not have logarithms*** *with respect to any base $a > 0$.*

III. *With* **$a > 1$,** *the logarithm function $\log_a$ is an* **increasing function** (*see Figure 90 on page 237*); *thus,*

$$x_1 < x_2 \quad \text{is equivalent to} \quad \log_a x_1 < \log_a x_2. \tag{7}$$

IV. *From the graph of $y = \log_a x$, with $a > 1$:*

$$\left\{ \begin{array}{c} \log_a x \to -\infty \quad \text{as} \quad x \to 0, \text{ or} \\ \text{the line } y = 0 \text{ is an asymptote of the graph.} \end{array} \right\} \tag{8}$$

$$\text{If } \quad x < 1, \quad \text{then} \quad \log_a x < 0. \tag{9}$$

$$\text{If } \quad x > 1, \quad \text{then} \quad \log_a x > 0. \tag{10}$$

Note 1. We do not use $a = 1$ as a base for logarithms because every power of 1 is 1, and hence no number except 1 could have a logarithm to the base 1.

Since $y = \log_a x$ means that $x = a^y$, it is seen that $\log_a x$ will be a *rational number* when and only when x is a power of a where the exponent is a *rational number.* Also, *all real numbers y occur as logarithms,* for x on the interval $0 < x < \infty$. In a certain sense, there are more irrational numbers than rational numbers. Hence, in this sense, $\log_a x$ *will be an irrational number more often than it is a rational number.*

EXERCISE 64

1. Draw a graph of $y = \log_{10} x$ with as large a distance as possible used for the unit of the scale on the y-axis. Then, from the graph, read approximate values, to one decimal place, for

$$\log_{10} 2; \quad \log_{10} .5; \quad \log_{10} 3; \quad \log_{10} 8; \quad \log_{10} 12.$$

Graph the equation. Obtain at least one solution $y = f(x)$, and a corresponding solution $x = g(y)$, with f and g defined by formulas, so that f and g are inverse solution functions of the equation. In each case, state the domain and the range of f and of g.

2. $3x + 4y = 12.$ **3.** $x = y^3.$ **4.** $x = y^2.$ **5.** $y = 4 - x^2.$

Express the power as a fraction.

6. $x^{-3}.$ **7.** $10^{-4}.$ **8.** $10^{-\sqrt{3}}.$ **9.** $10^{-4.7}.$

Express the radical by use of a fractional exponent.

10. $\sqrt[3]{a}.$ **11.** $\sqrt[4]{b}.$ **12.** $\sqrt[3]{9}.$

* In very advanced mathematics, the logarithm function is defined so that any complex number has infinitely many logarithms.

By use of (3) *on page 237, write an equivalent logarithmic equation.*

13. $N = 2^6$.
14. $N = 5^3$.
15. $N = 10^4$.
16. $N = 10^{-2}$.

17. $H = 4^{\frac{1}{3}}$.
18. $H = 5^{\frac{1}{2}}$.
19. $K = 10^{\frac{5}{3}}$.
20. $N = 10^{.35}$.

21. $N = 10^{-4}$.
22. $36 = 6^2$.
23. $16 = 2^4$.
24. $32 = 2^5$.

25. $81 = 3^4$.
26. $625 = 25^2$.
27. $625 = 5^4$.
28. $\frac{1}{49} = 7^{-2}$.

29. $\frac{1}{64} = 2^{-6}$.
30. $\frac{1}{27} = 3^{-3}$.
31. $\frac{1}{216} = 6^{-3}$.
32. $.0001 = 10^{-4}$.

Find the number whose logarithm is given.

33. $\log_6 N = 2$.
34. $\log_2 N = 3$.
35. $\log_{10} N = 4$.

36. $\log_7 M = 2$.
37. $\log_5 M = 3$.
38. $\log_{10} K = 0$.

39. $\log_{15} K = 1$.
40. $\log_{10} N = 1$.
41. $\log_5 N = -1$.

42. $\log_{10} M = -2$.
43. $\log_b M = 1$.
44. $\log_{11} N = -2$.

45. $\log_9 N = \frac{1}{2}$.
46. $\log_{64} N = \frac{1}{3}$.
47. $\log_{216} N = -\frac{1}{3}$.

48. $\log_4 N = \frac{3}{2}$.
49. $\log_{27} N = \frac{2}{3}$.
50. $\log_8 N = \frac{5}{3}$.

Find the following logarithms.

51. $\log_9 81$.
52. $\log_5 25$.
53. $\log_3 81$.
54. $\log_9 3$.

55. $\log_{10} 100$.
56. $\log_{10} 1000$.
57. $\log_3 243$.
58. $\log_{11} 121$.

59. $\log_{16} 4$.
60. $\log_{100} 10$.
61. $\log_7 \frac{1}{7}$.
62. $\log_4 \frac{1}{4}$.

63. $\log_3 \frac{1}{27}$.
64. $\log_2 \frac{1}{16}$.
65. $\log_{10} .001$.
66. $\log_{10} .0001$.

Find a, N, or x, whichever is not given.

67. $\log_a 9 = 2$.
68. $\log_a 64 = 3$.
69. $\log_a 10,000 = 4$.

70. $\log_a 10,000 = 2$.
71. $\log_a 2 = \frac{1}{2}$.
72. $\log_a 5 = \frac{1}{2}$.

73. $\log_a 4 = \frac{1}{3}$.
74. $\log_a 10 = \frac{1}{4}$.
75. $\log_a \frac{1}{20} = -1$.

76. $\log_a .0001 = -2$.
77. $\log_{49} N = \frac{3}{2}$.
78. $\log_{16} N = \frac{5}{4}$.

79. $\log_{27} N = -\frac{4}{3}$.
80. $\log_{256} 16 = x$.
81. $\log_a 4 = -\frac{2}{3}$.

103. Some properties of logarithms

Property I. *The logarithm of a product is equal to the sum of the logarithms of the factors, for instance,*

$$\log_a MN = \log_a M + \log_a N. \tag{1}$$

Illustration 1. $\qquad \log_{10} 897(596) = \log_{10} 897 + \log_{10} 596.$

Proof of (1). Let $x = \log_a M$ and $y = \log_a N$. Then,

$$M = a^x \quad \text{and} \quad N = a^y. \qquad \text{(Definition of a logarithm)}$$
$$MN = a^x a^y = a^{x+y}. \qquad \text{(A law of exponents)}$$

Therefore, by the definition of a logarithm, as in (4) on page 237,

$$\log_a MN = x + y = \log_a M + \log_a N.$$

Note 1. By use of (1) we can prove Property I for a product of any number of factors. Thus, since $MNP = (MN)(P)$,

$$\log_a MNP = \log_a MN + \log_a P = \log_a M + \log_a N + \log_a P.$$

Property II. *The logarithm of a quotient is equal to the logarithm of the dividend minus the logarithm of the divisor:*

$$\log_a \frac{M}{N} = \log_a M - \log_a N. \tag{2}$$

Illustration 2. $\qquad\qquad \log_{10} \frac{89}{57} = \log_{10} 89 - \log_{10} 57.$

Proof of (2). Let $\log_a M = x$ and $\log_a N = y$. Then,

$$\frac{M}{N} = \frac{a^x}{a^y} = a^{x-y}. \qquad \text{(A law of exponents)}$$

Hence, by the definition of a logarithm, we obtain (2):

$$\log_a \frac{M}{N} = x - y = \log_a M - \log_a N.$$

Illustration 3. By use of (1) and (2),

$$\log_a \frac{MK}{N} = \log_a MK - \log_a N = \log_a M + \log_a K - \log_a N.$$

Property III. *The logarithm of the kth power of a number N is equal to k times the logarithm of N:*

$$\log_a N^k = k \log_a N. \tag{3}$$

Illustration 4. $\qquad \log_a 7^5 = 5 \log_a 7. \quad \log_a \sqrt[4]{3} = \log_a 3^{\frac{1}{4}} = \frac{1}{4} \log_a 3.$

Proof of (3). Let $x = \log_a N$. Then, $N = a^x$ and

$$N^k = (a^x)^k = a^{kx}. \qquad \text{(A law of exponents)}$$

Hence, by the definition of a logarithm, we obtain (3):

$$\log_a N^k = kx = k \log_a N.$$

Since $\sqrt[h]{N} = N^{\frac{1}{h}}$, by use of (3) with $k = 1/h$ we obtain

$$\log_a \sqrt[h]{N} = \frac{1}{h} \log_a N. \tag{4}$$

Illustration 5. $\qquad \log_a \sqrt{N} = \frac{1}{2} \log_a N. \quad \log_a \sqrt[3]{25} = \frac{1}{3} \log_a 25.$

Logarithms to the base 10 are called **common logarithms** and are the most useful variety for computational purposes. Hereafter, unless otherwise stated, when we mention a *logarithm* we shall mean a *common* logarithm. For abbreviation, we shall write merely log N, instead of $\log_{10} N$, for the common logarithm of N. The following common logarithms will be useful later; the student should obtain them by use of (4) on page 237.

$N =$	.0001	.001	.01	.1	1	10	100	1000	10,000	100,000
$\log N =$	-4	-3	-2	-1	0	1	2	3	4	5

Illustration 6. If we are given log $3 = .4771$, then by use of Properties I, II, and III we obtain the following results:

$$\log 300 = \log 3(100) = \log 3 + \log 100 = .4771 + 2 = 2.4771;$$

$$\log .003 = \log \frac{3}{1000} = \log 3 - \log 1000 = .4771 - 3 = -2.5229;$$

$$\log \sqrt[4]{3} = \log 3^{\frac{1}{4}} = \tfrac{1}{4} \log 3 = \tfrac{1}{4}(.4771) = .1193.$$

EXERCISE 65

Find the common logarithm of each number by use of properties of logarithms and the following common logarithms.

$$\log 2 = .3010; \quad \log 3 = .4771; \quad \log 7 = .8451; \quad \log 17 = 1.2304.$$

1. 14. 2. 51. 3. 30. 4. 170. 5. 21. 6. 42.
7. $\frac{7}{2}$. 8. $\frac{17}{3}$. 9. $\frac{3}{7}$. 10. $\frac{10}{3}$. 11. $\frac{17}{14}$. 12. .7.
13. 200. 14. $\frac{34}{3}$. 15. $\frac{2}{21}$. 16. $\frac{100}{17}$. 17. $\frac{100}{21}$. 18. 49.
19. 32. 20. 81. 21. $\sqrt{3}$. 22. $\sqrt{14}$. 23. $\sqrt{\frac{7}{3}}$. 24. $\sqrt[3]{\frac{2}{17}}$.

Prove by the method employed in establishing Properties I, II, and III.

25. $\log_a M^2 P = 2 \log_a M + \log_a P.$
26. $\log_a (MN \div P) = \log_a M + \log_a N - \log_a P.$

104. Significant digits

During most of the present chapter, when we refer to a *number*, we shall think of it as represented by a *decimal*. With this understood, for any number N, let us read its digits from left to right. Then, we define the **significant digits** (or, figures) given for N to be *its digits, in order, starting with the first one not zero and ending with the last* one definitely specified* in the available decimal symbol for N. Notice that this definition does not involve any reference to the position of the decimal point in N. Usually, we do not mention final zeros at the right in referring to the significant digits of N except when it is specified as the approximate value of some item of data.

* We realize that any number N can be represented by an endless decimal. However, the notion of significant digits is important because, in applications, N may be specified only to a certain decimal place.

Illustration 1. The significant digits of .0041058 are (4, 1, 0, 5, 8).

If T is the true value, and A is an approximate value of some number, or of the measure of some quantity, we agree to call $|A - T|$ the **error*** of A.

Illustration 2. If $T = 35.62$, and if $A = 35.60$ is an approximation to T, then the error of A is $|35.60 - 35.62|$ or .02.

The significant digits in an approximate value A should indicate the maximum possible error of A. This error is understood to be *at most one half of a unit in the last significant place in A* or, which is the same, *not more than 5 units in the next place to the right.*

Illustration 3. If a surveyor measures a distance as 256.8 yards, he should mean that the error is at most .05 yard and that the true result lies between 256.75 and 256.85, inclusive, since the error might be .05.

In referring to the significant digits of an *approximate* value A, *it is essential to mention all final zeros designated in A.*

Illustration 4. To state that a measured weight is 35.60 pounds should mean that the true weight differs from 35.60 pounds by at most .005 pound. To state that the weight is 35.6 pounds should mean that the true weight differs from this by at most .05 pound.

For abbreviation, or to indicate how many digits in a number N are significant, we may write N as follows, in the so-called **scientific notation.**

Express the number N as the product of an integral power of 10 and a number equal to or greater than 1 but less than 10, with as many significant digits as are justified by the data.

Illustration 5. $385{,}720 = 3.8572(100{,}000) = 3.8572(10^5).$

$.000'000'368 = 3.68(.000'000'1) = 3.68(10^{-7}).$

Illustration 6. If 5,630,000 is an approximate value, its appearance fails to show how many zeros are significant. If five digits are significant, we write $5.6300(10^6)$, and if just three are significant, $5.63(10^6)$.

Suppose that the symbol for a number N is written in decimal form, and that $1 \leq W < 10$. Then, it is useful to observe the following facts.

$$\left\{ \begin{array}{l} \textit{If } N \geq 1 \textit{ and } N \textit{ has h digits to the left of the decimal point,} \\ \textit{then } k = h - 1 \textit{ in the scientific notation } N = W(10^k). \end{array} \right\} \quad (1)$$

$$\left\{ \begin{array}{l} \textit{If } 0 < N < 1, \textit{ and the first significant digit of } N \textit{ is in the kth dec-} \\ \textit{imal place, then } h = -k \textit{ in the scientific notation } N = W(10^h). \end{array} \right\} \quad (2)$$

---

* Sometimes, the error is defined as $(A - T)$, which thus is positive, negative, or zero. Then, a positive error means that $A > T$. Also, the error sometimes is defined as $(T - A)$, which reverses the preceding inequality. This lack of uniformity, and the frequent use of $|A - T|$ as the error, causes us to adopt this meaning.

Special cases of (1) and (2) were met in Illustration 5. To check (1), we notice that, in order to alter W into N, it is necessary to move the decimal point $(h - 1)$ places to the *right* in W, which corresponds to *multiplication* by 10^{h-1}; hence, $k = h - 1$. Under the conditions in (2), the decimal point in W must be moved k places to the *left* in order to obtain N, and this is equivalent to *dividing* W by 10^k, or multiplying W by 10^{-k}; hence $h = -k$.

105. Accuracy of computation

In referring to a *place* in a number, we shall mean any place where a significant digit stands. In referring to a *decimal place*, the word *decimal* will be used explicitly.

To round off N to k figures, or to write a *k-place approximation for N*, means to write an approximate value with k significant digits so that the error of this value is not more than one half of a unit in the kth place, or 5 units in the first neglected place. This condition leads to the following routine.

SUMMARY. **To round off a number N to k *places, drop off the part of N beyond the kth place (filling in zeros if necessary to the left of the decimal point) and then proceed as follows.***

1. *Leave the digit of N in the kth place* **unchanged** *or* **increase it by 1,** *according as the omitted part of N is* **less than** *or* **greater than 5 units** *in the $(k + 1)$th place.*

2. *If the omitted part is exactly 5 units in the $(k + 1)$th place,* **increase the digit in the kth place by 1 or leave the digit unchanged,** *with the object of making* **the final choice an even digit.** *

By illustrations, we can verify that the following rules do not *underestimate* the accuracy of computation. On the other hand, we admit that the rules sometimes *overestimate* the accuracy. However, we shall assume that a result obtained by these rules will have a negligible error in the last significant place which is specified.

  I. *In adding approximate values, round off the result in the first place where the last significant digit of any given value is found.*

  II. *In multiplying or dividing approximate values, round off the result to the smallest number of significant figures found in any given value.*

In problems where approximate values enter, or where approximate results are obtained from exact data, the results should be rounded off so as to avoid giving a false appearance of accuracy. No hard and fast rules for such rounding off should be adopted, and the final decision as to the accuracy of a result should be made only after a careful examination of the details of the solution.

* This agreement could be replaced by various similar and equally justified rules.

EXERCISE 66

Express as a power of 10.

1. 10,000,000.   **2.** 100,000.   **3.** .0001.   **4.** .01.   **5.** 1.

Round off, first to five and then to three significant digits.

6. 13.24683.   **7.** .2123589.   **8.** 215.634.   **9.** .00215388.

10. 6.312162.   **11.** .0493576.   **12.** 1,593,485.   **13.** 612,915.

Write the number in ordinary decimal form.

14. $2.63(10^3)$.   **15.** $1.598(10^7)$.   **16.** $3.4153(10^{-3})$.   **17.** $8.195(10^{-6})$.

Write as the product of a power of 10 *and a number between* 1 *and* 10.

18. 2,567,000.   '**19.** 89,315,000.   **20.** .0000578.   **21.** .00000364.

Write the number in the scientific notation under the assumption, first, that there are just five significant digits and, second, that there are just three significant digits.

22. 8,426,000.   **23.** 290,000.   **24.** 42,700,000.   **25.** 629,000,000.

106. Characteristic and mantissa

Every number, K, and hence every logarithm, can be written *in just one way* as the sum of *an integer and a decimal fraction*, which is positive or zero and less than 1. Then, the integer mentioned is *the largest integer n where* $n \leqq K$.

Illustration 1. $4.732 = 4 + .732; \quad -3.259 = -4 + .741.$

For any number $N > 0$, when $\log N$ is written as the sum of an integer and a nonnegative decimal less than 1, we call the integer the **characteristic** and the decimal the **mantissa** of $\log N$. That is,

$$\log N = \text{(an integer)} + \text{(a decimal, } \geqq 0, < 1), or \tag{1}$$

$$\log N = \text{characteristic} + \text{mantissa}. \tag{2}$$

Illustration 2. If $\log N = 4.6832 = 4 + .6832$, then .6832 is the mantissa and 4 is the characteristic of $\log N$.

Illustration 3. The following logarithms were obtained by later methods. The student should verify the three columns at the right.

	LOGARITHM	CHARACTERISTIC	MANTISSA
$\log 300 \quad = 2.4771$	$= \quad 2 + .4771$	2	.4771
$\log 50 \quad = 1.6990$	$= \quad 1 + .6990$	1	.6990
$\log .001 \quad = -3$	$= -3 + .0000$	-3	.0000
$\log 6.5 \quad = 0.8129$	$= \quad 0 + .8129$	0	.8129
$\log .0385 = -1.4145$	$= -2 + .5855$	-2	.5855
$\log .005 \quad = -2.3010$	$= -3 + .6990$	-3	.6990

Illustration 4. All numbers whose logarithms are given below have the same significant digits (3, 8, 0, 4). To obtain the logarithms, log 3.804 was found from a table to be discussed later; the other logarithms were obtained then by the use of Properties I and II.

$$\log 380.4 \;\; = \log 100(3.804) \;\; = \log 100 + \log 3.804 \;\; = \;\;\; 2 + .5802;$$

$$\log 38.04 \;\; = \log 10(3.804) \;\; = \log 10 + \log 3.804 \;\; = \;\;\; 1 + .5802;$$

$$\log 3.804 \;\; = .5802 \hspace{4.5cm} = \;\;\; 0 + .5802;$$

$$\log .3804 \;\; = \log \frac{3.804}{10} \;\; = \log 3.804 - \log 10 \;\; = \; -1 + .5802;$$

$$\log .03804 \;\; = \log \frac{3.804}{100} \;\; = \log 3.804 - \log 100 \;\; = \; -2 + .5802.$$

Similarly, if N is *any* number whose significant digits are (3, 8, 0, 4), then N is equal to 3.804 multiplied, or else divided, by a positive integral power of 10; hence, it follows as before that .5802 is the mantissa of log N.

If a number K is written in the form of *an integer plus a nonnegative decimal less than* 1, the integer involved will be *negative* if and only if K *is negative.* Hence, with log N written as in (1), *the characteristic of* log N *is negative if and only if* log N *is negative.* From the graph of $y = \log x$ in Figure 90 on page 237, $\log x < 0$ if and only if $0 < x < 1$. Hence, we reach the following conclusion.

$$\left\{ \begin{array}{c} \text{log } N \text{ is negative, and its characteristic is negative} \\ \textit{if and only if } \mathbf{0 < N < 1.} \end{array} \right\} \tag{3}$$

Special cases of (3) occurred in Illustration 3.

THEOREM II. *Suppose that* $N > 0$ *and* N *is represented in the scientific notation* $N = W(10^k)$, *where* $1 \leq W < 10$. *Then, the characteristic of* log N *is* k *and the mantissa of* log N *is* log W.

Proof. 1. By use of Property I for logarithms,

$$\log N = \log 10^k + \log W = k + \log W. \tag{4}$$

2. From (7) on page 238, since the function log x is an increasing function,

$$1 \leq W < 10 \qquad \textit{implies that} \qquad \log 1 \leq \log W < \log 10, \textit{ or}$$

$$0 \leq \log W < 1. \tag{5}$$

Statement (5) declares that log W is a *nonnegative decimal less than* 1. Thus, in (4), log N is expressed in the form (1), and hence log N has the characteristic k and mantissa log W.

THEOREM III. *The mantissa of* log N *depends only on the sequence of significant digits in* N. *That is,* **if two positive numbers differ only in the position of the decimal point,** *their logarithms have the* **same mantissa.**

Proof. Suppose that $M > 0$ and $N > 0$. If M and N differ only in the position of the decimal point, the expressions for M and N in scientific notation, as in Theorem II, differ only in the exponent for 10. That is, there exists W where $0 \leq W < 1$, and two integers u and v, so that

$$M = 10^u(W) \quad and \quad N = 10^v(W). \tag{6}$$

Hence, by Theorem II, the mantissa for both $\log M$ and $\log N$ is $\log W$, which proves Theorem III.

THEOREM IV. *If $N \geq 1$,* the characteristic of $\log N$ is a **nonnegative integer,** *which is* **one less than the number of digits in N to the left of the decimal point.**

THEOREM V. *If $0 < N < 1$,* the characteristic of $\log N$ is a **negative integer; if the first significant digit of N appears in the kth decimal place,** *then* **$-k$ is the characteristic of $\log N$.**

Proof of Theorem IV. Suppose that $N = 10^k(W)$, as in Theorem II, which states that k is the characteristic of $\log N$. If $N \geq 1$, statement (1) on page 242 describes k as specified for the characteristic in Theorem IV.

Proof of Theorem V. Let the scientific notation for N be $N = 10^h(W)$, where $0 < N < 1$. Then, h is the characteristic of $\log N$, and (2) on page 242 describes h precisely as specified by Theorem V.

Illustration 5. By use of Theorems IV and V, the characteristic of $\log N$ is found by merely inspecting N. Thus, by Theorem V, the characteristic of $\log .00039$ is -4 because "3" is in the 4th decimal place. By Theorem IV, the characteristic of $\log 1578.6$ is 3.

For convenience in computation, **if the characteristic of $\log N$ is negative, $-k$, change it to the equivalent value**

$$[(10 - k) - 10], \quad or \quad [(20 - k) - 20], \text{ etc.}$$

Illustration 6. Given that $\log .000843 = -4 + .9258$, we write

$$\log .000843 = -4 + .9258 = (6 - 10) + .9258 = 6.9258 - 10.$$

The characteristics of the following logarithms are obtained by use of Theorem V; the mantissas are identical, by Theorem III.

1st Signif. Digit in	Illustration	Log N	Standard Form
1st *decimal place*	$N = .843$	$-1 + .9258 =$	$9.9258 - 10$
2d *decimal place*	$N = .0843$	$-2 + .9258 =$	$8.9258 - 10$
6th *decimal place*	$N = .00000843$	$-6 + .9258 =$	$4.9258 - 10$

107. Tables of logarithms

Mantissas can be computed by advanced methods and, usually, are endless nonrepeating decimals. Computed mantissas are found in tables of logarithms, also called *tables of mantissas.*

Table V gives the mantissa of log N correct to four decimal places, if N has at most three significant digits aside from additional zeros at the right. A decimal point is understood at the left of each mantissa in the table. If N lies between 1 and 10, the characteristic of log N is *zero,* so that log N is *the same as its mantissa.* Hence, a four-place table of mantissas also is a table of *the actual four-place logarithms of all numbers with at most three significant digits from $N = 1.00$ to $N = 9.99$.* If $N \geqq 10$ or $N < 1$, we supply the characteristic of log N by use of Theorems IV and V of Section 106.

EXAMPLE 1. Find log .0316 from Table V.

Solution. 1. *The mantissa:* find "31" in the column headed N; in the row for "31," read in the column headed "6." The mantissa is .4997.

2. By Theorem V, the characteristic of log .0316 is -2, or $(8 - 10)$:

$$\log .0316 = -2 + .4997 = 8.4997 - 10.$$

Illustration 1. From Table V and Theorem IV, log 31,600 = 4.4997.

EXAMPLE 2. Find N if log $N = 7.6064 - 10.$

Solution. 1. *To find the significant digits of N:* the mantissa of log N is .6064; this is found in Table V as the mantissa for the digits "404."

2. *To locate the decimal point in N:* the characteristic of log N is $(7 - 10)$, or -3; hence, by Theorem V, $N = .00404.$

Illustration 2. If log $N = 3.6064$, the characteristic is 3 and, by Theorem IV, N has 4 figures to the left of the decimal point; the mantissa is the same as in Example 2. Hence, $N = 4040.$

DEFINITION IV. *To say that N is the* **antilogarithm** *of L means that* log $N = L$, *or $N = 10^{L}$, and we write $N =$* **antilog** *L.*

Illustration 3. Since log 1000 = 3, then 1000 = antilog 3.

Illustration 4. In Example 2 we found antilog $(7.6064 - 10) = .00404.$

EXERCISE 67

The given number is the logarithm of some number N. State the characteristic and the mantissa of log N.

1. 3.5217.   2. 25.3189.   3. −2.450.   4. 6.3159 − 10.
5. −3.1582.   6. −.6354.   7. 5.2891 − 10. 8. 9.1346 − 10.

Write the following negative logarithms in standard form.

9. $-2 + .1356.$ **10.** $.2341 - 3.$ **11.** $.5268 - 4.$ **12.** $-5.3214.$

State the characteristic of the logarithm of each number.

13. 41,356. **14.** 249. **15.** .000047. **16.** .0036. **17.** .000007.

Use Table V to find the four-place logarithm of the number.

18. 35.6. **19.** 124. **20.** 8950. **21.** .261. **22.** .495.

23. .0562. **24.** .00008. **25.** 20,900. **26.** .000419. **27.** .909.

28. .0861. **29.** 15,200. **30.** .000643. **31.** .0000219. **32.** 256,000.

Find the antilogarithm of the given logarithm by use of Table V.

33. 2.1335. **34.** 3.5263. **35.** $9.7185 - 10.$ **36.** $7.4183 - 10.$

37. 1.7459. **38.** 0.2148. **39.** $8.5752 - 10.$ **40.** $4.2945 - 10.$

41. 0.5198. **42.** 6.3096. **43.** $7.4669 - 10.$ **44.** $9.3201 - 10.$

45. 7.5172. **46.** 1.2304. **47.** $6.6325 - 10.$ **48.** $2.4955 - 10.$

49. Find N if (a) $\log N = -3.6021$; (b) $\log N = 7.6021 - 10.$

108. Interpolation in a table of logarithms

Interpolation in a table of mantissas is based on the assumption that, *for small changes in N, the corresponding changes in $\log N$ are proportional to the changes in N.* This **principle of proportional parts** is merely a useful approximation to the truth.

We agree that, when a mantissa is found by interpolation from a table, we shall express the result *only to the number of decimal places given in table entries.* Also, in finding N by interpolation in a table of mantissas when $\log N$ is given, we agree to specify just **four** or just **five** significant digits according as we are using a **four-place** or a **five-place*** table. No greater accuracy is justified by our methods.

In using a four-place table of logarithms, it is convenient to act as if each number N whose logarithm is mentioned has *just four significant digits,* perhaps including one or more zeros at the right. Thus, we attach one or more final zeros to the significant part of N if it has *less* than four significant digits. Or, we *round off* N to four significant digits if N initially has more than four-place accuracy. We then think of each entry in Table V as the mantissa for the logarithm of a number N with *four* significant digits, obtained by attaching a final zero to the part arising in the table.

Note 1. The first aim of training in computation is to develop the power to compute results with all the accuracy possible by the means at our disposal, *under the assumption that the data are exact.* Hence, in this book we shall assume that all numbers in the data are exact.

* Five-place tables will not be used in this text. However, our methods with four-place tables are designed so that they will apply without essential alterations to five-place tables.

EXAMPLE 1. Find log 13.86 by interpolation in Table V.

Solution. Since 13.86 has four significant digits, with the 4th not zero, the mantissa for log 13.86 cannot be read directly from the table. In the following table, log 13.80 and log 13.90 are obtained from Table V. The equation for x is a consequence of the principle of proportional parts.

$$.10 \left[.06 \left[\begin{array}{l} \log 13.80 = 1.1399 \\ \log 13.86 = \quad ? \\ \log 13.90 = 1.1430 \end{array} \right] x \right] 31$$

Tabular difference *is* .0031.

$$\frac{x}{31} = \frac{.06}{.10} \, ; \quad x = \frac{6}{10} \, (31).$$

$$x = .6(.0031) = .00186 = .0019, \textit{approximately};$$

$$\textbf{log 13.86} = \textbf{1.1399} + \textbf{.0019} = \textbf{1.1418.}$$

Comment. We found .6(31) = 18.6 by use of the table headed 31 under the column of *proportional parts* in Table V.

Note 2. When interpolating in a table of mantissas, if there is equal reason for choosing either of two successive digits, for uniformity we agree to make that choice which gives an **even digit** in the last significant place of the **final result** of the interpolation.

Illustration 1. To find log .002913 from Table V:

$$10 \left[3 \left[\begin{array}{l} 2910: \textit{mantissa is } .4639 \\ 2913: \textit{mantissa is } \quad ? \\ 2920: \textit{mantissa is } .4654 \end{array} \right] x \right] 15$$

Tabular difference *is*
.4654 − .4639 = .0015.
$$x = .3(15) = 4.5, \text{ or } 5.$$

Hence, the mantissa for 2913 *is* **.4639** + **.0005** = **.4644.**

By Theorem V, $\qquad$ log .002913 = $-3 + .4644 = 7.4644 - 10.$

We used .3(15) as 5, instead of 4, in agreement with Note 2.

EXAMPLE 2. Find N from Table V if log $N = 1.6187$.

Solution. 1. The mantissa .6187 is not in Table V but lies between the consecutive entries .6180 and .6191, the mantissas for 415 and 416.

2. Since .6187 is $\frac{7}{11}$ of the way from .6180 to .6191, we assume that N is $\frac{7}{11}$ of the way from 41.50 to 41.60. Thus, in the following table,

$$\frac{x}{.10} = \frac{7}{11}, \quad \textit{or} \quad x = \frac{7}{11} \, (.10).$$

$$11 \left[7 \left[\begin{array}{l} 1.6180 = \log 41.50 \\ 1.6187 = \log N \\ 1.6191 = \log 41.60 \end{array} \right] x \right] .10$$

$$41.60 - 41.50 = .10.$$
$$x = \tfrac{7}{11}(.10) = .064, \textit{ or}$$
$$\textit{approximately} \ .06.$$

$$N = 41.50 + \tfrac{7}{11}(.10) = \textbf{41.50} + \textbf{.06} = \textbf{41.56.}$$

Illustration 2. To find N if $\log N = 6.1053 - 10$:

$$34 \left[15 \left[\begin{array}{l} .1038, \textit{mantissa for } 1270 \\ .1053, \textit{mantissa for } \quad ? \\ .1072, \textit{mantissa for } 1280 \end{array} \right] x \right] 10 \qquad \begin{array}{l} \frac{15}{34} = .4. \;\; \textit{Hence,} \\ x = .4(10) = 4. \\ 1270 + 4 = 1274. \end{array}$$

Hence, .1053 is the mantissa for 1274 *and* $N = $ **.0001274.**

Comment. We obtain $\frac{15}{34} = .4$ by inspection of the tenths of 34 in the table. Thus,

$$13.6 = .4(34) \quad or \quad \frac{13.6}{34} = .4, \quad and \quad \frac{17}{34} = .5.$$

Since 15 is nearer to 13.6 than to 17, then $\frac{15}{34}$ is nearer to .4 than to .5.

Recall that, if N is written in the scientific notation, $N = W(10^k)$ with $1 \leq W < 10$, then $$\log N = k + \log W,$$

where k is the characteristic and $\log W$ is the mantissa of $\log N$.

Illustration 3. If $\log N = 9.7419$, and if we desire to write the form $N = W(10^k)$, we have $k = 9$ and $\log W = 0.7419$. Hence,

$$W = 5.520 \quad and \quad N = 5.520(10^9).$$

EXERCISE 68

Find the four-place logarithm of the number from Table V.

1. 1923.	**2.** 2725.	**3.** 5815.	**4.** 12.76.
5. 9.436.	**6.** .1787.	**7.** .7094.	**8.** .003196.
9. .005135.	**10.** .0001245.	**11.** .0002007.	**12.** $2.456(10^5)$.
13. 80,090.	**14.** 204,600.	**15.** 3.126.	**16.** 1.573.
17. 25,780.	**18.** $2.643(10^6)$.	**19.** $6.214(10^{-3})$.	**20.** $5.439(10^{-5})$.

Find the antilogarithm of the four-place logarithm, from Table V.

21. 1.6553.	**22.** 2.3468.	**23.** $9.0226 - 10$.	**24.** $8.1691 - 10$.
25. 0.5510.	**26.** 1.3754.	**27.** $8.6432 - 10$.	**28.** 0.5309.
29. 2.0360.	**30.** $7.4483 - 10$.	**31.** $6.0211 - 10$.	**32.** 2.0493.
33. $5.9367 - 10$.	**34.** 6.3194.	**35.** 7.0364.	**36.** 0.2779.
37. 3.3614.	**38.** 2.8547.	**39.** $9.9546 - 10$.	**40.** $9.9990 - 10$.
41. 0.9871.	**42.** $6.2338 - 10$.	**43.** 1.5648.	**44.** $3.1542 - 10$.

109. Computation of products and quotients

We continue to assume that the data of any given problem are *exact.* Under this assumption, the accuracy of a product, quotient, or power computed by use of logarithms depends on the number of places in the table being used. The result frequently is subject to an unavoidable error which usually is at most a few units in the last significant place given by interpolation. Hence, as a rule, we should compute with at least *five-place* logarithms to obtain *four-place accuracy*, and with at least *four-place* logarithms to obtain *three-place accuracy*. Usually, in any result, we shall give *all digits obtainable by interpolation* in the specified table.

EXAMPLE 1. Compute .0631(7.208)(.5127) by use of Table V.

Solution. Let P represent the product. By Property I, we obtain log P by adding the logarithms of the factors. We find the logarithms of the factors from Table V, add to obtain log P, and then finally obtain P from Table V. The computing form, given in boldface type, was made up completely as *the first step in the solution.*

log .0631 =	8.8000 − 10	(Table V)
log 7.208 =	0.8578	(Table V)
log .5127 =	9.7099 − 10	(Table V)
(*add*) log *P* =	19.3677 − 20 = 9.3677 − 10.	

Hence, *P* = .2332.   [= antilog (9.3677 − 10), Table V]

EXAMPLE 2. Compute $q = \dfrac{431.91}{15.6873}$ by use of Table V.

Solution. 1. By Property II, log q is equal to *the logarithm of the numerator minus the logarithm of the denominator*, or log q = log 431.91 − log 15.6873.

2. Before computing, we *round off* each given number to *four* significant digits because we are using a four-place table.

log 431.9 =	2.6354	(Table V)
(−) **log 15.69 =**	1.1956	(Table V)
log *q* =	1.4398. **Hence, *q* = 27.53.**	(Table V)

EXAMPLE 3. Compute $q = 257/8956$ by use of Table V.

Solution.   **log 257 =** 2.4099 = 12.4099 − 10
        (−) **log 8956 =** 3.9521 =   3.9521
        log *q* =   ?   =   8.4578 − 10;   ***q* = .02869.**

Comment. We saw that log q would be *negative* because log 8956 is *greater* than log 257. In order that log q should appear immediately in the *standard form for a negative logarithm*, we changed log 257 by adding 10 and then subtracting 10 to compensate for the first change. Actually,

$$\log q = 2.4099 - 3.9521 = -1.5422 = 8.4578 - 10.$$

Whenever it is necessary to subtract a logarithm from a smaller one in computing a quotient, add 10 to the characteristic of the smaller logarithm and then subtract 10 to compensate for the change.

EXAMPLE 4. Compute $q = \dfrac{(4.803)(269.9)(1.636)}{(7880)(253.6)}$.

Incomplete solution.   We make a **computing form,** to subtract the logarithm of the denominator from the logarithm of the numerator.

$(+) \begin{cases} \text{log } 4.803 = \\ \text{log } 269.9 = \\ \text{log } 1.636 = \end{cases}$

$\overline{}$

log numer. =

$(-)$ log denom. =

$\overline{}$

log *q* =

$(+) \begin{cases} \text{log } 7880 = \\ \text{log } 253.6 = \end{cases}$

$\overline{}$

log denom. =

Hence, *q* =

EXAMPLE 5.   Compute the reciprocal of 189 by use of Table V.

Solution.   Let $R = 1/189$.

$$\begin{aligned} \text{log } 1 &= 0.0000 = 10.0000 - 10 \\ (-) \text{ log } 189 &= 2.2765 = 2.2765 \end{aligned}$$

$\overline{}$

$$\begin{aligned} \text{log } R = \quad ? \quad &= 7.7235 - 10. \end{aligned}$$

Hence, *R* = .005290.

Comment.   In writing any approximate value, indicate all final zeros which are significant. In $R = .005290$ in Example 5, the final zero was essential.

Note 1.   *It is essential to become familiar with rounding off data, if necessary, to that number of significant digits which should be used with a given table of logarithms.* Retention of more than these digits causes unnecessary labor and does not increase accuracy. Recall that we round off data to *four figures* if *four-place* logarithms are in use, and to *five figures* if *five-place logarithms* are to be employed.

★110. Cologarithms

The logarithm of the *reciprocal* of N, that is, the logarithm of the fraction $1/N$, is called the *cologarithm* of N and is written **colog *N*.** Since log 1 = 0,

$$\text{colog } N = \text{log } \frac{1}{N} = 0 - \text{log } N. \tag{1}$$

Illustration 1.   Colog .031 = $\log \dfrac{1}{.031}$:

$$\begin{aligned} \text{log } 1 &= 10.0000 - 10 \\ (-) \text{ log } .031 &= 8.4914 - 10 \end{aligned}$$

$\overline{}$

$$\text{colog } .031 = 1.5086.$$

The positive part of colog N can be obtained quickly by inspection of log N: *subtract each digit (except the last) in the positive part of* log N *from 9, and subtract the last digit from 10.*

EXAMPLE 1. Compute $q = \dfrac{16.083 \times 256}{47 \times .0158}$ by use of cologarithms.

Solution. To *divide* by N is the same as to *multiply* by $1/N$. Hence, instead of *subtracting the logarithm* of each factor of the denominator, we *add the cologarithm* of the factor:

$$q = \frac{16.083 \times 256}{47 \times .0158} = (16.083 \times 256)\left(\frac{1}{47}\right)\left(\frac{1}{.0158}\right).$$

log 47 $= 1.6721$; **hence,**
log .0158 $= 8.1987 - 10$; **hence,**

log 16.08 =	1.2063
log 256 =	2.4082
colog 47 =	8.3279 $- 10$
colog .0158 =	1.8013

(*add*) log $q = 13.7437 - 10$
$= 3.7437.$
$q = 5542.$

EXERCISE 69

Compute by use of four-place logarithms.

1. 32.51×71.63.
2. $.8328 \times .0843$.
3. $913.421 \times .00314$.
4. $83.47 \times .156$.
5. $.0381 \times .25672$.
6. $3.14586 \times .00314$.
7. $(-31.92)(.0059)(.23646)$.
8. $(23.6)(153.867)(-.00076)$.

Hint. Recall that only positive numbers have real logarithms. First compute as if all factors were positive; then attach the proper final sign.

9. $\dfrac{483}{13.49}$.
10. $\dfrac{658.432}{748}$.
11. $\dfrac{.0359}{.7288}$.
12. $\dfrac{1}{4159.38}$.
13. $\dfrac{593.6}{25.89}$.
14. $\dfrac{634.157}{8349.6}$.
15. $\dfrac{1}{.00847}$.
16. $\dfrac{.0358}{.42849}$.
17. $\dfrac{26.037(198)}{54(.1475)}$.
18. $\dfrac{18.6(487)}{.721543(.582)}$.
19. $\dfrac{1}{628(.09372)}$.
20. $\dfrac{.4835(.846)}{.264536(.137)}$.
21. $\dfrac{6.39(.14758)}{23.1349(28.7)}$.
22. $\dfrac{1}{.0036(.2542)}$.
23. $\dfrac{-37(.045)(-.0026)}{(-2003.56)(4.53)}$.
24. $\dfrac{6.7(-39.42)(.8531)}{(-264)(-3.54293)}$.

Compute the reciprocal of the number.

25. 53847.
26. 16.2983.
27. $.03489$.
28. $.026(5.7426)$.

Compute by use of four-place logarithms.

29. $10^{-2.1567}$.
30. $2.314(10^{1.5872})$.
31. $4.738(10^{1.2678})$.
32. $1.57(10^{-1.6894})$.

Hint. $\log 10^{-2.1567} = -2.1567 = -3 + (\cdots)$.

33. Compute (*a*) $498(765)$; (*b*) $(\log 498)(\log 765)$.
34. Compute (*a*) $.483/.269$; (*b*) $(\log .483) \div (\log .269)$.

111. Computation of powers and roots

We recall that, if k is any real number and h is a positive integer,

$$\log N^k = k \log N; \qquad (1)$$

since $\sqrt[h]{N} = N^{\frac{1}{h}}$, $\qquad \log \sqrt[h]{N} = \dfrac{\log N}{h}. \qquad (2)$

EXAMPLE 1.   Compute $(.3156)^4$.

Solution. $\qquad \log (.3156)^4 = 4 \log .3156 = 4(9.4991 - 10).$

$\qquad\qquad \log (.3156)^4 = 37.9964 - 40 = 7.9964 - 10.$

$\qquad\qquad$ Therefore, $(.3156)^4 = .009918.$

EXAMPLE 2.   Compute $\sqrt[6]{.08351}$.

Solution.   By (2), $\log \sqrt[6]{N} = \frac{1}{6} \log N.$

$$\log \sqrt[6]{.08351} = \frac{\log .08351}{6} = \frac{8.9218 - 10}{6};$$

$$\log \sqrt[6]{.08351} = \frac{58.9218 - 60}{6} = 9.8203 - 10. \qquad (3)$$

$$\text{Therefore, } \sqrt[6]{.08351} = .6611.$$

Comment. Before dividing a negative logarithm by a positive integer, usually it is best to write the logarithm in such a way that *the negative part after division will be* -10. Thus, in (3), we altered $(8.9218 - 10)$ by *subtracting* 50 from -10 to make it -60, and by *adding* 50 to 8.9218 to compensate for the subtraction.

EXAMPLE 3.   Compute $q = \left(\dfrac{(.5831)^3}{65.3\sqrt{146}} \right)^{\frac{2}{5}}.$

Solution.   1. Let F represent the fraction. Then $\log q = \frac{2}{5} \log F.$

2. Notice that $\quad \log (.5831)^3 = 3 \log .5831; \quad \log \sqrt{146} = \frac{1}{2} \log 146.$

$$\begin{array}{ll}
\log .5831 = 9.7658 - 10 & \quad (+) \begin{cases} \log 65.3 = 1.8149 \\ \frac{1}{2}\log 146 = 1.0822 \end{cases} \\
\log 146 = 2.1644 & \\
\hline
3 \log .5831 = 9.2974 - 10 \\
(-) \log \text{denom.} = 2.8971 & \quad \log \text{denom.} = 2.8971. \\
\end{array}$$

$$\log F = 6.4003 - 10; \quad 2 \log F = 2.8006 - 10 = 42.8006 - 50.$$

$$\log q = \frac{2 \log F}{5} = \frac{42.8006 - 50}{5} = 8.5601 - 10; \quad q = .03632.$$

Note 1. Logarithms were invented by a Scotsman, JOHN NAPIER, Laird of Merchiston (1550–1617). His logarithms were not defined as exponents of powers of a base. Common logarithms were invented by an Englishman, HENRY BRIGGS (1556–1631), who was aided by Napier.

MISCELLANEOUS EXERCISE 70

Compute by use of four-place logarithms.

1. $(18.7)^3$.
2. $(4.1734)^4$.
3. $(.924)^5$.
4. $(.0327)^3$.

5. $\sqrt{35.6}$.
6. $\sqrt[3]{132.473}$.
7. $\sqrt[3]{.936}$.
8. $\sqrt[3]{.08572}$.

9. $\sqrt[4]{.00314787}$.
10. $(2.35)^6$.
11. $\sqrt[5]{10,000}$.
12. $(.31426)^{\frac{1}{5}}$.

13. $(173.215)^{\frac{1}{2}}$.
14. $(21.498)^{\frac{1}{4}}$.
15. $\sqrt[3]{.0001}$.
16. $(-38.9)^{\frac{1}{3}}$.

17. $(-248,742)^{\frac{1}{5}}$.
18. $(269)^{\frac{2}{3}}$.
19. $(-.00317)^3$.
20. $(-126.8)^3$.

21. $(.721317)^{\frac{3}{4}}$.
22. $(5.738)^{-4}$.
23. $(.13172)^{-2}$.
24. $(.2163)^{\frac{2}{3}}$.

Hint for Problem 22. Recall $(5.738)^{-4} = 1 \div (5.738)^4$.

25. $(757.2)^{\frac{3}{5}}$.
26. $(.63)^{-3}$.
27. $(1.03)^7$.
28. $(1.02)^{-3}$.

29. $(2.675)^{-4}$.
30. $(.0789268)^{-5}$.
31. $10^{3.56}(28)^4$.
32. $\sqrt[3]{258(64)}$.

33. (*a*) Compute $(1.04)^{100}$. (*b*) Given the seven-place $\log 1.04 = 0.0170333$, compute $(1.04)^{100}$ by starting with this logarithm, and finishing with the four-place table.

34. $675(8.39)^2$.
35. $.253\sqrt{.628}$.
36. $(3.41)^3\sqrt[3]{.849}$.

37. $10^{2.78}\sqrt{9.34}$.
38. $10^{1.56}(.631)^3$.
39. $10^{-3.24}(.163)^2$.

40. $\dfrac{.139(24.61)^3}{126.48}$.
41. $\dfrac{356.2(298)^2}{675\sqrt{4.1327}}$.
42. $\dfrac{.037(149)^3}{(2.16217)^2}$.

43. $\sqrt{\dfrac{653.2}{217(.0834)}}$.
44. $\sqrt[3]{\dfrac{25.682}{173(.0298)}}$.
45. $\dfrac{10^{.56}\sqrt{.38}}{(.813946)^2}$.

46. $\dfrac{\sqrt[3]{-264.137}}{\sqrt{14.2193}}$.
47. $\left(\dfrac{2139.27}{427.31\sqrt{.242}}\right)^{\frac{2}{3}}$.
48. $\left(\dfrac{621.9}{10^{1.48}\sqrt{69}}\right)^{\frac{1}{2}}$.

49. $(1.35)^{2.75}$.
50. $(21.98)^{.863}$.
51. $(69.3)^{-.26}$.
52. $(.03294)^{-.468}$.

Hint for Problem 51. $\log (69.3)^{-.26} = -.26(1.8407) = -.4786$.

Note 1. Observe that no property of logarithms is available to simplify the computation of a *sum*. Use logarithms below wherever possible.

53. $\dfrac{(26.8)^2 + 49.316}{\sqrt{69} + 1.589}$.
54. $\dfrac{\sqrt[3]{67} - 268.42}{(.7531)^3 + 89.2}$.
55. $\dfrac{\sqrt{29} - \sqrt{156}}{253(.210317)}$.

112. Exponential and logarithmic equations

A *logarithmic equation* is one in which there appears the logarithm of some expression involving the variable.

EXAMPLE 1. Solve for x: $\log x + \log \dfrac{2x}{5} = 6$.

Solution. By use of Properties I and II of logarithms,

$$\log x + \log 2 + \log x - \log 5 = 6.$$
$$2 \log x = 6 + \log 5 - \log 2 = 6.3980; \quad x = 1581. \qquad \text{(Table V)}$$

An equation where the variable appears in an exponent is called an *exponential equation*. Sometimes, an exponential equation can be solved by equating the logarithms of the members of the equation.

EXAMPLE 2. Solve $16^x = 74$.

Solution. Equate the logarithms of the two sides: $x \log 16 = \log 74$;

$$x = \frac{\log 74}{\log 16} = \frac{1.8692}{1.2041}.$$

$$\begin{array}{l} \log 1.869 = 0.2716 \\ (-) \log 1.204 = 0.0806 \\ \hline \log x = 0.1910 \; ; \quad \textit{hence} \quad x = 1.552. \end{array}$$

113. Logarithms to various bases

The base 10 is convenient for logarithms when they are being used to simplify computation. The only other base which is used appreciably is the irrational number $e = 2.71828 \cdots$. Logarithms to the base e are called **natural logarithms,** and are indispensable, for noncomputational purposes, in calculus and other parts of advanced mathematics.

Recall that the equations $N = a^x$ and $x = \log_a N$ are equivalent. Hence, if N and a are given, we can find $\log_a N$ by solving the exponential equation $N = a^x$ by use of *common* logarithms. In particular, the natural logarithm of N can be found by solving $N = e^x$ for x. For future use, notice that

$$\log_{10} e = 0.4343; \quad \log_{10} .4343 = 9.6378 - 10. \tag{1}$$

Illustration 1. To obtain $\log_e 35$, we let $x = \log_e 35$. Then we obtain $e^x = 35$. On solving this exponential equation for x as in Section 112, we obtain the desired result.

EXERCISE 71

Solve for x, or for n, or compute the specified logarithm by use of four-place logarithms.

1. $15^x = 32$.   2. $28^x = 478$.   3. $6^{2x} = 30(3^x)$.   4. $12^{3x} = 98(3^x)$.
5. $.87^x = 12$.   6. $.075^x = 15$.   7. $16^{x^2} = 85$.   8. $6.58^{-x} = .0893$.
9. $5^{x^2+x} = 23$.   10. $(1.04)^n = 1.562$.   11. $(1.02)^{-n} = .721$.
12. $\log x^3 - \log \frac{2}{5}x = 7.42$.   13. $\log 6x^2 + \log (3/x) = 6.789$.
14. $\log_e 85$.   15. $\log_e 1250$.   16. $\log_e 125$.   17. $\log_e 10$.
18. $\log_e 100$.   19. $\log_{12} 500$.   20. $\log_6 1.08$.   21. $\log_{.7} 24.6$.

22. Find the natural logarithm of (*a*) 529.7; (*b*) 5.297.

23. A given radioactive substance decomposes at such a rate that, if B is the initial number of atoms of the substance and N is the number remaining at the end of t hours, then $N = Be^{-kt}$, where k is a constant and $e = 2.71828 \cdots$. Given that, out of 17,000 atoms, 14,500 remain at the end of $\frac{1}{2}$ hour, (*a*) find k; (*b*) find when only $\frac{1}{2}$ of the atoms will remain.

Chapter 10 Mathematical Induction

114. A property of integers; mathematical induction

In this chapter, the word *integer* always will refer to a *positive integer*. In a logical foundation of the number system, we find that the following axiom or some equivalent postulate about the positive integers is of basic importance. We shall use the property stated by the axiom.

AXIOM OF INDUCTION. *If T is a set of positive integers with the following two properties, then T consists of **all positive integers***:

I. *The integer 1 belongs to T.*

II. *If the integer k belongs to T, then $(k + 1)$ belongs to T.*

This axiom becomes the foundation for a powerful method of proof called *mathematical induction*, which we proceed to illustrate.

Note 1. If property I of the Axiom is changed to read *"the integer h belongs to T,"* the conclusion would be that T consists of all integers $\geq h$.

EXAMPLE 1. By use of the Axiom of Induction, prove that, if the first term of an A.P. is a and the common difference is d, then the nth term is

$$[a + (n - 1)d].$$

Proof.* 1. Let $l_n = a + (n - 1)d$. Let T be the set of all integers n for which l_n is the nth term of the A.P. We wish to prove that T consists of *all* integers n.

---

* It should not be inferred that the previous proof of this result on page 120 was lacking in completeness, for any reader who could appreciate the verbal demonstration on page 120. However, some people would consider the proof in Example 1 more satisfying. Similar remarks could be made about various other proofs requested in this chapter.

2. *Verification of property* I *of the Axiom.* If $n = 1$, the first term is known to be a, and we verify that $l_1 = a + 0d = a$. Hence, T contains the integer 1 (that is, the stated result is true when $n = 1$).

3. *Verification of property* II *of the Axiom.* Our *hypothesis* is that the kth term of the A.P. is given by $l_k = a + (k - 1)d$. We wish to *prove* that the $(k + 1)$th term also is given by the formula for l_n. By the definition of an A.P.,

$$[(k + 1)\text{th } term] = l_k + d = a + (k - 1)d + d$$
$$= a + kd = a + [(k + 1) - 1]d. \tag{1}$$

In (1), notice that the result is that which is obtained if $n = k + 1$ in

$$l_n = a + (n - 1)d.$$

Hence, we have proved that, if the stated result of Example 1 is true when $n = k$, then the result also is true when $n = k + 1$.

4. We have shown that T has properties I and II of the Axiom. Hence, T contains *all* integers, or the nth term is $a + (n - 1)d$ for *all* values of n.

The method of proof in Example 1 is called *mathematical induction.* A proof by this method may be compared to climbing a ladder, where each rung corresponds to a special case of the theorem. In verifying property I of the Axiom, we show that we can climb onto the 1st rung (or, we may feel more comfortable if we verify that we can climb up the first few rungs). Then, in proving property II of the Axiom, we show that we can pass *from rung to rung.* Thus, the Axiom states that we can reach *all* rungs of the ladder.

Let the sequence $\{H_n\}$ represent a theorem which has $H_1, H_2, H_3, \cdots$, $H_n, \cdots$ as its special cases. That is, we are dealing with a theorem whose special cases can be arranged in a one-to-one correspondence with the set of all* positive integers, $1, 2, 3, \cdots, n, \cdots$. We refer to H_n as the nth *case*, or the *general case* of the theorem. Mathematical induction sometimes can be used to prove that H_n is true for all values of n, as follows.

METHOD. *Proof of a theorem* $\{H_n\}$ *for all values of* n *by* **mathematical induction.**

A. *Let* T *be the set of integers* $\{n\}$ *for which* $\{H_n\}$ *is true. Verify that* H_n *is true when* $n = 1$ *(and perhaps* $n = 2$, *and* $n = 3$ *for appreciation† of the nature of the theorem). (Part* I *of the Axiom of Induction.)*

B. *Proof of an* **auxiliary theorem** *which states that, if the* kth *case* H_k *is true then the* $(k + 1)$th *case* H_{k+1} *is true. (Part* II *of the Axiom.)*

Conclusion. *A clear statement that parts* I *and* II *of the Axiom of Induction have been established for the set* T, *and hence that* T *contains all integers, or* H_n *is true for all values of* n.

* Or, with all of them from a certain point on.
† Verification for the case $n = 1$ is all that is logically necessary.

EXAMPLE 2.   *If n is any positive integer, prove that*

$$2 + 4 + 6 + \cdots + 2n = n(n + 1), \tag{2}$$

or, the sum of the first n positive even integers is $n(n + 1)$.

Note 2. There are n terms on the left in (2), and $2n$ is not only the nth *term*, but also is a formula from which any term may be computed. Hence, we refer to $2n$ as the *general term* in (2).

Proof of (2). The theorem $\{H_n\}$ is summarized in (2). Let T be the set of all integers n for which (2) is true. We divide our proof into two parts, corresponding to A and B on page 258.

Part A. *Verification of special cases.*

When we place $n = 1$ in (2): $2 = 1(1 + 1)$, *or* $2 = 2$.
When we place $n = 2$ in (2): $2 + 4 = 2(2 + 1)$, *or* $6 = 6$.
When we place $n = 3$ in (2): $2 + 4 + 6 = 3(3 + 1)$, *or* $12 = 12$.

Hence, equation (2) is true when n is 1, 2, or 3. We have verified that T contains the integers $n = 1, 2$, and 3, or property I of the Axiom is true for T.

Part B. *Auxiliary Theorem: If k is a value of n for which equation (2) is true, then it is true also when $n = k + 1$.*

Proof. 1. By hypothesis, equation (2) is true when $n = k$, or

$$2 + 4 + 6 + \cdots + 2k = k(k + 1). \tag{3}$$

By use of (3), we wish to prove that

$$2 + 4 + 6 + \cdots + 2(k + 1) \stackrel{?}{=} (k + 1)[(k + 1) + 1]$$
$$\stackrel{?}{=} (k + 1)(k + 2), \tag{4}$$

which results from (2) when $n = k + 1$. In (4), we place "?" over "=" because the equality is not yet proved. Recognize that

$$2 + 4 + \cdots + 2(k + 1) = 2 + 4 + \cdots + 2k + 2(k + 1). \tag{5}$$

By (5), the equation (4) which we wish to establish becomes

$$2 + 4 + 6 + \cdots + 2k + 2(k + 1) \stackrel{?}{=} (k + 1)(k + 2). \tag{6}$$

Our *hypothesis* is stated by equation (3); by means of it we desire *to prove* that equation (6) is true.

2. Add $2(k + 1)$ to both sides of (3):

$$2 + 4 + 6 + \cdots + 2k + 2(k + 1) = k(k + 1) + 2(k + 1)$$
(factoring) $$= (k + 1)(k + 2). \tag{7}$$

Hence, each side in (7) is the same as the corresponding side of (6). Therefore, (6) is true if (3) is true, which proves the auxiliary theorem.

Conclusion. *We have shown that the set T of all values of n for which (2) is true contains the integer n = 1 (part I of the Axiom) and, also, that part II of the Axiom is true. Hence, by the Axiom, T contains all integers, or (2) is true for all values of n.*

EXAMPLE 3. *If n is any positive integer, prove that*

$$1 \cdot 2 + 2 \cdot 3 + \cdots + n(n + 1) = \tfrac{1}{3}n(n + 1)(n + 2). \tag{8}$$

Proof of (8). Let T be the set of all integers n for which (8) is true.

Part A. *Verification of special cases.* We verify (8) when $n = 1$ and $n = 2$:

When $n = 1$, $\qquad\qquad\qquad\qquad 1 \cdot 2 = \tfrac{1}{3}(1)(1 + 1)(1 + 2)$, *or* $2 = 2$.

When $n = 2$, $\qquad\qquad 1 \cdot 2 + 2 \cdot 3 = \tfrac{1}{3}(2)(2 + 1)(2 + 2)$, *or* $8 = 8$.

Hence, the set T contains the integers $n = 1$ and $n = 2$.

Part B. *Auxiliary Theorem: If k is any value of n for which equation (8) is true, then it is true also when n = k + 1.*

Proof. 1. By hypothesis, (8) is true when $n = k$, or

$$1 \cdot 2 + 2 \cdot 3 + \cdots + k(k + 1) = \tfrac{1}{3}k(k + 1)(k + 2). \tag{9}$$

Under this hypothesis we wish to show the truth of the following equation, which is obtained by placing $n = k + 1$ in (8):

$$\left. \begin{aligned} &1 \cdot 2 + 2 \cdot 3 + \cdots + (k + 1)[(k + 1) + 1] \\ &\overset{?}{=} \tfrac{1}{3}(k + 1)[(k + 1) + 1][(k + 1) + 2]. \end{aligned} \right\} \tag{10}$$

2. On explicitly indicating the kth term on the left in (10), we obtain

$$\left. \begin{aligned} &1 \cdot 2 + 2 \cdot 3 + \cdots + k(k + 1) + (k + 1)(k + 2) \\ &\overset{?}{=} \tfrac{1}{3}(k + 1)(k + 2)(k + 3). \end{aligned} \right\} \tag{11}$$

To establish (11), add $(k + 1)(k + 2)$ to both sides of (9):

$$\left. \begin{aligned} &1 \cdot 2 + 2 \cdot 3 + \cdots + k(k + 1) + (k + 1)(k + 2) \\ &= \tfrac{1}{3}k(k + 1)(k + 2) + (k + 1)(k + 2). \end{aligned} \right\} \tag{12}$$

In (12), when the right-hand side is simplified, we obtain

$$\frac{k(k + 1)(k + 2) + 3(k + 1)(k + 2)}{3} = \frac{1}{3}(k + 1)(k + 2)(k + 3).$$

Since each side of (12) is the same as in (11), we have shown that (10) is true if (9) is true. The student now should supply a concluding statement.

Both Part A and Part B of a proof by mathematical induction are necessary. Thus, Part A alone would be insufficient, because verification of any number of special cases of a theorem would not prove that all of its cases are true.

Illustration 1. It can be verified that $(n^2 - n + 41)$ is a prime number when $n = 1, 2, 3, \cdots, 40$. Hence, it might be inferred, incorrectly, that $(n^2 - n + 41)$ is a prime integer for all values of the integer n. This result is *not* true because, if $n = 41$,

$$n^2 - n + 41 = (41)^2 - 41 + 41 = (41)^2,$$

which is not a prime integer (being 41×41).

We note also that Part B, alone, of a proof by mathematical induction would not constitute a proof.

Illustration 2. If we should forget the necessity for Part A (verification of special cases), apparently we could prove the false statement that, *if n is any positive integer, then*

$$2 + 4 + 6 + \cdots + 2n = 20 + n(n + 1). \tag{13}$$

When we compare this equation with (2) on page 259, we see that the present equation (13) is *not* true for any value of n. Nevertheless, we can prove the auxiliary theorem of Part B, which would state that, if

$$2 + 4 + 6 + \cdots + 2k = 20 + k(k + 1), \tag{14}$$

then $\qquad 2 + 4 + 6 + \cdots + 2(k + 1) = 20 + (k + 1)(k + 2). \tag{15}$

We could verify (15) by adding $2(k + 1)$ on both sides of (14).

The student must not infer that mathematical induction applies only when the theorem is stated by means of an *equation*. In the next example, no equation is written to summarize the statement (although this could be done).

EXAMPLE 4. *Prove that, if n is any positive integer, then $(x^{2n} - y^{2n})$ has $(x + y)$ as a factor.*

Solution. **A.** When $n = 1$, $(x^{2n} - y^{2n})$ becomes $(x^2 - y^2)$, which is seen to have $(x + y)$ as a factor.

B. *Auxiliary Theorem: If $(x^{2n} - y^{2n})$ has $(x + y)$ as a factor when $n = k$, then $(x^{2n} - y^{2n})$ has $(x + y)$ as a factor also when $n = k + 1$.*

Proof. 1. If $(x^{2n} - y^{2n})$ has $(x + y)$ as a factor when $n = k$, then

$$x^{2k} - y^{2k} = (x + y)F, \tag{16}$$

where F represents the other factor. If $n = k + 1$, $(x^{2n} - y^{2n})$ becomes $(x^{2k+2} - y^{2k+2})$. On dividing $(x^{2k+2} - y^{2k+2})$ by $(x^{2k} - y^{2k})$, we find

$$x^{2k+2} - y^{2k+2} = x^2(x^{2k} - y^{2k}) + y^{2k}(x^2 - y^2). \tag{17}$$

2. Hence, by use of (16) and (17), we obtain

$$x^{2k+2} - y^{2k+2} = x^2(x + y)F + y^{2k}(x + y)(x - y)$$
$$= (x + y)[x^2F + y^{2k}(x - y)].$$

Therefore, $(x^{2k+2} - y^{2k+2})$ has the factor $(x + y)$ if $(x^{2k} - y^{2k})$ has the factor $(x + y)$, and hence the auxiliary theorem has been proved. The student should supply the concluding statement for the solution.

Note 3. In the natural sciences, a general conclusion often is reached, although not demonstrated in the mathematical sense, by a consideration of what happens in a number of special cases. Such reasoning is called *ordinary*, or *incomplete*, induction. In contrast to it, mathematical induction often is called *complete* induction.

EXERCISE 72

By mathematical induction, prove the statement for all positive integral values of n.

1. Suppose that a geometric progression has the first term a and common ratio r. Prove that the nth term, l_n, is given by the formula $l_n = ar^{n-1}$.
2. $4 + 8 + 12 + \cdots + 4n = 2n(n + 1)$.
3. $1 + 2 + 3 + \cdots + n = \frac{1}{2}n(n + 1)$.
4. The sum of the first n positive integral multiples of 3 is $\frac{3}{2}n(n + 1)$.
5. The sum of the first n positive integral multiples of 6 is $3n(n + 1)$.
6. The sum of the first n terms of the A.P. met in Example 1 on page 257 is $\frac{1}{2}n[2a + (n - 1)d]$.
7. The sum of the first n terms of the G.P. of Problem 1 is $(a - ar^n)/(1 - r)$.

If the statement is true for all positive integral values of n, prove this fact by mathematical induction. Otherwise, prove that your conclusion is correct.

8. $1 + 3 + 5 + \cdots + (2n - 1) = n^2$. (State this theorem in words.)
9. $1 + 5 + 9 + \cdots + (4n - 3) = n(2n - 1)$.
10. $2 + 5 + 8 + \cdots + (3n - 1) = \frac{1}{2}(5n^2 - 5n + 4)$.
11. $3 + 3^2 + 3^3 + \cdots + 3^n = \frac{1}{2}(3^{n+1} - 3)$.
12. $1 + 2 + 2^2 + \cdots + 2^{n-1} = 2^n - 1$.
13. $1 + 6 + 6^2 + \cdots + 6^{n-1} = \frac{1}{5}(6^n - 1)$.
14. $1^2 + 2^2 + 3^2 + \cdots + n^2 = \frac{1}{6}n(n + 1)(2n + 1)$.
15. $1^3 + 2^3 + 3^3 + \cdots + n^3 = \frac{1}{4}n^2(n + 1)^2$.
16. $1 \cdot 3 + 2 \cdot 4 + 3 \cdot 5 + \cdots + n(n + 2) = \frac{1}{6}n(n + 1)(2n + 7)$.
17. $\dfrac{1}{1 \cdot 2} + \dfrac{1}{2 \cdot 3} + \dfrac{1}{3 \cdot 4} + \cdots + \dfrac{1}{n(n + 1)} = \dfrac{n}{n + 1}$.
18. $1^3 + 3^3 + 5^3 + \cdots + (2n - 1)^3 = 2n^4 - 3n + 2$.
19. If n is any integer, then $\frac{1}{3}(n^3 + 2n)$ is an integer.
20. The sum of the cubes of the first n positive even integers is $2n^2(n + 1)^2$.
21. If n is a positive integer, then $(x^n - y^n)$ has $(x - y)$ as a factor.
22. If n is a positive integer, then $(x^{2n-1} + y^{2n-1})$ has $(x + y)$ as a factor.
★23. Suppose that n is a positive integer. Prove that, if

$$1 + 4 + 7 + \cdots + (3n - 2) = \tfrac{1}{2}(3n^2 - n + 1) \qquad (1)$$

is true when $n = k$, then (1) is true when $n = k + 1$. Then, try to prove that (1) is true for all values of n.

Prove the stated result by mathematical induction.

★24. If z is any complex number, where $z = a + bi$, prove that

$$|z^n|^2 = (a^2 + b^2)^n$$

for all positive integral values of n. Do not use the trigonometric form of z.

★25. Prove that, for all values of the positive integer $n > 1$,

$$(1 + x)^n > 1 + nx,$$

if $-1 < x$ and $x \neq 0$.

★26. Prove that, for all values of the positive integer $n > 1$,

$$\frac{1}{\sqrt{1}} + \frac{1}{\sqrt{2}} + \cdots + \frac{1}{\sqrt{n}} > \sqrt{n}.$$

★27. Prove that, for all values of the positive integer $n > 1$,

$$\frac{1}{\sqrt[3]{1}} + \frac{1}{\sqrt[3]{2}} + \cdots + \frac{1}{\sqrt[3]{n}} > \sqrt[3]{n^2}.$$

★28. For every positive integer n, $(x + y)^n$ is given by the expansion (1) on page 140. That is, prove the binomial theorem by mathematical induction.

Comment. The resulting demonstration is one of the classical proofs of mathematics. However, the natural complexity of the proof compares very unfavorably with the simple demonstration of the theorem on page 300. In Part B of the requested proof, the expansion of $(x + y)^k$ must be written, with both the rth and the $(r - 1)$th terms given explicitly. Then, after multiplication by $(x + y)$ to obtain $(x + y)^{k+1}$, it must be shown that the term involving $x^{k+1-r}y^r$ has the correct coefficient.

★29. By use of the results in Problems 15 and 20, obtain a formula for the sum of the cubes of the first n odd integers. Then, prove that this formula is correct for every positive integer n by mathematical induction.

Chapter 11   General Systems of Linear Equations

115. Systems of n linear equations in n variables

Let any system of n linear equations in n variables be written in the following form, illustrated for $n = 3$, with the variables x, y, and z:

$$\textbf{(A)} \quad \begin{cases} a_1x + b_1y + c_1z = k_1, & (1) \\ a_2x + b_2y + c_2z = k_2, & (2) \\ a_3x + b_3y + c_3z = k_3. & (3) \end{cases}$$

In (A), the characteristic feature is that all terms in the variables, *in a definite order*, are in the left-hand members, and the constant term (possibly zero) in each equation is on the right. A **solution** of (A) is an ordered triple of numbers (α, β, γ) such that all of the equations are satisfied when $(x = \alpha, y = \beta, z = \gamma)$. The system, or its set of equations, is called *consistent* if there is a solution (at least one), and otherwise is called *inconsistent*. We accept the fact that Theorem VIII on page 93, as extended to a system of any number of equations, justifies the following statement.

Fundamental Principle. *A system of n linear equations in any number of variables is equivalent to (has the same solutions as) the new system which results on replacing any given equation, $H = W$, by the new equation $R = S$ obtained as follows:*

$$\textbf{(B)} \quad \begin{cases} \textit{Multiply both sides of } H = W \textit{ by a constant, not zero;} \\ \textit{multiply both sides of a second equation, } U = V, \textit{ of} \\ \textit{the system by a constant, not zero; add the correspond-} \\ \textit{ing sides of the two new equations to obtain } R = S. \end{cases}$$

In some form, (B) is applied again and again in many of the methods available for solving (A), with any number of variables.

116. Triangular form for a system, and matrices*

Let us phrase our remarks for the case of a system (A) on page 264, for three variables. On the basis of (B) on page 264, we may eliminate one variable, say z, by use of (1) and (2) of (A) to obtain a new equation (1)′ to replace (1). By use of (2) and (3), we may eliminate z again, to obtain a new equation (2)′ in x and y to replace (2). Then, we consider [(1)′, (2)′, (3)] as the new system. Here, we may use (1)′ and (2)′ to eliminate y and obtain a new equation (1)″ to replace (1)′; equation (1)″ will involve *only* x. Then, in general, the system [(1)″, (2)′, (3)] is immediately solvable. For a reason evident in the following example, this system is said to be in a **triangular form,** and is equivalent to the given system (A).

Note 1. Instead of having (1)″ involving x, we might equally well choose to have (1)″ involve y, or z, as proves convenient, which amounts merely to altering the order in which we refer to the variables.

EXAMPLE 1.   Solve for x, y, and z:

$$\begin{cases} 3x + y - z = 11, & (1) \\ x + 3y - z = 13, & (2) \\ x + y - 3z = 11. & (3) \end{cases}$$

Solution. 1. Subtract,† (2) from (1): $\qquad 2x - 2y = -2.$ (4)

Multiply by 3 in (2): $\qquad\qquad 3x + 9y - 3z = 39.$ (5)

Subtract, (3) from (5): $\qquad\qquad 2x + 8y = 28.$ (6)

Subtract, (4) from (6): $\qquad\qquad 10y = 30.$

Thus, system [(1), (2), (3)] is equivalent to the following system, which we shall say is in a triangular form:

$$\begin{cases} 10y = 30, & (7) \\ 8y + 2x = 28, & (8) \\ y + x - 3z = 11. & (9) \end{cases}$$

2. From (7), $y = 3$; then, from (8), we have $2x = 28 - 24$ or $x = 2$; then, from (9), we have $3z = 3 + 2 - 11 = -6$ or $z = -2$. Thus, the given system has the single solution

$$(x = 2, y = 3, z = -2).$$

We shall refer to the preceding method as a solution by *changing to a triangular form.*

A **matrix** (of numbers) with h rows and k columns is an array of hk numbers, each called an **element** of the matrix, arranged in h rows and k columns. If $h = k$, the matrix is said to be a **square matrix.** If a matrix has h rows and k columns, we refer to it as an "h by k matrix," written "$h \times k$ matrix."

* In this chapter, all numbers will be real in the illustrations and examples, but the results and proofs will apply when the arbitrary numbers are any complex numbers.
† Meaning, subtract *corresponding sides* in the stated order.

Illustration 1. The coefficients of the variables in [(1), (2), (3)] in the order (x, y, z) form a square matrix; these coefficients, with an *added column* consisting of the *constant terms* on the right in the equations, form a rectangular matrix of three rows and four columns. Thus, we arrive at two matrices:

$$\begin{bmatrix} 3 & 1 & -1 \\ 1 & 3 & -1 \\ 1 & 1 & -3 \end{bmatrix} ; \begin{bmatrix} 3 & 1 & -1 & 11 \\ 1 & 3 & -1 & 13 \\ 1 & 1 & -3 & 11 \end{bmatrix} . \tag{10}$$

In (10), we have a 3×3 square matrix and a 3×4 matrix.

We call the matrix at the left in (10) the **coefficient matrix** and the matrix at the right the **augmented matrix** for the given system.

Recall the nature of Step 1 of the solution of Example 1, and our switch of y to the place of honor as the "1st *variable*" in writing (7), (8), and (9). We conclude that the following operations on the augmented matrix in (10) lead to a new matrix of 3 rows and 4 columns, which is *the augmented matrix for a system equivalent to* [(1), (2), (3)], where we refer to these equations as if they formed a general system.

I. *Interchange any two rows.*
II. *Interchange any two columns of the coefficient matrix.*
III. *Multiply the elements of any row by a constant, not zero.*
IV. *After applying operation III to any two specified rows, add (or subtract) their corresponding elements, and use the result as a replacement for any one of the two specified rows.*

Operation I is equivalent to rewriting the system with the equations in a different order. Operation II is equivalent to altering the order in which the variables are written in the equations. Operation III is equivalent to replacing any equation by a new equivalent equation obtained by multiplying both of its sides by a nonzero constant. Operations III and IV are equivalent to (B) of page 264. Instead of the solution given for Example 1, we could proceed as follows, to obtain a new augmented matrix where the matrix of coefficients (consisting of the first 3 columns) is in **triangular form** (*zeros* above the so-called **"main diagonal,"** starting at the *upper left-hand corner*).

Matrix solution of Example 1. We write the matrices (10). Instead of saying "*eliminate z,*" we shall say "*manipulate the augmented matrix*" to obtain zeros in two places in the 3d column. We subtract the elements of the 2d row from those of the 1st row; then multiply elements of the 2d row by 3 and subtract the elements of the 3d row from the new elements in the 2d row. We thus obtain

$$\begin{bmatrix} 2 & -2 & 0 & -2 \\ 1 & 3 & -1 & 13 \\ 1 & 1 & -3 & 11 \end{bmatrix} ; \quad then \quad \begin{bmatrix} 2 & -2 & 0 & -2 \\ 2 & 8 & 0 & 28 \\ 1 & 1 & -3 & 11 \end{bmatrix} . \tag{11}$$

In the matrix at the right in (11), multiply the elements of the 1st row by 4, and then add to these elements the corresponding elements of the 2d row, to obtain a triangular form for the coefficient matrix (3 columns at the left):

$$\begin{bmatrix} 10 & 0 & 0 & 20 \\ 2 & 8 & 0 & 28 \\ 1 & 1 & -3 & 11 \end{bmatrix} \quad for \quad \begin{cases} 10x & = 20, \\ 2x + 8y & = 28, \\ x + y - 3z = 11. \end{cases} \tag{12}$$

From (12), we obtain $(x = 2, y = 3, z = -2)$.

The convenience of the matrix method becomes more apparent as the number of equations increases.

The remarks following Theorem VIII on page 93 apply to a system of n equations in n variables, for any positive integer n, in recognizing when the equations are inconsistent. If the equations, in our process of solution, lead to a contradictory statement $c = 0$, where $c \neq 0$, the given system is *inconsistent*. If we are led to an identity $0 = 0$ as one new equation, we thus are left with a system containing fewer equations than variables. In such a case, the equations of the given system would be called **dependent,** but nevertheless they might be inconsistent; usually, however, the system would have infinitely many solutions, as discussed later in this chapter.

Suppose that the method of changing to a triangular form is used, with matrices involved. Then, the method leads to a unique solution of the given system if all numbers in the main diagonal of the coefficient matrix, in triangular form, are *not zero*. In such a case, each corresponding equation in the final form determines uniquely the value of one of the variables.

SUMMARY. *To change the augmented matrix of a system of n linear equations in n variables to a form where the coefficient matrix is in triangular form.*

1. *Manipulate rows by use of operations* III *and* IV *to obtain* 0 *in the nth column, 1st row. Repeat, to obtain* 0 *in all places in the nth column above the last row.*

2. *Use operations* III *and* IV *to obtain* 0 *in the* $(n - 1)$th *column in all rows except the last two rows. Continue until each element is* 0 *above the main diagonal of the coefficient matrix.*

EXERCISE 73

Solve by changing to the triangular form, or prove that the system is inconsistent, by matrix manipulations. In Problem 1, also solve as in Example 1 on page 265.

1. $\begin{cases} 6x + 4y - z = 3, \\ x + 2y + 4z = -2, \\ 5x + 4y = 0. \end{cases}$
  2. $\begin{cases} x + y - 2z = 7, \\ 2x - 3y = 2z, \\ x - 2y - 3z = 3. \end{cases}$

3. $\begin{cases} 2s + 4y - 5t = 1, \\ s + 2y - 3t = 1, \\ s - 3t = 2. \end{cases}$
  4. $\begin{cases} 3x + 4y + z = -1, \\ 2x - y + 2z + 1 = 0, \\ x + 3y - z = 2. \end{cases}$

5. $\begin{cases} x + y - z = 1, \\ 12x - 2y + 3z = 3, \\ 3x + y - 3z = 6. \end{cases}$

6. $\begin{cases} 9x + 2y + 3z = 3, \\ y - 12x - 12z + 6 = 0, \\ 2z - y - 2x = 4. \end{cases}$

7. $\begin{cases} x - 2y + z + 3w = 7, \\ x + y + 3z + 2w = 6, \\ x + y - 2z + w = 9, \\ 3x + 4y + 4z + 2w = 16. \end{cases}$

8. $\begin{cases} 6y - 4z - w + 3 = 0, \\ 2x + y - z - 2w = 7, \\ x - 2y + 8z = 7, \\ 3x - 4y + 4z - w = 12. \end{cases}$

9. $\begin{cases} 2y + z = 0, \\ -x + 3y + 5z = 0, \\ 3x + 4y - z = 0. \end{cases}$

10. $\begin{cases} x - 3y + 2z = 0, \\ 2x + y + 4z = 0, \\ -2x + y + 3z = 0. \end{cases}$

11. $\begin{cases} 3x + 3y - 7z = 7, \\ x + 2y - 3z = 3, \\ x - y - z = 2. \end{cases}$

12. $\begin{cases} 2x + 6y + 2z = 11, \\ 2x + y - z = 2, \\ x - 2y - 2z = -2. \end{cases}$

13. $\begin{cases} 2x - y + 3z - w = 9, \\ x - 4y + z = 11, \\ 3x - 5z + 2w = 13, \\ 8x + y + 4z - 2w = 30. \end{cases}$

14. $\begin{cases} 3x - 4y + 12z + 4w + 2v = 0, \\ 5 + 2y + 3v + 2w = 0, \\ z + v + 1 = 0, \\ 4 - x + 4y - 4z - 4w + 2v = 0, \\ x - 4y + 8z - 6w = 4. \end{cases}$

15. $\begin{cases} 2x + 6y + 2z - u + 2v + 3 = 0, \\ -6y + 8z + 2u - 2v = 1, \\ 2x + y + z - v = -1, \\ 6x + 4y - 2z + u = 4, \\ -8y + 6z - u + 4v = 3. \end{cases}$

117. The determinant* of a 2 × 2 matrix

If a, b, c, and d are any complex numbers, Example 4 on page 92 proves that

the system
$$\begin{cases} ax + by = e, \text{ and} & (1) \\ cx + dy = f, & (2) \end{cases}$$

has the unique solution
$$\left(x = \frac{de - bf}{ad - bc}, \quad y = \frac{af - ce}{ad - bc} \right). \qquad (3)$$

The symmetrical form of the numerators and denominators in (3) was noticed by early mathematicians, and led to the following concept of a *determinant*.

Let A represent the 2 × 2 matrix formed by the coefficients of x and y, in order, in system [(1), (2)]:

$$A = \begin{bmatrix} a & b \\ c & d \end{bmatrix}.$$

Then, the **determinant** of A, represented by $|A|$, is defined as follows:

$$|A| = ad - bc, \quad or \quad \begin{vmatrix} a & b \\ c & d \end{vmatrix} = ad - bc. \qquad (4)$$

---

* If the class is to study determinants on the basis of Note 6 of the Appendix, the remainder of this chapter might be delayed until Chapter 12 has been studied.

We read (4) as follows: *The determinant of A is* $(ad - bc)$; or, *the determinant of the matrix* $(a, b; c, d)$, reading the elements by rows, *is* $(ad - b\overset{.}{c})$. We refer to $(ad - bc)$ in (4) as the *expansion* of $|A|$.

Illustration 1. $\begin{vmatrix} 3 & 2 \\ -4 & -5 \end{vmatrix} = 3(-5) - (-4)(2) = -15 + 8 = -7.$

By the definition of a determinant in (4), if $ad - bc \neq 0,$ the solution of system $[(1), (2)]$ in (3) can be written as follows:

$$x = \frac{\begin{vmatrix} e & b \\ f & d \end{vmatrix}}{\begin{vmatrix} a & b \\ c & d \end{vmatrix}} ; \quad y = \frac{\begin{vmatrix} a & e \\ c & f \end{vmatrix}}{\begin{vmatrix} a & b \\ c & d \end{vmatrix}} . \tag{5}$$

We refer to $[(1), (2)]$ as the *standard form* for a system of two linear equations in two variables. In this form, the terms in the variables are in the left-hand members, with the order of the variables *the same in both equations.* The terms in the right-hand members then are called the *constant terms.* The solution in (5), for a system in standard form, is summarized by the following rule, due to the Swiss mathematician CRAMER (1704–1752). This rule is stated for a system of n equations, but at present has meaning only for the case $n = 2$, as illustrated by system $[(1), (2)]$.

Cramer's rule. *In a system of n linear equations in n variables, suppose that the determinant of the coefficient matrix for the variables is not zero. Then, the system has a single solution. In it, the value of each variable can be expressed as the quotient of two determinants, as follows:*

1. *The denominator is the* **determinant of the coefficient matrix** *for the variables.*

2. *For any variable, the numerator is the determinant of the matrix obtained from the coefficient matrix* **by replacing the column of coefficients of the variable by the column of constant terms** *in the augmented matrix for the system.*

Illustration 2. In (5), the constant terms e and f are in the 1st column in the numerator for x, and in the 2d column for y.

EXAMPLE 1. Solve by determinants: $\begin{cases} 2x - 4y = -14, \\ 3x + 7y = 5. \end{cases}$

Solution. From (5), $x = \dfrac{\begin{vmatrix} -14 & -4 \\ 5 & 7 \end{vmatrix}}{\begin{vmatrix} 2 & -4 \\ 3 & 7 \end{vmatrix}},$ and $y = \dfrac{\begin{vmatrix} 2 & -14 \\ 3 & 5 \end{vmatrix}}{\begin{vmatrix} 2 & -4 \\ 3 & 7 \end{vmatrix}}.$

On computing the determinants, we obtain $x = -3$ and $y = 2$.

Note 1. As far as the Western world is concerned, determinants were invented in 1693 by the German mathematician LEIBNIZ (1646–1716). However, determinants were invented at least ten years earlier by SEKI-KOWA (1642–1708), the great Japanese mathematician. The work of SEKI-KOWA had no influence on mathematical development outside of Japan.

EXERCISE 74

Expand the determinant.

1. $\begin{vmatrix} 2 & 1 \\ 4 & -5 \end{vmatrix}$. **2.** $\begin{vmatrix} 5 & 7 \\ 8 & 2 \end{vmatrix}$. **3.** $\begin{vmatrix} c & 3 \\ 3 & -1 \end{vmatrix}$. **4.** $\begin{vmatrix} h & m \\ k & n \end{vmatrix}$.

Solve by use of determinants, if possible.

5–15. Solve Problems 5–15, respectively, on page 94.

Solve for x and y by use of determinants.

16. $\begin{cases} cx + by = 1, \\ bx - ay = 1. \end{cases}$ **17.** $\begin{cases} dx - hy = k, \\ fx + by = h. \end{cases}$ **18.** $\begin{cases} 2bx - 3ay = 4b^2, \\ x + 3y = 4b + a. \end{cases}$

118. The determinant of an $n \times n$ matrix

Consider any $n \times n$ matrix, such as H or K below, where $n = 3$ for H and $n = 4$ for K.

$$H = \begin{bmatrix} a_1 & b_1 & c_1 \\ a_2 & b_2 & c_2 \\ a_3 & b_3 & c_3 \end{bmatrix}; \quad K = \begin{bmatrix} a_1 & b_1 & c_1 & d_1 \\ a_2 & b_2 & c_2 & d_2 \\ a_3 & b_3 & c_3 & d_3 \\ a_4 & b_4 & c_4 & d_4 \end{bmatrix}. \tag{1}$$

In any matrix, A, suppose that all elements in certain rows and certain columns are deleted (blotted out). Then, the remaining elements of A form an array referred to as a **submatrix** of A.

Illustration 1. If the 2d row and 3d column of K in (1) are deleted, we obtain the following submatrix of K:

$$\begin{bmatrix} a_1 & b_1 & d_1 \\ a_3 & b_3 & d_3 \\ a_4 & b_4 & d_4 \end{bmatrix}.$$

Let A represent any $n \times n$ matrix. Then, the symbol "$|A|$" will be read **"the determinant of A."** We shall call $|A|$ a *determinant of the nth order* because A is an $n \times n$ matrix. We shall define $|A|$ after introducing auxiliary terminology. In the following Definitions I and II, we assume that, for any square matrix A, eventually we shall assign a corresponding value for $|A|$.

DEFINITION I. *In a square matrix A, suppose that the row and column containing a certain element α are deleted, to give a submatrix S of A. Then, $|S|$ is called the **minor** of α in $|A|$.*

Note 1. To avoid confusion between a notation $|S|$ for a determinant and $|x|$ for the absolute value of a number x, we shall use capital letters only for *matrices* and *determinants* in this chapter.

Illustration 2. To find the minor of a_2 in $|H|$, where H is in (1), we delete the 1st column and 2d row of H to obtain the submatrix

$$\begin{bmatrix} b_1 & c_1 \\ b_3 & c_3 \end{bmatrix} ; \quad \textit{hence, the minor of } a_2 \textit{ is } \begin{vmatrix} b_1 & c_1 \\ b_3 & c_3 \end{vmatrix}.$$

If A is a 1×1 matrix, $A = [e]$, apart from future definitions we *define* $|A| = e$. Then, in any reference to a *minor* in a determinant, hereafter we shall assume that it is of order $n \geq 2$. Then, the minor of an element in a determinant of order n is a determinant of order $(n - 1)$.

DEFINITION II. *In a determinant, $|A|$, of any order, let α be the element which is in row i and column j of A, and let M be the minor of α. Then, the* **cofactor,** *C, of α in $|A|$ is defined by $C = (-1)^{i+j}M$. That is, $C = +M$ if $(i + j)$ is an* **even** *integer, and $C = -M$ if $(i + j)$ is an* **odd** *integer.*

Illustration 3. With H from (1), if M_2 represents the minor of a_2, then the cofactor C_2 of a_2 in $|H|$ is given by $C_2 = (-1)^{2+1}M_2 = -M_2$. For any determinant, $|A|$, the signs to attach to the minors of the elements of A in the various locations, to obtain the cofactors of the elements, can be remembered by use of the adjoining diagram. The signs alternate in proceeding to the right in any row or moving down in any column of A. The sign for the leading element at the top in the main diagonal of A is $+$; that is, $C = +M$ for this element.

$$\begin{vmatrix} + & - & + & \cdot & \cdot & \cdot & \cdot \\ - & + & - & \cdot & \cdot & \cdot & \cdot \\ + & - & + & \cdot & \cdot & \cdot & \cdot \\ - & + & - & \cdot & \cdot & \cdot & \cdot \\ \cdot & \cdot & \cdot & \cdot & \cdot & \cdot & \cdot \end{vmatrix}$$

Illustration 4. For the following determinant of the 2d order, the minor of a_1 is b_2, and of a_2 is b_1. The cofactor, C_1, of a_1 is $+b_2$; the cofactor, C_2, of a_2 is $-b_1$. We verify, from page 268, that the determinant of a 2×2 matrix can be written as follows in terms of cofactors:

$$\begin{vmatrix} a_1 & b_1 \\ a_2 & b_2 \end{vmatrix} = a_1 b_2 - a_2 b_1 = a_1 C_1 + a_2 C_2. \tag{2}$$

We proceed to define the value of *any* determinant of *order n* in terms of *determinants of order $(n - 1)$*. From (2), the following definition is seen to give the value as previously defined for a determinant of order $n = 2$. Then, the Axiom of Induction on page 257 assures us that the definition has meaning for all integers $n \geq 2$, because the definition has meaning for $n = k + 1$ if there is a well-defined meaning when $n = k$.

DEFINITION III. *Let A be any $n \times n$ matrix. For any column of A, with the elements, say, p_1, p_2, p_3, $\cdots$, p_n, let the corresponding cofactors in $|A|$ be $C_1, C_2, \cdots, C_n$. Then, we define*

$$|\mathbf{A}| = p_1 C_1 + p_2 C_2 + \cdots + p_n C_n. \tag{3}$$

We refer to (3) as the expansion of $|A|$ *by the elements and cofactors of the specified column.* In (3), each cofactor is the product of either $+1$ or -1 and a determinant of *order* $(n - 1)$. Hence, (3) defines a determinant of order n *in terms of determinants of order* $(n - 1)$, as stated earlier. In Note 6 of the Appendix, equation (3) will be proved as a *theorem*, with $|A|$ defined in an entirely different way which has great merit as a basis for the theory of determinants. Definition III is being used to permit rapid introduction to determinants, and also to illuminate the proofs in Note 6 of the Appendix.

We accept the following theorem without proof, and merely verify the result for the case where $|A|$ is of the 3d order.*

THEOREM I. *The value of $|A|$ as obtained in (3) corresponding to any column of A is the same as obtained if any other column of A is used. Also, $|A|$ is correctly given in (3) if $(p_1, p_2, \cdots, p_n)$ represent the elements of any row of A, and C_i is the cofactor of p_i in $|A|$.*

On the basis of Theorem I, we may expand $|A|$ by the elements and cofactors of any *row* or *column* of A, as we please.

Illustration 5. With H from (1), if we expand $|H|$ by the elements and cofactors of the 1st column of H, and use (3), we obtain

$$|H| = \begin{vmatrix} a_1 & b_1 & c_1 \\ a_2 & b_2 & c_2 \\ a_3 & b_3 & c_3 \end{vmatrix} = a_1 \begin{vmatrix} b_2 & c_2 \\ b_3 & c_3 \end{vmatrix} - a_2 \begin{vmatrix} b_1 & c_1 \\ b_3 & c_3 \end{vmatrix} + a_3 \begin{vmatrix} b_1 & c_1 \\ b_2 & c_2 \end{vmatrix}$$

$$= a_1(b_2 c_3 - b_3 c_2) - a_2(b_1 c_3 - b_3 c_1) + a_3(b_1 c_2 - b_2 c_1), \text{ or}$$

$$\begin{vmatrix} a_1 & b_1 & c_1 \\ a_2 & b_2 & c_2 \\ a_3 & b_3 & c_3 \end{vmatrix} = a_1 b_2 c_3 + a_2 b_3 c_1 + a_3 b_1 c_2 - a_1 b_3 c_2 - a_2 b_1 c_3 - a_3 b_2 c_1. \tag{4}$$

On expanding $|H|$ by the elements and cofactors of the 2d row of H, we obtain

$$|H| = -a_2 \begin{vmatrix} b_1 & c_1 \\ b_3 & c_3 \end{vmatrix} + b_2 \begin{vmatrix} a_1 & c_1 \\ a_3 & c_3 \end{vmatrix} - c_2 \begin{vmatrix} a_1 & b_1 \\ a_3 & b_3 \end{vmatrix}$$

$$= -a_2(b_1 c_3 - b_3 c_1) + b_2(a_1 c_3 - a_3 c_1) - c_2(a_1 b_3 - a_3 b_1),$$

which we observe is the same as in (4). The student should verify that (4) is obtained by expanding $|H|$ by use of cofactors in a few other ways.

---

* Proofs of properties of determinants on the basis of Definition III would be relatively inelegant. The logical basis for our discussion of determinants is in the Appendix.

Illustration 6. For the following determinant, we expand by the elements and cofactors of the 1st column of the matrix, and use (4) on page 268:

$$\begin{vmatrix} 1 & 5 & 2 \\ 4 & 7 & 3 \\ 2 & -3 & 6 \end{vmatrix} = 1 \begin{vmatrix} 7 & 3 \\ -3 & 6 \end{vmatrix} - 4 \begin{vmatrix} 5 & 2 \\ -3 & 6 \end{vmatrix} + 2 \begin{vmatrix} 5 & 2 \\ 7 & 3 \end{vmatrix}$$

$$= (42 + 9) - 4(30 + 6) + 2(15 - 14) = -91.$$

Illustration 7. We expand by the elements and cofactors of the 2d row of the matrix of the following determinant.

$$\begin{vmatrix} 3 & -1 & 5 & 0 \\ -1 & 0 & -4 & 2 \\ 2 & 3 & -2 & 6 \\ 4 & -2 & -3 & -1 \end{vmatrix}$$

$$= -(-1) \begin{vmatrix} -1 & 5 & 0 \\ 3 & -2 & 6 \\ -2 & -3 & -1 \end{vmatrix} + 0 - (-4) \begin{vmatrix} 3 & -1 & 0 \\ 2 & 3 & 6 \\ 4 & -2 & -1 \end{vmatrix} + 2 \begin{vmatrix} 3 & -1 & 5 \\ 2 & 3 & -2 \\ 4 & -2 & -3 \end{vmatrix} \cdot$$

Then, we would continue by computing each of the preceding determinants of the 3d order in accordance with Definition III. The result is -295.

EXERCISE 75

1. Expand the determinant of the adjoining matrix by the elements and cofactors of the 1st column; of the 2d column; of the 3d row.

$$\begin{bmatrix} c_1 & m_1 & v_1 \\ c_2 & m_2 & v_2 \\ c_3 & m_3 & v_3 \end{bmatrix}$$

Evaluate by expansion by use of cofactors. Notice that it is convenient to use the cofactors of the elements in any row or column having one or more zero elements.

2. $\begin{vmatrix} 1 & 4 & 2 \\ 4 & 3 & 3 \\ 2 & -5 & 6 \end{vmatrix} \cdot$ 3. $\begin{vmatrix} 4 & 3 & -2 \\ 1 & -1 & 4 \\ -2 & 0 & 3 \end{vmatrix} \cdot$ 4. $\begin{vmatrix} -2 & 0 & 2 \\ -3 & -3 & 3 \\ 4 & -2 & 3 \end{vmatrix} \cdot$

5. $\begin{vmatrix} 5 & 4 & 2 \\ -6 & 0 & -5 \\ 6 & -3 & 4 \end{vmatrix} \cdot$ 6. $\begin{vmatrix} a & c & b \\ 2a & 2 & 3 \\ c & b & 8a \end{vmatrix} \cdot$ 7. $\begin{vmatrix} 1 & x & y \\ 1 & x^2 & y^2 \\ 1 & x^3 & y^3 \end{vmatrix} \cdot$

8. $\begin{vmatrix} 1 & 2 & 3 & 1 \\ 3 & 0 & 0 & 2 \\ -2 & -1 & 4 & -3 \\ 1 & 3 & 2 & -4 \end{vmatrix} \cdot$ 9. $\begin{vmatrix} 2 & -1 & 2 & 3 \\ -1 & 1 & 0 & -2 \\ 5 & 3 & 0 & 1 \\ 7 & 2 & 4 & -5 \end{vmatrix} \cdot$

10. Suppose that $|A|$ is of order n, with A having arbitrary numbers as elements, and is expanded by use of Definition III, successively, until the expansion is obtained as a polynomial in the n^2 elements of A. By mathematical induction, prove that $|A|$ is equal to a polynomial consisting of $n!$ terms. (This result is almost an immediate consequence of the definition of $|A|$ met in Note 6 of the Appendix.)

119. Properties of determinants

A few of the properties of determinants can be proved easily by use of (3) on page 272. However, several fundamental properties require somewhat elaborate proofs, which are best presented by the method of Note 6 of the Appendix. We shall give proofs here only where they can be developed conveniently on our limited basis. All of the properties can be verified easily for a determinant of order 3.

Let A be a given matrix. Then, the **transpose** of A is defined as that matrix A' obtained if *the rows and columns of A are interchanged.*

Illustration 1. A matrix A and its transpose A' are given by

$$A = \begin{bmatrix} a_1 & b_1 & c_1 \\ a_2 & b_2 & c_2 \\ a_3 & b_3 & c_3 \end{bmatrix} \quad and \quad A' = \begin{bmatrix} a_1 & a_2 & a_3 \\ b_1 & b_2 & b_3 \\ c_1 & c_2 & c_3 \end{bmatrix}. \tag{1}$$

Property I. *If A is a square matrix, whose transpose is A', then $|A| = |A'|$.*

A proof of Property I is found in Note 6 of the Appendix. We shall verify Property I when $|A|$ is of order 3.

Illustration 2. On expanding $|A'|$ from Illustration 1 by the elements and cofactors of the 1st row of A', we obtain

$$|A'| = a_1(b_2c_3 - b_3c_2) - a_2(b_1c_3 - c_1b_3) + a_3(b_1c_2 - c_1b_2).$$

The student may verify that $|A'| = |A|$, as given in (4) on page 272.

By use of Property I, it is seen that, for every theorem about $|A|$ referring to the *columns* of A, there is a corresponding theorem referring to the *rows* of A, because $|A| = |A'|$, and A' is obtained by interchanging the rows and columns of A. Hence, we shall state various following properties of $|A|$ as applying to *both rows and columns*, but shall give verification or proof only for the case referring to *columns*. In the following discussion, A continues to represent *any square matrix.*

Property II. *If all elements of a column (or row) of A are multiplied by the same number, k, to obtain a new matrix B, then $|B| = k|A|$.*

Proof. Consider (3) on page 272 for $|A|$, with A as an $n \times n$ matrix:

$$|A| = p_1C_1 + p_2C_2 + \cdots + p_nC_n. \tag{2}$$

If each element in the column of p's in A is multiplied by k to obtain a new matrix B, then the corresponding column in B consists of the elements $(kp_1, kp_2, \cdots, kp_n)$. Since none of the other elements of A are altered, the cofactor in $|B|$ of the element kp_i will be the *same as for p_i in $|A|$*. Hence,

$$|B| = kp_1C_1 + kp_2C_2 + \cdots + kp_nC_n = k|A|.$$

Illustration 3.   By Property II, $k \begin{vmatrix} 3 & 4 \\ 5 & 7 \end{vmatrix} = \begin{vmatrix} 3 & 4k \\ 5 & 7k \end{vmatrix}$.

A special case of the following result is observed in Illustration 3. The general result is an immediate consequence of Property II.

Property III.   *If all elements of a column (or row) of a square matrix B have a common factor $k \neq 0$, and if A is the matrix obtained on dividing all elements of the column of B by k, then $|B| = k|A|$. That is, in obtaining $|B|$, the common factor k may be divided out if it is used to multiply the determinant of the new matrix A which arises.*

Property IV.   *If each element of a column (or row) of A is zero, then the determinant of A is zero, $|A| = 0$.*

Proof.   In the expansion of $|A|$ in (3) on page 272 by the elements and cofactors of the specified column, each term is zero because one factor of the term is zero, and hence $|A| = 0$.

Property V.*   *If two columns (or rows) in A are interchanged, to give a new matrix B, then $|B| = -|A|$.*

Illustration 4.   If $D = \begin{vmatrix} a_1 & b_1 & c_1 \\ a_2 & b_2 & c_2 \\ a_3 & b_3 & c_3 \end{vmatrix}$ *and* $T = \begin{vmatrix} c_1 & b_1 & a_1 \\ c_2 & b_2 & a_2 \\ c_3 & b_3 & a_3 \end{vmatrix}$,

then Property V states that $D = -T$. The student can verify this most easily by expanding D by the elements and cofactors of the third column of the matrix, and T by the first column of the new matrix involved. Identical expressions with signs changed are obtained in this fashion.

Property VI.   *If two columns (or rows) of a matrix A are identical, then the determinant of A is 0, $|A| = 0$.*

Proof.   If the two identical columns of A are interchanged, then the matrix is unaltered, so that, in the statement of Property V, $B = A$. Hence, $|A| = -|A|$ and thus $2|A| = 0$ or $|A| = 0$.

Illustration 5.   By Property VI, $\begin{vmatrix} a & x & x \\ b & y & y \\ c & z & z \end{vmatrix} = 0$.

Property VII.   *In a matrix A, suppose that each element p_i of some column (or row) is expressed as $p_i = p_i' + p_i''$. Then, $|A|$ can be expressed as the sum of the determinants of two matrices, where one has a column consisting of the numbers $\{p_i'\}$, and the other matrix has a column consisting of the numbers $\{p_i''\}$.*

* For a proof, see Note 6 in the Appendix.

Proof. We shall phrase our remarks for the determinant on the left below; Property VII states that the following equation should be true.

$$\begin{vmatrix} a_1 & (b_1 + d_1) & c_1 \\ a_2 & (b_2 + d_2) & c_2 \\ a_3 & (b_3 + d_3) & c_3 \end{vmatrix} = \begin{vmatrix} a_1 & b_1 & c_1 \\ a_2 & b_2 & c_2 \\ a_3 & b_3 & c_3 \end{vmatrix} + \begin{vmatrix} a_1 & d_1 & c_1 \\ a_2 & d_2 & c_2 \\ a_3 & d_3 & c_3 \end{vmatrix}. \tag{3}$$

Let B_1, B_2, and B_3 be the cofactors of the elements $(b_1 + d_1)$, $(b_2 + d_2)$, and $(b_3 + d_3)$ for the determinant on the left in (3). Since these cofactors depend only on the elements of the matrix in the 1st and 3d columns, (B_1, B_2, B_3) also are the cofactors of the elements in the 2d column of the matrix for each determinant on the right in (3). On expanding the determinant at the left in (3) by use of (3) on page 272, we obtain

$$(b_1 + d_1)B_1 + (b_2 + d_2)B_2 + (b_3 + d_3)B_3, \text{ or}$$
$$(b_1B_1 + b_2B_2 + b_3B_3) + (d_1B_1 + d_2B_2 + d_3B_3),$$

which is the sum of the expansions of the determinants on the right in (3). Hence, (3) is true. A similar proof, merely involving more notation, would apply in demonstrating Property VII for the determinant of any matrix A.

Property VIII. *In a matrix A, suppose that one column consists of the elements $(p_1, p_2, \cdots, p_n)$ and a second column consists of $(t_1, t_2, \cdots, t_n)$. If k is any constant, let a new matrix B be obtained by replacing p_i by $(p_i + kt_i)$. Then, $|A| = |B|$. Thus, addition of k times each element of one column of a matrix to the element of another column, in the same row, does not alter the determinant of the matrix.*

Proof. 1. We shall phrase our discussion for the matrix A of (1) on page 274, and prove that the following determinants D and R are equal.

$$D = \begin{vmatrix} a_1 & b_1 & c_1 \\ a_2 & b_2 & c_2 \\ a_3 & b_3 & c_3 \end{vmatrix}. \qquad R = \begin{vmatrix} a_1 & (b_1 + kc_1) & c_1 \\ a_2 & (b_2 + kc_2) & c_2 \\ a_3 & (b_3 + kc_3) & c_3 \end{vmatrix}.$$

2. On applying Property VII, and then Property III, we obtain

$$R = \begin{vmatrix} a_1 & b_1 & c_1 \\ a_2 & b_2 & c_2 \\ a_3 & b_3 & c_3 \end{vmatrix} + \begin{vmatrix} a_1 & kc_1 & c_1 \\ a_2 & kc_2 & c_2 \\ a_3 & kc_3 & c_3 \end{vmatrix} = D + k \begin{vmatrix} a_1 & c_1 & c_1 \\ a_2 & c_2 & c_2 \\ a_3 & c_3 & c_3 \end{vmatrix} = D, \tag{4}$$

because the determinant in (4) with two identical columns is zero, on account of Property VI.

120. Evaluation of determinants

A determinant of order 2 should be computed by use of the expansion (4) on page 268. If A is an $n \times n$ matrix where $n > 2$, usually it is best to compute $|A|$ as follows.

1. *By use of* Property VIII, *applied to both rows and columns, alter A to a form where all except a few of the elements in some particular column (or row) are zeros, and thus obtain a new matrix B, such that* $|A| = |B|$.

2. *Expand* $|B|$ *by the elements and cofactors of the column (or row) containing the zeros. For each minor in this expansion, if the order of the minor is greater than 2, proceed again as in the first stage.*

EXAMPLE 1.   Compute the determinant of the following matrix:

$$A = \begin{bmatrix} 5 & 7 & 8 & 6 \\ 11 & 16 & 13 & 11 \\ 14 & 24 & 20 & 23 \\ 7 & 13 & 12 & 2 \end{bmatrix}.$$

Solution.   1. In A, subtract the 1st row from the 4th row (that is, subtract each element of the 1st row from the corresponding element of the 4th row); twice the 1st row from the 2d row; three times the 1st row from the 3d row. Then, we obtain

$$|A| = \begin{vmatrix} 5 & 7 & 8 & 6 \\ 1 & 2 & -3 & -1 \\ -1 & 3 & -4 & 5 \\ 2 & 6 & 4 & -4 \end{vmatrix} = 2\begin{vmatrix} 5 & 7 & 8 & 6 \\ 1 & 2 & -3 & -1 \\ -1 & 3 & -4 & 5 \\ 1 & 3 & 2 & -2 \end{vmatrix}, \tag{1}$$

where Property III was used at the right in dividing each element by 2 in the 4th row of the determinant at the left.

2. In the matrix for the determinant at the right in (1), subtract the 2d row from the 4th row; subtract five times the 2d row from the 1st row; add the 2d row to the 3d row; then expand the determinant of the matrix by the elements and cofactors of the 1st column; finally, compute the determinant of the 3d order below by use of the elements and cofactors of some row or column:

$$|A| = 2\begin{vmatrix} 0 & -3 & 23 & 11 \\ 1 & 2 & -3 & -1 \\ 0 & 5 & -7 & 4 \\ 0 & 1 & 5 & -1 \end{vmatrix} = 2\left\{ -(1) \cdot \begin{vmatrix} -3 & 23 & 11 \\ 5 & -7 & 4 \\ 1 & 5 & -1 \end{vmatrix} \right\}$$

$$= 2(-598) = -1196.$$

Sometimes, it may be convenient to calculate $|A|$ by first arranging to alter A to triangular form, as met on page 266. Refer to operations* I–IV on page 266, as involved in changing the coefficient matrix of a system of linear equations to triangular form. By Property V, operation I, or II, if applied to A, would yield a new matrix B such that $|A| = -|B|$. Operation IV of page 266, if applied to A, yields a new matrix B such that $|A| = |B|$, because of Property

* Where any word *row* may be changed to *column*, and vice versa.

VIII. However, if operation III of page 266 is applied to A, with k as the constant employed, to obtain a new matrix B, it is necessary to remember that $|A| = |B|/k$. If changes of sign and constant divisors are duly noted, the process leading from A to a matrix B in *triangular form* is desirable on many occasions; the student will verify easily that $|B|$ is equal simply to **the product of the elements in the main diagonal of B.**

Illustration 1. To calculate $|A|$, where

$$A = \begin{bmatrix} 3 & 1 & 1 \\ 1 & 3 & 1 \\ -2 & 1 & 3 \end{bmatrix},$$

we may first alter A to triangular form as follows: Subtract the 2d row from the 1st row; then, multiply the elements of the 2d row by 3 (therefore, the determinant of any final matrix must be divided by 3, which we indicate for future use at the right):

$$A, \text{ then } \begin{bmatrix} 2 & -2 & 0 \\ 1 & 3 & 1 \\ -2 & 1 & 3 \end{bmatrix}; \quad \text{then} \quad \begin{bmatrix} 2 & -2 & 0 \\ 3 & 9 & 3 \\ -2 & 1 & 3 \end{bmatrix} = B. \quad (\div 3)$$

Then, subtract the 3d row from the 2d row; then, add the 1st column to the 2d column:

$$B, \text{ then } \begin{bmatrix} 2 & -2 & 0 \\ 5 & 8 & 0 \\ -2 & 1 & 3 \end{bmatrix}; \quad \text{then} \quad \begin{bmatrix} 2 & 0 & 0 \\ 5 & 13 & 0 \\ -2 & -1 & 3 \end{bmatrix} = W.$$

We have W in triangular form, and $|A| = \frac{1}{3}|W|$. On expanding $|W|$ by elements and cofactors of the 1st row, we find just one nonzero term:

$$|A| = \frac{1}{3} \cdot 2 \cdot \begin{vmatrix} 13 & 0 \\ -1 & 3 \end{vmatrix} = \frac{1}{3} \cdot 2 \cdot (39) = 26.$$

EXERCISE 76

1-4. Compute the determinants in Problems 2–5, respectively, of Exercise 75 by first altering the matrix involved so that it will have two zeros in some row or column. In at least one problem, also apply the triangulation method of Illustration 1 above.

5-6. Compute the determinants in Problems 8 and 9, respectively, of Exercise 75, by first arranging to have three zeros in some row or column.

Evaluate the determinant.

7. $\begin{vmatrix} 1 & -2 & 3 & 7 \\ -1 & -1 & 5 & 8 \\ 2 & 6 & -2 & -4 \\ 4 & 7 & 3 & 3 \end{vmatrix}.$

8. $\begin{vmatrix} 2 & -1 & 2 & 3 \\ 1 & 0 & 2 & 1 \\ 5 & 3 & 0 & 1 \\ 7 & 2 & 4 & -5 \end{vmatrix}.$

9. $\begin{vmatrix} 2 & -1 & 3 & 7 \\ 3 & 1 & 5 & 8 \\ 6 & -2 & -2 & -4 \\ 8 & -4 & -3 & 3 \end{vmatrix}.$ 10. $\begin{vmatrix} 2 & 3 & 1 & 4 \\ 3 & -5 & -1 & -1 \\ 0 & 1 & 2 & -5 \\ 3 & 3 & 2 & 3 \end{vmatrix}.$

11. Without expanding, show that the adjoining equation is satisfied when $x = 2$ and $x = 3$. Hence, what factors has the determinant? Check by expanding. $\begin{vmatrix} 1 & 3 & 2 \\ 1 & x & 2 \\ 1 & 2 & x \end{vmatrix} = 0.$

12. Without expanding, show that the adjoining determinant has the factors $(x - y)$, $(y - w)$, and $(x - w)$, and find a factored expression for the determinant. $\begin{vmatrix} 1 & 1 & 1 \\ x & y & w \\ x^2 & y^2 & w^2 \end{vmatrix}$

13. Without expanding the determinant, prove that the adjoining equation is the equation of the line through the points (x_1, y_1) and (x_2, y_2). Then, use this form to obtain the line through the points $(2, -3)$ and $(4, 1)$. $\begin{vmatrix} 1 & x & y \\ 1 & x_1 & y_1 \\ 1 & x_2 & y_2 \end{vmatrix} = 0.$

121. A property of cofactors

Let A be any square matrix, illustrated by $A = \begin{bmatrix} a_1 & b_1 & c_1 \\ a_2 & b_2 & c_2 \\ a_3 & b_3 & c_3 \end{bmatrix}.$ (1)

In dealing with $|A|$, let the cofactor for each element of A be represented by the corresponding capital letter with a subscript as on the element. Thus, for (1), we have the cofactors A_1, A_2, A_3, B_1, etc.

THEOREM II. *In the expansion of $|A|$ by the elements and cofactors of a given column (or row), if the elements are replaced by any numbers, then the result is the determinant of a new matrix where the given column of A is replaced by the new numbers.*

Proof, with remarks specialized to A of (1). Consider the expansion of $|A|$ by the elements and cofactors of any column, for instance,

$$\begin{vmatrix} a_1 & b_1 & c_1 \\ a_2 & b_2 & c_2 \\ a_3 & b_3 & c_3 \end{vmatrix} = b_1B_1 + b_2B_2 + b_3B_3.$$ (2)

In the identity (2), replace (b_1, b_2, b_3) on both sides by any numbers (k_1, k_2, k_3). Then, we obtain the following statement, which proves Theorem II.

$$\begin{vmatrix} a_1 & k_1 & c_1 \\ a_2 & k_2 & c_2 \\ a_3 & k_3 & c_3 \end{vmatrix} = k_1B_1 + k_2B_2 + k_3B_3.$$ (3)

THEOREM III. *In the expansion of $|A|$ by the elements and cofactors of a given column (or row), if its elements are replaced by the corresponding elements of another column (or row), the result is identically zero.*

Proof. If (k_1, k_2, k_3) in (3) are the elements of another column of A, not the column used in (2), then the matrix of the determinant in (3) has two identical columns, and hence the determinant is zero.

122. Solution of linear systems by determinants

Let any system of n linear equations in n variables be written in the following normal form, illustrated for the case $n = 3$, with the variables x, y, and z:

$$\textbf{(I)} \quad \begin{cases} a_1x + b_1y + c_1z = k_1, & (1) \\ a_2x + b_2y + c_2z = k_2, & (2) \\ a_3x + b_3y + c_3z = k_3. & (3) \end{cases}$$

In system (I), the characteristic feature is that all terms in the variables, *in a definite order*, are in the left-hand members, and the constant term (possibly zero) in each equation is on the right. In (I) we have a coefficient matrix, H, and its determinant, as follows:

$$H = \begin{bmatrix} a_1 & b_1 & c_1 \\ a_2 & b_2 & c_2 \\ a_3 & b_3 & c_3 \end{bmatrix}; \quad |H| = \begin{vmatrix} a_1 & b_1 & c_1 \\ a_2 & b_2 & c_2 \\ a_3 & b_3 & c_3 \end{vmatrix}. \quad (4)$$

Let three matrices (K_1, K_2, K_3) be defined as follows:

$$K_1 = \begin{bmatrix} k_1 & b_1 & c_1 \\ k_2 & b_2 & c_2 \\ k_3 & b_3 & c_3 \end{bmatrix}; \quad K_2 = \begin{bmatrix} a_1 & k_1 & c_1 \\ a_2 & k_2 & c_2 \\ a_3 & k_3 & c_3 \end{bmatrix}; \quad K_3 = \begin{bmatrix} a_1 & b_1 & k_1 \\ a_2 & b_2 & k_2 \\ a_3 & b_3 & k_3 \end{bmatrix}. \quad (5)$$

THEOREM IV. **Cramer's rule,** *as stated on page 269, applies in the case of a system of n linear equations in n variables, for every integer n.*

Proof, for the case $n = 3$, with system (I). 1. First, let us show that, **IF** (x, y, z) have values which satisfy (I), then

$$x \cdot |H| = |K_1|; \quad y \cdot |H| = |K_2|; \quad z \cdot |H| = |K_3|. \quad (6)$$

2. For the elements of H, let capital letters A_1, B_1, etc., as in Section 121, represent the cofactors of the elements, for $|H|$. Then, to establish, for instance, $y \cdot |H| = |K_2|$, multiply both sides of (1), (2), and (3), respectively, by B_1, B_2, and B_3, which gives

$$a_1B_1x + b_1B_1y + c_1B_1z = k_1B_1, \quad (7)$$
$$a_2B_2x + b_2B_2y + c_2B_2z = k_2B_2, \quad (8)$$
$$a_3B_3x + b_3B_3y + c_3B_3z = k_3B_3. \quad (9)$$

On adding corresponding members of (7), (8), and (9) and collecting terms, the coefficient of y is found to be

$$b_1B_1 + b_2B_2 + b_3B_3, \quad (10)$$

which is seen to be $|H|$, expanded by the elements and cofactors of the 2d column of H. On adding in (7), (8), and (9), as above, the coefficient of x on the left is found to be $(a_1B_1 + a_2B_2 + a_3B_3)$, which is the same as (10) except that a's replace the b's in (10). Hence, by Theorem III, the coefficient just found for x is zero. Similarly, the coefficient for z is zero. Thus, on adding in (7), (8), and (9), we obtain

$$y \cdot |H| = k_1B_1 + k_2B_2 + k_3B_3. \tag{11}$$

In (11), the right-hand side is the same as (10), except that the b's of (10) are replaced by the k's. Hence, by Theorem II, the right-hand side of (11) is the expansion of the determinant of the matrix obtained on replacing the b's in H by the k's, which gives $|K_2|$. Hence, (11) becomes $y \cdot |H| = |K_2|$.

3. To establish $z \cdot |H| = |K_3|$, we would multiply in (1), (2), and (3), respectively, by the cofactors (C_1, C_2, C_3) of the column of coefficients of z in $|H|$, and then add. To obtain $x \cdot |H| = |K_1|$, we would multiply similarly by the cofactors (A_1, A_2, A_3).

4. **IF** $|H| \neq 0$, from (6) we obtain the following results, as described in Cramer's rule:

$$x = \frac{|K_1|}{|H|} ; \quad y = \frac{|K_2|}{|H|} ; \quad z = \frac{|K_3|}{|H|} . \tag{12}$$

5. Suppose, now, that $|H| \neq 0$. Then, to complete the proof of Theorem IV, we should show that the values of (x, y, z) in (12) satisfy system (I). This substitution and verification is very simple if certain theorems about matrices are available.* However, in the absence of such theorems, we shall omit the substitution.

EXAMPLE 1. Solve: **(II)**
$$\begin{cases} 2x - y + 2z + w = 12, & (13) \\ 2x - y + 3z - 4w = 5, & (14) \\ 5x + y + z = 6, & (15) \\ -2y + z + w = 9. & (16) \end{cases}$$

Solution. We use Cramer's rule.

$$|H| = \begin{vmatrix} 2 & -1 & 2 & 1 \\ 2 & -1 & 3 & -4 \\ 5 & 1 & 1 & 0 \\ 0 & -2 & 1 & 1 \end{vmatrix} = 48; \quad K_3 = \begin{vmatrix} 2 & -1 & 12 & 1 \\ 2 & -1 & 5 & -4 \\ 5 & 1 & 6 & 0 \\ 0 & -2 & 9 & 1 \end{vmatrix} = 144.$$

Hence, $z = (|K_3|/|H|) = 3$. Similarly, $y = -2$. Instead of using determinants to obtain the values of x and w, it is convenient to proceed as follows:

Substitute $(y = -2, z = 3)$ in (15) and (16). Then, from (15) we obtain $x = 1$; from (16) we obtain $w = 2$. Thus, the solution of (II) is seen to be $(x = 1, y = -2, z = 3, \text{and } w = 2)$.

---

* For these omitted details, see Note 8 in the Appendix, where Theorem IV is proved by use of matrix algebra.

Let us understand that the notations for system (I) are to extend to *any* system of n linear equations in n variables, with H as the coefficient matrix for the system. The complete discussion of the solution of such a system when $|H| = 0$ is too complicated for treatment in this text. The system may be consistent (have solutions), and then can be proved to have infinitely many solutions. Usually, however, the system is inconsistent (has no solution) if $|H| = 0$. The most simple condition for inconsistency in this case is as follows:

THEOREM V. *Suppose that, in a system of the form* (I) *in n variables, the determinant of the coefficient matrix is zero,* $|H| = 0$, *and that at least one of the numerator determinants* $|K_1|, |K_2|, \cdots$ *of Cramer's rule is not zero. Then, the system is inconsistent.*

Proof, for the case of system (I). (*Indirect method.*) Assume that the conclusion of Theorem V is *false;* that is, assume that *there is a particular triple of numbers* (x, y, z) *which satisfy* (I). Then, (6) is true for (x, y, z). Since $|H| = 0$, then $x \cdot |H| = |K_1| = 0$. Similarly, $|K_2| = 0$ and $|K_3| = 0$. Thus, we have arrived at a contradiction to the hypothesis of Theorem V that *at least one* of $(|K_1|, |K_2|, |K_3|)$ is *not zero*. Hence, *our present assumption that* (I) *has a solution* (x, y, z) *cannot be true*, or (I) *must be inconsistent*.

EXERCISE 77

1–15. Solve Problems 1–15, respectively, on pages 267–268, if possible, or prove that the system is inconsistent, by use of determinants.

123. Homogeneous systems

A linear equation is said to be *homogeneous* in case the constant term in it is equal to zero. Thus, in (I) on page 280, to say that the equations are homogeneous means that $k_1 = k_2 = k_3 = 0$. By substitution, we see that any system of homogeneous linear equations is satisfied when each variable has the value zero. Frequently, such a solution is useless, and hence it is called the **trivial solution.** To say that a solution of the system is **nontrivial** means that, in it, *at least one of the variables is not equal to zero.*

THEOREM VI. *If a system of n homogeneous linear equations in n variables has a nontrivial solution, then the determinant of the coefficient matrix is equal to zero.*

Proof. 1. Consider system (I) on page 280 with $k_1 = k_2 = k_3 = 0$. By hypothesis, (I) has a nontrivial solution.

2. (*Indirect method.*) Let us assume that, in (4) on page 280, $|H| \neq \mathbf{0}$. From (5) on page 280,

$$|K_1| = |K_2| = |K_3| = 0,$$

because each of (K_1, K_2, K_3) has a column of zeros. Since $|H| \neq 0$, from (12) on page 281 we find that the *unique* solution of (I) is $(x = 0, y = 0, z = 0)$. This fact *contradicts the hypothesis that* (I) *has a nontrivial solution.* Therefore, the assumption that $|H| \neq 0$ is *false*, and thus $|H| = 0$.

THEOREM VII. *If the determinant of the coefficient matrix is zero in a system of n homogeneous linear equations in n variables, then the system has infinitely many nontrivial solutions.*

The proof of Theorem VII is beyond the scope of this text. However, for a homogeneous system as in Theorem VII, nontrivial solutions usually can be obtained as follows.

1. *Solve* $(n - 1)$ *of the equations for* $(n - 1)$ *of the variables in terms of the other variable, call it x.*

2. *Assign any value, not zero, to x and compute the values of the other variables by use of the preceding results. Each set of corresponding values of the n variables thus obtained is a solution of the system.*

EXAMPLE 1.   Discuss the following system:

$$\begin{cases} 3x + 2y - 3z = 0, & \text{(1)} \\ 4x - y + 7z = 0, & \text{(2)} \\ x - 3y + 10z = 0. & \text{(3)} \end{cases}$$

Solution.   1. The determinant of the coefficient matrix is

$$\begin{vmatrix} 3 & 2 & -3 \\ 4 & -1 & 7 \\ 1 & -3 & 10 \end{vmatrix} = 0.$$

Hence, by Theorem VII, the system has nontrivial solutions.

2. On solving (1) and (2) for x and y in terms of z, we obtain $x = -z$ and $y = 3z$. By substitution, it is found that these values for x and y satisfy (3) for every value of z.

3. From the preceding details, if $z = 2$, then $x = -2$ and $y = 6$, so that $(-2, 6, 2)$ is one solution. Similarly, corresponding to any value of z, we obtain a solution for the system. Thus, it has infinitely many solutions, given by $(x = -h, y = 3h, z = h)$, for any value of h.

124. More variables than equations

A system of m linear equations in n variables, where $n > m$, usually has *infinitely many solutions* but may be inconsistent. Generally, we can obtain solutions by solving the m equations for m of the variables in terms of the others and then substituting values arbitrarily for them.

Illustration 1. Consider the following system:

$$\left.\begin{cases} 3x - y - 2z = 1, \\ 2x + y - 3z = -1. \end{cases}\right\} \tag{1}$$

In (1), the determinant of the coefficient matrix for the variables (x, y) is not zero. Hence, we can solve (1) for x and y in terms of z by use of determinants, to obtain $(x = z, y = z - 1)$. Then, if $z = 2$, we find $x = 2$ and $y = 1$; thus, $(2, 1, 2)$ is a solution of (1). Similarly, for any value of h, with $z = h$ we obtain the solution $(x = h, y = h - 1, z = h)$ for (1). Thus, (1) has infinitely many solutions.

125. More equations than variables

A system of m linear equations in n variables, with $m > n$, usually is *inconsistent*. However, suppose that we can solve a certain n of the equations for the variables. If the values thus obtained also satisfy the other $(m - n)$ equations, then the system is consistent.

Illustration 1. In the system

$$\left.\begin{aligned} x - 2y + 7 &= 0, \\ 3x + 7y - 5 &= 0, \\ x + y + 1 &= 0, \end{aligned}\right\} \tag{1}$$

the first two equations have the single solution $(x = -3, y = 2)$. By substitution, these values are found to satisfy the third equation in (1). Hence, the system has just one solution.

A system of n linear equations in $(n - 1)$ variables can be written in the following standard form (illustrated for $n = 3$):

$$\left.\begin{aligned} a_1x + b_1y + c_1 &= 0, \\ a_2x + b_2y + c_2 &= 0, \\ a_3x + b_3y + c_3 &= 0. \end{aligned}\right\} \tag{2}$$

THEOREM VIII. *In a system of n linear equations in $(n - 1)$ variables in the standard form (2), let H be the matrix of coefficients of the variables, and the constant terms. Then, if $|H| \neq 0$, the system is inconsistent.*

Proof, for the case $n = 3$. 1. By hypothesis, $|H| \neq 0$. In (2), change (c_1, c_2, c_3) to (c_1z, c_2z, c_3z), respectively, to obtain the following homogeneous system in (x, y, z):

$$\left.\begin{aligned} a_1x + b_1y + c_1z &= 0, \\ a_2x + b_2y + c_2z &= 0, \\ a_3x + b_3y + c_3z &= 0. \end{aligned}\right\} \tag{3}$$

2. *(Indirect proof.)* Assume that (2) is *consistent*, with a solution $(x = h, y = k)$. Then, (3) has the nontrivial solution $(x = h, y = k, z = 1)$,

because (3) becomes (2) when $z = 1$. Thus, by Theorem VI on page 282, we should have $|H| = 0$. But, this contradicts the hypothesis that $|H| \neq 0$. Hence, *the assumption that* (2) *is consistent is false*, and thus (2) is *inconsistent*. The preceding remarks also prove the following result.

Corollary 1. *If system* (2) *is consistent, then* $|H| = 0$.

EXERCISE 78

Find two nontrivial solutions or prove that none exist.

1. $\begin{cases} x - 4y - 6z = 0, \\ 3x + 10y + 4z = 0, \\ 3x - y - 7z = 0. \end{cases}$

2. $\begin{cases} 3u - 2v - 13w = 0, \\ u + 4v + 5w = 0, \\ 2u + v - 4w = 0. \end{cases}$

3. $\begin{cases} 2x - 3y + 3z = 0, \\ 4x - 6y + 5z = 0, \\ 3x - 4y + 3z = 0. \end{cases}$

4. $\begin{cases} x + 3y + z = 0, \\ 3x - y - 2z = 0, \\ 2x - 4y - 3z = 0. \end{cases}$

Find two solutions of the system.

5. $\begin{cases} 2x - 3y = z - 8, \\ x + 2y - 4z = 3. \end{cases}$

6. $\begin{cases} 3x - y - 2z = 4, \\ 2x + 5y - 7z = 3. \end{cases}$

Prove inconsistent, or find a solution.

7. $\begin{cases} 2x + 9y - 12 = 0, \\ x - 2y + 7 = 0, \\ 3x + 7y = 5. \end{cases}$

8. $\begin{cases} x - 3y - 2 = 0, \\ x - 2y + 5 = 0, \\ 3x + 5y + 2 = 0. \end{cases}$

9. $\begin{cases} 4x - 7y = 13, \\ x - 2y = 3, \\ 2x - 3y = 7. \end{cases}$

10. $\begin{cases} x - 2y + 2 = 0, \\ 2x - 4y + 7 = 0, \\ 3x - y + 5 = 0. \end{cases}$

Given that the system is consistent, find the value of the constant k.

11. $\begin{cases} kx + 2y + k = 0, \\ 3x + 14ky - 5k = 0, \\ 2kx + 5y + k = 0. \end{cases}$

12. $\begin{cases} x - y + k = 0, \\ 6kx + ky - 2 = 0, \\ 2x + y + 2 = 0. \end{cases}$

Given that nontrivial solutions exist, find the value of the constant k.

13. $\begin{cases} kx - y + 2kz = 0, \\ 8x + 10y + kz = 0, \\ 2x + 2y + z = 0. \end{cases}$

14. $\begin{cases} 3kx - 2y + 2w = 0, \\ 4y + kw = 0, \\ kx + 6y - w = 0. \end{cases}$

If (x, y, z) *represents any solution of the system, find numbers* (g, h, k) *such that* (x, y, z) *are proportional to* (g, h, k), *or* $x : y : z = g : h : k$.

15. $\begin{cases} x - 2y + 3z = 0, \\ 2x + 4y - z = 0. \end{cases}$

16. $\begin{cases} 3x - y + z = 0, \\ 2x + 3y - 2z = 0. \end{cases}$

Chapter **12** Combinations and Permutations

126. A multiplication principle

The present chapter will develop methods for finding how often specified events can occur. The following result is useful in many situations.

Multiplication Principle. *For successive or simultaneous events.*

If an event E_1 can occur in h_1 ways and if, after its occurrence or at the same time, an event E_2 can occur in h_2 ways, then the two events can occur in the stated fashion in h_1h_2 ways. Similarly, if events E_1, E_2, $\cdots$, E_k can occur successively or, in part, simultaneously in h_1, h_2, $\cdots$, h_k ways, respectively, then all of the events can occur as stated in $h_1h_2 \cdots h_k$ ways.

Illustration 1. If there are 5 ways of going from A to B and 4 ways of going from B to C, then we can go from A to B to C in $5 \cdot 4$ or 20 ways.

Illustration 2. Suppose that a mouse is motivated to go through a maze which has two doors for entrance to some first chamber, two exits from it to arrive at some second chamber, and three exits from it to arrive at some terminal, with a food reward available at only one of the possible terminals. Then, the mouse must make three choices E_1, E_2, and E_3, where the numbers of options are $h_1 = 2$, $h_2 = 2$, and $h_3 = 3$, respectively. By the multiplication principle, the mouse has $2 \cdot 2 \cdot 3$ or 12 ways of arriving at a terminal, u. This result is illustrated in the logical *"tree"* in Figure 91, where the mouse starts at S.

Figure 91

Note 1. In this chapter and the next, unless otherwise specified, the word *number* will refer to a *positive integer*.

EXAMPLE 1. How many numbers of three different digits each can be formed by use of the digits 1, 2, 3, 5, 8, and 9.

Solution. We can choose any one of the six digits for the units' place, indicated by 6 in the right-hand box below; then, any one of the five remaining digits for the tens' place; then, any one of the four remaining digits for the hundreds' place. Hence, by the multiplication principle, we can form $6 \cdot 5 \cdot 4$ or 120 different numbers of the specified type.

(4)	(5)	(6)

In applying the multiplication principle to a complicated act, it is best to analyze it, if possible, into two or more successive or simultaneous acts of a more simple nature. Then, the principle should be applied first to each of the simpler acts, and finally to their joint performance.

EXAMPLE 2. In how many ways can 4 boys and 3 girls be seated in a row of 7 seats if the end seats are to be occupied by boys?

Solution. The 1st seat can be filled in 4 ways; then, the 7th seat in 3 ways, by any one of the 3 remaining boys; then, the 2d seat in 5 ways, by any one of the 5 remaining boys and girls; then, the 3d seat in 4 ways, etc., as in the diagram. Hence, the 7 seats can be filled by the boys and the girls in the specified manner in $4 \cdot 3 \cdot 5 \cdot 4 \cdot 3 \cdot 2 \cdot 1$ or 1440 ways.

(4)	(5)	(4)	(3)	(2)	(1)	(3)

EXAMPLE 3. In how many ways can 3 men be assigned consecutive seats in a row of 7 seats?

Solution. 1. *Analysis.* To seat the men in any one of the ways,

(a) *choose 3 consecutive seats, and then*

(b) *seat the men in the 3 seats just chosen.*

2. We can perform act (a) in 5 ways (think first of the 3 seats being at the left-hand end, and then move to the right-hand end, in 4 steps).

3. After any choice of 3 seats, by the multiplication principle, the 3 men can be assigned these seats in $3 \cdot 2 \cdot 1$ ways, or (b) can be performed in 6 ways.

4. Hence, by the multiplication principle, (a) and (b) can be done in succession, or the men can be seated, in $5 \cdot 6$ or 30 ways.

Comment. In the analysis, observe that we thought of how we might proceed, in stages, to perform the specified act in *just one way*.

127. Combinations; arrangements, or permutations

When we refer simply to a *set* (or, *collection*) of objects, with the "undefined" meaning used for *set* on page 19, it is assumed that *no question of order or arrangement for the objects is involved*. Thus, in mentioning a set of ten men, we think of them in a *group*, unordered. In speaking of the elements of a set (or of a subset of some fundamental set), frequently we shall refer to the set as a **combination** of its elements. Many problems in this chapter will be stated in colloquial language. In such a case, we agree that the word *group* may be used to mean *combination*.

Illustration 1. A subset of three men from a group of men is a combination of the men of the group, taken three at a time. A combination of three digits selected from $(1, 2, 3, 4, 5)$ is a subset of three digits, say $\left\{ \begin{matrix} & 2 & \\ 4 & & 5 \end{matrix} \right\}$, where we write them in this way to emphasize that no order is assigned to them.

A particular order can be specified among the elements of a set by arranging them in a sequence, by placing them in earmarked locations of special significance, or in other ways. Thus, in each of Examples 1 and 2 of the preceding section, we were concerned with *ordering* a set of elements (digits in one case; boys and girls in the other case). The placement of a set of elements in a definite order may be called an **arrangement** of the elements. The technical word **permutation** also will be used frequently in place of arrangement.

Illustration 2. From the combination or group of digits $\left\{ \begin{matrix} & 2 & \\ 4 & & 5 \end{matrix} \right\}$ in Illustration 1, we can form the following six permutations, or arrangements of the digits:

$$254; \quad 245; \quad 425; \quad 452; \quad 524; \quad 542.$$

This illustrates the fact that, with the usual place system for writing numerals, every number symbol is a permutation of the digits of the symbol.

The solutions of Examples 1 and 2 of the preceding section show that the multiplication principle frequently is useful in finding the number of permutations of a specified nature.

SUMMARY. *A* **combination** *of certain elements consists of the elements without any specification of relative order among them. A* **permutation** *of certain elements consists of the elements* **arranged in a particular order.**

In a **permutation, order is significant.**	(1)
In a **combination, order is not involved.**	(2)

Illustration 3. From a group consisting of Jones, Johnson, Hansen, and Watson, we can form a combination, or group, of two men in the following 6 different ways, where the order of writing the names is immaterial.

$$\left\{\begin{array}{l}\text{(Jones, Johnson);} \quad \text{(Jones, Hansen);} \quad \text{(Jones, Watson);} \\ \text{(Johnson, Hansen);} \quad \text{(Johnson, Watson);} \quad \text{(Hansen, Watson).}\end{array}\right\} \quad (3)$$

Now, consider filling the positions of president and treasurer in a club by selections from the four men. There are 4 ways of choosing the president, and then 3 ways of selecting the treasurer from the remaining 3 men. By the multiplication principle, there are $4 \cdot 3$ or 12 ways of filling the offices. In this case, the order, or names (*pres.*, *treas.*), is a fundamental feature. Thus, there are 12 *permutations* of the 4 men taken two at a time. The student may verify that these permutations, two at a time, are obtained by using each of the combinations (3) in turn for the officers. Thus, with (Jones, Johnson), we can have

$$(pres. \text{ Jones, } treas. \text{ Johnson}) \quad or \quad (pres. \text{ Johnson, } treas. \text{ Jones}).$$

In this chapter, we shall be interested in finding the number of combinations, or of permutations, of given elements under various conditions. The concept of a combination is more simple than that of a permutation. However, it will prove convenient to develop, first, formulas for numbers of permutations, and then to employ these results in obtaining formulas for numbers of combinations. At present, problems involving permutations should be solved by direct use of the multiplication principle. Combinations will be met later.

Illustration 4. The permutations of the letters a, b, and c, taken two at a time, are ab, ba, ac, ca, bc, and cb; their permutations, taken three at a time, are abc, acb, bac, bca, cab, and cba.

EXAMPLE 1. Find the number of permutations of seven different things taken three at a time.

Solution. In forming permutations, we can fill the first place in 7 ways, then the second place with any one of the 6 things remaining after the first place is filled, and finally the last place in 5 ways. Hence, there are $7 \cdot 6 \cdot 5$ or 210 permutations of the specified kind.

EXERCISE 79

1. From the digits 1, 2, 3, 4, 5, 7, and 8, (*a*) how many numbers of four different digits each can be formed; (*b*) how many odd numbers of this character can be formed?

2. In how many ways can 4 people seat themselves in 6 given seats?

3. Each of 3 departments in a store needs a secretary. There are 6 applicants for the positions. In how many ways can the positions be filled?

4. Two cubical dice, each with its faces numbered 1, 2, 3, 4, 5, and 6, are tossed. In how many ways can they fall?

5. How many permutations (*numbers*) can be written by use of the digits 2, 3, 4, 7, and 8 taken three at a time? Write out these permutations.

6. Find an expression for the number of permutations of n different things taken 4 at a time; taken 8 at a time, assuming that $n > 7$.

7. In how many ways can 3 students choose sections in registering for a course where 6 sections are taught at the same hour?

8. How many permutations are there of the letters a, d, h, k, and w taken three at a time? Write out all of these permutations.

9. If all possible numbers of five different digits each are written by use of the digits 1, 2, 3, 4, 5, 6, 7, 8, and 9, (a) how many are written? Also, find how many are (b) even; (c) divisible by 5; (d) begin with an even digit and end with an odd digit.

10. From the letters of the word "decimal," all permutations of 5 different letters each will be formed. (1) How many of them are formed? Also, how many (2) begin and end with a *consonant;* (3) have d or c in the center; (4) have consonants and vowels alternating?

11. How many numbers without repeated digits can be written by use of the digits 1, 2, 3, 4, 5, and 6?

12. In how many ways can 4 men choose movies to attend, if 6 different movies are being shown?

13. In how many ways can 6 men be arranged in a row for a minstrel show if just 4 men are capable of acting as end men?

14. How many flag signals can be shown by a ship if the signal mast has five positions, the flags have different colors, and any signal with less than five flags uses the top positions on the pole? Five flags are available.

15. Four travelers arrive in a town with five hotels. In how many ways can they (a) take up quarters; (b) take up quarters, with each traveler staying at a different hotel?

16. (a) How many numbers of four different digits each can be written by use of the digits 0, 2, 3, 5, 6, and 9? Of these numbers, how many (b) are even; (c) are divisible by 5?

17. In how many ways can 7 people be assigned consecutive positions in a receiving line if the first 2 positions must be filled by selections from 4 of the people?

18. In how many ways can 4 girls and 4 boys be assigned seats in a row at a theater if boys and girls are to alternate?

19. In how many ways can 4 different novels and 3 different mystery stories be arranged in a row on a shelf, with books of the same variety together?

20. The captain of a baseball team assigns himself to the 4th place in the batting order. In how many ways can he assign the remaining places to his 8 teammates, if just 3 men are considered eligible for the 1st position?

21. How many distinct license plates for automobiles can be made up if each plate label consists of two different capital Roman letters (not O) at the ends, and a number, not 0, less than 100,000 between the ends.

22. A group of six speakers consists of two politicians and four lawyers who are not politicians. In arrangements for a speaking order at a meeting, the politicians will speak in succession and the lawyers in succession. In how many ways can the order be arranged?

128. Formulas for numbers of permutations

Let $_nP_r$ represent the number of permutations of n different things taken r at a time.

THEOREM I. *The number of permutations of n different things taken r at a time is $n(n-1)(n-2) \cdots (n-r+1)$, or*

$$_nP_r = n(n-1)(n-2) \cdots (n-r+1). \qquad (1)$$

Proof. In any permutation, we can fill the 1st place by any one of the n things, then the 2d place by any of the $(n-1)$ things remaining after the 1st place is filled, then the 3d place by any one of the $(n-2)$ things remaining, $\cdots$, finally the rth place by any one of the $[n-(r-1)]$ things remaining after the $(r-1)$th place is filled. Hence, by the multiplication principle, all r places in a permutation of the n things, taken r at a time, can be filled in

$$n(n-1)(n-2) \cdots (n-r+1) \text{ different ways.}$$

Corollary 1. *The number of permutations of n different things, taken n at a time, is n!.*

Proof. We place $r = n$ in (1) and obtain

$$_nP_n = n(n-1)(n-2) \cdots 3 \cdot 2 \cdot 1 = n!. \qquad (2)$$

Illustration 1. $_7P_4 = 7 \cdot 6 \cdot 5 \cdot 4 = 840$; $_nP_3 = n(n-1)(n-2)$.

Note 1. The student should remember that the multiplication principle has wider application than (1) and (2), which were derived by use of the principle.

EXAMPLE 1. In how many relative orders can 7 people take seats at a round table?

Solution. Think of *a particular one* of the people as being seated, and consider his position permanently fixed. Since only *relative* order is involved, it does not matter where he is located. Then, the number of different orders for the 7 people is the number of ways in which six of them can be arranged in *the other* 6 seats, which is $_6P_6$ or 6!, or 720 ways.

In Example 1, we dealt with **cyclical permutations,** or arrangements in a *ring.* In contrast, permutations as otherwise described can be referred to as **linear permutations,** or arrangements in ordered places in a line. By the method of Example 1, we obtain the following result, because the number of *cyclical* permutations of n different things is equal to the number of *linear* permutations of $(n-1)$ of the things.

THEOREM II. *The number of cyclical permutations of n different things taken n at a time is $(n-1)!$.*

EXAMPLE 2. In how many ways can 4 boys and 3 girls be seated in a row of 7 seats with the girls in consecutive seats?

First solution. 1. *Analysis.* We may seat the boys and girls by performing the following successive acts:

(a) *Select 3 consecutive seats.*

(b) *Arrange the girls in these 3 seats.*

(c) *Arrange the boys in the remaining 4 seats.*

2. We can perform (a) in 5 ways. The number of ways for performing (b) is $_3P_3$ or 3!, and for (c) is $_4P_4$ or 4!. Hence, by the multiplication principle, we can perform (a), (b), and (c) in 5(3!)(4!) or 720 ways.

Second solution. 1. *Analysis.* At first, think of the girls as if tied together, giving 5 things for arrangement, the girls as a unit and 4 boys. Then:

(a) *Choose seats for the 4 boys and the "unit" of girls.*

(b) *Seat the 3 girls in the 3 seats chosen for them.*

2. The number of ways for performing (a) is $_5P_5$ or 5!, for (b) is $_3P_3$ or 3!, and for (a) and (b) is 5!(3!) or 720 ways.

It is easily seen that there are fewer permutations of *like* things than of *unlike* things. For instance, there are 6 permutations of (a, b, c) taken all at a time, whereas the only permutation of (a, a, a), taken all at a time, is aaa.

EXAMPLE 3. Find the number of permutations of (a, a, a, b, c) taken five at a time.

Solution. 1. Let P be the desired number of permutations.

2. Consider (a_1, a_2, a_3, b, c) where all letters are different; their number of permutations taken five at a time is 5!. We can obtain these as follows:

I. *Take in turn each distinct permutation of* (a, a, a, b, c).

II. *Replace the a's in all possible ways by* (a_1, a_2, a_3).

We can perform act I in P ways, act II in 3! ways, and hence acts I and II in $P(3!)$ ways. Therefore,

$$P(3!) = 5!, \qquad or \qquad P = \frac{5!}{3!} = 20.$$

THEOREM III. *If P represents the number of distinct permutations of n things taken all at a time when, of the n things, there are u alike, v others alike, w others alike, etc., then*

$$\boldsymbol{P} = \frac{n!}{u!\,v!\,w!\cdots}. \tag{3}$$

Proof. 1. For concreteness, let the n things consist of u like things represented by a's, and v other like things represented by b's.

2. Replace the u letters "a" by u different letters $a_1, a_2, \cdots, a_u$ and the v letters "b" by v different letters $b_1, b_2, \cdots, b_v$, thus obtaining n *different* letters. We can create all of their permutations taken n at a time as follows:

i.   *Take in turn each permutation of the given u letters "a" and v letters "b."*

ii. *Then, replace the u letters "a" of the permutation in all possible ways by the u different letters, $a_1, a_2, \cdots, a_u$.*

iii. *Replace the v letters "b" in all possible ways by the v different letters $b_1, b_2, \cdots, b_v$.*

We can do (i) in P ways, (ii) in $u!$ ways, and (iii) in $v!$ ways. Hence, we can do (i), (ii), and (iii) in succession in $P(u!)(v!)$ ways. But, this is equal to the number of permutations of the n different letters n at a time, or $n!$. Hence,

$$P(u!)(v!) = n!, \qquad or \qquad P = \frac{n!}{u!\,v!}. \tag{4}$$

Illustration 2. The number of permutations of the letters in *attention* taken all at a time is $9!/(3!\,2!)$, because there are three t's and two n's.

EXERCISE 80

Read the symbol and compute its value.

  1. $_6P_3$.   **2.** $_7P_4$.   **3.** $_4P_4$.   **4.** $_8P_6$.   **5.** $_{10}P_3$.

Find the number of distinct permutations of the letters or digits, taken all at a time.

  6. $(d, d, c, c, c, c, b, b, b)$.   **7.** $(3, 3, 3, 3, 2, 5, 5, 5, 6, 6)$.

  8. How many distinct permutations can be made of the letters of the word *commotion*, taken all at a time?

  9. How many different numbers of eight digits each can be written by use of three 1's, two 4's, one 5, and two 7's?

 10. With 5 green hats and 3 red hats, all alike except for color, in how many distinct ways can 8 boys be provided with hats?

 11. (a) In how many relative orders can a host seat himself and 4 guests around a table? (b) In how many ways can the host seat his guests after he has chosen his own seat?

 12. In how many ways can 4 pennies, 5 nickels, and 3 dimes be distributed among 12 children, if each is to receive one coin?

 13. In how many distinguishable ways can 9 similar spherical beads of different colors be strung on a circular wire?

 14. How many numbers of five different digits each can be written by use of 2, 3, 5, 7, and 8, with 2, 3, and 5 consecutive in each number?

 15. By use of 8 flags, identical except for color, how many signals can be formed by arranging all of the flags in 8 positions on a pole, if 3 flags are red, 3 are green, and 2 are yellow?

 16. How many permutations can we form by use of (a, b, c, d, e, h) taken all at a time, with (a, b, e, h) consecutive?

17. By use of 3 different red flags, and 4 different green flags, how many different signals can be formed by flying all of the flags from seven positions on a pole, if flags of the same color are to be consecutive?

18. In how many ways can 2 men, 3 boys, and 4 girls be seated in a row of 9 seats, with a man at each end and with the boys and girls, respectively, in consecutive seats?

19. In how many different relative orders can 4 men and 4 women be seated around a table, with men and women alternating?

20. In how many ways can we seat 3 girls and 2 boys in a row of 5 seats if the boys are *not* to sit in consecutive seats?

21. Five girls are to be seated at a table, and then each of 5 boys is to be assigned a position behind a girl. In how many different ways can couples thus be arranged, if only their relative order around the table is of importance?

22. In how many ways can 4 men and 4 women be assigned positions as the first 4 couples in a grand march?

Note 1. We define a **complete permutation** of the integers $(1, 2, 3, \cdots, n)$ as a permutation of all of them leaving no integer in its place in natural order. Let γ_n be the number of such permutations. Problem 23 involves γ_3, where careful analysis, instead of mere use of formulas, yields the solution.

★23. In how many ways can 3 men and their wives be matched by lot for a dance so that no man obtains his wife for a partner?

★24. Prove that, if $n \geqq 3$, γ_n of Note 1 satisfies the recursion formula
$$\gamma_n = (n-1)\gamma_{n-1} + (n-1)\gamma_{n-2}.$$
Also, show that $\gamma_1 = 0$ and $\gamma_2 = 1$. Then find $\gamma_3, \gamma_4, \gamma_5, \gamma_6$.

★25. A cloakroom attendant receives the hat of each of 5 men, forgets to attach numbered checks to the hats, and later hands out the hats at random to the men. In how many ways could the attendant hand out the hats so that no man receives his own hat?

129. Formulas for numbers of combinations

Recall that a *combination* of all or part of a set of elements is merely a *subset* of the elements, and that *no question of relative order arises in a set unless order is specifically mentioned.*

Illustration 1. The different combinations of a, b, c, and d, taken 3 at a time, are (a, b, c), (a, b, d), (a, c, d), and (b, c, d). From each combination we can form 3! or 6 different permutations of the 4 letters taken 3 at a time. Thus, from (a, b, c) we can form the permutations abc, acb, bac, bca, cab, and cba. In other words, there are only *four combinations*, whereas there are $4 \cdot 6$, or 24, *permutations* of the 4 letters taken 3 at a time.

We use the symbol $_nC_r$ to denote the number of combinations of n different things taken r at a time.

THEOREM IV. *The number of combinations of n different things taken r at a time is equal to the number of permutations of n different things, taken r at a time, divided by r!.*

Proof. With each combination containing r of the things, we can form $r!$ permutations of the things taken r at a time. Hence, since there are $_nC_r$ different combinations, there are $_nC_r \cdot (r!)$ different permutations. That is,

$$_nC_r \cdot (r!) = {_nP_r}, \quad or \quad _nC_r = \frac{_nP_r}{r!}. \tag{1}$$

EXAMPLE 1. From 10 people, in how many ways can we (*a*) select a group of 6 people; (*b*) fill 6 different offices in a club?

Solution. (*a*) The number of groups which can be formed is the number of combinations of 10 things taken 6 at a time, or $_{10}C_6$. From (1),

$$_{10}C_6 = \frac{_{10}P_6}{6!} = \frac{10 \cdot 9 \cdot 8 \cdot 7 \cdot 6 \cdot 5}{1 \cdot 2 \cdot 3 \cdot 4 \cdot 5 \cdot 6} = 210. \tag{2}$$

(*b*) The result is $_{10}P_6$ or 151,200.

When we *pick a subset of r elements* from a set of *n* elements, we *leave a subset of* $(n - r)$ *elements*. Thus, the number of combinations of the *n* elements taken *r* at a time is the same as the number of combinations of the *n* elements taken $(n - r)$ at a time, or

$$_nC_r = {_nC_{n-r}}. \tag{3}$$

We may use (3) to compute $_nC_r$ if *r is close to n*.

Illustration 2. $_{50}C_{48} = {_{50}C_2} = \dfrac{50 \cdot 49}{2} = 1225.$

Formula (1) is useful for computation, as seen in (2). However, other convenient formulas for $_nC_r$ can be obtained. Thus, by use of Theorem I, page 291, formula (1) gives

$$_nC_r = \frac{n(n - 1)(n - 2) \cdots (n - r + 1)}{r!}. \tag{4}$$

If both numerator and denominator in (4) are multiplied by $(n - r)!$, the new numerator is

$$1 \cdot 2 \cdot 3 \cdots (n - r)(n - r + 1) \cdots (n - 2)(n - 1)n,$$

or $n!$, and therefore

$$_nC_r = \frac{n!}{r!(n - r)!}. \tag{5}$$

We may prove (3) by use of (5). Thus, from (5),

$$_nC_{n-r} = \frac{n!}{(n - r)![n - (n - r)]!} = \frac{n!}{(n - r)!r!} = {_nC_r}.$$

Illustration 3. From (5), $\,_7C_3 = \dfrac{7!}{3!4!} = \dfrac{5 \cdot 6 \cdot 7}{6} = 35.$

EXAMPLE 2. If 7 coins are tossed, in how many ways can it happen that exactly 5 coins fall tails?

Solution. For any way of picking a subset of 5 coins from the 7 coins, there is just *one way* of placing the subset with tails up, and the other coins with heads up. Hence, the number of ways in which 5 coins can fall tails is equal to $\,_7C_5$, or 21 ways.

Note 1. The symbol $\begin{pmatrix} n \\ r \end{pmatrix}$ is met frequently in place of $\,_nC_r$. We shall use $\begin{pmatrix} n \\ r \end{pmatrix}$ occasionally, but shall prefer $\,_nC_r$ partly because of convenience in printing. For reference, notice that

$$\begin{pmatrix} n \\ r \end{pmatrix} = \frac{n!}{r!(n-r)!} \,; \quad \begin{pmatrix} n \\ r \end{pmatrix} = \begin{pmatrix} n \\ n-r \end{pmatrix}. \tag{6}$$

In place of $\,_nC_r$, we also meet, occasionally, $C_{n,r}$ or $C_n^{(r)}$. In place of $\,_nP_r$, we may meet $P_r^{(n)}$ or $P_{n,r}$.

130. Mutually exclusive events

If a certain two events *cannot occur simultaneously*, we call them **mutually exclusive.** For such events, we observe the following simple counting principle.

Addition Principle. *For mutually exclusive events.*

If a first event can occur in h ways and a second event in k ways, and if the two events are mutually exclusive, then one or the other of the events can occur in $(h + k)$ ways.

In the preceding principle, if we label each way of occurrence as an *element* of a corresponding set of elements, set terminology permits an instructive restatement of the principle. Thus, suppose that A and B are sets of elements where $A \cap B = \emptyset$ (which translates the condition above of the events being *mutually exclusive*). Then, the principle states that, *if A consists of h elements and B consists of k elements, the* **union** *of A and B, or $A \cup B$, consists of $(h + k)$ elements.* The phrasing of the principle in colloquial language as above is useful in obtaining quick reactions to situations as met in applications.

Illustration 1. Suppose that a bag contains 5 white, 6 black, and 4 red balls. By the *addition principle*, we can draw a white ball **OR** a black ball from the bag in $(5 + 6)$ or 11 ways. On the other hand, by the *multiplication principle* for successive events, we can draw a white ball **AND** a black ball in $5 \cdot 6$ or 30 ways. The key words AND and OR are the essential clues leading to use of the corresponding principles.

EXAMPLE 1. From 6 men and 5 women, in how many ways can we select a group of (*a*) 4 men alone or 3 women alone; (*b*) 4 men and 3 women?

Solution. 1. The number of ways of selecting a group of 4 men is $_6C_4$ or 15 ways, and the number of ways for a group of 3 women is $_5C_3$ or 10 ways.

2. By the addition principle, the number of ways for selecting a group of 4 men alone **OR** 3 women alone is $(15 + 10)$ or 25 ways.

3. By the multiplication principle, the number of ways for selecting a group of 4 men **AND** 3 women is $15 \cdot 10$ or 150 ways.

131. Miscellaneous methods

In finding the number of ways of performing a complicated act, it is advisable to make a preliminary analysis of the act into either *successive simpler acts* or into various *mutually exclusive simpler acts.*

EXAMPLE 1. How many numbers of five different digits each can be written if each number involves three odd and two even digits and no digit 0?

Solution. 1. *Analysis.* In writing a number, we may

(*a*) *select a group of three odd digits from* (1, 3, 5, 7, 9),

(*b*) *select a group of two even digits from* (2, 4, 6, 8), *and then*

(*c*) *form a permutation of the five digits selected in* (*a*) *and* (*b*).

2. The number of ways for performing (*a*) is $_5C_3$ or 10 ways, and for (*b*) is $_4C_2$ or 6 ways. For each way of performing (*a*) and (*b*), the number of ways for performing (*c*) is $_5P_5$ or 5! ways. Hence, by the multiplication principle, the number of ways for performing (*a*), (*b*), and (*c*) is $10 \cdot 6 \cdot 5!$ or 7200 ways.

EXAMPLE 2. How many numbers greater than 5000, with no repeated digits, can be written by use of the digits 0, 3, 6, 7, 4, 2?

Solution. 1. *Analysis.* Consider the following mutually exclusive types:

(*a*) *Numbers of six digits each.*

(*b*) *Numbers of five digits each.*

(*c*) *Numbers of four digits each.*

2. *For type* (*a*): the left-hand end can be filled in just 5 ways (with 3, 6, 7, 4, or 2); then the next place in 5 ways, because 0 is now eligible; etc.; the number of these numbers is $5 \cdot 5 \cdot 4 \cdot 3 \cdot 2 \cdot 1$, or 600 numbers. Similarly, there are 600 numbers of type (*b*).

3. *For type* (*c*): the left-hand end can be filled with 6 or 7; then the next place in 5 ways; etc.; we find $2 \cdot 5 \cdot 4 \cdot 3$ or 120 numbers of type (*c*).

4. The number of numbers of all types is $(600 + 600 + 120)$ or 1320, by the addition principle.

EXAMPLE 3. A bag contains 7 black and 6 white balls. In how many ways can we draw from the bag groups of 5 balls involving *at least* 3 black balls?

Solution. 1. We obtain *at least* 3 black balls if we obtain

(*a*) EXACTLY 3 black balls and 2 white balls; OR

(*b*) EXACTLY 4 black balls and 1 white ball; OR

(*c*) EXACTLY 5 black balls.

2. Since (*a*), (*b*), and (*c*) are *mutually exclusive events*, we *add* their numbers of ways of occurrence and obtain the following final result:

$$(_7C_3)(_6C_2) + (_7C_4)(_6C_1) + _7C_5 = 756 \ ways.$$

Comment. Notice the preliminary analysis of "AT LEAST" into various mutually exclusive possibilities involving "EXACT" situations, to which our methods apply more easily. A similar analysis is usually advisable in any problem involving "AT MOST" in its statement.

MISCELLANEOUS EXERCISE 81

1. Write out (*a*) all the combinations of (*H, K, M, N*) taken three at a time; (*b*) all the permutations of (*H, K, M, N*) taken three at a time.
2. Read each symbol and compute it: $_9C_3$; $_8C_6$; $_{12}C_5$.
3. From a group of 8 people, how many different committees may be appointed consisting of (*a*) 4 people each; (*b*) 4 or 5 people each?
4. From a cent, a nickel, a dime, a quarter, and a half-dollar, how many sums can be formed consisting of (*a*) 3 coins each; (*b*) at least 3 coins each?
5. From a set of 6 elements, how many subsets can be formed where each consists of (*a*) 3 elements; (*b*) 4 elements?
6. How many different groups of 2000 people each could be formed from 2003 people?
7. From a suit of 13 playing cards, (*a*) how many hands of 5 cards each can be dealt to a player; (*b*) how many of these hands will include the king?
8. If 5 coins are tossed, in how many ways can they fall?
9. A bag contains 6 black, 7 white, and 8 green balls.* In how many ways can we select sets of balls where each set consists of (*a*) 4 black or 4 white balls; (*b*) 4 black and 4 white balls; (*c*) 4 balls all of the same color; (*d*) 4 balls of each color?
10. In how many ways can a hostess select 6 luncheon guests from 10 women, if she is to avoid having a particular two of the women together at the luncheon?
11. From a group of 7 girls and 8 boys, how many committees of six each can be formed, involving (*a*) 3 girls and 3 boys; (*b*) 6 girls or 6 boys; (*c*) at least 5 girls?
12. By use of the digits (1, 2, 3, 4, 5, 6, 7), how many numbers of four different digits each can be written, if each number involves two odd and two even digits?
13. In how many ways can 6 different presents be given to 5 children?
14. In how many ways can we fill 7 numbered seats with 3 men and 4 women, by selections from 6 men and 5 women?

* Indistinguishable except as to color. This assumption will persist in all such problems.

15. In how many ways can 7 boys choose places in a row of 10 seats?

16. From a bag containing 5 white and 9 black balls, in how many ways can we form a set of 5 balls involving (a) exactly 3 white balls; (b) at least 3 white balls?

17. In how many ways can 9 different books be divided among A, B, and C, so that they receive 4, 3, and 2 books, respectively?

18. By use of the digits (1, 2, 3, 4, 5, 6, 7, 8, 9), how many numbers of 7 different digits each can be written in which odd and even digits alternate?

19. If two dice* are tossed, in how many ways can they show a total of 6?

20. In how many ways can 8 people be arranged with 4 people at each of two round tables, and only relative order of importance at any table?

21. How many committees of 6 men each can be selected from 9 men, if a certain 2 men refuse to serve together on any committee?

22. If 6 coins are tossed together, in how many ways can it result that (a) all fall heads; (b) just two fall heads; (c) at least four fall heads?

23. If 7 coins are tossed together, in how many ways can they fall with at most 3 heads?

24. In how many relative orders can we seat 7 people at a round table, with a certain 3 people (a) side by side; (b) not in consecutive chairs?

25. One bag contains 6 white and 8 black balls, and a second bag contains 3 white and 6 black balls. How many sets of 6 balls each can be selected consisting of 4 black and 2 white balls, (a) if all balls come from the same bag; (b) if the white balls come from one bag and the black balls from the other bag; (c) if there is no restriction in regard to the bags from which the balls come?

26. From a set of 4 elements, how many subsets can be formed?

27. In how many ways can two numbers whose sum is even be chosen from the numbers (1, 2, 3, 8, 9, 10, 11)?

28. From a suit of 13 cards, in how many ways can we select a set of 5 cards including the king, or the jack, or both?

29. How many distinguishable combinations can be formed of the digits (2, 2, 2, 3, 4, 5, 6), taken three at a time?

30. In how many ways can 10 convention guests be divided, with 3 guests going to a theater, 4 guests to a dance, and 3 guests to a concert?

31. From the letters (a, o, e, i, r, s, t), how many permutations of 5 different letters each can be formed, if each permutation involves 2 consonants and 3 vowels?

32. From a set of 7 different books, in how many ways can we choose subsets of (a) exactly 4 books each; (b) at least 4 books each; (c) at most 4 books each?

33. From a group of 6 representatives of labor, 5 representatives of business, and 8 representatives of the general public, how many committees of six can be formed consisting of 2 people from each group?

34. In how many ways can 12 different presents be distributed to 4 children, with each to receive 3 presents?

35. From a group of 5 freshmen, 6 sophomores, and 8 seniors, how many committees can be formed if each consists of 3 members of each of two classes?

* Any die referred to is a cube, with the faces numbered 1, 2, 3, 4, 5, and 6, respectively.

36. How many parallelograms are formed if a set of 4 parallel lines is met by another set of 6 parallel lines, not parallel to the 1st set?

37. In how many ways can 7 dice fall, with all of 1, 2, 3, 4, 5, 6 up?

38. In how many ways can a total of 8 be thrown if 3 dice are tossed?

39. How many combinations of 3 letters each can be formed by use of (a, b, c, d, e) if repetitions are allowed?

40. (*a*) How many different hands of 13 cards each can be made from a usual deck of 52 cards? (*b*) In how many ways can 4 players in a game be dealt hands of 13 cards each? Leave the results in factored form.

132. The binomial theorem

On page 140, we met the expansion of $(x + y)^n$, where n is a positive integer, but no proof was given for the result. We shall prove that

$$\left. \begin{aligned} (x + y)^n &= x^n + {}_nC_1 x^{n-1} y + {}_nC_2 x^{n-2} y^2 + \cdots \\ &\quad + {}_nC_r x^{n-r} y^r + \cdots + {}_nC_{n-1} x y^{n-1} + {}_nC_n y^n, \end{aligned} \right\} \tag{1}$$

and then compare the coefficients in (1) with those on page 140. By use of the summation notation on page 132, we may write (1) as follows.

$$(x + y)^n = \sum_{r=0}^{n} {}_nC_r x^{n-r} y^r,$$

where we define ${}_nC_0 = 1$. This result is called the **binomial theorem**, or the **binomial formula.**

Proof of (1). 1. By definition,

$$(x + y)^n = (x + y)(x + y) \cdots (x + y). \tag{2}$$

The expansion of the product of the n factors $(x + y)$ in (2) on the right consists of the sum of the results obtained by taking, *in all possible ways*, one term out of each of the factors and multiplying the selected terms.

2. We obtain x^n in the expansion of (2) by selecting x out of *each* factor $(x + y)$; since this can be done in just *one way*, we obtain x^n with the coefficient 1 in the expansion, in agreement with (1).

3. We obtain a term of the type $x^{n-1}y$ in the expansion of (2) by selecting y out of just *one factor* on the right, which can be done in n *ways*, and x out of the remaining $(n - 1)$ factors. Thus we get the term $x^{n-1}y$ exactly n *times*, or we obtain $n x^{n-1} y$ on the right in (1). We note that $n = {}_nC_1$. Etc.

4. We obtain a term of the type $x^{n-r}y^r$ in expanding on the right in (2) by selecting y out of r of the factors $(x + y)$ and x out of the other $(n - r)$ factors. The number of ways of selecting r letters y out of the n factors is ${}_nC_r$ (the number of *combinations* of r letters y out of n letters y, because the *order of selection is of no importance*). Hence, the term $x^{n-r}y^r$ is obtained ${}_nC_r$ times; or, ${}_nC_r$ is the coefficient of $x^{n-r}y^r$ in the expansion of $(x + y)^n$.

Note 1. We verify that $_nC_1 = n$, $_nC_2 = \frac{1}{2}n(n-1)$, and observe the expression for $_nC_r$ in (4) on page 295. Then, on comparing (1) on page 140 with (1) of this section, we see that the results on page 140 were correct. Also, notice the successive terms, the $(r+1)$th term and the $(r+2)$th term counting from the left in (1):

$$_nC_r x^{n-r}y^r \quad and \quad _nC_{(r+1)}x^{n-r-1}y^{r+1}. \tag{3}$$

From (4) on page 295, with r replaced by $(r+1)$,

$$_nC_{(r+1)} = \frac{n(n-1)\cdots[n-(r-1)](n-r)}{(r!)(r+1)} = \frac{n-r}{r+1}\,_nC_r. \tag{4}$$

Observe that (4) proves the following fact:

$$\left\{\begin{array}{l}\textit{To obtain the coefficient of the term involving } x^{n-r-1}y^{r+1} \textit{ in (1),}\\ \textit{multiply the coefficient of the preceding term by the exponent of x in that}\\ \textit{term, and divide by the number of that term, counting from the left.}\end{array}\right\} \tag{5}$$

The student should verify that, in establishing (5), we have proved Rule IV of page 140, where no proof of the rule was included. We notice that Rule V on page 140 is demonstrated by the fact that $_nC_r = _nC_{n-r}$. That is, the coefficients of $x^{n-r}y^r$ and $x^r y^{n-r}$ on the right in (1) are equal.

Illustration 1. From (1),

$$(x-y)^5 = x^5 - {_5C_1}x^4y + {_5C_2}x^3y^2 - {_5C_3}x^2y^3 + {_5C_4}xy^4 - {_5C_5}y^5, \textit{ or}$$
$$(x-y)^5 = x^5 - 5x^4y + 10x^3y^2 - 10x^2y^3 + 5xy^4 - y^5.$$

To obtain any particular term in the expansion (1) of a binomial, we refer to the following formula, which we call the general term in (1):

Term of $(x+y)^n$ involving y^r is $_nC_r x^{n-r}y^r$. \qquad (6)

Illustration 2. By use of (6) with $n=7$ and $r=5$, the term of the expansion of $(x^3 + 2y^2)^7$ where y^{10} occurs is

$$_7C_5(x^3)^{7-5}(2y^2)^5 = {_7C_2}x^6(2^5y^{10}) = 21(32)x^6y^{10} = 672x^6y^{10}.$$

EXAMPLE 1. Obtain the 8th term of the expansion of $(3a^{\frac{1}{2}} - b)^{11}$ when the terms are arranged in ascending powers of b.

Solution. In the 8th term, the exponent of b is 7. Hence, we use (6) with $x = 3a^{\frac{1}{2}}, y = -b, n = 11$, and $r = 7$;

$$_{11}C_7(3a^{\frac{1}{2}})^4(-b^7) = -{_{11}C_4}(3^4a^2b^7) = -26{,}730a^2b^7.$$

If we place $x = 1$ and $y = 1$ in (1), we obtain

$$2^n = 1 + {_nC_1} + {_nC_2} + \cdots + {_nC_r} + \cdots + {_nC_n}, \textit{ or}$$
$$_nC_1 + {_nC_2} + \cdots + {_nC_n} = 2^n - 1.$$

Thus, *the total number of combinations of n things taken 1 at a time, or 2 at a time, $\cdots$, or n at a time, is $(2^n - 1)$.*

Note 2. The use of $_nC_r$ as in (1) is so important that, frequently, $_nC_r$ is called the rth *binomial coefficient* in the expansion of $(x + y)^n$, without mentioning the meaning of $_nC_r$ as a *number of combinations.*

133. Pascal's triangle for $_nC_r$

THEOREM V. (Pascal's formula.) *If* $1 \le r \le n$, *then*

$$_{(n+1)}C_r = {}_nC_{(r-1)} + {}_nC_r. \tag{1}$$

Proof. 1. Let $(n + 1)$ things be given. Consider a particular one, u, of these things. Then, the combinations of the $(n + 1)$ things taken r at a time consist of the combinations in the following two categories:

A. *Those involving u, together with a combination of the other n things taken $(r - 1)$ at a time.*

B. *Those not involving u, and hence consisting of a combination of the other n things taken r at a time.*

2. The number of combinations of type A is the first term on the right in equation (1). The number of type B is the second term on the right in (1). By the addition principle of page 296, since types A and B are mutually exclusive, it follows that the sum on the right in (1) is equal to $_{(n+1)}C_r$.

By use of (1), we justify use of the triangular array called *Pascal's triangle* for obtaining binomial coefficients on page 141. Now, we may call this array *Pascal's triangle for $_nC_r$.* To verify this statement, we proceed as follows. For every integer $n \ge 1$, we have defined $_nC_0 = 1$, the coefficient of x^n in (1) on page 300. Also, we define $_0C_0 = 1$. Then, consider the following three rows:

$$\left\{ \begin{array}{ccc} & {}_0C_0 & \\ {}_1C_0 & & {}_1C_1 \\ {}_2C_0 & {}_2C_1 & {}_2C_2 \end{array} \right\} \tag{2}$$

The second row in (2) is $(1 \quad 1)$, the coefficients of $(x + y)^1$; the third row is $(1 \quad 2 \quad 1)$, the coefficients of the expansion of $(x + y)^2$. Also, because of (1), with $n = 1$ and $r = 1$,

$$_2C_1 = {}_1C_0 + {}_1C_1.$$

Hence, $_2C_1$ is obtained by adding the two numbers above it. Similarly, consider the following two rows of coefficients for $(x + y)^n$ and $(x + y)^{n+1}$:

$$_nC_0 \qquad {}_nC_1 \cdots\cdots {}_nC_{r-1} \qquad {}_nC_r \cdots\cdots {}_nC_n$$

$$_{n+1}C_0 \qquad {}_{n+1}C_1 \cdots\cdots\cdots\cdots {}_{n+1}C_r \cdots\cdots\cdots\cdots {}_{n+1}C_{n+1}.$$

Again by use of (1), we notice that $_{n+1}C_r$ can be obtained by *adding its closest neighbors in the preceding row.* This justifies the routine used on page 141 to form Pascal's triangle.

In Problem 19 on page 334, it will be proved that, if $n \geq 2$, the *largest coefficient* of the terms in (1) on page 300 occurs at the *middle term* if n is even, and at each of the *two middle terms* if n is odd. These facts can be anticipated by recalling the details of the construction of Pascal's triangle.

Illustration 1. In the expansion of $(x + y)^{14}$, the middle term involves $x^7 y^7$ and has the coefficient $_{14}C_7$, which is the largest coefficient of the expansion.

EXERCISE 82

Write out the expansion of the power by use of combination symbols and then compute the coefficients. Check by use of Pascal's triangle.

1. $(x + y)^6$.
2. $(x - y)^5$.
3. $(x^3 - 3y^2)^5$.
4. $(2x^2 + y^3)^6$.
5. $(x^{\frac{1}{3}} - y^{\frac{2}{3}})^8$.
6. $(x^{-\frac{1}{2}} + 2y^{-1})^7$.
7. $(2y^{-2} - \frac{1}{2}x^{\frac{1}{4}})^9$.
8. $(3y^{-3} - z^2)^6$.

Find only the specified term in the expansion of the power of the binomial by use of the general term.

9. $(x + y)^8$; term involving y^6.
10. $(2y - x)^{10}$; term involving y^6.
11. $(x - 2z^{\frac{1}{2}})^{12}$; term involving z^4.
12. $(x^{\frac{1}{3}} + w^2)^7$; term involving $x^{\frac{5}{3}}$.
13. $(1 - .02)^9$; term involving $(.02)^6$.
14. $(1 + .03)^{10}$; term involving $(.03)^5$.
15. $(y^{\frac{1}{2}} - 2x^{\frac{1}{4}})^7$; term involving $x^{\frac{3}{2}}$ as the power of x.
16. $(2x^{\frac{1}{5}} - z^{\frac{1}{3}})^8$; term involving $z^{\frac{5}{3}}$ as the power of z.
17. The 8th term of $(2 - x^{\frac{1}{2}})^{12}$ in ascending powers of x.
18. The 10th term of $(a - \frac{1}{3}w)^{11}$ in descending powers of a.
19. The middle term of $(x + \frac{1}{2}y^{\frac{1}{2}})^8$.

20. Compute the largest coefficient and the corresponding term of the expansion of $(x + y)^{12}$.
21. Compute the largest absolute value attained by the coefficients in the expansion of $(x - y)^{11}$ and find each corresponding term.
22. How many committees of one or more people can be made up from a group of 7 people?
23. How many sums of money can be made up by use of combinations of a cent, a nickel, a dime, a quarter, a dollar, a $5 bill, a $10 bill, and a $100 bill?
24. Obtain the expansion of $(x + y + z)^n$ by use of combination symbols for the coefficients. Use the method of proof employed on page 300.
25. How many subsets of one or more elements can be formed from a set consisting of 12 elements?

Chapter 13 Probability

134. The role of probability

The word *probability* is in common use colloquially, usually as a means for expressing varying degrees of confidence, not clearly defined, in the possibility of the occurrence of some uncertain event. Whenever the word probability is introduced mathematically, an explicit definition of its meaning should be given. The importance of probability as a part of applied mathematics comes from its application to concrete situations. Let us refer to the typical application as a *random experiment*. We shall use the qualifying word *"random"* whenever we feel it desirable to emphasize that the experimenter will introduce probabilities in connection with the experiment. In his use of probability, his procedure should involve two fundamental steps, as follows:

1. *A decision that a certain abstract* **mathematical model for defining probability** *will be satisfactory as a basis for later decisions, when the elements in this model are thought of as items related to the experiment.*

2. *Computation of probabilities based on the abstract model and interpretation of these results in terms of the elements of the experiment.*

These steps are the logical basis for any sound procedure in the field called statistical inference. We proceed to define probability for certain models.

135. Probability defined for a finite sample space

Consider a set T consisting of N distinct abstract elements, and let r be a variable with the domain T. We write $T = \{r\}$, and we may read "$\{r\}$" as *"the set of all elements r."* It will be an aid to intuition if we refer to T as the set of possible outcomes of a *random experiment*, which may produce any one of the N outcomes in $\{r\}$ whenever the experiment is performed. We shall call T the basic **sample space.** When we apply this name to a set T, we shall imply that *an associated concept of probability is to be introduced in connection*

304

with T. We call *T* a *finite sample space* because it has just a *finite number of elements*. We proceed to formulate probability for *T*.

Let *H* represent a *subset* of *T*; that is, *H* consists of a certain number, say *S*, of the *N* possible outcomes of *T*. Let $F = N - S$. We shall refer to *H* as an *event*, made possible by any trial of the experiment. When we examine a particular outcome $\hat{r}$ of *T*, we shall say that *H* **occurs** if $\hat{r}$ is in *H* and shall call the outcome $\hat{r}$ a **success**. If $\hat{r}$ is *not* in *H*, we shall refer to $\hat{r}$ as a **failure** relative to *H*. Thus, *T* consists of *S* outcomes (*those in H*) which are successes and *F* outcomes (*those not in H*) which are failures relative to *H*. These *F* outcomes make up the set *H'*, which we have called the *complement* of *H*. *H* and *H'* are mutually exclusive sets, and the *union* of *H* and *H'* is the whole space *T*, or $T = H \cup H'$ and $H \cap H' = \emptyset$, the empty set.

Illustration 1. A bag contains 4 white and 3 black balls. Let an experiment consist of drawing 2 balls together from the bag, and identify the possible outcomes of this experiment as the set *T* mentioned above. Then, the total number of outcomes is $N = {}_7C_2$ or $N = 21$. Let *H* be the event of obtaining a black ball and a white ball at any trial; the number of outcomes of this variety is $S = 4(3) = 12$.

DEFINITION I. *To each outcome r of the finite sample space T, let there be assigned a positive number p_r, to be called the* **probability of r,** *where the sum of the numbers in the set $\{p_r\}$ for all outcomes of T is 1. Then, the* **probability of any event H** *is defined as the sum of the probabilities of those outcomes of the sample space which belong to H.*

We use functional notation, *P(H)*, to represent *"the probability of H."* Sometimes we may call *P(H)* the probability of *success for H at any trial of the experiment* which gives rise to the set of outcomes which form the sample space *T*. Thus, we have defined a **probability function P,** whose domain is all subsets *{H}* of *T*. That is, *P* is a *set function*, or a function of sets of outcomes. If $\emptyset$ as usual denotes the empty set, containing no outcomes of *T*, we define $P(\emptyset) = 0$. From Definition I, when $H = T$, we obtain $P(T) = 1$. For any sample space *T*, the range of *P*, or the set of all values of *P(H)*, consists of a certain set of numbers from 0 to 1 inclusive.

Illustration 2. Let the random experiment be the tossing of a die, numbered as usual, and observing which number falls up. First, suppose that the experimenter assigns the probability $\frac{1}{6}$ to each of the 6 possible outcomes. Let *H* be the event that, at a trial of the experiment, the die falls with a face up which is numbered *greater than* 4. Then, *H* consists of two outcomes, 5 up and 6 up, and $P(H) = \frac{1}{6} + \frac{1}{6} = \frac{1}{3}$. Next, as a new basis for probability, suppose that the experimenter knows that the die is biased or loaded, and accordingly assigns the probability $\frac{1}{3}$ to each of faces 1 and 6, and $\frac{1}{12}$ to each of faces 2, 3, 4, and 5. Let *H* be the event that, at any throw of the die, it will fall with a face up *numbered less than* 3; then $P(H) = \frac{1}{3} + \frac{1}{12} = \frac{5}{12}$.

In any acceptance of Definition I as the model for probability, an experimenter would first identify the possible outcomes of his experiment as the elements of the sample space T. Then, on the basis of past experience with the experiment, or theoretical knowledge of its nature, the experimenter would arbitrarily select the individual probabilities of the outcomes. Thereafter, he would use the result $P(H)$ given by Definition I. In particular, for each element r in T, $P(r) = p_r$ as mentioned in Definition I, because "r" itself is a *subset* of T, and hence* "r" is a special case of the notation "H" for an event.

For any event H, the complementary event "*not H*," denoted by H', consists of all outcomes of the sample space T which are failures relative to H. We shall refer to $P(H')$ as the probability of *failure* of H.

THEOREM I. *For any event H, the sum of the probabilities of success and failure is 1. That is,*

$(H'$ means not $H)$ $$P(H) + P(H') = 1. \tag{1}$$

Proof. The outcomes in H and those which are in H' (that is, *not in H*) make up all of the outcomes of T. Hence, $P(H) + P(H')$ is just the sum of the probabilities of *all* outcomes, and hence is equal to 1.

We shall say that H is *certain to occur* at any trial of the experiment in case $P(H) = 1$. The condition $P(H) = 1$ is equivalent to stating that H consists of *all* outcomes of T, so that $H = T$. If $P(H) = 1$, it follows from (1) that $P(H') = 0$, or the probability of failure for H is zero. To say that H is *certain to fail* at any trial will mean that $P(H) = 0$. In this case, from (1), $P(H') = 1$, or the probability of success is zero and of failure is 1.

If all of the N outcomes in the sample space T are assigned *equal probabilities*, we shall say that the outcomes are *equally likely*. In such a case, each outcome r has the probability $1/N$.

THEOREM II. *Suppose that the N outcomes of the sample space T are equally likely, and that H is an event consisting of S outcomes (successes), with F outcomes (failures) not in H, where $F = N - S$. Then, at any trial of the experiment, the probability of success for H is*

$$P(H) = \frac{S}{N} = p, \tag{2}$$

and the probability of H failing to occur is

$$P(H') - \frac{F}{N} = q. \tag{3}$$

---

* Logically there is a difference between the *element r* of T and the *subset* of T consisting of *r alone*. However, we agree to use the same symbol, r, for both entities, with the context relied upon to clarify the meaning. Thus, in $P(r)$, the symbol r represents the subset (or event) consisting of r alone.

Proof. By Definition I, with each outcome having the probability $1/N$, the sum of the probabilities of the S outcomes of H is $S \cdot (1/N)$, or $P(H)$ is given by (2). Similarly, the sum of the probabilities of the F failures in H' is $F \cdot (1/N)$, or the probability of failure of H is $P(H') = F/N$, as in (3).

Hereafter in this chapter, a moderate number of problems will occur where the outcomes of the sample space are *not* equally likely; this case is absolutely essential for the development of statistics. However, unless otherwise stated in a problem, Theorem II will apply. In any experiment, *"to draw"* or *"to perform an act"* will imply that this is done *"at random"* in the colloquial sense. Then, we shall assume that the possible outcomes are to be taken as the sample space T of Definition I with the outcomes considered as *equally likely*, unless the context implies that they may have unequal probabilities.

Illustration 3. If a bag contains 7 black and 3 white balls, the probability that a ball drawn at random will be black is $\frac{7}{10}$.

Note 1. As a special case of (1), from (2) and (3) we obtain $p + q = 1$. If the event H is *certain to occur*, then $p = 1$ and $q = 0$. If H is *certain to fail*, then $p = 0$ and $q = 1$.

In using (2), we first decide on the *random experiment* which produces the outcomes. Then, with an event H, we compute separately the number, S, of successful outcomes, and the total number, N, of outcomes for the act.

EXAMPLE 1. A bag contains 5 red and 6 white balls. If we draw 4 balls *together* (or, *in succession without replacement*), find the probability that (a) two are red and two are white; (b) all are of the same color; (c) at least three are white.

Solution. 1. The *random experiment* is that we draw 4 balls. The number of outcomes for this act is $_{11}C_4$, or $N = 330$.

2. Let H_1 be event (a). *Successful outcomes:* the number of ways of drawing 2 reds and 2 whites is $(_5C_2)(_6C_2) = 150$, or H_1 contains 150 outcomes. Hence, $P(H_1) = \frac{150}{330} = \frac{5}{11}$.

3. Let H_2 be event (b). *Successful outcomes:* the number of ways of drawing 4 reds is $_5C_4$ or 5, and of drawing 4 whites is $_6C_4$ or 15; hence, by the addition principle on page 296, the number of ways of drawing 4 balls of the *same color* is $(5 + 15)$ or 20, the number of outcomes in H_2. Hence, $P(H_2) = \frac{20}{330} = \frac{2}{33}$.

4. Let H_3 be event (c). *Successful outcomes:* at least 3 of the 4 balls are white if (i) exactly 3 are white or (ii) exactly 4 are white.

(i) *The number of ways of drawing exactly 3 white balls, and hence just 1 red ball, is $(_6C_3)(_5C_1)$ or 100 ways.*

(ii) *The number of ways of drawing 4 whites is $_6C_4$ or 15.*

By page 296, the number of outcomes in H_3 is $(100 + 15)$; $P(H_3) = \frac{115}{330} = \frac{23}{66}$.

EXAMPLE 2.   A number of five different digits is written at random by use of the digits $(1, 2, 3, 4, 5, 6, 8)$. Find the probability that the number will have even digits at each end.

Solution.   1. The *random experiment* is the writing of a number of five different digits. The number of ways of doing this is $_7P_5$, or $N = 2520$.

2. *Successful outcomes.*   By the multiplication principle on page 286, the number of ways in which we can write a number of five different digits having even digits at the ends is $4 \cdot 3 \cdot 5 \cdot 4 \cdot 3$, or $S = 720$.

3. From (2), the desired probability is $p = \frac{720}{2520}$, or $p = \frac{2}{7}$.

Probability as in Definition I is referred to as *"a priori"* probability because, in any application to an experiment, we assume that, in *advance* of a trial, the number and nature of the possible outcomes are known. In the mathematical model used as a basis for probability in Definition I, the *"probability of an outcome"* is an *undefined term*, subject only to the restriction that it is positive and the sum of the probabilities of all outcomes is 1. However, the experimenter is at liberty to think of the probability which he assigns to any outcome as a measure of his *confidence* in the appearance of the outcome at any trial.

EXAMPLE 3.   In a random group of six people, what is the probability that at least two have their birthdays on the same day of the year?

Solution.   1. Suppose that any year consists of 365 days. Let the random experiment be six selections of a day for a birthday, from the 365 days of the year. Then, the sample space, T, for use in Definition I, consists of all possible random selections of the six birthdays; the number of selections is $N = 365^6$.

2. We look upon the birthdays of the given six people as the outcome of a trial of the experiment. Let H be the event that *at least two* of the people have the same birthday. Let H' be the complementary event *"not H,"* or the event that *all of the six birthdays are different*. It will be easier to obtain $P(H')$ than $P(H)$, as often is the case; finally we shall use (1) to obtain $P(H)$.

3. The number of elements in the set H' is the number of ways of assigning birthdays, *all different*, to six people, or $_{365}P_6$. Hence, by Theorem II,

$$P(H') = \frac{365 \cdot 364 \cdot 363 \cdot 362 \cdot 361 \cdot 360}{365^6} = .9594; \quad \text{(Table V)}$$

$$P(H) = 1 - P(H') = .0406.$$

A good approximation to $P(H')$ is obtained by writing

$$P(H') = (1 - \tfrac{1}{365})(1 - \tfrac{2}{365})(1 - \tfrac{3}{365})(1 - \tfrac{4}{365})(1 - \tfrac{5}{365}) \qquad (4)$$

$$(approximately) \approx 1 - \frac{1 + 2 + 3 + 4 + 5}{365} = 1 - .041 = .959, \quad (5)$$

obtained by omitting all products of two or more fractions in (4).

Note 2. In Example 3, suppose that there are n people in the group, where $n \leq 365$. If a person were asked to guess the least value of n so that $P(H)$, as in Example 3, would be *greater than* .5, it is likely that the guess would be much too large. Actually (see Problem 30 on page 311), $P(H) > .5$ if $n = 23$. This illustrates the fact that mere intuition can lead to very wrong estimates of a probability.

EXERCISE 83

1. A man has in his pocket a nickel, a dime, a quarter, a half-dollar, and a silver dollar. He will draw two coins together at random from his pocket. In a table having a row and a column corresponding to each coin, list the set of pairs of coins which form the sample space for this experiment. Find the probability that (*a*) both coins drawn will be silver; (*b*) the value of the two coins will be an integral multiple of ten cents; (*c*) the value of the two coins will be an integral multiple of five cents.

2. An experimenter will throw a loaded die at random. He assigns the probabilities $\frac{1}{6}$, $\frac{1}{12}$, $\frac{1}{4}$, $\frac{1}{3}$, $\frac{1}{12}$, and $\frac{1}{12}$ to the faces 1, 2, 3, 4, 5, and 6, respectively, as possible outcomes for the face up on a throw. Let H be the event of obtaining, at any trial, a face numbered (*a*) less than 5; (*b*) more than 2. In each case find $P(H)$ and $P(H')$.

3. An experimenter will throw, together, a *warped coin* and a *loaded die*. For the coin thought of alone, he would assign a probability of $\frac{1}{3}$ to obtaining a head, and $\frac{2}{3}$ to obtaining a tail at any throw. For the die alone, he would assign the probability $\frac{1}{12}$ to each of faces 1, 2, 3, and 4, and $\frac{1}{3}$ to each of faces 5 and 6, as outcomes of any throw. For the *joint experiment* of throwing *the coin and the die*, he decides to assign to each joint outcome a probability equal to *the product of the probabilities of the particular face on the coin and the face on the die* which land up. (Thus, to the outcome heads and 3 on the die, he assigns the probability $\frac{1}{3} \cdot \frac{1}{12}$ or $\frac{1}{36}$.) (*a*) Make up a table with 2 rows and 6 columns showing the probability of each outcome of the experiment, and verify that the sum of the assigned probabilities is 1. (*b*) Let H be the event of obtaining, at any trial, a tail and at least 3 on the die; find $P(H)$ and $P(H')$.

4. A bag contains 5 white, 6 red, and 15 green balls. If 1 ball is drawn, find the probability that it will be (*a*) red; (*b*) white or green.

5. If a die is tossed, what is the probability that it will show (*a*) 3 or 4; (*b*) at least 4?

6. From a deck of 52 cards, 1 card is to be drawn. What is the probability that it will be (*a*) a queen; (*b*) an ace, king, or jack?

7. A bag contains 3 white and 5 red balls. If 2 balls are drawn together, find the probability that (*a*) both balls are white; (*b*) both are red; (*c*) one is white and one is red; (*d*) all are of the same color.

8. From 5 men and 7 women, a committee of four is chosen by lot. Find the probability that the committee will involve (*a*) 4 men; (*b*) 2 men and 2 women; (*c*) all men or all women; (*d*) at least 3 women.

9. In a single toss with two dice, find the probability of throwing a total of (*a*) 7; (*b*) 9; (*c*) 11; (*d*) at most 5.

10. From a deck of 52 cards, 4 cards will be drawn together. Find the probability that those drawn will be (a) spades; (b) all of the same suit; (c) all face cards or aces.

11. If a number of six different digits is written at random by use of the digits (1, 2, 3, 4, 5, 6, 7), find the probability that the number will be (a) odd; (b) even; (c) divisible by 5; (d) greater than 500,000.

12. Four roads meet at an intersection. If each of 2 people chooses a road at random, find the probability that they will choose the same road.

13. A 1st group consists of 4 men and 2 women, and a 2d group consists of 5 men and 10 women. If 1 person is chosen by lot from each group, find the probability that (a) both are women; (b) both are men; (c) one is a man and one is a woman; (d) at least one is a man.

14. If 5 coins are tossed together (or, if one coin is tossed 5 times), find the probability that they will fall with (a) just 3 heads; (b) just 3 heads or just 2 heads.

15. If a hand of 13 cards is dealt from a deck of 52 cards, find the probability that the hand will contain all of the aces and kings.

16. A 1st bag contains 4 red and 6 green balls, and a 2d bag contains 5 red and 8 black balls. If we draw a ball from each bag, find the probability that we obtain (a) a red ball and a black ball; (b) a red ball and one not red; (c) at least 1 red ball.

17. If 2 balls are drawn together from each bag in Problem 16, find the probability of obtaining (a) 2 red and 2 black balls; (b) just 1 red ball from each bag; (c) no red ball.

18. A bag contains 10 black and 5 red balls. If we draw 2 balls in succession, find the probability that both are black, if the 1st ball drawn (a) *is replaced* before the 2d is drawn; (b) *is not replaced*. If we draw 3 balls in succession, without replacement, find the probability that (c) all are red; (d) the 1st and 2d balls drawn are black and the 3d is red.

19. The buyer of a lot of 25 transistor radios will test the lot by examining 2 radios selected at random. If one or both of these is defective, the lot will be rejected. Suppose that just 5 of the radios are defective. What is the probability that the lot will be rejected by the buyer?

20. If 3 men and 3 women are seated at random at a round table, find the probability that (a) men and women will alternate; (b) a certain man and his wife, in the group, will be seated side by side.

21. A wholesaler's stock of 80 motors contains 8 defective motors. If 5 motors are selected at random for shipment to a purchaser, find the probability that (a) none of these is defective; (b) at most 1 motor in the shipment is defective. Logarithms would be useful.

22. A 1st bag contains 5 white and 10 black balls, and a 2d bag contains 20 white and 10 black balls. The experiment consists of selecting a bag at random and then drawing a ball. We decide to use $\frac{1}{2}$ as the probability in equal shares for all outcomes from any bag. Thus, each *outcome* (a *ball*) from the 1st bag has the probability $\frac{1}{2} \cdot \frac{1}{15}$ or $\frac{1}{30}$, and $\frac{1}{2} \cdot \frac{1}{30}$ or $\frac{1}{60}$ for each outcome from the 2d bag. By use of Definition I, find the probability of drawing (a) a white ball; (b) a white ball from the 1st bag; (c) a black ball.

23. In a matching question on an examination, 8 events in history are to be matched with 8 specified dates, where each item is to be used just once. A student is sure of 4 dates, and chooses to match the others at random. Find his probability of matching correctly (*a*) all items; (*b*) at least 6 dates.

24. Six dice are tossed. Find the probability that all of the numbers 1, 2, 3, 4, 5, and 6 will appear.

25. A first die is biased so that, at any toss of this die alone, the probabilities of throwing 1, 2, 3, 4, 5, or 6 would be chosen as, respectively, $\frac{1}{12}, \frac{1}{12}, \frac{1}{12}, \frac{1}{3}, \frac{1}{12}$, and $\frac{1}{3}$. For a second biased die, the corresponding probabilities are $\frac{1}{4}, \frac{1}{12}, \frac{1}{12}$, $\frac{1}{4}, \frac{1}{4}$, and $\frac{1}{12}$. The experiment will consist, now, of throwing the dice together. (*a*) Define *sensible* probabilities for each of the 36 possible outcomes, and show them in a table. (*b*) Find the probabilities of throwing each of the following totals at any trial: (*i*) 9, consisting of 4 on the 1st die and 5 on the 2d die; (*ii*) 3; (*iii*) at least 9; (*iv*) 8.

26. A die is loaded so that the probability of falling up when the die is cast will be the same for each even-numbered face, and proportional to the number of dots for each odd-numbered face, with the total probability $\frac{2}{3}$ for the odd faces. (*a*) Specify the probability for each face. (*b*) Find the probability that the die will fall with a face up numbered more than 3.

27. A purchaser will accept a consignment of 12 electric clocks if a random sample of 3 clocks selected by him shows no defectives. If 2 clocks of the lot are defective, find the probability that the lot will be rejected.

★**28.** Three men and their wives are matched by lot for a dance. Find the probability that no man obtains his wife for a partner.

★**29.** In a random group of 10 people, what is the probability that at least two have the same birthday? (*a*) Use logarithms; (*b*) use the approximate method of (5) on page 308.

★**30.** Repeat Problem 29 for a group of 23 people. Logarithms should be used; the method of (5) on page 308 would give a result badly in error since 23 is too large to justify the approximation.

★**31.** Solve Problem 28 for the case of 6 men and their wives. Compare with the result for Problem 28. Recall Problem 24 on page 294.

136. Random variables

The outcomes of a random experiment are not necessarily *numbers*. However, mathematical analysis is likely to be facilitated when data are arranged to yield numbers. Hence, it is frequently convenient to associate each of the outcomes of a random experiment with a corresponding *number*, and thereafter to deal with the resulting set of numbers instead of with the original sample space. The basis for such a procedure is the concept of a *random variable*, which we proceed to introduce.

Let T be a sample space with the outcomes $\{r_i\}$, $i = 1, 2, \cdots, N$. Then, corresponding to each r_i of T, let a real number x_i be specified. Thus, we obtain a set of N ordered pairs:

$$(r_1, x_1), (r_2, x_2), \cdots, (r_i, x_i), \cdots, (r_N, x_N), \tag{1}$$

where the first components are the outcomes of T with no repetitions, and the second component of each pair is a number, x_i for the ith pair. The set of pairs in (1) form a *function* whose *domain* is the set $T = \{r_i\}$ and *range* is the set of distinct numbers among $x_1, x_2, \cdots, x_N$. Let X represent this function; for any outcome r of T, the value of X is $X(r)$. We shall give a special name to a function such as X.

DEFINITION II. *Let T be a finite* sample space. Then, a* **random variable** *X on T is a real-valued function whose domain is T. That is, for each outcome r of T, there is defined a real number $x = X(r)$. The set of all values of X, or the set $V = \{x\}$, will be called the* **value space** *for X.*

Certain events and their probabilities in the sample space T now may be described briefly by reference to V. Thus, if x is any particular number in V,

$$P[\text{event that } X(r) = x] \quad \textit{may be abbreviated by} \quad \textbf{P[X(r) = x].} \tag{2}$$

Let f be a function whose domain is the value space $V = \{x\}$ for X, where

$$f(x) = P[X(r) = x]. \tag{3}$$

We shall call f the **probability function for X,** and shall say that f defines a **probability distribution** over the value space for X.

Illustration 1. If a true coin is tossed, let the sample space be $T = \{r\}$, where r is either *head* or *tail*. Let X be a random variable on T with $X(r) = 1$ if r is *head*, and $X(r) = 0$ if r is *tail*. The range of X is $V = \{0, 1\}$. With f as the probability function for X,

$$P[X(r) = 0] = f(0) = \tfrac{1}{2}; \quad P[X(r) = 1] = f(1) = \tfrac{1}{2}.$$

Illustration 2. A merchant has six new baseballs in a box, where three baseballs are perfect and three are defective. If a baseball is drawn at random, the sample space $T = \{r\}$ has six elements (baseballs). Let X be a random variable on T with $X(r) = 1$ if r is a perfect baseball, and $X(r) = 0$ if r is defective. Then, the value space for X is $V = \{0, 1\}$, with

$$f(0) = P[X(\cdot) = 0] = \tfrac{1}{2}; \quad f(1) = P[X(\cdot) = 1] = \tfrac{1}{2}. \tag{4}$$

In (4), we use "$(\cdot)$" instead of "(r)" to emphasize that, after V and f are known, the elements of T recede into the background.

Notice that the random variables in Illustrations 1 and 2 are *different*, because the domains of the variables are distinct sample spaces. However, the value space $\{0, 1\}$ with its associated probabilities is the *same* for the two variables. Hence, these variables are equivalent in the probability sense. This illustrates the fact that, by considering a single random variable with a given value space, and specified probabilities for each number in this space, it may be possible to unify probability considerations for different sample spaces.

---

* The notion of a random variable extends to sample spaces with infinitely many elements.

Illustration 3.   Let the random experiment be the tossing of a blue die and a white die together, and observing the number of dots b on the upper face of the blue die and w on the upper face of the white die after the dice fall. Then, the set T of equally likely outcomes consists of 36 pairs of numbers (b, w) as follows:

$$T = \begin{cases} (1, 1); & (1, 2); & (1, 3); & (1, 4); & (1, 5); & (1, 6); \\ (2, 1); & (2, 2); & \cdot & \cdot & \cdot & ; & (2, 6); \\ \cdot & \cdot & \cdot & \cdot & ; & \cdot \\ \cdot & \cdot & \cdot & \cdot & ; & \cdot \\ \cdot & \cdot & \cdot & \cdot & ; & \cdot \\ (6, 1); & (6, 2); & \cdot & \cdot & ; & (6, 6). \end{cases} \qquad (5)$$

For each outcome r in (5), define $X(r) = b + w = x$. The range of X, or its value space, is the set

$$V = \{2, 3, 4, 5, 6, 7, 8, 9, 10, 11, 12\} = \{x\}, \qquad (6)$$

where x is a variable with the domain $2, \cdots, 12$. From (5),

$$f(3) = P[X(\cdot) = 3] = \tfrac{1}{18}; \quad f(5) = P[X(\cdot) = 5] = \tfrac{1}{9}; \text{ } etc., \text{ } as \text{ } below.$$

$x =$	2	3	4	5	6	7	8	9	10	11	12
$f(x) =$	$\frac{1}{36}$	$\frac{1}{18}$	$\frac{1}{12}$	$\frac{1}{9}$	$\frac{5}{36}$	$\frac{1}{6}$	$\frac{5}{36}$	$\frac{1}{9}$	$\frac{1}{12}$	$\frac{1}{18}$	$\frac{1}{36}$

A graph of the probability function f, that is, a graph of $y = f(x)$, is shown in Figure 92. The graph consists of just 11 points. The broken lines in Figure 92 are included merely to emphasize the points on the graph; it is called *a graph of the probability distribution* over the range of X.

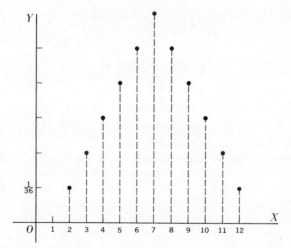

Figure 92

We could solve *only certain types of probability problems about T* in (5) by use of X as defined. Thus, by use of X, we could not find the probability of the event that the first component of the pair (b, w) in (5) is 1. This illustrates the fact that the choice of a random variable X for a sample space T depends on the type of problem which is to be considered.

For a given random experiment with sample space $T = \{r_j\}$, where $j = 1, \cdots, N$, suppose that we have defined a random variable X on T. Let the value space for X be $V = \{x_1, \cdots, x_k\}$, and the probability function for X be f. First, note that $k \leq N$ because V consists of the *distinct* numbers in the set $X(r_1), \cdots, X(r_N)$, among which there may be *duplicates*. Hence, with T as a finite sample space, the value space V for X is a finite set of numbers. We observe that *the sum of the probabilities of all numbers in V is* 1, or

$$\sum_{i=1}^{k} f(x_i) = \sum_{j=1}^{N} P(r_j) = 1. \tag{7}$$

This is true because each outcome, r_j, contributes its probability, $P(r_j)$ as defined for T, to *just one* of the probabilities $P[X(\cdot) = x_i]$, or $f(x_i)$. Then, for probability purposes where X is useful, we may think of V (instead of T) *as if V were a sample space* in the sense of Definition I on page 305. Then, each outcome of the experiment is considered as producing a value of X in V.

Illustration 4. In Illustration 3, $x = 3$ for the two outcomes $(1, 2)$ and $(2, 1)$ in (5), and hence we found the probability

$$f(3) = P[(1, 2)] + P[(2, 1)] = \tfrac{1}{36} + \tfrac{1}{36} = \tfrac{1}{18}.$$

Note 1. In a sequence of n elements of just two kinds, let any unbroken sequence of one or more elements of the same kind be called a **run**.

Illustration 5. If a coin is tossed five times and if it falls (H, T, H, H, T), respectively, in the tosses, the sequence exhibits 4 runs. The least number of runs which could be exhibited by the experiment is 1; the greatest number is 5, obtained for (H, T, H, T, H), or (T, H, T, H, T).

EXERCISE 84

Specify all numbers in the value space for X and find all values of the probability function f for X. Draw a graph of $y = f(x)$.

1. For any outcome r in the sample space T of (5) on page 313, let $X(r) = b + 2w$.
2. Repeat Problem 1 if $X(r) = w - b$.
3. A bag contains 3 white balls, 6 black balls, and 9 red balls. The random experiment consists of drawing a ball at random from the bag. For any outcome, r, of the experiment, define $X(r) = 2$ if r is a white ball, $X(r) = 1$ if r is a black ball, and $X(r) = 4$ if r is a red ball.
4. The random experiment is that a coin will be tossed three times, and the succession of heads (H) and tails (T) will be observed. (Recall Note 1 and Illustration 5 on this page.) For any outcome, r, of three tosses, let $X(r)$ be the number of runs exhibited in the sequence of three letters, each H or T.

5. A bag contains 2 white balls, 3 black balls, and one red ball. The random experiment consists of drawing 2 balls together from the bag. A prize of \$2 will be given for the drawing of any white ball, \$1 for any black ball, and \$4 for any red ball. For each outcome, r, of the experiment, define $X(r)$ as the number of dollars in the prize which will be obtained.

137. Expected value of a random variable

After a random variable X has been defined on a sample space $T = \{r\}$, the essential data become the range of X, or its value space $V = \{x\}$ where $X(r) = x$, and the probability function f for which $f(x) = P[X(\cdot) = x]$. Thereafter, frequently, T no longer need be mentioned. Thus, we find that a substantial part of probability theory involves concepts defined directly in terms of the values, $\{x\}$, of a random variable, X, and the corresponding probabilities $\{f(x)\}$. We proceed to introduce the most elementary concept of this nature.

DEFINITION III. *Let X be a random variable defined on some sample space $T = \{r\}$, where $X(r) = x$ and the value space for X is $V = \{x_i\}$, with $i = 1$, $2, \cdots, k$. Let f be the probability function for X. Then, the* **expected value** *of X, represented by $E(X)$, is defined as*

$$E(X) = \sum\nolimits_{i=1}^{k} f(x_i)x_i; \tag{1}$$

or, $E(X)$ is the sum of the products of each value of X times the probability of X assuming that value.

In V, if the probability $f(x_i)$ is the same for each value of i, we would say that the numbers of V are *equally likely*. Then, $f(x_i) = 1/k$ and, from (1),

$$E(X) = \sum\nolimits_{i=1}^{k} \frac{1}{k} x_i = \frac{\sum_{i=1}^{k} x_i}{k}. \tag{2}$$

In this case, $E(X)$ is merely the *average* of the values of X. In any case, from (1), $E(X)$ can be thought of as a *weighted average* of $(x_1, x_2, \cdots, x_k)$. In statistics, $E(X)$ also is called the **mean** of X, and is denoted by μ.

Illustration 1. Let the random experiment be the drawing of 1 ball from a bag containing 4 white and 6 black balls; the 10 outcomes are equally likely. Consider a game where the person making the draw will be paid \$2 if he draws a white ball and \$3 if he draws a black ball. For each outcome r of the sample space $T = \{r\}$, define $X(r) = x$, where \$x$ is the payoff corresponding to outcome r. If r is a white ball, then $x = 2$; if r is a black ball, then $x = 3$. Thus, we have defined a random variable X on T; the range of X is the set $V = \{2, 3\}$. With f as the probability function for X, we find that

$$P[X(\cdot) = 2] = \tfrac{4}{10} = \tfrac{2}{5} = f(2); \quad f(3) = \tfrac{3}{5}. \tag{3}$$

From (1), $\qquad\qquad E(X) = \tfrac{2}{5}(2) + \tfrac{3}{5}(3) = \tfrac{13}{5} = 2.6. \tag{4}$

Consider a random game where the possible outcomes form the sample space $T = \{r\}$. Let $X(r) = x$, where $\$x$ is the payoff to a player if outcome r arises at any trial of the game. In this case, we may call X the *payoff function* for the game. Then, the following terminology becomes useful.

DEFINITION IV. *In a game with possible outcomes* $T = \{r\}$, *where the payoff function for a player is* X, *the* **mathematical expectation** *of the player is defined as the expected value of* X, *or* $E(X)$ *(in money units).*

Illustration 2. In Illustration 1, the mathematical expectation of the player is \$2.60, which happens to be the average of the total of possible payoffs in the game. This feature is due to the fact that the outcomes of the game are equally likely, and hence $E(X)$ could be obtained from

$$E(X) = \tfrac{1}{10}(2) + \tfrac{1}{10}(2) + \tfrac{1}{10}(2) + \tfrac{1}{10}(2) + \tfrac{1}{10}(3) + \cdots + \tfrac{1}{10}(3) \qquad (5)$$

$$= \tfrac{4}{10}(2) + \tfrac{6}{10}(3) = \frac{4(2) + 6(3)}{10} = \tfrac{26}{10}.$$

The first four terms on the right in (5) are grouped (with the same value of X) to give $\tfrac{2}{5}(2)$, as in (4); the last six terms on the right in (5) give $\tfrac{3}{5}(3)$.

Suppose that a given random experiment produces the sample space $T = \{r\}$, and let H be the event in T consisting of the outcomes $(r_1, r_2, \cdots, r_m)$. Then, by Definition I on page 305,

$$P(H) = \sum_{i=1}^{m} P(r_i).$$

Now, consider a game where the player makes a trial of the experiment, and is promised a prize $\$W$ if event H occurs, and no payment if H fails to occur. Let us define a random variable X on T by specifying $X(r) = W$ if r is in H, and $X(r) - 0$ if r is in H', or *"not H."* The value space for X is $V = \{W, 0\}$;

$$P[X(r) = W] = \sum_{i=1}^{m} P(r_i) = P(H).$$

By Definition IV, the mathematical expectation of the player, in dollars, is

$$E(X) = WP(H) + 0 = WP(H). \qquad (6)$$

If we let $p = P(H)$, then (6) justifies the following statement.

$$\left\{ \begin{array}{l} \textit{If p is the probability of a player in a game receiving} \\ \textit{a prize } \$W, \textit{ his mathematical expectation is } \$pW. \end{array} \right\} \qquad (7)$$

<hr>

EXERCISE 85

X and f will represent a random variable and the probability function for X, respectively.

1. The value space for a random variable X is the set $V = \{2, 4, 6, 11\}$, and the numbers in V are equally likely. Find $E(X)$.
2. In Problem 1, find $E(X)$ if the probability function, f, for X has $f(2) = .3$, $f(4) = .1$, and $f(6) = .2$.

3. Let the sample space T consist of the 6 outcomes of the experiment of tossing a die, where the outcomes 1, 2, 3, 4, 5, and 6 are assigned the probabilities $\frac{1}{12}, \frac{1}{12}, \frac{1}{3}, \frac{1}{3}, \frac{1}{12}$, and $\frac{1}{12}$, respectively, and where the corresponding values of a random variable X are 12, 10, 8, 6, 4, and 2. Find $E(X)$. Draw a graph of the probability function f for X.

4. A game consists of drawing two balls together from a bag containing 6 white balls and 4 black balls. The player will receive $2 if he draws 2 white balls, $3 if he draws 2 black balls, and $1 if he draws one ball of each color. Define appropriately the values of a payoff random variable X, and find $E(X)$.

5. A merchant has 8 golf balls in a box, where 3 are defective and 5 are perfect. A single golf ball is drawn at random. For any outcome, r, of the drawing, define $X(r) = 0$ if the golf ball is defective and $X(r) = 1$ if the golf ball is perfect. Find $f(0)$ and $f(1)$; compute $E(X)$.

6. A bag contains 5 black and 10 white balls. At a charity bazaar, $6 is charged a player for the privilege of drawing a ball at random, with a promised prize of $8 if the ball drawn is black, and $2 if it is white. Define a payoff function X on the sample space for the game, and find the mathematical expectation of the player. Is the game likely to be profitable for the sponsors of the bazaar? What criterion for *"profitable"* did you use?

7. Let the random experiment be the tossing of a die. For any outcome r, define $X(r)$ as *"the number of dots"* observed. List the numbers in the value space V for X, find all values of the probability function for X, and compute the expected number of dots to be observed.

8. In Illustration 3 on page 313, specify all numbers in the value space for X, find all values of the probability function f for X, and compute $E(X)$, if $X(r) = 2b - w$ for any outcome r. Graph the probability function f.

9. In Illustration 3 on page 313, for any outcome r, define $X(r) = |b - w|$. Repeat Problem 8 for this variable X.

10. As the basis for a game, a coin and a die are tossed, and the upper face of the coin, and the number of dots, y, on the upper face of the die are observed. The player will receive $10 if the outcome is *(heads, y)* with $y = 1$ or $y = 6$, $5 if the outcome is *(heads, y)* with $2 \leq y \leq 5$, and nothing if the outcome is *(tails, y)*, for any y. List the outcomes of the sample space for the game. Define X as the payoff function; specify the numbers in its value space; compute the mathematical expectation of the player.

11. A consignment of 12 portable radios contains just 3 defective radios. Three radios will be drawn together at random from the lot. For any outcome r of this experiment, let $X(r)$ be *"the number of defectives among the three drawn."* Specify the value space $V = \{x\}$ for X, and compute the expected number of defectives in the random drawing. Graph the probability function f for X.

12. On an examination, a student is asked to match the dates (1863, 1815, 1769) with the following events: the Battle of Gettysburg; the Battle of Waterloo; the birth of Napoleon Bonaparte. If the student guesses without knowledge of the true dates, list the possible outcomes of his random experiment, in the order given above for the events. For any outcome r, define $X(r)$ as *"the number of correct dates in the outcome."* Compute the expected value of the number of correct dates in the student's answer.

★**13.** Refer to Note 1 on page 314. Three boys and two girls take seats at random in a row of five seats at a lunch counter. For any outcome, r, let X be the number of runs of boys or girls exhibited by r. Find the values of the probability function f for X and $E(X)$.

★**14.** Refer to Illustration 5 on page 314. For any outcome r, let $X(r)$ be the number of runs in r. Find $E(X)$.

138. A Bernoulli random variable

Consider any sample space $T = \{r\}$, and an event H in T, where $P(H) = p$, and $1 - p = q$. On T, let us define a random variable X by specifying that $X(r) = 1$ if r is in the event H (or, if H occurs at any trial), and $X(r) = 0$ if r is in H', or *"not H."* Then, the value space for X is $V = \{0, 1\}$. If f is the probability function for X then

$$f(1) = P(H) = p; \quad f(0) = P(H') = 1 - p = q. \tag{1}$$

A random variable X is called a **Bernoulli variable** in case the value space for X is $\{0, 1\}$, with $f(0) = q$ and $f(1) = p$, where $p + q = 1$. Hence, in arriving at (1), we introduced a Bernoulli variable. Occasionally, we may call the set $\{0, 1\}$ with its associated probabilities a **Bernoulli space.** After a Bernoulli random variable has been introduced relative to an event H, we may look at a trial of the random experiment as a random selection of a number, 0 or 1, from the new sample space $\{0, 1\}$. *"Occurrence of H"* would mean that 1 has been selected; also, $P(H) = f(1) = p$.

Illustration 1. A Bernoulli variable was introduced in Illustration 2 on page 312.

Suppose that we are asked to proceed on the basis of a statement that *"the probability of the occurrence of a certain event H at any trial of a given experiment is p,"* without sufficient information to compute the probability. Then, *we agree to act as if the experiment is equivalent to a random selection of a number from the Bernoulli space* $\{0, 1\}$, with the probabilities $f(0) = q$ and $f(1) = p$. Also selection of "1" means occurrence of H and selection of "0" means failure of H. In particular, this agreement will apply if we seek a mathematical expectation based on event H. Essentially, we have agreed *to legalize the unsupported announcement* that $P(H) = p$ within the framework of our Definition I. Regardless of any theoretical basis, the agreement just made is in accordance with our intuitions.

Illustration 2. If the probability is $\frac{1}{5}$ that driver A will win the first prize of $20,000 in a cross-country automobile race, his mathematical expectation in dollars is $\frac{1}{5}(\$20,000)$ or $4000.

Note 1. The mathematician JAKOB (or, JACQUES) BERNOULLI (1654–1705), whose home was in Basle, Switzerland, may be regarded as the founder of probability as a branch of mathematics, although the roots of probability extend back as far as the early 16th Century. In a posthumous book by Jakob Bernoulli entitled *Ars conjectandi*, published in 1713, he aimed at a fusion of methods of *a priori* probability and early statistical theory based on observation of past trials of a random experiment (*a posteriori* methods, to be met on page 320). The name *Bernoulli* occurs frequently in the modern development of probability theory. Jakob Bernoulli was in the first generation of a famous Basle family which, in three generations, produced eight outstanding mathematicians. The most prominent of these were Jakob and his brother JOHANN (1667–1748). These brothers worked partly on the same problems, which created jealousy and even public quarrels. The most famous son of Johann was DANIEL BERNOULLI (1700–1782), who also worked in the field of probability. Daniel received a prize from the French Academy ten times for mathematical results.

139. The language of "odds"

Suppose that $m > 0$ and $n > 0$. Then, to state that *"the **odds** are m to n,"* written $m : n$, that a certain event H will occur, means that the probabilities p and q of success and failure, respectively, for H satisfy

$$p : q = m : n, \quad and \quad p + q = 1. \tag{1}$$

From (1),
$$\frac{q}{p} = \frac{n}{m}; \quad q = \frac{np}{m}; \quad p + \frac{np}{m} = 1.$$

Hence, $p(m + n) = m$, or

$$p = \frac{m}{n + m} \quad and\ then \quad q = \frac{n}{n + m}. \tag{2}$$

If $m > n$ in (1), the odds are said to be $m : n$ *in favor of the occurrence of H;* if $n > m$, the odds are $n : m$ *against occurrence of H*. With odds assigned outright, we use p from (2) on the basis described for an *unsupported* statement of a probability in the preceding section. That is, we agree to act as if the experiment is equivalent to a random selection of a number from a Bernoulli space $\{0, 1\}$ with the probabilities $f(1) = p$ and $f(0) = q$.

Illustration 1. If the odds are 5 : 3 against Jones winning $64 in a game, then his probability of winning is $\frac{3}{8}$ and his mathematical expectation is $\$\frac{3}{8}(64)$.

EXAMPLE 1. Jones places a $2 bet with a gambler G at odds of 1 : 4 that a horse Lazybones will win a certain race. If the horse wins, how much will Jones receive, if it is understood that, before the race, Jones and G had *equal mathematical expectations*, under the assumption that the odds stated the correct probabilities of the horse winning, and of it losing in the race?

Solution. From (2), the probability of Jones winning is $p = \frac{1}{5}$ and of Jones losing is $q = \frac{4}{5}$. Let $\$S$ be the amount Jones will receive if he wins. Then, the mathematical expectations, in dollars, of Jones and G are $\frac{1}{5}S$ and $\frac{4}{5}(2)$, respectively. Hence, $\frac{1}{5}S = \frac{4}{5}(2)$, or $S = 8$.

140. The expected number of successes in n trials

Consider a random experiment, Z, whose outcomes form the sample space $T = \{r\}$, and let H be an event in T with $P_0(H) = p$. Suppose that n successive trials of Z are made, where no trial has any effect on the outcome of any other trial. In Section 143 on page 330, we shall consider "n successive trials of Z" as a *new* random experiment, L. Each trial of L will exhibit just a certain number, x, of successes for H, where x has the domain $\{0, 1, 2, \cdots, n\}$. Each of these possibilities will have a *probability of occurrence*. At this point in the chapter, we merely state that *the most probable number of successes for H in n trials of L is approximately np*. Also, np is called the *expected number of successes in n trials*. This name is appropriate because it is found that $np = E(X)$, where X is a random variable on the sample space for L with the value of X, for any n trials, equal to the number of successes for H in those trials. The so-called "*law of large numbers*" in probability states that, under reasonable hypotheses, we can expect the relative frequency of successes, x/n, in n trials to be near p if n is large. However, if n is small, we would have no reason to expect x/n to be near p. Even when n is large, the law of large numbers allows for the possibility that x/n may differ substantially from p, although this would be anticipated as a rare occurrence.

Illustration 1. Suppose that $\frac{3}{5}$ is the probability that Jones will win a certain game whenever he plays. If, for instance, Jones plays 1000 games, the most probable number of wins is $\frac{3}{5}(1000)$ or 600. Since 1000 is large, we would expect the relative frequency of his wins to be approximately $\frac{3}{5}$. If he plays only a few games, we would not be surprised if the relative frequency of his wins differed considerably from $\frac{3}{5}$.

Consider a random experiment whose outcomes are known to form a sample space T, perhaps not finite as in Definition I on page 305, and let H be an event in T whose probability is $P(H) = p$. Assume that we do not have enough knowledge of T to permit computation of p by *a priori* methods (methods *in advance of experimenting*). Suppose, now, that we observe n trials of the experiment and find that H occurs in just x of these trials. On the basis of the law of large numbers, we shall accept *the relative frequency of successes, x/n*, as a desirable approximation to the unknown probability, p, for the event H at any future trial of the experiment, and simply say that $p = x/n$. Then, x/n may be called an experimental, or empirical, or an "*a posteriori*" probability (because it is determined from data observed in the past). If we use $p = x/n$, then we may also associate each trial of the experiment with a Bernoulli random variable having the values $\{0, 1\}$ as was described for an assumed probability in the preceding section.

Illustration 2. The Commissioners Standard Ordinary Mortality Table (Table VII, abbreviated CSO Table) embodies the results of extensive observation of the ages at death of people who have carried life insurance. The table may be thought of as a record of the year in which death occurred for each of 1,023,102 people who were born at the same time. A mortality table can be used as the basis for obtaining empirical probabilities concerning living and dying for a person of any given age.

EXAMPLE 1. If a man is alive at age 30, find the probability that he will live at least 14 years.

Solution. In Table VII, we observe 924,609 men alive at age 30, and 859,464 of these remain alive 14 years later. Hence, the (empirical) probability of living at least 14 years is $p = 859,464/924,609$, or $p = .9295$, by logarithms.

Illustration 3. If a man plays a game where the prize is $100, and the probability of winning is $\frac{3}{5}$, his mathematical expectation in dollars is $\frac{3}{5}(\$100)$ or $60. Now, suppose that a professional gambler offers to play this game against any man who will pay his expectation ($60) as a fee for playing. If a great many players enter the game, the professional operator may feel safe in assuming that the relative frequency of wins will be approximately $\frac{3}{5}$, or that about $\frac{3}{5}$ of the players will win. Thus, if 100 players enter, they pay $6000 in fees; if $\frac{3}{5}(100)$ or 60 players win, they collect $6000, and in this case the operator has no gain or loss. To avoid possible loss, however, the operator should charge more than the mathematical expectation as a fee because more than $\frac{3}{5}$ of the players may win.

EXAMPLE 2. An insurance policy written for a man, A, aged 30 promises to pay him an endowment of $1000 at age 50 if he is alive then. What is his mathematical expectation?

Solution. Let p be the probability that A will be alive at age 50. From the CSO Table VII, $p = 810,900/924,609$, or $p = .877$, which is the probability of the payment being made. Hence, the value of the mathematical expectation of A in dollars is $1000(.877)$ or $877, payable at age 50.

The principle involved in Illustration 3 is important in the conduct of a life insurance company, or of any financial enterprise involving the sharing of natural risks by a group of people. The fact that the risks are unavoidable, instead of being assumed voluntarily, as in a game of chance, does not alter the nature of the problem essentially. The financial safety of the operating company demands that the fees charged shall be more than the corresponding mathematical expectations and that many people should participate.

Illustration 4. In Example 2, for financial safety, the insurance company should charge the policy holder, A, premiums whose value exceeds $877, the mathematical expectation of A. The excess would have to provide for administrative expenses of the company, in addition to giving a margin of safety in view of the fact that a random experiment is involved in writing the policy.

Note 1. An *n*-year term insurance policy for $W on the life of a man A is a contract (by an insurance company) to pay $W to a stated beneficiary B when A dies, provided that he dies within *n* years after the day of issue of the policy. Such a contract would call for the payment of a premium, or premiums, to the insurance company.

EXAMPLE 3. An insurance company, K, sells a $1000, one-year term insurance policy to a man A, of age 35, in return for a premium of $12 payable immediately. Find the mathematical expectation of the beneficiary B of the policy. Does K have a margin of financial safety?

Solution. 1. Consider A as a man selected at random from the 906,554 men of his age listed in CSO Table VII. Let *H* be the event that A will die within one year. Then,

$$P(H) = \frac{d_{35}}{l_{35}} = \frac{4161}{906,554} = .00459.$$

2. If *H* occurs, then B will receive $1000. Hence,

$$(mathematical\ expectation\ of\ \text{B}) = .00459(\$1000) = \$4.59.$$

Since the premium was $12, there is a margin of safety for K, ($12 − 4.59), or $7.41, to provide for administrative costs, and possibly unfavorably high mortality among the whole group of people insured by K.

Note 2. The *mathematics of investment** may be described as the study of the equivalence of the values of pairs of sets of designated payments of money, under the assumptions (1) that the payments are *certain* to be made on given dates, and (2) that the effects of investment of money at compound interest will be taken into account in equivalence relations. On the other hand, the mathematical theory of life insurance and life annuities, called *actuarial theory*, deals with *contingent* payments, that is, payments where each one has a certain probability of being paid on a specified date. This probability, in actuarial mathematics, is determined by the probabilities of death or survival of one or more people of given initial ages. The basis of actuarial science then is the mathematics of investment, plus the concept of the mathematical expectation of a contingent payment.

EXERCISE 86

1. Find the mathematical expectation of a man whose probability of winning $500 in a game is $\frac{1}{20}$.
2. On a bank night in a chain of theaters, the pot contains $3500, and each of the 15,000 patrons has an equal probability of winning the pot. Find the mathematical expectation of each person.
3. If the odds are 5 : 3 in favor of a man K receiving $100 if a certain random act is performed, find the probability (*a*) of K receiving $100; (*b*) of K not receiving $100. Also, find K's mathematical expectation.

* See *The Mathematics of Investment, Fourth Edition,* by WILLIAM L. HART; D. C. Heath and Company, publishers.

4. If the odds are 5 : 7 against a man receiving $50 if a certain random experiment is performed, find (a) his probability of receiving $50; (b) his mathematical expectation.

5. Suppose that a gambler A bets $W against a gambler G that a certain event H will occur at a trial of a specified random experiment, L. Let the odds for the bet be m : n that H will occur. We agree that the arrangement will be fair to both A and G if their mathematical expectations are equal. If H fails to occur, then A must pay $W to G. If H occurs, then G must pay a certain amount $U to A. Prove that W : U = m : n, by use of (2) on page 319.

6. A man, K, bets $75 at odds of 3:7 that the horse Darling Daisy will win in a race. (a) What is the assumed probability that the horse will win? (b) How much will K receive if the horse wins?

Find the probability of the event by use of the mortality table. Leave the result as a fraction, except as directed by the instructor. If decimal values are desired, logarithms should be used.

7. That a boy aged 10 will be alive 30 years later.

8. That a man aged 24 will live at least 20 years.

9. (a) That a person aged 30 will live at least 35 years; (b) that he will die between ages 65 and 70.

10. That a person aged 21 will die (a) within 5 years; (b) during the 5th year.

11. That a person aged 20 will die (a) within 1 year; (b) during his 36th year.

12. That a person aged 65 will die within 1 year.

13. An insurance policy, written for a man now aged 30, promises an endowment of $1000 to him at the end of 20 years, if he is alive then. Find his mathematical expectation to the nearest dollar.

14. A true die has been tossed 239 times, and the face with 6 dots has been up 39 times. The die is tossed again. What is the probability that the upper face will show 6 dots?

15. A true coin will be tossed 400 times. What is the expected number of heads?

16. A true coin has been tossed 480 times, and it has fallen heads just 235 times. Then, the coin will be tossed 20 more times. What is the expected number of heads in the 20 tosses?

17. A man is now 25 years old and his wife is 21 years old. They are promised a gift of $5000 at the end of 15 years if both are alive then. Find the mathematical expectation of the man and his wife.

141. Probability of the event "*H or K*"

Consider a random experiment with a finite sample space $T = \{r\}$, as in Definition I. Let H and K be two events (subsets) of T. Then, "*the event H or K*" consists of all outcomes in H *alone*, or in K *alone*, or in *both H and K*, when they have common outcomes. Thus, "*the event H or K*" is the *union* of H and K, or $H \cup K$, as defined on page 59. We wish to investigate $P(H \cup K)$, which we shall write frequently as $P(H$ *or* $K)$, for quick appreciation.

Illustration 1. A bag contains 4 black balls, 5 white balls, 3 black cubes, and 6 white cubes. Let the random experiment be the drawing of a single object from the bag. The sample space T has 18 equally likely outcomes. Let the event of drawing a white object be H, and of drawing a ball be K. Then,

$$H = \{6 \text{ white cubes; 5 white balls}\} ; \tag{1}$$

$$K = \{5 \text{ white balls; 4 black balls}\} ; \tag{2}$$

$$H \cap K = \{5 \text{ white balls}\} ; \tag{3}$$

$$H \cup K = \{6 \text{ white cubes; 5 white balls; 4 black balls}\} . \tag{4}$$

In Figure 93, we represent H by the region with horizontal rulings and K by the region with vertical rulings. Then, $H \cup K$ is represented by all ruled points in the figure; $H \cap K$ is represented by the doubly ruled region where H and K overlap. By counting outcomes, we obtain

$$P(H) = \tfrac{11}{18}; \quad P(K) = \tfrac{9}{18}; \quad P(H \cap K) = \tfrac{5}{18}; \quad P(H \cup K) = \tfrac{15}{18}. \tag{5}$$

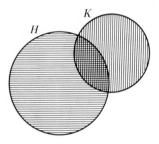

Figure 93

With the aid of Figure 93, we decide that the number of outcomes in $H \cup K$ is equal to the number of outcomes in H, *plus* the number in K, *minus* the number of outcomes in $H \cap K$, because these occur in *both H and K* and thus were counted *twice* in considering H alone and K alone. Hence, in (5) it should be true that

$$\frac{15}{18} = \frac{11}{18} + \frac{9}{18} - \frac{5}{18} \text{, which checks.} \tag{6}$$

THEOREM III. *If H and K are events which may occur at any trial of a certain random experiment, as considered in Definition I, then*

$$P(H \cup K) = P(H) + P(K) - P(H \cap K). \tag{7}$$

Proof. Let H and K be represented in Figure 93. With the aid of this diagram, as in Illustration 1, we conclude that $P(H \cup K)$ is equal to the sum of the probabilities of all outcomes in H, and of all in K, minus the sum of the probabilities of the outcomes in both H and K, to correct for having added these probabilities *twice*. Thus, to obtain $P(H \cup K)$, we compute $P(H) + P(K)$, and subtract $P(H \cap K)$, as in (7).

Illustration 2. We met a special case of (7) in (6).

Corollary 1. *If H_1 and H_2 are* **mutually exclusive events,** *then*

$$P(H_1 \text{ or } H_2) = P(H_1 \cup H_2) = P(H_1) + P(H_2). \tag{8}$$

Proof. By hypothesis, $H_1 \cap H_2 = \emptyset$. Also, $P(\emptyset) = 0$. Hence, with $H = H_1$ and $K = H_2$ in (7), we obtain (8).

Illustration 3. A bag contains 3 white, 7 black, and 10 yellow balls. The random experiment consists of drawing a ball from the bag. Let the events of drawing a white ball, and a black ball, be H_1 and H_2, respectively. Then the sample space T consists of 20 outcomes, H_1 of 3 outcomes, and H_2 of 7 outcomes. Also, $H_1 \cap H_2 = \emptyset$. The event $(H_1 \text{ or } H_2)$ is the event of obtaining *a white ball or a black ball.* By use of (8),

$$P(\text{white or black}) = P(\text{white}) + P(\text{black}) = \tfrac{3}{20} + \tfrac{7}{20} = \tfrac{1}{2}.$$

Equation (8) is a special case of the following result, whose proof does not have to be based on (7).

THEOREM IV. *Let $H_1, H_2, H_3, \cdots$ be mutually exclusive events in the sample space T, for a random experiment, L. Then, at a trial of L, the probability of the event, H, that at least one of $H_1, H_2, H_3, \cdots$ will occur is the sum of their separate probabilities, or*

$$P(H) = P(H_1, \text{ or } H_2, \text{ or } H_3, \cdots) = P(H_1) + P(H_2) + P(H_3) + \cdots. \quad (9)$$

Proof (for just three events). By Definition III on page 59,

$$H = (H_1, \text{ or } H_2, \text{ or } H_3) = H_1 \cup H_2 \cup H_3. \quad (10)$$

No outcome of T is in *more than one* of (H_1, H_2, H_3) because they are mutually exclusive, as illustrated in Figure 94; that is,

$$H_1 \cap H_2 = H_1 \cap H_3 = H_2 \cap H_3 = \emptyset.$$

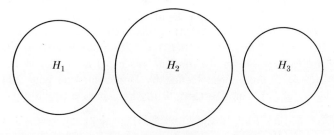

Figure 94

Hence, the outcomes of H consist of the outcomes *of H_1, and of H_2, and of H_3,* where no outcome is involved *more than once.* Therefore, $P(H)$ is the sum of the probabilities of those outcomes in H_1, and those in H_2, and those in H_3, or

$$P(H) = P(H_1) + P(H_2) + P(H_3).$$

Illustration 4. A bag contains 5 white balls, 6 black balls, 4 green balls, and 3 yellow balls. If one ball is drawn,

$$P(\text{ball is black, or white, or yellow}) =$$

$$P(\text{black}) + P(\text{white}) + P(\text{yellow}) = \tfrac{6}{18} + \tfrac{5}{18} + \tfrac{3}{18} = \tfrac{14}{18} = \tfrac{7}{9}.$$

142. Independent experiments

Consider two random experiments L_1 and L_2:

$$L_1; \text{ with sample sp. } T_1 = \{r\}; \text{ prob. function } P_1; \text{ event } H_1 \text{ in } T_1. \qquad (1)$$

$$L_2; \text{ with sample sp. } T_2 = \{s\}; \text{ prob. function } P_2; \text{ event } H_2 \text{ in } T_2. \qquad (2)$$

DEFINITION V. *Two random experiments L_1 and L_2 will be called* **independent** *in case they may be performed either simultaneously or in succession, and if the outcome r of L_1 has no influence on the outcome s of L_2, and s has no influence on the outcome r.*

When L_1 and L_2 are performed as in Definition V, let the *compound experiment* be represented by $L = (L_1, L_2)$. By Definition V, the sample space T for L consists of all ordered pairs (r, s) with r in T_1 and s in T_2; we shall write*
$T = (T_1, T_2) = \{all\ (r, s)\}$. One event of T will be the subset

$$H = \{all\ (r, s)\ with\ r\ in\ H_1\ and\ s\ in\ H_2\},$$

where we shall write $H = (H_1, H_2)$.

Illustration 1. A bag (I) contains 4 white and 6 black balls, and a bag (II) contains 5 red and 10 green cubes. Let the random drawing of a ball from bag (I) be experiment L_1, and of a cube from bag (II) be experiment L_2, with all outcomes, for each experiment, considered equally likely. Let the event that a white ball is drawn from bag (I) be H_1, and that a red cube is drawn from bag (II) be H_2. Let $L = (L_1, L_2)$ be the experiment of drawing an object from each bag. Experiments L_1 and L_2 are independent. The sample space for L is the set $T = \{all\ (ball, cube)\}$. It seems natural to consider the outcomes in T as equally likely. Thus, T has $10(15)$ or 150 equally likely pairs $(ball, cube)$. Let $H = (H_1, H_2)$, the event $(white\ ball, red\ cube)$ at a trial of L. Then, H consists of $4(5)$ or 20 outcomes. Hence, by Definition I on page 305, we have $P(H) = \frac{20}{150} = \frac{2}{15}$. We notice that, with the separate probability functions P_1 for L_1 and P_2 for L_2,

$$P_1(H_1) = \tfrac{2}{5}, \quad P_2(H_2) = \tfrac{1}{3}, \quad and \quad \tfrac{2}{5} \cdot \tfrac{1}{3} = \tfrac{2}{15}.$$

Hence, our definition of probability in T resulted in

$$P(H) = P(H_1, H_2) = P_1(H_1)P_2(H_2). \qquad (3)$$

Also, notice that the probability of each outcome in T_1 was $\frac{1}{10}$, in T_2 was $\frac{1}{15}$, and in T was $\frac{1}{150}$, which is equal to $\frac{1}{10}(\frac{1}{15})$. The *product feature* here was responsible for the *product feature* for $P(H)$ above.

Now, consider the data in (1) and (2), with the compound experiment $L = (L_1, L_2)$ whose sample space is $T = (T_1, T_2)$. We have the event

---

* In set terminology, T is called the *cartesian product* of T_1 and T_2, which is denoted by the symbol $T_1 \times T_2$. We prefer $T = (T_1, T_2)$, for our application, in order to associate T clearly with (L_1, L_2).

$H = (H_1, H_2)$ in T. Let $P_1(H_1) = p_1$, for experiment L_1, and $P_2(H_2) = p_2$, for experiment L_2. Then, we define the probability of (H_1, H_2) as follows.

DEFINITION VI. *Suppose that events H_1 and H_2 may occur, with probabilities p_1 and p_2, respectively, whenever the corresponding independent experiments L_1 and L_2 are performed. Then, the probability that H_1 and H_2 both will occur when L_1 and L_2 are both performed, in succession or simultaneously, is defined by*

$$P(H_1, H_2) = p_1 p_2. \tag{4}$$

Illustration 2. Equation (4) of Definition VI agrees with (3) as used in Illustration 1.

Note 1. Definition VI and its introduction were phrased so as to apply to sample spaces much more general (possibly infinite) than the space in Definition VI. Let W represent the set of all outcomes in the sample space T for (L_1, L_2) which are *not* in (H_1, H_2). Then, in addition to (4), it is implied that we define $P(W) = 1 - p_1 p_2$. The interested student would find it reasonably easy to prove that (4) and $P(W) = 1 - p_1 p_2$ are true if we define the probabilities for *each pair* (r, s) in T as follows:*

$$P[(r, s)] = P_1(r)P_2(s). \tag{5}$$

The preceding discussion relating to *just two* independent experiments becomes a basis for extending (4) to any finite number of experiments and corresponding events. Consider three or more experiments $L_1, L_2, L_3, \cdots$, with sample spaces $T_1 = \{r_1\}$, $T_2 = \{r_2\}$, $T_3 = \{r_3\}, \cdots$. Then $L_1, L_2, L_3, \cdots$ will be called *independent experiments* if any number of them can be performed simultaneously, or in succession, with the outcome of any particular experiment L_i not influenced by the outcomes of any of the other experiments. Let $H_1, H_2, H_3, \cdots$ be events which may occur at any trial of $L_1, L_2, L_3, \cdots$, respectively, with corresponding probabilities $p_1, p_2, p_3, \cdots$. With (4) applied first to the compound experiment (L_1, L_2) and the event (H_1, H_2), we find its probability $p_1 p_2$. Then, with experiment (L_1, L_2, L_3) considered as the performance of (L_1, L_2) and L_3, we may again apply (4) for the event $[(H_1, H_2), H_3]$ to obtain the following result for the probability of (H_1, H_2, H_3) occurring at any trial of (L_1, L_2, L_3):

$$P(H_1, H_2, H_3) = (p_1 p_2)p_3 = p_1 p_2 p_3. \tag{6}$$

Similarly, we extend (4) to any finite number of events, to obtain

$$P(H_1, H_2, H_3, \cdots) = p_1 p_2 p_3 \cdots. \tag{7}$$

EXAMPLE 1. A 1st bag contains 4 white and 6 black balls, and a 2d bag contains 5 white and 7 green balls. If a ball is drawn from each bag, find the probability (*a*) of obtaining a black ball and a green ball; (*b*) of obtaining a black ball (with no specification about the second ball).

---

* Note that (5) is a special case of (4), with H_1 consisting of *just outcome r*, and H_2 of *just outcome s*.

Solution. (a) Let the experiment of drawing a ball from the first bag be L_1, and from the second bag be L_2. These are independent experiments. Let the event of obtaining a black ball at a trial of L_1 be H_1, and a green ball at a trial of L_2 be H_2. Then, $P_1(H_1) = \frac{3}{5}$ and $P_2(H_2) = \frac{7}{12}$. With P as the probability function on the sample space of the compound experiment (L_1, L_2), from (4) we obtain $P(black\ ball,\ green\ ball) = \frac{3}{5} \cdot \frac{7}{12} = \frac{7}{20}$.

(b) The event of *any* outcome occurring at a trial of L_2 is T_2 itself, and $P_2(T_2) = 1$. Hence,

$$P(black\ ball,\ any\ second\ ball) = \frac{3}{5} \cdot 1 = \frac{3}{5}. \tag{8}$$

Let L be a given random experiment. Assume that, in repeated trials of L, the outcome at any trial is not influenced by the outcomes at other trials. Then, the repetitions of L form a set of independent experiments to which we may apply (7) to any number of corresponding events $H_1, H_2, H_3, \cdots$, all in the sample space for L.

EXAMPLE 2. A bag contains 10 white and 30 black balls. We draw 2 balls together, replace them, and then draw 2 more balls together. Find the probability of obtaining 2 white, and then 1 white and 1 black ball.

Solution. 1. Let L be the experiment of drawing 2 balls from the bag, and let P_1 be the probability function defined on the sample space for L. Then

$$p_1 = P_1(2\ white) = \frac{{}_{10}C_2}{{}_{40}C_2} = \frac{3}{52};$$

$$p_2 = P_1(1\ white\ and\ 1\ black) = \frac{10 \cdot 30}{{}_{40}C_2} = \frac{5}{13}.$$

2. Repetition of L creates a compound experiment $Z = (L, L)$. Let P be the probability function defined on the sample space for Z. Let

$$H_1 = (event\ of\ 2\ white) \qquad and \qquad H_2 = (event\ of\ 1\ white\ and\ 1\ black)$$

at a trial of L. Then, by use of (4),

$$P(H_1, H_2) = p_1 p_2 = \frac{3}{52} \cdot \frac{5}{13} = \frac{15}{676}.$$

EXAMPLE 3. The probability that Jones will win in a certain game when he plays is $\frac{1}{3}$. If he plays twice, find the probability that he will win just once.

Solution. 1. Let G represent the random experiment of playing the game. Repetitions of G are independent experiments. Jones engages in a trial of the compound experiment (G, G). Let P be the probability function on the sample space for (G, G).

2. Jones will win just once if

(a) *he wins the 1st game and loses the 2d game; or, if*

(b) *he loses the 1st game and wins the 2d game.*

Each of the mutually exclusive events (a) and (b) is an event in the sample space for (G, G). The probability that Jones will lose in any game is $\frac{2}{3}$. Hence, from (4) applied to (G, G) for event (a), and then for event (b),

$$P[(a)] = \tfrac{1}{3} \cdot \tfrac{2}{3} = \tfrac{2}{9}; \quad P[(b)] = \tfrac{2}{3} \cdot \tfrac{1}{3} = \tfrac{2}{9}.$$

By Theorem IV on page 325, $\qquad P[(a) \text{ or } (b)] = \tfrac{2}{9} + \tfrac{2}{9} = \tfrac{4}{9}.$

Comment. In Example 3, notice the convenience of first analyzing the specified event into a set of mutually exclusive events of more simple nature, and then using Theorem IV.

EXERCISE 87

Obtain the probability of any compound event by use of Sections 141 and 142.

1. In a game where only one player can win, the probability that Smith will win is $\frac{1}{4}$ and that Johnson will win is $\frac{1}{3}$. Find the probability that one of them will win.

2. The probability that Jones will win a certain game is $\frac{1}{4}$ and that Smith will win another game is $\frac{1}{3}$. If each man plays his game, find the probability that (a) both will win; (b) Smith will win and Jones will lose; (c) just one of the men will win.

3. Find the probability of throwing 5 heads in 5 tosses of a coin.

4. If a coin and a die are tossed, find the probability of obtaining (a) a tail and 3 on the die; (b) a head and at least 5 on the die.

5. Find the probability of throwing 11 each time in 3 tosses of 2 dice.

6. If a coin is tossed twice, find the probability that one fall is a head and the other is a tail.

7. The probability that Hansen will win a certain game whenever he plays is $\frac{1}{4}$. If he plays twice, find the probability that (a) he will win the 1st game and lose the 2d game; (b) he will win just one game; (c) he will win at least one game; (d) he will lose both games. [Why are results (c) and (d) related simply?]

8. The probability that a certain man will live 10 years is $\frac{1}{3}$, and that his wife will live 10 years is $\frac{3}{4}$. Find the probability that (a) the wife will live and the man will not live 10 years; (b) just one of them will remain alive at the end of 10 years.

A 1st bag contains 5 black and 10 white balls. A 2d bag contains 3 white and 5 black balls. Find the probability of the specified event.

9. If we draw a ball from each bag, we shall obtain (a) 2 white balls; (b) 2 balls of the same color; (c) 1 white and 1 black ball.

10. If 2 balls are drawn in succession from the 1st bag, *with replacement* of the 1st ball before the 2d ball is drawn, then (a) both will be white; (b) just one will be white; (c) at most one will be white.

11. If 2 balls are drawn together from each bag, (a) all balls obtained will be white; (b) 1 white and 1 black ball will be obtained from each bag; (c) all obtained will be of the same color; (d) 3 white balls and 1 black ball will be obtained.

12. From a well shuffled deck of 52 cards, we draw 3 cards in succession, with each one replaced before the next draw. Find the probability that we draw (a) all spades or clubs; (b) all of one suit; (c) all aces or jacks.

13. The probabilities of Jones, Smith, and Harrison living for 10 years are $\frac{1}{2}$, $\frac{1}{4}$, and $\frac{1}{3}$, respectively. Find the probability that (a) all will live for 10 years; (b) all will be dead at the end of 10 years; (c) just two will live 10 years.

14. From a deck of 52 cards, we draw 2 cards together, replace them, and repeat this act again. Find the probability that (a) all cards obtained are hearts; (b) all are of the same suit.

15. Johnson's probability of winning a certain game is $\frac{1}{4}$, and Jackson's probability of winning a different game is $\frac{1}{2}$. If each of them plays his game, find the probability that at most one will win.

16. Robert's probability of winning a certain game whenever he plays it is $\frac{1}{3}$. If he plays the game 3 times, find his probability of (a) winning each time; (b) winning twice and losing once.

    Hint for (b). He may (i) *win, win, lose;* (ii) *win, lose, win;* (iii) *lose, win, win.* Events (i), (ii), and (iii) are mutually exclusive.

17. Jordan's probability of winning a certain game whenever he plays it is $\frac{1}{4}$. If he plays the game 4 times, find his probability of winning just 3 times.

18. In answering true-false questions on an examination, a student chooses responses at random. Find his probability of answering the first 6 questions correctly and the next 4 questions incorrectly.

19. To determine who gets a prize, A tosses a coin with B, the winner tosses with C, and the winner tosses with D. The last winner obtains the prize. Find each person's probability of receiving the prize.

★20. For any subsets E and F of a space T, prove that $E = (E \cap F) \cup (E \cap F')$.

★21. In a sample space T, let E and F be events such that $P(E) = .6$, $P(F) = .5$, and $P(E \cap F') = .2$. By use of (7) on page 324 and other information, find the probabilities of E', $E \cap F$, $E \cup F$, $E' \cup F'$, and $E' \cap F'$.

★22. In Definition VI on page 327, let L be the compound experiment (L_1, L_2), with P_1, P_2, and P as the probability functions on the sample spaces T_1, T_2, and T of L_1, L_2, and L, respectively. In T, let H be the event $\{H_1 \ occurs\}$. Prove that $P(H) = P_1(H_1) = p_1$. (In this case, H_2 of Definition VI becomes T_2.) Similarly, in (7) on page 327, $p_i = P(H_i)$. Also, see (8) on page 328.

143. Successive trials of a random experiment

Let L be a random experiment with the sample space $T = \{r\}$, where $P(H)$ represents the probability of an event H (subset of T) which may occur at a trial of L. We agree, as in Section 142, that successive trials of L qualify as *independent experiments,* under the assumption that *the outcome space T for L remains the same at each trial.** Then, if L is to be repeated a given number of times, by use of (7) on page 327 we can find the corresponding probability of any specified sequence of successes and failures for H at the trials of L.

---

* When this is true, the trials may be referred to as *independent trials* of L.

EXAMPLE 1. The probability that Jones will win whenever he plays a certain game is $\frac{1}{4}$. If he plays 6 times, find his probability of winning 4 games and losing 2 games.

Solution. 1. Let L represent the random experiment (the game); let f be the probability function on the sample space $T = \{w, l\}$ of L, where "w" represents *win* and "l" represents *lose*. Then $f(w) = \frac{1}{4}$ and $f(l) = \frac{3}{4}$.

2. In 6 successive trials of L, Jones might have wins and losses as follows, where each subscript indicates the number of the game among the six played which is won or lost, when exactly four are won:

$$(w_1, w_2, l_3, l_4, w_5, w_6); \quad (l_1, w_2, w_3, l_4, w_5, w_6); \cdots . \qquad (1)$$

The number of mutually exclusive events in (1) is equal to the number of ways of selecting 4 games to be won out of 6 games to be played (or, is the number of permutations of 4 w's and 2 l's taken six at a time). This number of ways is $_6C_4$ or 15. Two of the ways are seen in (1). The student should write a few of the other possibilities.

3. Let P be the probability function for the random experiment consisting of L repeated six times, or (L, L, L, L, L, L). With $f(w_i) = \frac{1}{4}$ and $f(l_i) = \frac{3}{4}$ for each trial of L, from (7) on page 327 we obtain, for the 1st case in (1),

$$P(w_1, w_2, l_3, l_4, w_5, w_6) = f(w_1)f(w_2)f(l_3)f(l_4)f(w_5)f(w_6) \qquad (2)$$
$$= \tfrac{1}{4} \cdot \tfrac{1}{4} \cdot \tfrac{1}{4} \cdot \tfrac{1}{4} \cdot \tfrac{3}{4} \cdot \tfrac{3}{4} = (\tfrac{1}{4})^4(\tfrac{3}{4})^2.$$

It is seen that the order of the 4 w's and 2 l's is unimportant in (2). Thus, the probability of each of the 15 mutually exclusive events in (1) where 4 w's and 2 l's occur is $(\tfrac{1}{4})^4(\tfrac{3}{4})^2$. Hence, by (9) on page 325, the probability that one or other of the 15 events in (1) will occur is the sum of 15 probabilities, each equal to $(\tfrac{1}{4})^4(\tfrac{3}{4})^2$, or

$$P(4 \ wins \ and \ 2 \ losses) = 15(\tfrac{1}{4})^4(\tfrac{3}{4})^2 = 15\tfrac{9}{4096} = \tfrac{135}{4096}.$$

THEOREM V. *If the probability that an event H will occur at any trial of a random experiment L is p, and that H will not occur is q, then the probability that H will occur exactly k times in n trials is*

$$_nC_kp^kq^{n-k}. \qquad (3)$$

Proof. 1. By (7) on page 327, the probability that any particular k trials will be successful and the other $(n - k)$ trials will fail is

$$(p \cdot p \cdots to \ k \ factors) \cdot [q \cdot q \cdots to \ (n - k) \ factors], \quad or \quad p^kq^{n-k}. \qquad (4)$$

2. The number of ways for stipulating k successes out of n trials is $_nC_k$. The probability of each of these mutually exclusive combinations of k successes and $(n - k)$ failures is p^kq^{n-k}, by (4). Hence, by Theorem IV, the probability that k successes will occur in one of the mutually exclusive ways (whose number is $_nC_k$) is $_nC_kp^kq^{n-k}$.

Corollary 1. *The probability that H will occur at least k times in n trials of the experiment L is*

$$p^n + {}_nC_{n-1}p^{n-1}q + {}_nC_{n-2}p^{n-2}q^2 + \cdots + {}_nC_kp^kq^{n-k}. \qquad (5)$$

Proof. In (5), the 1st term is the probability of *exactly* n successes in n trials; the 2d term is the probability of *just* $(n-1)$ successes, etc.; the last term is the probability of *just* k successes. By Theorem V, and (9) on page 325, (5) is the probability of k *or more successes.*

Note 1. From page 301, recognize that ${}_nC_kp^kq^{n-k}$ is the term in the expansion of $(p+q)^n$ which involves p^kq^{n-k}. Also, (5) consists of the first $(n-k+1)$ terms in the expansion of $(p+q)^n$ in descending powers of p.

EXAMPLE 2. A bag contains 5 white and 10 black balls. If we draw 5 balls in succession, replacing each one before the next is drawn, find the probability that (a) just three drawn will be black; (b) at least three will be black.

Solution. 1. At any draw, since replacement occurs, the probability of obtaining a black ball is $\frac{2}{3}$. Hence, $p = \frac{2}{3}$ and $q = \frac{1}{3}$ in Theorem V.

2. For (a), the probability is ${}_5C_3(\frac{2}{3})^3(\frac{1}{3})^2$, or 80/243. From (5), with P as the probability function on the sample space for 5 successive trials,

$$P[(b)] = {}_5C_3(\tfrac{2}{3})^3(\tfrac{1}{3})^2 + {}_5C_4(\tfrac{2}{3})^4(\tfrac{1}{3}) + (\tfrac{2}{3})^5 = \tfrac{64}{81}.$$

THEOREM VI. *Under the conditions of Theorem V, where n is fixed and $0 < p < 1$, let $\sigma(k)$ represent the probability of exactly k successes in n trials, with $n > 2$. Then, the largest value of $\sigma(k)$ occurs for each integer k satisfying*

$$np - q \leq k \leq np + p. \qquad (6)$$

★*Proof.* 1. For any k where $1 \leq k < n$, from (3) we obtain

$$\sigma(k-1) = \frac{n(n-1)\cdots(n-k+2)}{(k-1)!}q^{n-k+1}p^{k-1}; \qquad (7)$$

$$\sigma(k) = \frac{n(n-1)\cdots(n-k+2)(n-k+1)}{k!}q^{n-k}p^k; \qquad (8)$$

$$\sigma(k+1) = \frac{n(n-1)\cdots(n-k+1)(n-k)}{(k+1)!}q^{n-k-1}p^{k+1}. \qquad (9)$$

2. If $\sigma(k)$, with $k \neq 0$ and $k \neq n$, has the *largest* value among

$$\sigma(0), \sigma(1), \sigma(2), \cdots, \sigma(k-1), \sigma(k), \sigma(k+1), \cdots, \sigma(n), \qquad (10)$$

then $\sigma(k)$ must be at least as large as *its predecessor and its successor* in (10). Hence, it is necessary that k should satisfy each of the following inequalities.

$$\frac{\sigma(k)}{\sigma(k-1)} \geq 1, \quad or \quad \frac{n-k+1}{k} \cdot \frac{p}{q} \geq 1. \qquad (11)$$

$$\frac{\sigma(k+1)}{\sigma(k)} \leq 1, \quad or \quad \frac{n-k}{k+1} \cdot \frac{p}{q} \leq 1. \qquad (12)$$

From (11), $$np + p \geqq k(p + q) = k. \qquad (13)$$

From (12), $$np - q \leqq k(p + q) = k. \qquad (14)$$

From (13) and (14), it is seen that k must satisfy (6) if $\sigma(k)$ has the largest value in (10).

3. In Figure 95 observe that (6) requires k to be on an interval of length 1, because

$$(np + p) - (np - q) = p + q = 1.$$

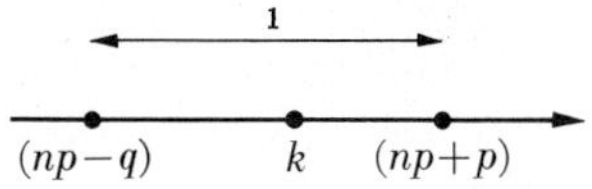

Figure 95

There is *at least one integer* on this interval; there are *two integers*, $(np + p)$ and $(np - q)$, on the interval if and only if each endpoint is an integer.

4. There *is* a largest number among the function values for σ in (10). Hence, when just one integer k satisfies (6), it follows that k successes has the greatest probability. If $np + p = h$, an integer, we verify that $k = h$ satisfies (11) and $k = h - 1 = np - q$ satisfies (12), or

$$\sigma(h) \geqq \sigma(h - 1) \qquad and \qquad \sigma(h) \leqq \sigma(h - 1).$$

Hence, in this case, $\sigma(h) = \sigma(h - 1)$, and both h successes and $(h - 1)$ successes have the largest probability. [In Problem 18 on page 345, the student may prove Theorem VI if $np - q \leqq 0$, or if $np + p \geqq n$.]

Note 2. For ease of reference, we recall (6) by stating that *the most probable number of successes for an event H in n trials is approximately np*, where p is the probability of success for H at each trial, and *is np if np is an integer*.

Illustration 1. If $p = \frac{1}{3}$, the most probable number of successes in 60 trials is $\frac{1}{3}(60)$, or 20. If $p = \frac{1}{3}$ then $q = \frac{2}{3}$. Hence, by (6), the most probable number of successes in 20 trials is any integer k satisfying

$$\tfrac{20}{3} - \tfrac{2}{3} \leqq k \leqq \tfrac{20}{3} + \tfrac{1}{3}, \qquad or \qquad 6 \leqq k \leqq 7.$$

Thus, the largest probability occurs for both 6 and 7 successes in the 20 trials.

Illustration 2. If $p = \frac{1}{4}$ and $n = 21$, then $q = \frac{3}{4}$, and (6) becomes

$$\tfrac{21}{4} - \tfrac{3}{4} \leqq k \leqq \tfrac{21}{4} + \tfrac{1}{4}, \qquad or \qquad 4\tfrac{1}{2} \leqq k \leqq 5\tfrac{1}{2}. \qquad (15)$$

Then, the most probable number of successes in 21 trials is 5.

EXERCISE 88

In certain problems, it may be advisable to use logarithms in computing the result.

1. The probability of Jones's winning whenever he plays a certain game is $\frac{1}{3}$. If he plays 4 times, find the probability that he wins (a) just twice; (b) at least twice; (c) at most twice.

2. The probability of Hansen's winning whenever he plays a certain game is .2. If he plays 5 times, find the probability that he wins (a) exactly 4 games; (b) at least 4 games; (c) at most 2 games.

3. If 6 coins are tossed (or, 1 coin is tossed 6 times), find the probability of tossing (a) just 3 heads; (b) at least 3 heads; (c) at most 2 heads; (d) the most probable number of heads.

4. If 3 dice are tossed, find the probability of throwing (a) just 2 aces (the number 1 is referred to as an ace); (b) at least 2 aces.

5. A bag contains 2 white and 6 black balls. If we draw 4 balls in succession, with each replaced before the next is drawn, find the probability that, of those drawn, (a) exactly three are white; (b) at least two are white; (c) at most three are white.

6. Find the probability of throwing just three 7's in 4 throws with 2 dice.

7. From a group of 2 men and 4 women, we make 5 random selections of a committee of 2 persons. Find the probability that exactly three of the committees consist entirely of men.

8. An examination of multiple-choice type has 10 problems, each with 3 responses, where just one is correct. If a student chooses a response at random for each problem, find the probability that he answers correctly in just (a) 4 problems; (b) 6 problems.

At any trial of a random experiment L, the probability of success for a specified event H has the given value p. If n independent trials of L are made, find the value, or values, of k for which the probability of k successes has the largest possible value.

9. $p = \frac{1}{4}$; $n = 80$. 10. $p = \frac{1}{5}$; $n = 44$.

11. $p = \frac{2}{3}$; $n = 85$. 12. $p = \frac{1}{4}$; $n = 161$.

13. Find the probability that, of 4 men, each of age 25, just three will remain alive at age 40. Use Table VII and logarithms.

14. Find the probability that, from 3 classmates each of age 21, just two will be alive 30 years later.

15. For a certain type of biological cell, the empirical probability that the cell will survive for a given time is .3. Find the probability that just 4 out of 6 cells will survive for this time.

16. A coin is to be tossed repeatedly. Find the probability that the 5th head will appear at the 8th toss.

17. A coin is to be tossed repeatedly. Find the probability that (a) the 3d head will appear on the 9th toss; (b) the kth head will appear on the nth toss.

18. Boys A, B, and C have probabilities $\frac{1}{3}$, $\frac{1}{6}$, and $\frac{1}{2}$, respectively, of winning whenever they play together in a game G where just one player will win. If they play six times, find the probability that C will win one game, B two games, and A three games.

★19. Let n be a positive integer. By use of Theorem VI with $p = \frac{1}{2}$, prove that the largest coefficient for the terms in the expansion of $(x + y)^n$ appears with the middle term if n is even, and with the two middle terms if n is odd.

★20. In Problem 18, let the probabilities of A, B, and C winning be p, q, and r, respectively. Suppose that they play four times. Show that all possible probabilities of winning and losing are given by the terms in the expansion of $(p + q + r)^4$.

★144. Conditional probability*

Let L be a random experiment with sample space $T = \{r\}$, where P is the probability function on T. Let H_1 and H_2 be two *events* (*subsets of T*) which may occur at a trial of L. Then, the intersection of H_1 and H_2, or $H_1 \cap H_2$, is the set of outcomes in both H_1 and H_2. If $W = H_1 \cap H_2$, we may refer to W as the event that "*both H_1 and H_2 occur*" at a trial of L. The Venn diagram in Figure 96 clarifies the connection between H_1, H_2, and their intersection W. We wish to develop a simple model for computing $P(H_1 \cap H_2)$ in certain situations.

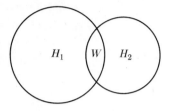

Figure 96

Illustration 1. Consider a bag containing 3 black and 7 white balls, and 5 black and 10 white cubes. Let L be the experiment of drawing an object from the bag, with the outcomes taken as equally likely. At any trial of L, let H_1 be the event of obtaining a *ball*, and H_2 be the event of obtaining a black object. Then, $P(H_1) = \frac{10}{25}; P(H_2) = \frac{8}{25}$. Also,

$$H_1 \cap H_2 = (3 \text{ black balls}) \quad and \quad P(H_1 \cap H_2) = \frac{3}{25}.$$

Let us consider a new concept which we shall call the

$$\left\{ \begin{array}{l} \textit{probability of obtaining a black ob-} \\ \textit{ject, } \textbf{knowing that a ball is drawn.} \end{array} \right\} \tag{1}$$

The "*probability*" requested in (1) is *not* a probability as defined on the sample space T, with 25 outcomes for experiment L. To give a sensible meaning to (1), we think of a *reduced sample space* T_0, consisting only of the *balls* in T. Thus, T_0 contains 10 *outcomes*. With a new meaning for probability based on T_0, we decide that the probability, P_0, requested in (1) can be taken as follows:

$$P_0 \text{ (black object, given that it is a ball)} = \frac{3}{10}. \tag{2}$$

With H_1 and H_2 used in (2), we verify that

$$P_0(H_2, \text{given } H_1) = \frac{P(H_1 \cap H_2)}{P(H_1)} = \frac{\frac{3}{25}}{\frac{10}{25}} = \frac{3}{10}. \tag{3}$$

The preceding discussion introduces the following terminology.

DEFINITION VII. *Let H_1 and H_2 be events which may occur at a trial of a random experiment L, with sample space T and probability function P defined on T. Then, if $P(H_1) \neq 0$, the* "**conditional probability of H_2, given that H_1 occurs,**" *in symbols, $P_c(H_2, \text{given } H_1)$, is defined as follows:*

$$P_c(H_2, \text{given } H_1) = \frac{P(H_1 \cap H_2)}{P(H_1)}. \tag{4}$$

* The remainder of the chapter is essential in the study of statistics.

In Definition I on page 305, the probability of any event H could be described as *the ratio of the probability of all outcomes in H to the probability, 1, of the whole sample space T*. In (4), similarly, we have $P_c(H_2,$ *given H_1*) defined as *the ratio of the probability of all outcomes in $H_1 \cap H_2$ (where both H_1 and H_2 occur) to the probability of H_1*. Thus, a conditional probability, with H_1 known to occur, can be thought of as an ordinary probability, as in Definition I, with respect to a *reduced sample space* consisting of the outcomes in H_1. If we are able to compute $P_c(H_2,$ *given H_1*) on the basis of the preceding remarks, then we obtain a means for computing $P(H_1 \cap H_2)$ as follows, by use of (4):

$$P(H_1 \cap H_2) = P(H_1)P_c(H_2, \text{given } H_1). \tag{5}$$

The following concept of *independence* for events in the same sample space is of great importance in statistics.

DEFINITION VIII. *Let L be a random experiment with sample space T, where P is the probability function on T, and let $\{H_1, H_2, H_3\}$ be events in T. Then, these events are called* **independent** *in the probability sense in case the probability of any two or more of the events occurring is equal to the product of their separate probabilities, or*

$$P(H_1 \cap H_2) = P(H_1)P(H_2); \quad P(H_1 \cap H_3) = P(H_1)P(H_3); \text{ etc.;} \tag{6}$$

$$P(H_1 \cap H_2 \cap H_3) = P(H_1)P(H_2)P(H_3). \tag{7}$$

We stated Definition VIII for three events for later convenience. The definition applies without alteration to any finite number of events. If the events are *not independent,* they are said to be *dependent.*

THEOREM VII. *If H_1 and H_2 are events in a sample space T and $P(H_1) \neq 0$, then H_1 and H_2 are independent if and only if*

$$P_c(H_2, \text{given } H_1) = P(H_2). \tag{8}$$

Proof. If (8) is true, from (4) we obtain

$$P(H_2) = \frac{P(H_1 \cap H_2)}{P(H_1)} \quad or \quad P(H_1 \cap H_2) = P(H_1)P(H_2),$$

so that H_1 and H_2 are independent. Conversely, if H_1 and H_2 are independent, from (4) and (6) we obtain

$$P_c(H_2, \text{given } H_1) = \frac{P(H_1)P(H_2)}{P(H_1)} = P(H_2). \tag{9}$$

This completes the proof of Theorem VII.

Illustration 2. In Illustration 1,

$$P(H_1) = \tfrac{2}{5}; \quad P(H_2) = \tfrac{8}{25}; \quad P(H_1 \cap H_2) = \tfrac{3}{25} \neq \tfrac{2}{5} \cdot \tfrac{8}{25}.$$

Hence, H_1 and H_2 are dependent events.

Illustration 3. A bag contains 3 black and 7 white balls and 6 black and 14 white cubes. Let L be the *drawing of an object from the bag*, with all outcomes taken equally likely. Let the event of obtaining a *ball* be H_1 and of obtaining a *black object* be H_2. By Definition I on page 305, we find

$$P(H_1) = \tfrac{1}{3}; \quad P(H_2) = \tfrac{3}{10}; \quad P(H_1 \cap H_2) = \tfrac{1}{10} = P(H_1)P(H_2).$$

Hence, H_1 and H_2 are independent events.

Let H_1, H_2, and H_3 be three events in T, where $P(H_1 \cap H_2) \neq 0$. Then, as in (4), we define the conditional probability

$$P_c(H_3, \text{ given } H_1 \cap H_2) = \frac{P(H_1 \cap H_2 \cap H_3)}{P(H_1 \cap H_2)}. \tag{10}$$

In words, (10) states that the conditional probability of H_3, given $H_1 \cap H_2$, is equal to the probability of the set of outcomes common to H_1, H_2, and H_3, divided by $P(H_1 \cap H_2)$. From (5) and (10),

$$P(H_1 \cap H_2 \cap H_3) = P(H_1)P_c(H_2, \text{ given } H_1)P_c(H_3, \text{ given } H_1 \cap H_2).$$

In (10), $P_c(H_3, \text{ given } H_1 \cap H_2)$ can be thought of as an ordinary probability of the set of outcomes common to H_1, H_2, and H_3 based on a *reduced sample space* composed of the outcomes common to H_1 and H_2. If H_1, H_2, and H_3 are independent events with $P(H_1 \cap H_2) \neq 0$, from (10) we obtain

$$P_c(H_3, \text{ given } H_1 \cap H_2) = \frac{P(H_1)P(H_2)P(H_3)}{P(H_1)P(H_2)} = P(H_3).$$

The conditional probability $P_c(H_4, \text{ given } H_1 \cap H_2 \cap H_3)$ can be defined in similar fashion, etc. for any number of events.

Note 1. In probability discussions, the context frequently should be relied upon to show that a reference to a *"probability"* means a *"conditional probability."*

★145. Probability of causes, or Bayes' theorem

Let T be the sample space for a given random experiment, with P as the probability function on T. Assume that there exists a set of k mutually exclusive events $\{H_1, \cdots, H_k\}$ in T such that

$$T = H_1 \cup H_2 \cup H_3 \cdots \cup H_k. \tag{1}$$

Then, we shall say that $H_1, \cdots, H_k$ form an **exhaustive set** for T. Thus, as a simple instance, any event H and its complementary event H' form an exhaustive set for T. For illustration, suppose that $k = 3$ in (1), and let W be any event in T. Then, W consists of those outcomes of T in $W \cap H_1$, those in $W \cap H_2$, and those in $W \cap H_3$, because each outcome of W must be in just one subset of the exhaustive set $\{H_1, H_2, H_3\}$. That is,

$$W = (W \cap H_1) \cup (W \cap H_2) \cup (W \cap H_3). \tag{2}$$

As an aid in visualizing (2), Figure 97 shows a representation of H_1, H_2, and H_3 as rectangular regions, with W as the ruled region, where we represent $W \cap H_1$ by the region with horizontal rulings, $W \cap H_2$ by the part ruled vertically, and $W \cap H_3$ by the part ruled obliquely. A natural extension of (2) applies in the case of an exhaustive set of any number, k, of mutually exclusive sets.

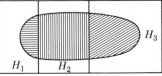

Figure 97

EXAMPLE 1. In the production for one day in an automobile factory, 40% of the engine blocks come from production line I, and 60% from line II. Previous experience leads to the conclusion that just one block per 1000 blocks from line I, and just two per 1000 from line II will be defective. Out of the production for one day, a block chosen at random is found to be defective. Find the probability that it came from (a) line I; (b) line II.

Solution. 1. The set of blocks produced in the day form the sample space, T, with probability function P. We take the given relative frequencies as probabilities in T. Let the event of a block coming from line I be H, a block from line II be K, and a block being defective be D. Then, $P(H) = .4$ and $P(K) = .6$. In a production of 10,000 blocks, the number of defectives is assumed to be $4(1) + 6(2) = 16$; hence, the relative frequency of defectives is 16/10,000, or $P(D) = .0016$. [Also, $P(D) = .4(.001) + .6(.002) = .0016$.]

2. We desire $P_c(H, \text{ given } D)$ and $P_c(K, \text{ given } D)$. To obtain them, first we observe the following conditional probabilities in the data:

$$P_c(D, \text{ given } H) = .001; \quad P_c(D, \text{ given } K) = .002. \tag{3}$$

We then compute $P(H \cap D)$ and $P(K \cap D)$ by use of (3), and (5) on page 336:

$$P(H \cap D) = P(H)P_c(D, \text{ given } H) = .4(.001) = .0004. \tag{4}$$

$$P(K \cap D) = P(K)P_c(D, \text{ given } K) = .6(.002) = .0012. \tag{5}$$

3. We employ (4) and (5), with $P(D) = .0016$, to compute the desired results by use of (4) on page 335:

$$P_c(H, \text{ given } D) = \frac{P(H \cap D)}{P(D)} = \frac{.0004}{.0016} = \frac{1}{4}; \tag{6}$$

$$P_c(K, \text{ given } D) = \frac{P(K \cap D)}{P(D)} = \frac{.0012}{.0016} = \frac{3}{4}. \tag{7}$$

Comment. The student is advised to make direct use of the definition of P_c, from (4) on page 335, in solving any problem such as Example 1. However, we may recognize (6) and (7) as special cases of *Bayes' theorem* (or, *Bayes' rule* for probability of causes) which follows. Thus, in (6) and (7), note that $\{H, K\}$ is an exhaustive set of mutually exclusive events for T. Hence, by (2),

$$D = (H \cap D) \cup (K \cap D); \quad P(D) = P(H \cap D) + P(K \cap D).$$

Then, for instance, $P_c(H, \text{ given } D) = \dfrac{P(H \cap D)}{P(H \cap D) + P(K \cap D)}$,

which is a special case of (8) below for just two *"causes,"* H and K.

THEOREM VIII. **(Bayes' rule.)** *If* $\{H_1, H_2, \cdots, H_k\}$ *is an exhaustive set of mutually exclusive events (subsets) for a sample space* T, *and if* W *is any event in* T, *then*

$$P_c(H_j, \text{ given } W) = \frac{P(H_j \cap W)}{\sum_{i=1}^{k} P(H_i \cap W)}. \tag{8}$$

Proof. From (2), the denominator in (8) is equal to $P(W)$. Then, the right-hand side of (8) becomes

$$P(H_j \cap W)/P(W); \tag{9}$$

by (4) on page 335, (9) is equal to $P_c(H_j, \text{ given } W)$.

Note 1. Any use of Bayes' rule is merely use of a conditional probability. In some cases, the denominator in (8) is given by the data.

EXERCISE 89

Venn diagrams will prove useful in solving the problems. Any given relative frequency should be used as a probability.

1. A group of children consists of 16 boys and 20 girls, where just 6 boys and 12 girls have blue eyes. A child will be picked at random from the group. Let H be the event of the child having blue eyes. Find $P(boy)$; $P(girl)$; $P(H)$; $P(boy \cap H)$; $P(girl \cap H)$; $P_c(H, \text{ given girl})$; $P_c(H, \text{ given boy})$; $P_c(girl, \text{ given } H)$; $P_c(boy, \text{ given } H)$. Also, translate each symbol for a conditional probability into words.

2. A bag contains 10 white balls, of which four have a red spot, and 15 green balls, of which ten have a red spot. A ball will be drawn at random. Let W, G, and S represent the events of the ball being white, green, and having a red spot, respectively. Find $P(W)$; $P(G)$; $P(S)$; $P(W \cap S)$; $P(G \cap S)$; $P_c(S, \text{ given } W)$; $P_c(S, \text{ given } G)$; $P_c(W, \text{ given } S)$; $P_c(G, \text{ given } S)$. Also, translate each symbol for a conditional probability into words.

3. A red die and a blue die will be tossed together. Given that, at a trial of this experiment, the dice will show a total of 8, find the conditional probability that the blue die will show at most 3. (Count outcomes.)

4. By use of the digits $\{2, 2, 5, 7\}$, all possible integers of four digits each will be written. Given that one of these integers is *odd*, find the conditional probability that the number has an odd digit also at the left end.

5. In a group of 100 men, just forty are overweight, just sixty wear glasses, and just 15 are overweight and do not wear glasses. The random experiment is that a man will be picked from the group. (*a*) Find the probability of the event that "he will not be overweight and will wear glasses." (*b*) Given that he is overweight, what is the probability that he wears glasses?

6. Suppose that 60% of the population of a city consists of males and 40% of females. Assume that 1% of the females and 4% of the males are color-blind. A person will be picked at random from the population. (a) Find the probability of the event that the person will be color-blind. (b) What conditional probabilities are given? (c) Given that the person who will be picked is color-blind, find the probability that the person is male; female.

7. In the manufacture of electric toasters in a plant, 30% of the toasters come from production line I and 70% from line II. It is known that just 3% of the products of line I are defective, and 2% of line II. A toaster will be picked at random from a day's production. If the toaster is defective, find the probability that it was produced by (a) line I; (b) line II.

8. Among the voters in a city, 40% are Republicans and 60% are Democrats. In regard to a recent action of the President, who is a Democrat, 30% of the Republicans and 50% of the Democrats are in favor of the action. If a voter chosen at random should be found in favor of the action, find the probability that he is (a) a Democrat; (b) a Republican.

9. In the manufacture of a variety of light bulbs in a plant, 25% of the bulbs come from machine A and 75% from machine B. It is known that just 3% of the bulbs from A are defective, and 5% from B. A bulb will be picked at random from the output for one day. If the bulb is not defective, find the probability that it was produced (α) by A; (β) by B.

10. In the manufacture of a type of wet battery in a plant, 15% of the batteries come from production line I, 25% from line II, and 60% from line III. It is admitted that 2% of the products of line I are defective, 3% of line II, and 1% of line III. A single battery from the output for one day is examined and found defective. Find the probability that the battery was produced by (a) line I; (b) line II; (c) line III.

Note 1. Problem 11 will show that merely *pairwise* independence of a set of more than two events does not imply their independence as described in Definition VIII on page 336. Problem 12 will show that, for more than two events, pairwise independence is not a consequence of an equation such as (7) on page 336.

11. A blue die and a red die are tossed together. Let E be the event of the dice falling with 1 up on the blue die, F the event of any face up numbered more than 1 on the red die, and G the event of the same number up on both dice. Show that (E, F, G) are pairwise independent, but not independent.

12. For the dice in Problem 11, let E be the event of 3 up on the blue die, and let F and G be the following events:

$$F = \{(\text{at most 3 up on both dice}) \text{ or } (\text{at least 4 up on both})\}.$$

$$G = \left\{ \begin{array}{l} \text{the same number, (1, 2, or 3), up on} \\ \text{both dice, or more than 3 up on both} \end{array} \right\}.$$

Show that (E, F, G) are not pairwise independent, but that

$$P(E \cap F \cap G) = P(E)P(F)P(G).$$

★13. Suppose that H and K are independent events in a sample space T. Prove that H and K', H' and K, and H' and K' are independent pairs of events.

★146. Dependent experiments

Consider a random experiment Z which can be analyzed into a sequence of two random experiments, Z_1 followed by Z_2. Assume that the nature and outcomes of Z_2 *may** be influenced by the preceding experiment Z_1. Then, let us call Z_1 and Z_2 *dependent experiments*.

Illustration 1. A 1st bag contains 5 white and 10 black balls, and a 2d bag contains 20 white and 10 black balls. Let Z be the experiment of (*drawing a ball from a bag selected at random*). We decide to consider each outcome as a ball; there are 45 outcomes. We obtain all of them by analyzing Z into the acts (Z_1, *then* Z_2), where Z_1 is (*select a bag at random*) and Z_2 is (*after selecting a bag, draw a ball*). Consider the event $H = $ (*obtaining a white ball from the* 1st *bag*). We are tempted to proceed as follows: With Z_1 thought of *alone*, the probability of selecting the 1st bag is $p_1 = \frac{1}{2}$. After this bag is selected, the probability of drawing a white ball is $p_2 = \frac{5}{15}$ or $p_2 = \frac{1}{3}$. Then, we conclude that $P(H) = \frac{1}{2} \cdot \frac{1}{3} = \frac{1}{6}$. We shall develop a model leading to this result.

Suppose that the experiment Z_1 has the sample space T_1 and probability function P_1 on T_1. Let A_1 be an event which may happen if Z_1 is performed, with $P_1(A_1) = p_1$ and $q_1 = 1 - p_1 = P_1(A_1')$, where A_1' means *not* A_1. The Venn diagram in Figure 98 helps in visualizing Z_1, A_1, and A_1'. If an outcome of A_1 appears at any trial of Z_1, assume that an experiment Z_2 can be performed, with sample space T_2 and probability function P_2 on T_2. Let A_2 be an event which may occur at a trial of Z_2, with $P_2(A_2) = p_2$ and $q_2 = 1 - p_2 = P_2(A_2')$. This sequence of experiments will be denoted by $Z = (Z_1, \text{then } Z_2)$. When Z_1 produces an outcome in A_1, then Z_2 will yield an outcome in A_2 or in A_2'.

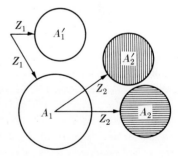

Let T be the set of outcomes of Z, with P as the probability function on T. We wish to define P sensibly. Let $\bar{A}_1$, $\bar{A}_2$, $\bar{A}_1'$, and K be events in T as follows.

Figure 98

$$\bar{A}_1 = \{the\ outcomes\ of\ Z\ where\ A_1\ occurs\}. \tag{1}$$

$$\bar{A}_2 = \{the\ outcomes\ of\ Z\ where\ A_1\ and\ then\ A_2\ occur\}. \tag{2}$$

$$\bar{A}_1' = \{the\ outcomes\ of\ Z\ where\ A_1'\ occurs\}. \tag{3}$$

$$K = \{the\ outcomes\ of\ Z\ where\ A_1\ and\ then\ A_2'\ occur\}. \tag{4}$$

We shall abbreviate (1)–(4) as follows, remembering that A_1 is an event at the first stage, and A_2 is an event at the second stage of Z:

---

* Thus, Z_2 may *not* be affected by Z_1, and then Z_1 and Z_2 are independent experiments. In this case, Section 142 would apply. Thus, the following results for dependent experiments include the content of Section 142 as a special case.

$$\left.\begin{array}{ll} \overline{A}_1 = \{A_1 \text{ occurs}\}; & \overline{A}_2 = \{A_1, \text{ then } A_2\}; \\ \overline{A}_1' = \{A_1' \text{ occurs}\}; & K = \{A_1, \text{ then } A_2'\}. \end{array}\right\} \tag{5}$$

In Figure 98, $\overline{A}_1$ is represented by the *whole ruled region*, $\overline{A}_2$ by the part *ruled horizontally*, and K by the part *ruled vertically*. We now think of Z_1 as an experiment to produce *final outcomes* of $Z = (Z_1, \text{ then } Z_2)$, and *temporarily disregard* Z_2. Since all of $\overline{A}_1$ (ruled) in the final sample space T for Z is a consequence of the occurrence of A_1 at the first stage Z_1, we decide to assign to $\overline{A}_1$ *the probability specified for* A_1 *in the space* T_1. Similarly, we shall assign to $\overline{A}_1'$ the probability of A_1' in T_1. Thus, we define

$$P(\overline{A}_1) = p_1 \quad and \quad P(\overline{A}_1') = q_1, \tag{6}$$

because $p_1 = P_1(A_1)$ and $q_1 = P_1(A_1')$. Then, Z_2 appears as an experiment *to select outcomes in the reduced sample space* $\overline{A}_1$, where A_1 has occurred. Hence, we interpret p_2 as the following *conditional probability:*

$$\boldsymbol{p_2 = P_c(\overline{A}_2, \textbf{ given } \overline{A}_1).} \tag{7}$$

We observe that $\overline{A}_2 \subset \overline{A}_1$ so that $\overline{A}_1 \cap \overline{A}_2 = \overline{A}_2$. Hence, from (7), and (5) on page 336, we obtain

$$P(\overline{A}_2) = P(\overline{A}_1 \cap \overline{A}_2) = P(\overline{A}_1)P_c(\overline{A}_2, \text{ given } \overline{A}_1), \text{ or}$$
$$\boldsymbol{P(\overline{A}_2) = p_1 p_2.} \tag{8}$$

Similarly, we define $P(K) = p_1 q_2$. Since $\overline{A}_1 = \overline{A}_2 \cup K$, we should have

$$P(\overline{A}_1) = P(\overline{A}_2) + P(K), \quad or \quad p_1 = p_1 p_2 + p_1 q_2 = p_1(p_2 + q_2),$$

which is true. Thus, our definitions of probabilities are consistent.

The preceding use of $\overline{A}_1$ and $\overline{A}_2$ instead of A_1 and A_2 was essential because A_1 and A_2 are subsets of T_1 and T_2, respectively, and we needed corresponding subsets $\overline{A}_1$ and $\overline{A}_2$ of T. Hereafter, however, in referring to A_1 and A_2 in connection with $Z = (Z_1, \text{ then } Z_2)$, *we agree to mean the corresponding sets of outcomes of Z exhibiting A_1 at the first stage and A_2 at the second stage.* Then (7) and (8) become

$$\boldsymbol{p_2 = P_c(A_2, \textbf{ given } A_1),} \text{ and} \tag{9}$$

$$\boldsymbol{P(A_1, \textbf{ then } A_2) = P(A_1)P_c(A_2, \textbf{ given } A_1) = p_1 p_2.} \tag{10}$$

Illustration 2. We employed (10) in Illustration 1, where

$$A_1 = \{\text{choose 1st bag}\} \quad and \quad A_2 = \{\text{obtain white ball}\}; \text{ then,}$$
$$P(\text{1st bag, then white ball}) = \tfrac{1}{2} \cdot \tfrac{1}{3} = \tfrac{1}{6}.$$

The agreements which led to (9) and (10) extend conveniently to the complex experiment in the following definition, where the outcome of Z_i may* depend on the outcome of the preceding sequence $Z_1, Z_2, \cdots, Z_{i-1}$.

* See footnote on page 341. Thus, (7) on page 327 is a special case of (12) on page 343, with the word *"then"* in (12) of no consequence.

DEFINITION IX. *Suppose that events* $A_1, A_2, \cdots, A_k$ *may occur in succession at a trial of the sequence of corresponding dependent experiments* $Z_1, Z_2, \cdots, Z_k$. *Let* p_i *be the probability of* A_i *occurring at a trial of* Z_i, *for* $i = 1, 2, \cdots, k$. *Then, in the sample space* T *for the complex experiment* $Z = (Z_1, \text{ then } Z_2, \cdots, \text{ then } Z_k)$, *we agree to assign probabilities to the outcomes so that* $p_1 = P(A_1)$,

$$\text{(with } i > 1) \qquad p_i = P_c(A_i, \text{ given } A_{i-1}), \text{ and} \qquad (11)$$

$$P(A_1, \text{ then } A_2, \text{ then } A_3, \cdots, \text{ then } A_k) = p_1 p_2 p_3 \cdots p_k. \qquad (12)$$

EXAMPLE 1.   There are 5 white and 10 black balls in bag I, and 20 white and 10 black balls in bag II. The random experiment Z consists of selecting a bag at random and then drawing a ball. (*a*) Find the probability of obtaining a black ball. (*b*) Given that the ball obtained is black, find the probability that it came from bag II.

Solution.   1. We have $Z = (Z_1, \text{ then } Z_2)$, where Z_1 is "*select a bag,*" and Z_2 is "*draw a ball.*" Let T be the sample space of outcomes (*balls*) of Z, with P as the probability function on T. Let B be the event of obtaining a black ball at a trial of Z. Let I and II be the events in T of a ball coming from bags I and II, respectively.

2. (*a*) At a trial of Z, a black ball is obtained if either of the following mutually exclusive events occurs:

$H = \{bag$ I *is selected, and then a black ball is drawn*$\}$.

$K = \{bag$ II *is selected, and then a black ball is drawn*$\}$.

We shall apply (10) to H and K separately, and use Theorem IV on page 325.

$P(H) = (prob.\ of\ selecting\ bag\ \text{I}) \cdot P_c(black,\ given\ \text{I}) = \frac{1}{2} \cdot \frac{2}{3} = \frac{1}{3}.$

$P(K) = (prob.\ of\ selecting\ bag\ \text{II}) \cdot P_c(black,\ given\ \text{II}) = \frac{1}{2} \cdot \frac{1}{3} = \frac{1}{6}.$

Hence, $P(B) = \frac{1}{3} + \frac{1}{6} = \frac{1}{2}.$

3. (*b*) We desire to obtain $P_c(\text{II}, given\ B)$. From details above, $K = \text{II} \cap B$. Hence, from (4) on page 335,

$$P_c(ball\ came\ from\ bag\ \text{II},\ given\ the\ ball\ is\ black)$$

$$= P_c(\text{II}, given\ B) = \frac{P(\text{II} \cap B)}{P(B)} = \frac{\frac{1}{6}}{\frac{1}{2}} = \frac{1}{3}.$$

EXAMPLE 2.   A bag contains 10 white and 5 black balls. If 3 balls are drawn in succession without replacement, find the probability that (*black, black, white*) are obtained (*a*) in that order; (*b*) in any order.

Solution.   (*a*) We apply (12) for 3 dependent experiments, successive draws without replacement. The probability of a black at the 1st draw is $\frac{5}{15}$. If the 1st draw is black, there remain 4 black and 10 white balls. Hence, prob. (2d *black if* 1st *is black*) $= \frac{4}{14}$; *etc.*

prob. (*black, black, white*) $= \frac{5}{15} \cdot \frac{4}{14} \cdot \frac{10}{13} = \frac{20}{273}$.

(*b*) In (*a*), let $p_1 = \frac{20}{273}$. Similarly, we must find

$p_2 = $ prob. (*black, white, black*)   *and* $p_3 = $ prob. (*white, black, black*),

and then compute $p = p_1 + p_2 + p_3$ as the desired result. The student may verify that $p = \frac{60}{273}$. This could be computed also by Definition I on page 305.

MISCELLANEOUS EXERCISE 90

Bag I *contains 5 white and 10 green balls; bag* II *contains 4 white and 2 black balls; bag* III *contains 6 black and 4 green balls. In Problems 1–6, find the probability of the specified event.*

1. If a ball is drawn from bag I, and a ball from bag II, both balls will be white.
2. If a bag is selected at random, and then a ball is drawn, it will be (*a*) white; (*b*) white or green.
3. If a bag is selected at random, and then 2 balls are drawn together, both will be (*a*) white; (*b*) green; (*c*) of the same color.
4. If 2 balls are drawn in succession from bag I and not replaced, the balls drawn will be white and green, in any order.
5. If 3 balls are drawn in succession from bag I, then all will be white, under the assumption that (*a*) none are replaced; (*b*) each is replaced before the next one is drawn.
6. If 3 balls are drawn in succession from bag I, and none are replaced, then they will appear (white, green, white), (*a*) in that order as drawn; (*b*) in any order.
7. One box contains 5 lemons and 8 oranges; a second box contains 4 lemons and 3 oranges. A man selects a box at random and then a piece of fruit at random. Let H, K, and W be the events of obtaining a lemon from the 1st box, a lemon from the 2d box, and a lemon, respectively. Find $P(H)$, $P(K)$, and $P(W)$. Also, if he obtains a lemon, find the probability that it came from the second box.

In Problems 8–9, cards will be dealt one at a time without replacement from a full deck of 52 cards, well shuffled.

8. Find the probability that the first king will be dealt as the 4th card.
9. Find the probability that just two of the first three cards dealt will be aces. Solve, *first*, by use of merely Definition I on page 305 and, *second*, by use of Section 146.
10. In tossing two dice repeatedly, find the probability that the first toss will total 5, the next two tosses will *not* total 5, 7, or 11, and the fourth toss will total 5.
11. A 1st bag contains 5 red and 8 white balls, and a 2d bag contains 9 red and 3 white cubes. Let Z be the experiment of drawing an object from a bag selected at random. Let H be the event of (*obtaining a ball*) and K be the event of (*obtaining a red object*). Let H' and K' be "*not H*" and "*not K*," respectively. Find $P(H)$; $P(K)$; $P(H')$; $P(K')$; $P(H \cap K)$; $P_c(K, given H)$. Prove that H and K are *not* independent.

12. Repeat Problem 11 if the 2d bag contains 10 red and 16 white cubes, but in this case prove that H and K are independent events.

13. A bag contains two markers numbered 1, and three markers numbered 2. A box, numbered 1, contains 4 white and 3 black balls. A box, numbered 2, contains 2 white and 4 black balls. A marker is drawn from the bag, and then a ball is drawn from that box having the number on the marker. (a) Find the probability of obtaining a white ball. (b) If a white ball is obtained, find the probability that it came from box 1.

14. A committee consists of 5 men and 9 women. In order to fill the positions of chairman, secretary, and treasurer for the committee, first a chairman will be selected by lot, then a secretary by lot, and then a treasurer by lot. Find the probability that the chairman and treasurer will be women and the secretary a man. Assume that no person will hold two positions.

15. A bag contains 3 white and 7 black balls. We draw 2 balls, replace them by green balls, and then draw 2 more balls. Find the probability that all balls drawn will have the same color.

16. Consider the data preceding Problem 1. Suppose that 2 bags are selected at random, and then 1 ball is drawn from each of these bags. Find the probability that each of these balls is green.

17. For a certain type of biological cell, the empirical probability of survival for 1 hour is .8. If the cell survives, then fission occurs, and the cell splits into two new cells of the same type. If a single cell starts the creation of a population of cells, find the probability that, at the end of 2 hours, there will be (a) 4 cells; (b) just 2 cells. (c) Check by computing the probability for no cells at the end of 2 hours. Assume that the survival of any cell is not affected by any coexisting cell.

18. By use of (12) and (14) on pages 332–333, prove that, if $np - q \leqq 0$ then $\sigma(0) \geqq \sigma(k)$ when $1 \leqq k \leqq n$. By use of (11) and (13) on pages 332–333, prove that, if $np + p \geqq n$ then $\sigma(k) \leqq \sigma(n)$ when $0 \leqq k < n$. Thus, prove that Theorem VI remains true if $np - q \leqq 0$ or if $np + p \geqq n$.

Chapter 14 Introduction to Linear Programming

147. Half planes and convex sets of points in an xy-plane

Any line l in an xy-plane divides the plane into two sets of points, say A and B, with l as the common boundary of A and B. We shall call each of A and B a *half plane*. If set A includes the boundary line l, then A is called a *closed half plane*. Otherwise, A is called an *open half plane*.

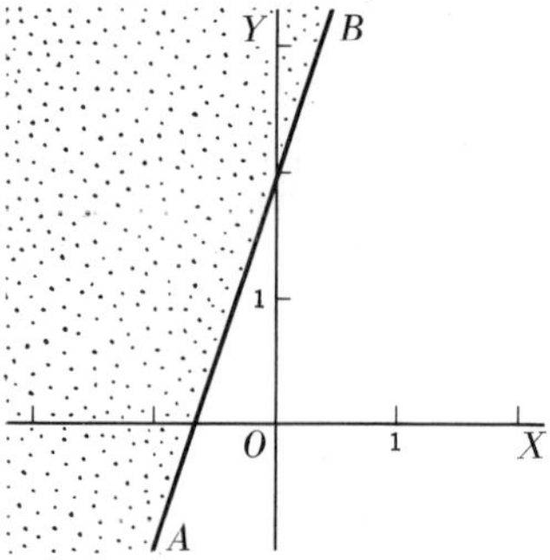

Figure 99

Illustration 1. The solution set [*pairs* (x, y), or *points*] of the inequality

$$y - 3x - 2 \geqq 0 \qquad (1)$$

is the closed half plane S which is dotted in Figure 99. S includes the line AB which is the graph of $y - 3x - 2 = 0$. Figure 99 can be verified by the method used on page 95.

In Figure 99, we illustrate the fact that any closed half plane is the graph of an inequality

$$ax + by + c \geqq 0 \qquad or \qquad ax + by + c \leqq 0, \qquad (2)$$

where a and b are not both zero. The line $ax + by + c = 0$ divides the xy-plane into two half planes, and forms their common boundary.

DEFINITION I. *A set, S, of points in an xy-plane is called a* **convex set** *of points, or a* **convex region,** *in case the following condition is true:*

$$\left\{ \begin{array}{l} \textit{If } P \textit{ and } Q \textit{ are distinct points in } S, \textit{ then} \\ \textit{all points of the line segment } PQ \textit{ are in } S. \end{array} \right\} \qquad (3)$$

346

Note 1. If S is the empty set of points, then (3) is satisfied in an uninteresting vacuous sense, because then no points P and Q exist in S.

From the observed nature of a half plane, we accept the following important result as geometrically evident.

THEOREM I. *A half plane, open or closed, is a convex set of points.*

THEOREM II. *If S and T are convex sets of points (not necessarily half planes) in the xy-plane, and if $U = S \cap T$, then U is a convex set.*

Proof. We assume that the intersection, U, of S and T is not empty. Figure 100 shows S and T as two half planes, with rulings; U is the set of points where double rulings occur. Suppose that P and Q are in U. Then, P and Q are in S and hence all points on segment PQ are in S, because S is convex. Similarly, P and Q are also in T; thus, all points of PQ are in T. Hence, all points of PQ are in *both* S *and* T, and accordingly are in $U = S \cap T$. Therefore, U is a convex set of points.

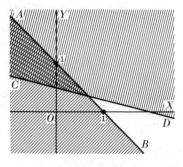

Figure 100

DEFINITION II. *The intersection, U, of two or more closed half planes is called a **polygonal set** of points. If U has an area (finite), then the boundary of U is called a **convex polygon**, and U will be called a **finite polygonal region**.*

Illustration 2. In Figure 100, the region S with rulings perpendicular to line AB is the graph of $x + y - 1 \leq 0$. The region T with rulings perpendicular to CD is the graph of $x + 4y - 2 \geq 0$. The *intersection*, U, of these closed half planes is an infinite polygonal region, and is the graph of the system of inequalities

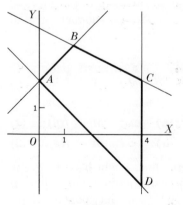

Figure 101

$$\left. \begin{array}{l} x + y - 1 \leq 0,\ and \\ x + 4y - 2 \geq 0. \end{array} \right\} \quad (4)$$

Illustration 3. The student should verify that the interior of the polygon $ABCD$ and its boundary (sides) in Figure 101 form the graph, S, of the solution set of the following system of four inequalities, where the word *"and"* is understood to apply between the last two inequalities at the right:

$$x \leq 4, \quad x - y + 2 \geq 0, \quad x + y \geq 2, \quad x + 2y - 8 \leq 0.$$

Thus, S is a finite polygonal region.

EXERCISE 91

In an xy-plane, indicate the convex set, T, which is the graph of the system of inequalities. The word "and" is understood between the two inequalities at the right.

1. $x \geq 0, y \geq 0, y \leq 3$.　　　　　　**2.** $x \geq -4, y \geq -2, y > x$.

3. $y - x \leq 3, y + x \geq 3, y - 2x + 6 \geq 0$.

4. $y \geq 0, x \geq 0, y - x \leq 1, x - y - 1 \leq 0, x + y - 2 \leq 0$.

5. $y \leq 5, x \leq 0, y \geq 0, x \geq -4, y - 2x \geq 2, y + x + 3 \geq 0$.

6. $x \geq 0, y \geq 1, y + x - 2 \geq 0, y - x \leq 3, y - 2x + 3 \geq 0$.

7. $x \geq 0, y \geq 0, 2y - x - 2 \geq 0, y - x \geq 1, 2y + 2x \leq 1$.

8. Can any region in the xy-plane bounded by a triangle fail to be a convex region? Give an argument based on remarks about half planes.

9. A region T in the xy-plane is bounded by a quadrilateral. Is it possible that T is not a convex region? Prove your statement.

10. Sketch a region T in the xy-plane bounded by a pentagon where T is *not* convex.

A convex polygon in the xy-plane has the specified vertices. Find a system of inequalities whose graph is the convex region bounded by the polygon.

11. $(3, 0), (6, 0), (6, 4), (3, 6)$.　　　　**12.** $(0, 0), (-2, 0), (4, 6)$.

13. $(1, -3), (3, -1), (4, 5), (2, 5)$.　　　**14.** $(-2, 1), (3, 3), (1, 5), (-4, 4)$.

148. Extrema of a linear function on an interval

Suppose that the domain of a function f is $D = \{\alpha \leq x \leq \beta\}$, and that there exists a largest value, M, and a smallest value, m, for f. Then, we refer to M as the **maximum**, and to m as the **minimum** of f, or of $f(x)$, on D. Either m or M can be called an **extremum** of f; m and M, together, are called the **extrema** of f. In any case, $m \leq M$. We have met illustrations of maxima and minima in graphing quadratic functions of x, and also polynomials in x of degree greater than 2.

THEOREM III.　*Let $f(t) = ct + d$, where c and d are constants and $c \neq 0$, with $\alpha \leq t \leq \beta$. Then, the extrema, m and M, of f occur when $t = \alpha$ and $t = \beta$. Moreover,*

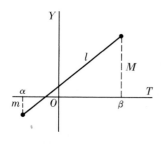

Figure 102

if $c > 0$:　　$m = f(\alpha)$　and　$M = f(\beta)$;　(1)

if $c < 0$:　　$M = f(\alpha)$　and　$m = f(\beta)$.　(2)

Proof. Consider the line, l, which is the graph of $y = f(t)$ in the ty-plane, as in Figure 102. If $c > 0$, as in Figure 102, then l has positive slope, so that $f(t)$ increases as t increases. Hence, the least value of f is $f(\alpha)$ and the greatest value is $f(\beta)$. If $c < 0$, then l has negative slope and $f(t)$ decreases as t increases; hence, $m = f(\beta)$ and $M = f(\alpha)$.

149. Parametric equations for a line*

Let l be the line through two distinct points $P_1:(x_1, y_1)$ and $P_2:(x_2, y_2)$ in an xy-plane. Let t be a variable whose domain consists of *all real numbers.* Then, we shall prove that, *for each value of t, the following equations* (1) *give the coordinates of a point* $P:(x, y)$ *on* l and, conversely, that *each point P is given by* (1) *for just one value of t.* We refer to (1) as *parametric equations for l,* and call the variable t the *parameter* in these equations.

$$x = x_1 + t(x_2 - x_1); \quad y = y_1 + t(y_2 - y_1). \tag{1}$$

Proof. 1. For our proof, designate l to be a *directed* line, with the positive direction *from* P_1 *to* P_2, and with distance on l to be measured in terms of *any* specified unit. If $P:(x, y)$ is any point on l, as in Figure 103, with $\overline{P_1P}$ and $\overline{P_1P_2}$ as the values of directed line segments, let a variable t be defined by

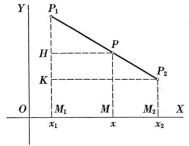

Figure 103

$$\frac{\overline{P_1P}}{\overline{P_1P_2}} = t, \text{ so that } \overline{P_1P} = t(\overline{P_1P_2}). \tag{2}$$

For each point P, a single value of t is determined by (2). Conversely, for each value of t, just one value of $\overline{P_1P}$, and hence just one point P, is determined by (2). Thus, (2) establishes a *one-to-one correspondence* between points on l and all real values of t. From (2), P is in the direction of P_2 *from* P_1 *if* $t > 0$, and in *the opposite direction if* $t < 0$.

2. Equations (1) are true when $t = 0$, with $P:(x, y)$ given as P_1. Suppose, now, that P is not P_1, and that l is *not vertical*, as in Figure 103.† From the similar triangles P_1HP and P_1KP_2, and (2), we obtain

$$\frac{\overline{HP}}{\overline{KP_2}} = \frac{\overline{P_1P}}{\overline{P_1P_2}}, \quad or \quad \frac{x - x_1}{x_2 - x_1} = t. \tag{3}$$

We note that (3) is true *regardless of the units of length used on OX and l*, because the value of each fraction in (3) is independent of the unit of length. From (3), $x = x_1 + t(x_2 - x_1)$. If l is vertical, then $x_2 = x_1$ and (1) gives $x = x_1$, which is true. Thus, (1) has been proved for x. Similarly, we may prove (1) for y.

Note 1. From (2), observe that $t = 0$ when $\overline{P_1P} = 0$, or $P = P_1$; also, $t = 1$ corresponds to $P = P_2$. Thus, the points on segment P_1P_2 are obtained as t varies from $t = 0$ to $t = 1$.

---

* The results of this section also can be obtained very simply by use of vector analysis.
† In Figure 103, P_1P and P_1P_2 have the same direction. The student may construct a corresponding figure and check the proof for a case where P_1P and P_1P_2 have opposite directions.

If $t = \frac{1}{2}$ in (2), then P is the **mid-point** of segment P_1P_2, and (1) becomes

$$(\text{mid-point of } P_1P_2) \qquad x = \tfrac{1}{2}(x_1 + x_2); \quad y = \tfrac{1}{2}(y_1 + y_2). \qquad (4)$$

The coordinates of that point $P:(x, y)$ dividing the segment P_1P_2 in any given ratio can be found from (1) with the proper value for t, as illustrated in (4). Hence, equations (1) sometimes are called **point of division formulas.**

EXAMPLE 1. Write parametric equations for the line l through $P_1:(2, 3)$ and $P_2:(-4, 5)$. Then, find the mid-point of P_1P_2; the points trisecting P_1P_2; the point P dividing P_1P_2 internally in the ratio $3 : 5$.

Solution. 1. From (1), parametric equations for l are

$$x = 2 - 6t; \quad y = 3 + 2t. \qquad (5)$$

2. *Mid-point:* use $t = \frac{1}{2}$ in (5), or use (4), to obtain $P:(-1, 4)$.

3. *Points of trisection:* use $t = \frac{1}{3}$ and $t = \frac{2}{3}$ in (5) to obtain P so that, respectively, $\overline{P_1P} = \frac{1}{3}\overline{P_1P_2}$ and $\overline{P_1P} = \frac{2}{3}\overline{P_1P_2}$:

When $t = \frac{1}{3}$, $(x = 0, y = \frac{11}{3})$. When $t = \frac{2}{3}$, $(x = -2, y = \frac{13}{3})$.

4. If P divides $\overline{P_1P_2}$ internally in the ratio $3:5$, as in Figure 104, then $\overline{P_1P}/\overline{PP_2}$ is equal to $\frac{3}{5}$, or $\overline{P_1P} = \frac{3}{8}\overline{P_1P_2}$. With $t = \frac{3}{8}$ in (5), we find $P:(-\frac{1}{4}, \frac{15}{4})$.

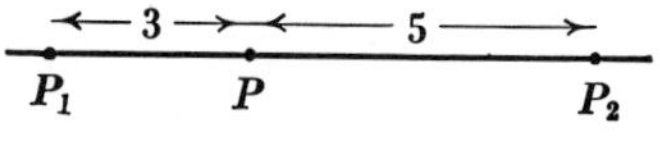

Figure 104

150. Extrema of $(ax + by + c)$ on a line segment

Consider two distinct points $P_1:(x_1, y_1)$ and $P_2:(x_2, y_2)$ in an xy-plane, and let T represent the line segment* P_1P_2. Let

$$f(x, y) = ax + by + c, \qquad (1)$$

where a, b, and c are constants. Then, we shall prove the following result.

THEOREM IV. *Let $P:(x, y)$ be restricted to segment P_1P_2. That is, let the domain of (x, y) be the number pairs which are coordinates of points on P_1P_2. Then, the extrema of $f(x, y)$ for (x, y) on P_1P_2 are attained at P_1 and P_2. Or,*

$$f(x_1, y_1) \qquad and \qquad f(x_2, y_2) \qquad (2)$$

are the maximum and the minimum, in some order, for $f(x, y)$ on P_1P_2.

Illustration 1. With $P_1:(1, 1)$, $P_2:(3, 3)$, and $f(x, y) = 3x - y + 7$, we obtain the function values

$$f(1, 1) = 9 \qquad and \qquad f(3, 3) = 13. \qquad (3)$$

* In referring to any *line segment*, we agree that its endpoints are included. Also, hereafter in this chapter, "*segment*" will mean "*line segment.*"

Hence, by Theorem IV, the minimum of f is 9 and the maximum of f is 13, when (x, y) is restricted to segment P_1P_2.

Proof of Theorem IV. 1. From (1) on page 349, parametric equations for line P_1P_2 with $P:(x, y)$ on the line, as in Figure 105, are

Figure 105

$$x = x_1 + t(x_2 - x_1) \qquad and \qquad y = y_1 + t(y_2 - y_1). \qquad (4)$$

From (2) on page 349, $t = \overline{P_1P}/\overline{P_1P_2}$, when line P_1P_2 is considered as a directed line with the positive direction from P_1 to P_2. If $P:(x, y)$ is given by (4), segment P_1P_2 is the locus of $P:(x, y)$ when $0 \leq t \leq 1$, with $P = P_1$ when $t = 0$ and $P = P_2$ when $t = 1$.

2. When equations (4) are used, let

$$f(x, y) = \phi(t) = f[x_1 + t(x_2 - x_1), y_1 + t(y_2 - y_1)]. \qquad (5)$$

We could obtain $\phi(t)$, with coefficients involving a, b, and c, by substituting (4) in (1). Without carrying out the details, it is sufficient to notice that $\phi(t)$ will be a polynomial in t of *degree* 1, *or a constant*. That is,

$$\phi(t) = At + B, \qquad (6)$$

where A and B are constants, and $0 \leq t \leq 1$.

3. If $A = 0$ in (6), then $\phi(t) = B$, a constant, so that both the maximum and the minimum of ϕ are equal to B, and Theorem IV is true.

4. By Theorem III on page 348, if $A > 0$ then ϕ attains its minimum, m, when $t = 0$ and its maximum, M, when $t = 1$. Then,

$$m = \phi(0) = f(x_1, y_1); \quad M = \phi(1) = f(x_2, y_2). \qquad (7)$$

Similarly, if $A < 0$, then m and M are interchanged in (7). This completes the proof of Theorem IV.

Illustration 2. In Illustration 1, by use of (1) on page 349, parametric equations for P_1P_2 are

$$x = 1 + 2t \qquad and \qquad y = 1 + 2t. \qquad (8)$$

By use of (8), with $f(x, y)$ given in Illustration 1,

$$f(x, y) = \phi(t) = 3(1 + 2t) - (1 + 2t) + 7, \text{ or}$$

$$\phi(t) = 9 + 4t.$$

Since $\phi(t)$ is an increasing function, the maximum, M, of ϕ for $0 \leq t \leq 1$ occurs at $t = 1$, and the minimum, m, at $t = 0$. Thus

$$m = \phi(0) = f(1, 1) = 9; \quad M = \phi(1) = f(3, 3) = 13.$$

These results check with (2) and (3).

EXERCISE 92

Find the maximum and the minimum of f on the domain D.

1. $f(x) = 4x - 7$; on D: $\{-4 \le x \le 3\}$.

2. $f(x) = 5 - 3x$; on D: $\{2 \le x \le 8\}$.

Write parametric equations for the line through the points. Then, find the mid-point and the points of trisection of the line segment joining the points.

3. $(2, 4)$; $(8, 10)$. **4.** $(0, 6)$; $(12, 0)$. **5.** $(-2, 3)$; $(-8, -3)$.

6. $(3, 5)$; $(9, 8)$. **7.** $(-4, 5)$; $(-10, -2)$. **8.** $(2, 3)$; $(6, 11)$.

9. Find the points for division into four equal parts in Problem 3.

On the line through $A:(-3, 4)$ and $B:(5, -2)$, find C.

10. C divides AB internally in the ratio 2 : 3.

11. AB is directed; $\overline{AC} = 3(\overline{AB})$. **12.** AB is directed; $\overline{AC} = -3(\overline{AB})$.

13. $A:(2, 3)$ is an endpoint and $(4, 7)$ is the mid-point of segment AC; find C.

14. If $(3, \frac{1}{2})$ is the center of a circle which passes through $(1, 2)$, find another point on the circle by use of Section 149.

15. If $(2, 2)$, $(3, -3)$, $(6, 4)$ are vertices of a parallelogram in counterclockwise order, find the other vertex by use of Section 149.

Let $f(x, y) = 3x - 2y + 7$. Write parametric equations for the line l through the given points, in terms of a parameter t as in (1) on page 349. Then, with $f(x, y) = \phi(t)$ at $P:(x, y)$ on l, calculate $\phi(t)$; find its maximum, M, and minimum, m; state at which point each extremum is attained.

16–19. The points in Problems 3–6, respectively.

Comment. Do Problem 16 in two ways, using the points in two distinct orders as P_1 and P_2 in (1) on page 349. Are the results for Problem 16 affected?

Note 1. A **median** of a triangle is a line segment from a vertex to the mid-point of the opposite side. A proof of the following theorem is requested in Problem 25. The medians of a triangle meet in a point which is $\frac{2}{3}$ of the way from any vertex to the mid-point of the opposite side.

★**20.** Verify the result stated in Note 1 for the triangle with the vertices $A:(1, 1)$, $B:(7, 9)$, and $C:(3, 5)$, by finding the specified point on each median.

★**21.** Obtain the coordinates of $P:(x, y)$ on the line through P_1 and P_2 of Figure 103 on page 349, with $\overline{P_1P}/\overline{PP_2} = k_1/k_2$.

★*Prove the stated result by an analytic method.*

22. An isosceles triangle has two equal medians.

23. The line segment joining the mid-points of opposite sides of a parallelogram is parallel to and has the same length as the other sides.

24. The line segment joining the mid-points of two sides of a triangle is one-half as long as the third side and parallel to it.

25. Prove the result stated in Note 1 for any triangle.

151. Extrema of $(ax + by + c)$ on a finite polygonal region

THEOREM V. *Let T represent a finite polygonal set of points in the xy-plane. Suppose that f is a function of two variables, with*

$$f(x, y) = ax + by + c, \tag{1}$$

where a, b, and c are constants, and the domain of f consists of all pairs (x, y) which are coordinates of points in T. Let S be the polygon which is the boundary of T. Then, f has a maximum value, M, and minimum value, m, on the domain T. Moreover, $f(x, y) = M$ at some vertex of S, and $f(x, y) = m$ at some vertex of S.

Proof. 1. By Theorem IV, if $P: (x, y)$ is restricted to any side $P_1 P_2$ of S, as in Figure 106, then the maximum and minimum values of $f(x, y)$ are attained at P_1 and P_2. Similar remarks apply to each side of S. Hence, with $P: (x, y)$ restricted to S, $f(x, y)$ has some maximum, M_0, and minimum, m_0, where $f(x, y) = M_0$ at some vertex of S, and $f(x, y) = m_0$ at some vertex.

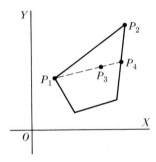

Figure 106

2. Now, let $P_3: (x_3, y_3)$ be any point in the interior of T, as in Figure 106. Let $P_1: (x_1, y_1)$ be a vertex of S such that $f(x_1, y_1) = M_0$. Connect P_1 and P_3 by a line l, and extend l through P_3 until l meets* a side of S, at $P_4: (x_4, y_4)$. By Theorem IV, if $P: (x, y)$ is on segment $\overline{P_1 P_4}$, then $f(x, y)$ has its maximum at P_1 or P_4; this maximum occurs at P_1 because $f(x_1, y_1) = M_0$, the maximum of $f(x, y)$ on S. Then, $f(x_4, y_4)$ is the minimum of $f(x, y)$ for $P: (x, y)$ on $P_1 P_4$; thus

$$m_0 \leqq f(x_4, y_4) \leqq f(x_3, y_3) \leqq M_0, \tag{2}$$

where m_0 can be inserted because it is the minimum of $f(x, y)$ on S.

3. From (2), at any point $P_3: (x_3, y_3)$ in the interior of T, the function value $f(x_3, y_3)$ cannot exceed the maximum of $f(x, y)$ on the boundary S, and cannot be less than the minimum m_0 on the boundary. Hence, M_0 and m_0 are the maximum and minimum, respectively, of $f(x, y)$ for all $P: (x, y)$ in T, and each extremum of the function f is attained at a vertex of the polygon which is the boundary of T.

Illustration 1. The four vertices $(-1, 0)$, $(1, -1)$, $(5, 3)$, and $(-2, 2)$ of a polygon, S, are shown in Figure 107, where S is the boundary of a convex region T. Let $f(x, y) = 3x - 2y + 5$. By Theorem V, to obtain the extrema of $f(x, y)$ for $P: (x, y)$ in T, we merely have to calculate $f(x, y)$ at each vertex of S. Then, the maximum and minimum of these numbers are the

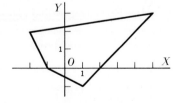

Figure 107

* Line l, as extended, must meet a side of S because T is finite.

corresponding extrema for $f(x, y)$, for all $P:(x, y)$ in T. From Figure 107, we compute f at the vertices of S, as follows:

$$f(-1, 0) = 2; \quad f(1, -1) = 10; \quad f(5, 3) = 14; \quad f(-2, 2) = -5.$$

By inspection, the maximum for $f(x, y)$ in T is 14, attained at vertex $(5, 3)$; the minimum is -5, attained at $(-2, 2)$.

If the convex region T of Theorem V is described as the graph of a system of linear inequalities, then it is necessary to solve the corresponding systems of linear equations, two by two, as necessary, in order to find the vertices of the polygon which is the boundary of T.

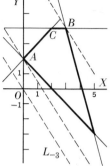

Figure 108

EXAMPLE 1. Obtain the extrema of f, if

$$f(x, y) = 3x + 2y - 3,$$

where the domain of (x, y) consists of all points which satisfy the following system of inequalities:

$$y \leqq 4, \quad x - y + 2 \geqq 0, \quad x + y - 2 \geqq 0, \quad 7x + 2y - 29 \leqq 0. \quad (3)$$

Solution. 1. The finite convex region T defined by (3) is shown in Figure 108. To find the vertices of T (meaning the vertices of the *polygon* which is the boundary of T), we solve each of the following systems:

$$\begin{cases} y = 4, \\ x - y + 2 = 0. \end{cases} \quad \begin{cases} y = 4, \\ 7x + 2y = 29. \end{cases} \quad \begin{cases} x = y - 2, \\ x + y = 2. \end{cases} \quad \begin{cases} x + y = 2, \\ 7x + 2y = 29. \end{cases} \quad (4)$$

From (4), the vertices are, respectively: $(2, 4)$; $(3, 4)$; $(0, 2)$; $(5, -3)$.

2. We find the following values of f at the vertices:

$$f(2, 4) = 11; \quad f(3, 4) = 14; \quad f(0, 2) = 1; \quad f(5, -3) = 6.$$

Hence, the maximum for $f(x, y)$ is 14 and the minimum is 1.

Comment 1. With 4 inequalities in (3), we could form $_4C_2$, or 6 systems of two equations each for boundaries. We used only 4 systems in (4) because Figure 108 showed that the other systems did not define vertices.

Comment 2. In Example 1, consider the line $L_k:[3x + 2y - 3 = k]$, for all values of k. Thus, L_k is the set of points in the xy-plane where $f(x, y) = k$. Example 1 asks for *the largest and smallest values of k for which L_k has at least one point in region T.*

We may write $\qquad\qquad L_k:[y = -\frac{3}{2}x + \frac{1}{2}(3 + k)]. \qquad\qquad (5)$

Think of any position of L_k, such as L_{-3}, which is the broken line through the origin in Figure 108. Consider moving L_k from position L_{-3} upward, always with slope $-\frac{3}{2}$. By observing the slopes of L_k and the sides of T, we see that the position of L_k with *smallest* y-intercept, and thus with smallest value of k in (5), occurs when L_k meets T at point $A:(0, 2)$. The *largest* y-intercept for L_k occurs when L_k meets T at $B:(3, 4)$. These graphical decisions agree with the solution of Example 1.

EXAMPLE 2.   Repeat Example 1 with $f(x, y) = 2x - 2y + 5$.

Solution.   We consider line $L_k:[f(x, y) = k]$, *or*

$$L_k:[y = x + \tfrac{1}{2}(5 - k)], \tag{6}$$

and apply the method of the preceding Comment 2. The lines of the set $\{L_k\}$, for all values of k, have slope 1. Since the y-intercept in (6) is $\tfrac{1}{2}(5 - k)$, when k *increases* the y-intercept *decreases*. The student should draw illustrations of L_k on a duplicate of Figure 108 (or slide a ruler with proper slope over that figure) and verify the following facts. *With L_k intersecting T:*

The smallest y-intercept for (6) *occurs when L_k goes through point* $(5, -3)$.
The largest y-intercept for (6) *occurs when L_k coincides with side AC of T.*

Hence, the *maximum* of f in T occurs at $(5, -3)$, where the maximum is $f(5, -3) = 21$; the *minimum* of f occurs *at all points on side AC.* Thus, at $A:(0, 2)$ and $C:(2, 4)$

$$f(0, 2) = 1 = f(2, 4).$$

The results here could be verified by calculating $f(x, y)$ at each vertex of T.

Note 1.   In Example 2, we showed that, in Theorem V, we may add the remark that *either extremum of $f(x, y)$ may be attained at all points of some side of T.* This occurs only when the values of $f(x, y)$ are the same at the endpoints of a side, because then the maximum and the minimum of $f(x, y)$ on this side are equal, and hence $f(x, y)$ is a constant on the side.

EXERCISE 93

By use of Theorem V, find the maximum and minimum of the specified function f if the domain of f consists of the convex set T defined by the indicated inequalities, or bounded by the polygon S with the given vertices. Check the result graphically by considering a family of lines $\{L_k\}$ as in Example 2 above.

1. $f(x, y) = 4x - 3y - 7$; T defined in Problem 3, page 348.
2. $f(x, y) = -3x - 5y + 4$; T defined in Problem 5, page 348.
3. $f(x, y) = 3x + 9y - 8$; T defined in Problem 6, page 348.
4. $f(x, y) = -4x - y - 3$; S has the vertices in Problem 11, page 348.
5. $f(x, y) = 5x - 3y + 4$; S has the vertices in Problem 12, page 348.
6. $f(x, y) = 9x + y - 20$; S has the vertices in Problem 13, page 348.
7. $f(x, y) = -8x + 3y - 15$; S has the vertices in Problem 14, page 348.
8. $f(x, y) = 2x - 4y + 7$; T is the solution set of the following system of inequalities:

$$\left.\begin{array}{ll} x \geq 0, \quad x \leq 8, \quad y \geq 0, \quad y \leq 10, \\ x + y - 12 \leq 0, \quad x + y - 12 \geq 0. \end{array}\right\} \tag{1}$$

Comment.   The two inequalities in the line above are equivalent to $x + y - 12 = 0$. Hence, the region T collapses to simply a line segment. An *equality* always can be thought of in this way as a corresponding *system of two inequalities.*

152. Linear programming with two variables

Let x and y be variables associated with a problem which, for concreteness, we shall refer to as a *business problem*, being managed by a man K. Suppose that conditions of the problem restrict the domain of (x, y) in such a manner that (x, y) must satisfy a certain system of linear inequalities. Also, suppose that K wishes to choose (x, y) so that a certain linear function $f(x, y)$ will have either its maximum or its minimum value, subject to the given restrictions. Then, the determination of the proper values (x, y) is referred to as a problem in *linear programming*. Our basis for solving such a problem is Theorem V on page 353. Problems of this nature, for the case of two or more variables, arise with great frequency in economics, business management, logistics in any field (for instance, in military affairs), etc.

EXAMPLE 1. The operator, K, of a saw mill is able to produce 175 wholesale trade units of two by four lumber per week. He can arrange to turn out lumber of three different grades, A, B, and C, where the cost of production per unit is the same for each grade. He has contracted to sell 50 units of A and 25 units of C per week. He can sell all that he produces of C, but can sell at most 100 units of A and 80 units of B. His profit per unit on A is \$35, on B is \$30, and on C is \$25. (*a*) How much of each grade should he produce for maximum profit? (*b*) What product mix would yield the least profit?

Solution. 1. Let the number of units produced of A be x, and of B be y. Then, $(175 - x - y)$ units of C are produced. The problem requires

$$x \geq 0; \quad x \geq 50; \quad x \leq 100; \quad y \geq 0; \quad y \leq 80; \quad (175 - x - y) \geq 25. \quad (1)$$

We call (1) the **constraints** of the problem. The condition $x \geq 0$ is redundant, because $x \geq 50$ also is required. Let $f(x, y)$ dollars be the profit of K per week:

$$f(x, y) = 35x + 30y + 25(175 - x - y), \text{ or}$$
$$f(x, y) = 10x + 5y + 4375. \quad (2)$$

We desire a pair (x, y) to **maximize** $f(x, y)$, if (x, y) is in the convex region, T, defined by (1).

2. The inequality at the right in (1) becomes

$$150 - x - y \geq 0.$$

The polygon S shown by unbroken lines in Figure 109 is the boundary of the region T defined by (1). The vertices of S are:

$(50, 80); \ (70, 80); \ (100, 50); \ (100, 0); \ (50, 0).$

The corresponding values of $f(x, y)$ are:

$5275; \quad 5475; \quad 5625; \quad 5375; \quad 4875.$

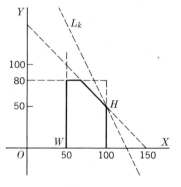

Figure 109

By Theorem V, maximum profit is obtained if K produces 100 units of A, 50 units of B, and 25 units of C, corresponding to vertex H of S. Minimum profit occurs if K produces 50 units of A, and 125 units of C, corresponding to vertex W of the polygon S.

Comment. To check the results of Example 1 graphically, as in Example 2 on page 355, we consider the family of lines

$$L_k : [10x + 5y + 4375 = k], \quad \text{or} \quad L_k : [y = -2x + (k - 875)].$$

The vertex of T where $f(x, y)$ attains its maximum is that vertex met by L_k with the *greatest y-intercept* for which L_k intersects T. The corresponding line L_k is shown through vertex H in Figure 109 on page 356.

EXAMPLE 2.   A farmer wishes to mix three materials, A, B, and C, in suitable proportions to form fertilizer. Material A contains 25% nitrogen, 10% phosphate, and 30% potash; B contains 25% nitrogen, 50% phosphate, and 10% potash; C contains 15% nitrogen, 25% phosphate, and 30% potash. The fertilizer is to contain at least 20% of each chemical. The costs per pound of A, B, and C are 2 cents, 3 cents, and 5 cents, respectively. Find how many pounds of each material should be used per 100 pounds of the mixture, to minimize the cost of the fertilizer.

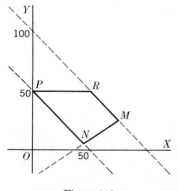

Figure 110

Solution.   1. Let x, y, and z be the numbers of pounds of A, B, and C respectively, in 100 pounds of the mixture. Then, the constraints of the problem are as follows:

$$x \geq 0; \quad y \geq 0; \quad z \geq 0; \tag{3}$$
$$.25x + .25y + .15z \geq 20; \tag{4}$$
$$.10x + .50y + .25z \geq 20; \tag{5}$$
$$.30x + .10y + .30z \geq 20; \tag{6}$$
$$x + y + z = 100. \tag{7}$$

We wish to minimize the cost, $f(x, y, z)$, in cents per 100 pounds, where

$$f(x, y, z) = 2x + 3y + 5z. \tag{8}$$

2. By use of (7), we have $z = 100 - x - y$. When this is used in (3)–(6), after simplification we obtain the constraints in *two* variables:

$$x \geq 0; \quad y \geq 0; \quad 100 - x - y \geq 0; \tag{9}$$
$$x + y - 50 \geq 0; \tag{10}$$
$$100 - 3x + 5y \geq 0; \tag{11}$$
$$50 - y \geq 0. \tag{12}$$

The graph of the solution set of (9)–(12) consists of the convex set of points (x, y) in the region T bounded by polygon $PRMN$ in Figure 110. From (8), by use of (7), $f(x, y, z)$ becomes $F(x, y)$, where

$$F(x, y) = 500 - 3x - 2y. \tag{13}$$

We wish to find the minimum of F when (x, y) has the domain T. In Problem 3 below, the student will be asked to finish the solution.

Note 1. By geometrical methods similar to those used in this chapter, linear programming can be discussed for problems where the constraints involve three independent variables. Then, systems of linear inequalities in three variables, say (x, y, z), would be involved. The graph of the linear equation related to any one of the inequalities would be a *plane* in an xyz-system of rectangular coordinates in space of three dimensions. The graph of any linear inequality in (x, y, z) would be a *half space* on one side of a corresponding plane. The intersection of closed half spaces is a *convex polyhedral region*, with edges, and vertices at which edges would intersect. Suppose that $f(x, y, z) = ax + by + cz + d$, where (a, b, c, d) are constants, and let the domain of (x, y, z) be a finite polyhedral region, T, in xyz-space. Then, it can be proved that f has a maximum, M, and a minimum, m, for (x, y, z) in T, and that f attains the value M at some vertex of T, and the value m at some vertex of T.* In case more than three variables enter, a discussion of linear programming involves a mathematical foundation far above the level of the present text.

EXERCISE 94

Solve each problem by the method of Example 1 on page 356. Then check the solution by carrying through the graphical method of Example 2 on page 355.

1. A manufacturer, K, produces two varieties of power lawnmowers, where variety A is a riding mower, and variety B must be guided by hand. K can sell all mowers which he can produce. K uses two types, R and S, of workmen. To manufacture one of style A requires two man-days of type R and three of type S. To manufacture one of style B requires three man-days of type R, and one of type S. K has at most 2400 man-days of type R, and 1500 man-days of type S available per month. The profit per machine of style A is $75, and of style B is $60. How many of style A and of style B should K produce per month to obtain maximum profit?

2. A farmer has 200 acres available for planting with crops A, B, and C. He is assured of profits per acre of $40 on A and $30 on B. He cannot take care of more than 100 acres of A, or 120 acres of C. How many acres should he assign to each crop in order to maximize his profit if the profit per acre on C is (*i*) $25; (*ii*) $45?

3. Solve Example 2 on page 357.

4. A manufacturer, K, produces three varieties of products, A, B, and C. The number of manufacturing time units to be used is 600 per month. The time units required for the output of each A-unit is 2 time units, of each B-unit is 8 time units, and of each C-unit is 2 time units. The profits per unit output on A, B, and C are $40, $100, and $20, respectively. K has contracted to sell 60 units of C, 20 units of A, and 20 units of B per month, and cannot produce more than 100 units of A and 45

---

* For a proof of the results for linear programming with three independent variables, see page 478, in *Algebra, Elementary Functions, and Probability*, by William L. Hart; D. C. Heath and Company (1965).

units of B. If K can sell all that he is able to produce, find how many units he should produce of each product per month to maximize his profit.

5. A manufacturer of plastic boxes is considering the use of a mixture composed of three different compounds A, B, and C, whose costs per pound are 15 cents, 12 cents, and 10 cents, respectively. If the mixture, M, contains more than 30% of A, then M will have the proper color. If M contains more than 20% of B, then M will have the proper strength in cold weather. If M contains more than 20% of C, then M will have the proper hardness in warm weather. The ratio of the amount of A to the amount of C in the mixture must be at least 1 on account of chemical properties. Find how much of A, of B, and of C should be used per 100 pounds of the mixture to minimize the cost, with proper color, strength, and hardness.

6. A food compound, M, is to be composed of three components (A, B, C). Component A contains 20% protein, 10% carbohydrates, and 10% fats; B contains 20% protein, 50% carbohydrates, and 25% fats; C contains 5% protein, 10% carbohydrates, and 25% fats. To make M palatable, there must be at least as much of A as of B. Also, M is to contain at least 11% protein, 14% carbohydrates, and 14.5% fats. The costs of A, B, and C per pound are 4 cents, 6 cents, and 3 cents, respectively. How much of A, of B, and of C should be used per 100 pounds of M to make it palatable, and also otherwise satisfactory, with minimum cost?

7. A drug company will produce a cough syrup involving a combination of three drugs, a sedative A, an expectorant B, and an antihistamine C. In the mixture of A, B, and C the following conditions must be satisfied:

I.   At least 15% and not more than 30% is A.

II. The amount of B must be at most four times the amount of A.

III. At least 40% is B.

IV. The amount of C is at least 10%, and at most as large as the amount of B.

The costs of A, B, and C per ounce are $4, $5, and $8, respectively. What proportions of A, B, and C should be used to minimize the cost of the mixture of A, B, and C? (Work with 100 ounces of the mixture.)

8. A drug manufacturer will prepare a tonic, H, to remedy a deficiency in thiamine (T) and nicotinic acid (N) by a mixture of ingredients (M, P, R) containing the following numbers of milligrams (mg.) of N and T per gram: M:(5 mg. N, 20 mg. T); P:(25 mg. N, 10 mg. T); R:(15 mg. N, 15 mg. T). The costs in cents per gram of (M, P, R) are (25, 30, 40). At most 50% of H will be R. Also, H must contain at least 15 mg. of T per gram. The amount of M must be at most three times the amount of P. The costs in cents per gram of (M, P, R) are (25, 30, 10). How many grams of (M, P, R) per 100 grams of H should be used to minimize the cost?

9. The dietician in a school is considering the amounts of three foods (A, B, C) to include in a specified total of pounds of these foods. The costs of (A, B, C) in cents per pound are (80, 30, 60). To make the food palatable, at least 25% but not more than 60% should be A. For a rounded diet: at least 10% should be C; the amount of C must not exceed "three times the amount of B" plus "the amount of A"; the amount of B must not exceed twice the amount of A. (i) Find the proportions of (A, B, C) to use in order to minimize the total cost under the given conditions. (ii) Find the minimum and the maximum costs per 100 pounds.

Note 1. In an xy-plane, let T be a polygonal region which does *not* have a finite area. Thus, T has infinite extent. Let $f(x, y) = ax + by + c$, where a, b, and c are constants, with a and b not zero. Then, f may have a *maximum value, M*, but no minimum when the point (x, y) has the domain T; or, a *minimum value, m*, but no maximum; or, *neither a maximum nor a minimum*. It is found that any maximum or minimum of f is attained at a vertex of T (possibly along the whole of a boundary line of T). To prove the preceding fact in any particular case, geometrical reasoning as in Comment 2 on page 354 may be used. The following problems should be solved in this manner.

Prove geometrically that f has an extremum, or no extremum if the domain of (x, y) is the specified set W. Find any extremum which exists, and where f takes on this value.

10. $f(x, y) = 5x + 2y - 3$, and W is the solution set of the system

$$y + 3x \geq 4, \qquad 2y - 2x \leq 3, \qquad and \qquad x + 2y \geq 2.$$

11. $f(x, y) = 4 - 2y - 5x$, and W is the solution set of the system

$$x \geq 3, \qquad 3x - 4y \leq 12, \qquad and \qquad 2y \geq x.$$

12. $f(x, y) = 3y - 2x$, and W is the solution set of the system

$$y - x \leq 2, \qquad 2y - x \leq 5, \qquad and \qquad x + y \leq 7.$$

13. Solve Problem 12 if $f(x, y) = x - y$.

14. Solve Problem 12 if $f(x, y) = y - 4x$.

15. An automobile manufacturer has 300 automobiles of a certain model at plant A and 300 of this model at plant B. Retail dealers G, H, and K order 200, 150, and 250 cars, respectively, of this model. The costs of shipping one automobile to each of these dealers from A and from B are as follows:

	To G	*To* H	*To* K
From A	$50	$150	$200
From B	$50	$200	$ 50

How should the orders be filled, to minimize shipping costs?

Hint. Let x cars go from A to G, and y cars from A to H. Then, $(200 - x)$ go from B to G; $(300 - x - y)$ go from A to K; etc. Then, $200 - x \geq 0$; $300 - x - y \geq 0$; etc.

16. Let $f(x, y) = 3y + 2x$, and T be the graph of the system

$$x \geq 0, \qquad y \leq 0, \qquad 2x + 3y \leq 2, \qquad and \qquad 2x + 3y \geq -3.$$

Show that f has both a maximum and a minimum for (x, y) in T. Hence, besides the possibilities for f in Note 1, both extrema may exist for f in a polygonal region of infinite extent.

Appendix

NOTE 1
The Irrationality of $\sqrt{2}$

If there exists a rational number which is a square root of 2, then there exist two positive integers m and n, such that
$$\sqrt{2} = \frac{m}{n}, \qquad (1)$$
where m/n is a fraction in lowest terms. Or, if $\sqrt{2}$ is rational, there exist two integers m and n, **without a common factor which is an integer, not 1,** such that (1) is true. Let us show that this assumption leads to a contradiction.

1. Square both sides of (1):
$$2 = \frac{m^2}{n^2}; \qquad or \qquad 2n^2 = m^2. \qquad (2)$$

We see that 2 is a factor of the left-hand member of $2n^2 = m^2$; hence 2 is a factor of the right-hand member. Therefore 2 is a factor of m because otherwise 2 is not a factor of m^2. Or, $m = 2k$, where k is some positive integer.

2. Place $m = 2k$ in (2):
$$2n^2 = (2k)^2 = 4k^2; \quad or \quad n^2 = 2k^2. \qquad (3)$$

Since 2 is a factor of the right-hand member in (3), then 2 is a factor of n.

3. We have shown in Steps 1 and 2 that m and n have 2 as a factor. This contradicts our assumption that m and n have no common factor except 1. Hence, the assumed equation (1) has led us to a contradiction, and it follows that (1) itself must be false. Therefore no rational number exists which is a square root of 2, or $\sqrt{2}$ *is an irrational number.*

Comment. We verify that $(1.4)^2 = 1.96$; $(1.41)^2 = 1.9881$; $(1.414)^2 = 1.999396$; $(1.4142)^2 = 1.99996164$; etc. On considering
$$1.4, \quad 1.41, \quad 1.414, \quad 1.4142, \quad 1.41421, \quad \cdots, \qquad (4)$$
we see that the square of each number in (4) is less than 2 but that, on proceeding to the right in (4), the squares of the numbers give improving approximations to 2. We may obtain (4) by carrying out the square root process of arithmetic to find $\sqrt{2}$.

NOTE 2

Axioms for the System of Real Numbers

There are two main methods for studying the system, R, of real numbers. One, which we shall call the *constructive method*, has been illustrated in the student's experience in elementary mathematics, with many logical details treated informally, but nevertheless involved in a reasonably complete fashion. In brief, the constructive method could proceed as follows. We start with a relatively *primitive basis*,* such as the set, S_1, of *natural numbers*, $(1, 2, 3, \cdots)$, also called *whole numbers*, and finally called the *positive integers*. (For convenience, we use the word *positive* here because of its necessary presence later.) Then, we join to S_1 the new number *zero*, 0, to obtain a system S_2, consisting of 0 together with all numbers in S_1. Next, we define the positive rational numbers a/b, where a and b are in S_2 and $b \neq 0$, and join these new numbers to S_2, thus obtaining a system S_3, consisting of zero and all positive rational numbers. Then, the positive irrational numbers can be defined in terms of the rational numbers, as suggested very informally in Section 1 on page 4. On adjoining the irrational numbers to S_3, we obtain a system S_4. Finally, corresponding to each nonzero number in S_4, we may define a *negative number*, as was done in Section 2, on page 7. On adjoining the negative numbers to S_4, we finally obtain the system, R, of real numbers. At each stage in a constructive development of R as just illustrated, of course it is necessary to define addition and multiplication, as the student has seen in more elementary mathematics.

Another method of studying R is to give a description of the system, which we assume to exist, by means of a *basic set of properties* from which all other properties can be proved. This method will be referred to as the *descriptive method*,† which we proceed to treat briefly. In this method, we commence by stating fundamental postulates, as follows, called the *axioms for the real numbers*. We shall introduce the axioms in stages.‡

Let R be a set of elements, called *numbers*, to be represented by lower case letters such as $a, b, x, y, \cdots$. We stipulate that two binary operations, *addition* and *multiplication*, are defined in R, with the following axioms specified for the operations (to be indicated by the usual notational system of algebra).

I. AXIOMS FOR ADDITION.

I_1. *Any two numbers, x and y, have a unique sum, $(x + y)$, and the determination of a sum is called* addition.

---

* Or, with a *more* primitive basis, such as the "*Peano Axioms*," which permit definition of the natural numbers. For this type of basis, see *Foundations of Analysis* by Edmund Landau, Chelsea Publishing Company, publishers.

† For a detailed account of this method, going very far beyond the relatively brief content of the present appendix note, see *The Real Number System*, by John M. H. Olmsted, Appleton-Century-Crofts, publishers. The discussion in the present note (with many omissions) is modeled after the beginning of the treatment by Olmsted.

‡ As mentioned later, we shall omit the so-called axiom of *completeness*, leading to consideration of irrational numbers.

I_2. *Addition is* **associative.** *That is, for any numbers* x, y, *and* z,

$$x + (y + z) = (x + y) + z.$$

I_3. *There exists a number* **zero,** 0, *called an* **additive identity element** *of* R, *such that, for any number* x, *we have* $x + 0 = x$.

I_4. *Corresponding to any number* x, *there exists a number* $-x$, *called an* **additive inverse element** *for* x, *such that* $x + (-x) = 0$.

I_5. *Addition is* **commutative.** *That is, for any numbers* x *and* y, $x + y = y + x$.

II. AXIOMS FOR MULTIPLICATION.

II_1. *Any two numbers* x *and* y *have a unique product,* xy, *and the determination of a product is called* **multiplication.**

II_2. *Multiplication is* **associative.** *That is, for any numbers* x, y, *and* z, *we have* $x(yz) = (xy)z$.

II_3. *There exists a number* $1 \neq 0$, *such that, for any number* x, *we have* $x \cdot 1 = x$; *we call* 1 *a* **multiplicative identity element** *of* R, *and refer to* 1 *as* **one.**

II_4. *Corresponding to any number* $x \neq 0$, *there exists a number* x^{-1}, *called an* **inverse element** *for* x, *such that* $x(x^{-1}) = 1$.

II_5. *Multiplication is* **commutative.** *That is, for any numbers* x *and* y, *we have* $xy = yx$.

III. AXIOM FOR ADDITION AND MULTIPLICATION.

Multiplication is **distributive** *with respect to addition. That is, if* x, y, *and* z *are any numbers, then* $x(y + z) = xy + xz$.

A **field** is defined as any set, R, of *elements* (called *numbers* above) satisfying axioms I–III. Hence, with the observation that I–III are satisfied in the system, R, of real numbers, we conclude that R can be referred to as the *field of real numbers*. On analyzing the foundation for the system, C, of complex numbers on pages 177–182, it is seen that C can be referred to as *the field of complex numbers*.

PROPOSITION 1. *There is just one additive identity element in* R, *or zero is unique.*

Proof. Suppose that both 0 and $0'$ are zero numbers satisfying (I_3). *Then, since* $x + 0 = x$ *for every number* x, *we may let* $x = 0'$, *and thus obtain*

$$0' + 0 = 0'. \tag{1}$$

Also, since $x + 0' = x$ for every number x, we may let $x = 0$, and thus obtain

$$0 + 0' = 0. \tag{2}$$

By (I_5), we have $0 + 0' = 0' + 0$, and hence (1) and (2) show that $0 = 0'$.

PROPOSITION 2. (*The cancellation law for addition.*) *If* $x + y = x + z$, *then* $y = z$.

Proof. Suppose that $x + y = x + z$. Let $-x$ be an additive inverse for x, as in (I$_4$). Then,

$$(-x) + (x + y) = (-x) + (x + z). \tag{3}$$

By (I$_2$), from (3) we obtain

$$[(-x) + x] + y = [(-x) + x] + z, \quad \text{or} \quad 0 + y = 0 + z.$$

Hence, $y + 0 = z + 0$ and thus, by (I$_3$), we have $y = z$.

PROPOSITION 3. *For any number* x, *we have* $x \cdot 0 = 0$.

Proof. We have $0 + 0 = 0$. Then, on multiplying by x on each side, we obtain

$$x(0 + 0) = x \cdot 0, \quad \text{or} \quad x \cdot 0 + x \cdot 0 = x \cdot 0.$$

By (I$_3$), $$x \cdot 0 + 0 = x \cdot 0.$$

Hence, $$x \cdot 0 + x \cdot 0 = x \cdot 0 + 0.$$

Therefore, by Proposition 2, $$x \cdot 0 = 0.$$

PROPOSITION 4. *If* $x \neq 0$ *and* $y \neq 0$, *then* $xy \neq 0$. *Or, if* $xy = 0$, *then at least one of* x *and* y *is* 0.

Proof. (*Indirect method of proof.*) Suppose that x and y are numbers such that $xy = 0$, where $x \neq 0$ and $y \neq 0$. Then, with x^{-1} from (II$_4$),

$$x^{-1}(xy) = x^{-1}(0), \quad \text{or} \quad (x^{-1}x)y = 0.$$

Since $x(x^{-1}) = 1$, we have $1 \cdot y = 0$, or $y = 0$. This contradicts the condition that $y \neq 0$. Hence, the assumption "$xy = 0$ *with* $x \neq 0$ *and* $y \neq 0$" is *false*. Therefore, $xy \neq 0$ when $x \neq 0$ and $y \neq 0$.

PROPOSITION 5. *If* $x \neq 0$, *then* $x^{-1} \neq 0$.

Proof. (*Indirect method.*) Suppose that there exists a number $x \neq 0$ such that $x^{-1} = 0$, where (II$_4$) is true. Then,

$$x(x^{-1}) = x \cdot 0, \quad \text{or} \quad 1 = 0,$$

which contradicts (II$_3$), which states that $1 \neq 0$.

PROPOSITION 6. *For any number* x, *there exists just one additive inverse*, $-x$, *as described in* (I$_4$). *That is, the additive inverse of* x *is unique*.

Proof. Suppose that y is any number such that $x + y = 0$. From (I$_4$), there is one number $-x$ such that $x + (-x) = 0$. Hence,

$$x + y = x + (-x).$$

Thus, by Proposition 2, $y = -x$, or $-x$ is the only additive inverse for x.

Hereafter, for any x in R, we define the **negative** of x as $-x$, the unique *additive inverse* of x.

DEFINITION I.   *The* **difference** *between x and y is defined as $[x + (-y)]$, and will be represented by $(x - y)$. That is, by definition,*

$$x - y = x + (-y).$$

The operation of obtaining a difference will be called **subtraction.** Thus, the result of subtracting y from x is represented by $(x - y)$.

PROPOSITION 7.   *There is just one number 1 with the properties specified in* (II_3). *Or, the multiplicative identity element, 1, is unique.*

Proof.   Suppose that 1 and 1' both satisfy (II_3). Then,

$$x \cdot 1 = x \cdot 1'.$$

With $x \neq 0$, let x^{-1} be an inverse of x. Then,

$$x^{-1}(x \cdot 1) = x^{-1}(x \cdot 1'), \qquad or \qquad (x^{-1}x) \cdot 1 = (x^{-1}x)1'.$$

Since $x^{-1}x = 1$, we have $1 \cdot 1 = 1 \cdot 1'$. But, $1 \cdot y = y$ for every y. Therefore, $1 = 1'$.

PROPOSITION 8.   *For any number $x \neq 0$, there exists just one number y such that $xy = 1$. That is, the inverse of x is unique.*

Proof.   From (II_4), there is at least one number x^{-1} such that $xx^{-1} = 1$. Let y be any number such that $xy = 1$. Then, $xx^{-1} = xy$. Hence,

$$x^{-1}(xx^{-1}) = x^{-1}(xy), \qquad or \qquad (x^{-1}x)x^{-1} = (x^{-1}x)y.$$

Since $x^{-1}x = 1$, we then have $1 \cdot x^{-1} = 1 \cdot y$, or $x^{-1} = y$, as we desired to prove.

PROPOSITION 9.   *(Cancellation law for multiplication.)   If $x \neq 0$ and $xy = xz$, then $y = z$.*

The student may prove this by use of x^{-1}.

PROPOSITION 10. $(-1)(-1) = 1$.

Proof.   We have $1 + (-1) = 0$. Hence,

$$(-1)[1 + (-1)] = (-1) \cdot 0 = 0, \qquad or \qquad (-1) + (-1)(-1) = 0.$$

On adding 1 to each side of the equation, we obtain

$$1 + [(-1) + (-1)(-1)] = 1, \quad or \quad [1 + (-1)] + (-1)(-1) = 1.$$

Thus, $0 + (-1)(-1) = 1$, or $(-1)(-1) = 1$.

DEFINITION II.   *To* **divide** *x by $y \neq 0$, means to find a number z such that $x = yz$. We call z the* **quotient** *of x divided by y, and write $x \div y = z$, or $\dfrac{x}{y} = z$.*

PROPOSITION 11. *If $y \neq 0$, the quotient $x \div y$ exists and is unique, with*
$$\frac{x}{y} = xy^{-1}.$$

Proof. 1. If $x = yz$, on multiplying on both sides by y^{-1}, we obtain $z = xy^{-1}$. Hence, if there exists *any* number z satisfying Definition II, we must have $z = xy^{-1}$.

2. It remains to prove that, if $z = xy^{-1}$, then $x = yz$. The student should perform this step.

The student should find it interesting to prove the following additional results:

$$-0 = 0. \quad -(-x) = x. \quad 0 - x = -x. \quad 1^{-1} = 1. \quad \frac{1}{x} = x^{-1}.$$

If $x \neq 0$ and $y \neq 0$, then

$$(xy)^{-1} = x^{-1}y^{-1} = \frac{1}{xy} = \frac{1}{x} \cdot \frac{1}{y};$$

$$\frac{a}{x} = \frac{ay}{xy}; \quad \frac{a}{x} \cdot \frac{c}{y} = \frac{ac}{xy}.$$

PROPOSITION 12. *If $x \neq 0$ and $y \neq 0$, then*

$$\frac{a}{x} + \frac{c}{y} = \frac{ay + cx}{xy}. \tag{4}$$

Proof. By Proposition 11, used at the start, and again at the final stage,

$$\frac{ay + cx}{xy} = (ay + cx)(xy)^{-1} = x^{-1}y^{-1}(ya) + y^{-1}x^{-1}(xc)$$

$$= x^{-1}a + y^{-1}c = ax^{-1} + cy^{-1} = \frac{a}{x} + \frac{c}{y}.$$

PROPOSITION 13. $(-1)x = -x.$

Proof. We have $1 + (-1) = 0$. Hence,

$$x[1 + (-1)] = x \cdot 0 = 0, \quad or \quad x + x(-1) = 0.$$

By Proposition 6, $-x$ is the unique number satisfying $x + (-x) = 0$. Hence, $-x = (-1) \cdot x$.

It is suggested that the student should prove the following results.

$$(-x)(-y) = xy. \quad -(xy) = (-x)y = x(-y).$$

If $y \neq 0$, then

$$-\frac{x}{y} = \frac{-x}{y} = \frac{x}{-y}.$$

Comment 1. A set of elements $R = \{all\ x\}$, for which there is defined a single binary operation (call it *addition*), is called a **group** if axioms (I_1)–(I_4) are satisfied. Let us call the operation, in R, the "*group operation.*" The student may desire to prove that the *nonzero* elements of any field form a group, with respect to *multiplication* as the group operation.

We now add to the sets of axioms I, II, and III the following *axioms of order*. Any field, such as the system, R, of real numbers, which also satisfies the axioms listed in (IV) below is called an **ordered field.**

IV. AXIOMS OF ORDER. *There exists a set P of numbers in R satisfying the following conditions.*

IV₁. *If x is in P and if y is in P, then $(x + y)$ is in P.*

IV₂. *If x and y are in P, then xy is in P.*

IV₃. *For every number x in R, just one of the following statements is true:*

$$x \text{ is in } P; \quad x = 0; \quad -x \text{ is in } P. \tag{5}$$

DEFINITION III. *To state that x is less than y, or y is greater than x, means that $(y - x)$ is in P, and we write $x < y$, or $y > x$.*

We call each of the statements $x < y$ and $y < x$ an *inequality*.

We agree that $x \leq y$ means that *either $x = y$ or $x < y$*, and similarly for $x \geq y$. Also, we shall call $x \leq y$ or $x \geq y$ an *inequality* in this note.

DEFINITION IV. *To state that a number x is* **positive** *means that x belongs to P. To state that x is* **negative** *means that $-x$ belongs to P.*

From (5), it is seen that *we do not call 0 either positive or negative*, and that 0 is the *only* number with this character.

With the basis furnished by axioms IV, with Definitions III and IV, we then could develop the usual properties of inequalities, and discuss equivalent equalities. Many of the associated details would correspond to the discussion about inequalities in Chapter 2.

In order to bring into focus the properties of the real number system associated with irrational numbers, another axiom called the *axiom of completeness* would have to be introduced with respect to R. The student is referred to page 120 in the book by Olmsted cited in the footnote on page 362, or to other books of an advanced nature, for discussion of completeness and irrational numbers.

NOTE 3
Proof of the Index Laws for Rational Exponents

A complete proof that the index laws hold for any rational exponents could be constructed by showing, in succession, that the laws hold (1) if the exponents are any positive rational numbers; (2) if the exponents are zero, or positive, or negative rational numbers. Without giving a complete discussion, we shall indicate the methods involved by proving some of the necessary theorems. For convenience, we shall assume that the *base* is positive. In our proofs, we use the index laws for positive integral exponents and the definitions of Sections 21 and 23 on pages 35 and 37.

THEOREM I. *If m, n, and p are positive integers,* $\left(a^{\frac{m}{n}}\right)^p = a^{\frac{mp}{n}}$.

Proof. $\left(a^{\frac{m}{n}}\right)^p = \left[\left(a^{\frac{1}{n}}\right)^m\right]^p = \left(a^{\frac{1}{n}}\right)^{mp}$;   [(3), page 37; (II), page 18]

or, $\left(a^{\frac{m}{n}}\right)^p = a^{\frac{mp}{n}}$.   [(3), page 37]

THEOREM II. *If m, n, p, and q are positive integers, then*

$$a^{\frac{m}{n}}a^{\frac{p}{q}} = a^{\frac{m}{n}+\frac{p}{q}} = a^{\frac{mq+np}{nq}}.$$

Proof. $\left(a^{\frac{m}{n}}a^{\frac{p}{q}}\right)^{nq} = \left(a^{\frac{m}{n}}\right)^{nq}\left(a^{\frac{p}{q}}\right)^{nq}$ [(IV), page 18]

$$= a^{mq}a^{pn}.$$ (Theorem I)

Hence, $\left(a^{\frac{m}{n}}a^{\frac{p}{q}}\right)^{nq} = a^{mq+pn}.$ [(I), page 18]

Therefore, by the definition of an nqth root,

$$a^{\frac{m}{n}}a^{\frac{p}{q}} = (a^{mq+pn})^{\frac{1}{nq}} = a^{\frac{mq+pn}{nq}}.$$

THEOREM III. $\left(a^{\frac{m}{n}}\right)^{\frac{p}{q}} = a^{\frac{mp}{nq}}.$

Suggestion for proof. Compute $\left[\left(a^{\frac{m}{n}}\right)^{\frac{p}{q}}\right]^{nq}$.

In the remainder of this note we shall assume that the index laws have been completely established for all positive rational exponents.

THEOREM IV. *Law* I *of Section* 8 *on page* 18 *holds if the exponents are any positive or negative rational numbers.*

Comment 1. We are assuming that Law I has been established if both exponents are positive. Hence, it remains to show that, if h and k are any positive rational numbers,

$$a^{-h}a^{-k} = a^{-h-k}, \quad and \quad a^{h}a^{-k} = a^{h-k}.$$

Incomplete proof. By the definition of a negative power,

$$a^{-h}a^{-k} = \frac{1}{a^h}\cdot\frac{1}{a^k} = \frac{1}{a^{h+k}}; \quad or, \quad a^{-h}a^{-k} = a^{-(h+k)}.$$

NOTE 4

Rational Numbers as Repeating Decimals

We shall restrict the remarks to positive rational numbers.

Illustration 1. To obtain $106/33$, we carry out the following long division.

$$
\left.
\begin{array}{r}
3.21\cdots\cdots \\
33\overline{\smash{\big)}\,106.0000\cdots} \\
\underline{99} \\
(I)\rightarrow\quad 7\,0 \\
\underline{6\,6} \\
40 \\
\underline{33} \\
(II)\rightarrow\quad 7
\end{array}
\right\}
$$

If we disregard the location of the decimal point, the remainder, 7, at stage (II) is the same as at stage (I). Hence, the first digits "21" of the quotient repeat if we continue beyond (II), and then repeat again, etc., because 7 would be obtained after each two steps in the division. Thus, we make the conjecture that 106/33 is equal to the repeating decimal 3.2121 ⋯ .

To verify the preceding conjecture, let

$$r_{2k} = 3.2121 \cdots 21, \text{ to } 2k \text{ decimal places.} \tag{1}$$

Then, from the division process above, carried to the stage where $2k$ decimal places have been obtained in the quotient, we have

$$\frac{106}{33} = r_{2k} + \frac{7}{33(10^{2k})}, \text{ where} \tag{2}$$

the remainder is 7 in the $(2k)$th decimal place. Let $t_k = 7/[33(10^{2k})]$. Then,

$$\lim_{k\to\infty} t_k = 0.$$

From (2),
$$\frac{106}{33} = r_{2k} + t_k, \text{ or}$$

$$r_{2k} = \frac{106}{33} - t_k.$$

Hence,
$$\lim_{k\to\infty} r_{2k} = \frac{106}{33} - \lim_{k\to\infty} t_k = \frac{106}{33} + 0.$$

From Definition IV on page 137, the repeating decimal $3.\dot{2}\dot{1}$ has the following value, with r_{2k} as defined in (1):

$$3.\dot{2}\dot{1} = \lim_{k\to\infty} r_{2k}.$$

Hence we conclude that $\frac{106}{33}$ is equal to the repeating decimal $3.\dot{2}\dot{1}$.

The preceding discussion concerning $\frac{106}{33}$ can be repeated, with moderate alterations, in the case of any rational number. We shall give in detail only the initial stage, relating to the division process, for an arbitrary rational number. It is clear that we may limit our treatment to positive rational numbers, because any negative rational number would be equal to the negative of any decimal obtained for a corresponding positive rational number.

THEOREM I. *Let p/q be any rational number, where p and q are positive integers, with $q \neq 0$. Then, if the usual long division process is carried out for $p \div q$, an endless repeating decimal will be obtained (where, possibly, the decimal may terminate, and thus end with repeated zeros.)*

Proof. 1. By division, p/q can be expressed as an integer, perhaps 0, plus a positive rational number m/n where $m < n$. We shall prove Theorem I for m/n, which will imply the same result for p/q.

2. Consider dividing m by n, as in Illustration 1. The division may terminate, due to 0 appearing as the remainder at some stage, and then m/n is equal to a terminating decimal.

3. Suppose that 0 is *not* obtained as the remainder at any stage of the division. Then, the quotient arising from the division process will be an *endless decimal.* At any stage in the division, the remainder (disregarding the position of the decimal point) is one of the integers $1, 2, \cdots, (n - 1)$. Hence, after at most $(n - 1)$ steps, we must meet a particular remainder, W, which repeats one previously obtained, h *steps earlier.* Then, the next h steps of the division will introduce digits in the quotient which are the same as those obtained in the preceding h steps; etc., without end. Thus, the quotient is a repeating decimal, where the repeating part consists of h figures.

As stated above, we shall omit the discussion leading to the conclusion that m/n, from Theorem I, can be approximated as closely as we please by using an approximation to the repeating decimal (from Theorem I), terminated with sufficiently many decimal places.

NOTE 5

Translation of Axes, with Applications to Conics

In Figure 111, let OX and OY be original axes; let $O'X'$ and $O'Y'$ be new axes, respectively parallel to OX and OY, with the same positive directions, the same scale unit on OX as on $O'X'$, and the same unit on OY as on $O'Y'$. A change of coordinate systems of this nature is called a **translation of axes to the new origin** O'. If O' has original coordinates ($x = h, y = k$), we shall prove that the coordinates (x, y) and (x', y') of any point P satisfy

$$x = x' + h; \quad y = y' + k. \tag{1}$$

Or, $$x' = x - h; \quad y' = y - k. \tag{2}$$

Proof. Let the projection of $P:(x, y)$ on $O'X'$ be M' and on OX be M, and the projection of O' on OX be N. Since all line segments to be mentioned in Figure 111 are directed, for any position of P we obtain the following results:

$$h = \overline{ON}; \quad x' = \overline{O'M'} = \overline{NM};$$
$$x = \overline{OM} = \overline{ON} + \overline{NM} = h + x'.$$

Similarly, by projecting P on $O'Y'$ and OY, we would obtain $y = k + y'$.

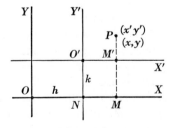

Figure 111

Illustration 1. Let the new origin be $O':(x = 2, y = -3)$. Then, from (2), the point $(x = -1, y = 4)$ has new coordinates

$$x' = -1 - 2 = -3 \quad \text{and} \quad y' = 4 - (-3) = 7.$$

A major objective in transformation of coordinates is the simplification of equations in terms of the new coordinates.

EXAMPLE 1. Transform the following equation by translating axes to the new origin $(x = 2, y = -3)$:

$$2x^2 - 8x + y^2 + 6y + 11 = 0. \tag{3}$$

Solution. 1. From (1), substitute $x = x' + 2$ and $y = y' - 3$ in (3):

$$2(x' + 2)^2 - 8(x' + 2) + (y' - 3)^2 + 6(y' - 3) + 11 = 0, \text{ or}$$
$$2x'^2 + y'^2 = 6. \tag{4}$$

2. The locus of (4) is an ellipse with center $(x' = 0, y' = 0)$, with $O'X'$ and $O'Y'$ as axes of symmetry, x'-intercepts $\pm\sqrt{3}$ and y'-intercepts $\pm\sqrt{6}$. The graph of (4), with reference to $O'X'$ and $O'Y'$, is in Figure 112. Hence, the locus of (3) is an ellipse with center $(x = 2, y = -3)$, and the lines $x = 2$ and $y = -3$ as axes of symmetry.

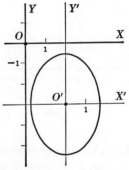

We may use (1) to transform an equation from an xy-system to the $x'y'$-system, and (2) for the *inverse* transformation from the $x'y'$-system to the xy-system. Thus, above, if we use $(x' = x - 2, y' = y + 3)$ in (4), we obtain the original equation (3). Since (1) and (2) are *linear* in x, y, x', and y', *the degree of an equation is unchanged by translating axes.*

Figure 112

By use of translation of axes and results from Chapter 6, we may obtain new standard equations for conics in more general locations, where the requirement is that *any axis of symmetry of any conic is parallel to a coordinate axis.*

Any equation of the second degree which does not involve the product xy is equivalent to an equation of the form

$$Ax^2 + Cy^2 + Dx + Ey + F = 0, \tag{5}$$

where A, C, D, E, and F are constants, and A and C are not both zero. By completing a square (multiplied by a constant) in the x-terms of (5) when $A \neq 0$, and in the y-terms when $C \neq 0$, we can change (5) to one of the following forms:

$(C \neq 0, D \neq 0)$ $C(y - k)^2 + D(x - h) = 0;$ (6)

$(A \neq 0, E \neq 0)$ $A(x - h)^2 + E(y - k) = 0;$ (7)

$(A \text{ and } C \text{ not both zero})$ $A(x - h)^2 + C(y - k)^2 = G.$ (8)

Then, in (6), (7), and (8), we may translate axes to the point (h, k) as a new origin, by use of (2), and thus obtain

$$Cy'^2 + Dx' = 0; \quad Ax'^2 + Ey' = 0; \quad Ax'^2 + Cy'^2 = G. \quad (9)$$

In (9), the two equations at the left represent parabolas. The equation at the right has no real locus, or represents either an ellipse, hyperbola, or a degenerate conic, with center at $x' = y' = 0$, and the various possibilities as to curves as stated in (2)–(4) on page 152 in regard to A, C, and G.

EXAMPLE 2. Remove linear terms by translating axes and graph

$$9x^2 - 36x + 25y^2 - 150y + 36 = 0. \quad (10)$$

Solution. 1. Complete squares with the terms in x and in y:

$$9(x^2 - 4x + 4) + 25(y^2 - 6y + 9) = -36 + 225 + 36, \; or \quad (11)$$

$$9(x - 2)^2 + 25(y - 3)^2 = 225, \quad (12)$$

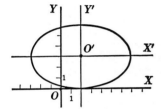

Figure 113

2. Let $x' = x - 2$ and $y' = y - 3$, which shifts the $x'y'$-origin to the point $(x = 2, y = 3)$ in the xy-plane. Then, (12) becomes

$$9x'^2 + 25y'^2 = 225, \quad (13)$$

whose graph is an ellipse with x'-intercepts ± 5 and y'-intercepts ± 3. The graph of (10), or (13), with all axes shown, is in Figure 113.

EXAMPLE 3. Graph the equation

$$9x^2 + 54x - 16y^2 + 64y = 127. \quad (14)$$

Solution. Complete squares with the terms in x and in y:

$$9(x^2 + 6x + 9) - 16(y^2 - 4y + 4) = 127 + 81 - 64 = 144; \; or \quad (15)$$

$$9(x + 3)^2 - 16(y - 2)^2 = 144. \quad (16)$$

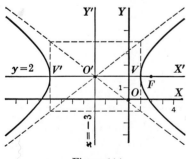

Figure 114

With $x' = x - (-3)$ and $y' = y - 2$, (16) becomes

$$\frac{x'^2}{16} - \frac{y'^2}{9} = 1, \quad (17)$$

whose graph is the hyperbola in Figure 114, with x'-intercepts ± 4 and the fundamental rectangle having one vertex at the point $(x' = 4, y' = 3)$. The $x'y'$-axes have the new origin $(x = -3, y = 2)$.

EXAMPLE 4. Graph the equation $\qquad x^2 - 4x + 8y = -36. \quad (18)$

Solution. On completing a square with the x-terms, we obtain

$$x^2 - 4x + 4 = -8y - 36 + 4, \text{ or}$$
$$(x - 2)^2 = -8[y - (-4)]. \qquad (19)$$

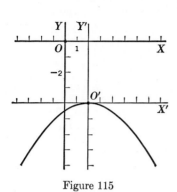

Figure 115

With $x' = x - 2$ and $y' = y - (-4)$, the new origin is $(x = 2, y = -4)$, and the new equation for (19) is

$$x'^2 = -8y', \qquad (20)$$

whose graph is the parabola in Figure 115.

As a special case of the method of Example 4, we shall prove that *the graph of a quadratic function of just one variable is a parabola* (this fact was stated without proof on page 103). Let

$$f(x) = ax^2 + bx + c, \qquad where \qquad a \neq 0.$$

First, we note that the graph of the quadratic function f is the graph of

$$y = ax^2 + bx + c. \qquad (21)$$

On dividing by a, and then adding $b^2/4a^2$ to complete a square, we obtain

$$\left(x + \frac{b}{2a}\right)^2 = \frac{1}{a}(y - k), \quad or \quad \left[x - \left(-\frac{b}{2a}\right)\right]^2 = \frac{1}{a}(y - k), \qquad (22)$$

where $k = (4ac - b^2)/4a$. With

$$x' = x - \left(-\frac{b}{2a}\right) \qquad and \qquad y' = y - k,$$

equation (22) becomes $x'^2 = y'/a$, which represents a parabola whose vertex is $(x' = 0, y' = 0)$ and axis is the line $x' = 0$, or $x - (-b/2a) = 0$. By reference to Figures 59 and 60 on page 157, we see that the parabola is concave *upward* or *downward* according as $a > 0$ or $a < 0$. Our conclusions justify the following statement.

> If $f(x) = ax^2 + bx + c$ where $a \neq 0$, the graph of f, or of the equation $y = f(x)$, is a **parabola** *with the following characteristics: it is concave in the **positive** y-direction when $a > 0$, and in the **negative** y-direction when $a < 0$; at the **vertex**, $x = -b/2a$; the **axis** is the line $x = -b/2a$.* $\qquad (23)$

If $A \neq 0$, $C = 0$, and $E \neq 0$ in (5) on page 371, the equation is linear in y. Then, on solving for y in terms of x, we find that the equation defines y as a quadratic function of x. To graph the equation, it usually is more convenient to use (23), which is equivalent to the earlier method of the Summary on page 103, instead of completing a square to change the equation to a standard form, as in Example 4. Similarly, if $A = 0$, $C \neq 0$, and $D \neq 0$ in (5), we solve for x, note that the equation defines x as a quadratic function of y, and use (23) with the roles of x and y interchanged. Thus, with $a \neq 0$, the graph of

$$x = ay^2 + by + c$$

is a parabola at whose *vertex* $y = -b/2a$; the *axis* is the line $y = -b/2a$.

EXERCISE 95

1. Find the new coordinates of $(3, 7)$, $(-4, 6)$, $(-1, -2)$, and $(0, 0)$, if the axes are translated to the new origin $O':(2, 4)$. Plot all points and both sets of axes.

Graph the equation by first translating the origin conveniently. Draw the asymptotes for any hyperbola. Show both sets of coordinate axes.

2. $(y - 2)^2 = 4(x - 3)$.

3. $25(x - 4)^2 + 9(y - 5)^2 = 225$.

4. $\dfrac{(x - 3)^2}{9} - \dfrac{(y + 5)^2}{16} = 1$.

5. $\dfrac{(y + 3)^2}{144} - \dfrac{(x + 6)^2}{25} = 1$.

After completing one or more squares, translate the origin conveniently and draw the graph, showing any asymptotes.

6. $x^2 - 2x + y^2 - 6y + 6 = 0$.

7. $y^2 - 8y - 6x + 28 = 0$.

8. $9x^2 + 36x + 4y^2 - 24y + 36 = 0$.

9. $4x^2 + 9y^2 + 24x = 0$.

10. $y^2 + 6x - 4y = 14$.

11. $2x^2 - 8x - 15y = -53$.

12. $4y^2 + 24y = x^2 - 20$.

13. $25x^2 - 100x - 4y^2 - 32y = 64$.

14. $y^2 + 4x^2 + 10y + 32x + 25 = 0$.

15. $3x^2 + 4y^2 - 12x + 8y + 19 = 0$.

16. $4x^2 - 25y^2 - 8x + 50y - 9 = 0$.

17. $x^2 + 4y^2 = 4y - 1$.

18. $4x^2 - 4x = 3 - 12y + 9y^2$.

19. $5x^2 + 20x - 4y^2 - 40y - 160 = 0$.

Graph by the method based on (23) on page 373.

20. $y = x^2 - 4x + 7$.

21. $4x - 2x^2 = y - 3$.

22. $x = 8y - 2y^2 - 6$.

NOTE 6*

Determinant Theory Based on Inversions in Indices

In a permutation of any number of positive integers arranged in a row, as read from left to right, we shall say that there is an **inversion** whenever one of the integers precedes another which is *smaller*.

Illustration 1. In the permutation $(1, 5, 3, 2, 4)$, there are four inversions, because 5 precedes 3, 2, and 4, while 3 precedes 2.

Similarly in a *permutation of letters*, as read from left to right, we shall say that there is an inversion whenever a letter *precedes* one which occurs earlier in the alphabet, or in some previously specified standard order.

* Chapters 11 and 12 are a prerequisite for the study of this note.

Illustration 2. In the permutation (d, a, f, b), there are 3 inversions because d precedes a and b, and f precedes b.

A permutation of integers, or letters, will be called an *even* or an *odd* permutation according as it exhibits an *even* or an *odd* number of inversions. Thus, we met an even permutation in Illustration 1 and an odd permutation in Illustration 2. We shall use the notion of inversions, as just presented, in a fundamental fashion in the following discussion of determinants.

In this note of the Appendix, *"matrix"* will mean *"square matrix."* As a basis for definitions and theorems about the determinant of a matrix, unless otherwise stated, we shall represent each element of the general matrix by a letter with a subscript showing the number of the row where the element lies. Also, we shall use the same letter for all elements in any given column. The column letters are to be chosen without duplications. Thus, a 4×4 matrix A is written as follows.*

$$A = \begin{bmatrix} a_1 & b_1 & c_1 & d_1 \\ a_2 & b_2 & c_2 & d_2 \\ a_3 & b_3 & c_3 & d_3 \\ a_4 & b_4 & c_4 & d_4 \end{bmatrix} \tag{1}$$

We shall proceed as if Definition III of page 272 had not been given, and make a fresh start on the theory of determinants of order $n \geq 1$.

DEFINITION I. *Let A be a square matrix, with the notation for the elements as in (1). Then, the* **determinant** *of A, denoted by $|A|$, is defined as the sum of all possible terms $\{T\}$ obtained as follows:*

(*i*) *Write a product p by taking as factors just one element from each row and from each column of A.*

(*ii*) *Arrange the factors of p with the letters in the order in which they appear in the columns of A. Then, to obtain T, prefix a plus sign or a minus sign to p according as the subscripts of the factors, as now arranged, form an even or an odd permutation. That is, if s is the number of inversions in the subscripts in p, then*

$$T = (-1)^s p. \tag{2}$$

The sum of the signed products described in Definition I is called the *expansion* of the determinant. Thus, the determinant of A is a *polynomial in the elements of the matrix A.*

Illustration 3. We obtain the terms in the expansion of the following determinant by first attaching $(1, 2, 3)$ in every possible order to "$a \quad b \quad c$," which gives $a_1 b_2 c_3$, $a_3 b_2 c_1$, etc. The sign to prefix to each product is determined by reference to paragraph (*ii*) of Definition I. Thus, we prefix a *plus* sign to

---

* In more elaborate introductions to determinants, it is essential to use the same letter for *all* elements, with *two* subscripts, where one indicates the row and the other shows the column where the element lies. Since our illustrations will apply with the order $n \leq 4$ for any determinant, our chosen notation is more convenient for our purposes.

$a_2 b_3 c_1$ because $(2, 3, 1)$ shows two inversions, and $(-1)^2 = +1$. We prefix a *minus* sign to $a_2 b_1 c_3$ because $(2, 1, 3)$ shows just one inversion. Hence, we obtain

$$\begin{vmatrix} a_1 & b_1 & c_1 \\ a_2 & b_2 & c_2 \\ a_3 & b_3 & c_3 \end{vmatrix} = a_1 b_2 c_3 + a_3 b_1 c_2 + a_2 b_3 c_1 - a_3 b_2 c_1 - a_1 b_3 c_2 - a_2 b_1 c_3. \qquad (3)$$

Expansion (3) is the same as (4) on page 272. Similarly, Definition I yields the expansion on page 271 for a determinant of order 2. Hence, Definition I, and Definition III on page 272, give the same values for $|A|$ when $|A|$ is of order $n = 2$ or $n = 3$.

THEOREM I. *If A is an $n \times n$ matrix, the expansion of $|A|$ is a polynomial of $n!$ terms in the elements of A.*

Proof. The number of terms is the same as the number of ways in which we can attach the subscripts $1, 2, \cdots, n$ to the n letters used to denote columns. This number of ways is $_nP_n$, or $n!$.

Illustration 4. The expansion of a determinant of the 4th order contains 4!, or 24 terms.

Comment 1. In a matrix A, let us use the same letter for all elements of any given row, with row letters in alphabetical order (or, in some specified order), as in the matrix below. Also, let each letter have a subscript showing the number of the

$$\begin{bmatrix} a_1 & a_2 & a_3 \\ b_1 & b_2 & b_3 \\ c_1 & c_2 & c_3 \end{bmatrix}$$

column where the letter stands. Then, we would rewrite paragraph *(ii)* of Definition I as follows: *Arrange the product p with the subscripts in natural order. Then, prefix a plus sign or a minus sign to p according as the letters representing the factors of p form an even or an odd permutation.*

EXERCISE 96

Determine whether the permutation is even or odd.

1. $5, 2, 4, 1, 7, 9$.   2. $6, 1, 4, 3, 5, 2$.   3. $1, 4, 3, 2, 6, 5$.
4. a, b, d, c, f.   5. c, a, g, b, d.   6. h, a, d, f, b, c.

7. By use of Definition I, write the expansion of $|A|$ for the matrix A in (1) on page 375.

THEOREM II. *In any permutation of integers (or letters), if two adjacent integers (or letters) are interchanged, the number of inversions is increased by or decreased by 1.*

Illustration 5. In $(1, 5, 3, 2, 4)$ there are four inversions; on interchanging 2 and 3, we obtain $(1, 5, 2, 3, 4)$, with only three inversions.

Proof. Let x and y be adjacent integers in the permutation $WxyZ$, where W and Z represent the sequences of integers which, respectively, precede and follow xy. On interchanging x and y, we obtain $WyxZ$. Any inversions in W, or in Z, and any due to the fact that W precedes x and y, or that Wxy precedes Z, are present in both $WxyZ$ and $WyxZ$. The only change in inversions is due to the fact that, if xy *shows* an inversion, then yx *does not show* an inversion, and $WxyZ$ *shows one more inversion than* $WyxZ$. Or, if xy *does not show* an inversion then yx *does show* an inversion, and $WyxZ$ *shows one less inversion than* $WyxZ$. Hence, we have proved Theorem II for the case of integers. The same remarks apply equally well to the case of inversions in letters.

For any matrix A as in (1), consider the product p of elements of A in (2), with the factors of p arranged in an arbitrary fashion for present purposes. In p, let s and l be the numbers of inversions in the subscripts on the elements of A, and in the letters for these elements, respectively.

THEOREM III. *If two adjacent factors of p are interchanged, the sum $(s + l)$ of the numbers of inversions in subscripts and in letters in p is increased by 2, or by -2, or by 0.*

Illustration 6. If $p = a_1 b_4 d_3 c_2$, then $(s + l) = 3 + 1 = 4$; on interchanging d_3 and c_2, we obtain $p = a_1 b_4 c_2 d_3$, where $(s + l) = 2 + 0 = 2$.

Proof. If we interchange two adjacent factors in p, we interchange two adjacent letters and two adjacent subscripts. Hence, by Theorem II, we increase s by ± 1 and l by ± 1. Therefore, we increase $(s + l)$ by $(\pm 1 \pm 1)$, which is either $+2$, or -2, or 0.

THEOREM IV. *If the factors of p are arranged in any order, the sum, $(s + l)$, of the numbers of inversions in subscripts and in letters for the factors is either always even or always odd.*

Proof. Any order for the factors can be obtained from any other order by successive interchanges of adjacent factors. Each interchange increases $(s + l)$ by $+2$, or -2, or 0, each of which is *even*. Hence, if $(s + l$ is *even* (or *odd*) for one order of the factors, it is *even* (or *odd*) for all orders.

We shall state and number properties of determinants as on pages 274–276.

Property I. *If A is a square matrix whose transpose is A', then $|A| = |A'|$.*

Proof. 1. In A, we assume that the letters used for column elements are in alphabetical order from left to right. Matrix A' is obtained by interchanging rows and columns in A.

2. Let any term in the expansion of $|A|$ be $T = (-1)^s p$, as in (2) on page 375, where the factors of p are arranged as specified in Definition I, and s is the number of inversions in the *subscripts* of the factors. On account of paragraph (*i*) of Definition I, a term T' occurs in the expansion of $|A'|$ where T' differs from T *at most in sign*. Let $T' = (-1)^\lambda p'$, where p' has its factors (elements of A) arranged as directed in Comment 1 on page 376, with λ as the number of inversions in the *letters* in the factors of p'. We have $p = p'$. Thus,

$$\text{if } |A| = \begin{vmatrix} a_1 & b_1 & c_1 \\ a_2 & b_2 & c_2 \\ a_3 & b_3 & c_3 \end{vmatrix}, \text{ then } |A'| = \begin{vmatrix} a_1 & a_2 & a_3 \\ b_1 & b_2 & b_3 \\ c_1 & c_2 & c_3 \end{vmatrix};$$

one term in the expansion of $|A|$ is $T = -a_2 b_1 c_3$; the corresponding term for $|A'|$ is $T' = -b_1 a_2 c_3$.

3. With $T = (-1)^s p$, the sum of the numbers of inversions in the subscripts and in the letters in p is s, because there are *no inversions in the letters*. Similarly with $T' = (-1)^\lambda p'$, and the factors of p' arranged as specified in Comment 1 on page 376, the sum of the numbers of inversions in the subscripts and in the letters in p' is λ, because there are *no inversions in the subscripts*. By Theorem IV, s and λ are both *even* or both *odd*. Hence, $T = T'$ because $p = p'$ and $(-1)^s = (-1)^\lambda$. Therefore, $|A| = |A'|$, because each term in the expansion of $|A|$ is equal to the term with the same elements as factors in the expansion of $|A'|$.

Comment 2. Because of Property I, we recall that, for any theorem about $|A|$ referring to *columns* of A, there is a corresponding theorem referring to *rows* of A.

Property II. *If all elements of a column (or row) of A are multiplied by the same number, k, to obtain a new matrix B, then $|B| = k|A|$.*

Proof. Let T_1 be a term in the expansion of $|A|$ formed as in paragraph (*ii*) of Definition I, and let T_2 be the corresponding term in the expansion of $|B|$. Then, $T_2 = kT_1$, because just one element of B occurs from the column obtained on multiplying by k in a column of A. Hence, $|B| = k|A|$, because each term in the expansion of $|B|$ is k times a corresponding term in the expansion of $|A|$.

Property III. We recall from page 275 that this is an immediate consequence of Property II.

Property IV. *If each element of a column (row) of A is zero, then $|A| = 0$.*

Proof. Each term of the expansion of $|A|$ is zero because the term has a factor from the column of zeros. Hence, $|A| = 0$.

Property V. *If two columns (rows) in A are interchanged, to give a new matrix B, then $|B| = -|A|$.*

Proof. 1. First, suppose that B is obtained by interchanging two *adjacent* columns of A. In the expansion of $|A|$, let T_1 be any term, with $T_1 = \pm p$, where p is a product of elements of A, and the factors of p are arranged, and the sign is specified as in Definition I. In the expansion of $|B|$, let T_2 be that term having as factors the same elements of A which are factors of T_1. Then, $T_2 = \pm p$, where the factors of p are arranged, and the sign is specified as in

Definition I. For instance, if $\quad A = \begin{bmatrix} a_1 & b_1 & c_1 \\ a_2 & b_2 & c_2 \\ a_3 & b_3 & c_3 \end{bmatrix} \quad and \quad B = \begin{bmatrix} a_1 & c_1 & b_1 \\ a_2 & c_2 & b_2 \\ a_3 & c_3 & b_3 \end{bmatrix}$,

one term in the expansion of $|A|$ is $T_1 = a_3 b_1 c_2$. The corresponding term in the expansion of $|B|$ is $T_2 = -a_3 c_2 b_1$. By Theorem II, the number of inversions in the subscripts of factors in T_1 is *even* or *odd*, according as the number of inversions in the subscripts of factors in T_2 is *odd* or *even*. Hence, by paragraph (*ii*) of Definition I, the signs in $T_1 = \pm p$ and in $T_2 = \pm p$ are opposites, or $T_2 = -T_1$. Therefore, $|A| = -|B|$, because corresponding terms in the expansions of the determinants occur with opposite signs.

2. Now, let U and V represent *any* two columns of A, with U to the left of V and with h columns between U and V. We can accomplish the interchange of U and V by $(2h + 1)$ successive interchanges of adjacent columns as follows:

Interchange U, in succession, with each of the h columns between U and V; this brings U next to V. Then, interchange V, in succession, with U and the h columns originally between U and V.

With A as the original matrix, let S_k be the matrix resulting after k of the preceding $(2h + 1)$ interchanges have been made. Then,

$$|S_1| = -|A|; \; |S_2| = -|S_1| = (-1)^2 |A|, \cdots, |B| = |S_{2h+1}| = (-1)^{2h+1}|A|.$$

Since $(2h + 1)$ is *odd*, we have $|B| = -|A|$, which proves Property V.

We recall that Property VI on page 275 is easily proved by use of Property V. Also, Property VII on page 275, and Property VIII on page 276 can be proved as in Chapter 11, after Definition III on page 272 (for expansion by use of cofactors) has been proved as a theorem, to be stated as Property X.

Property IX. *In any $n \times n$ matrix A, let a_1 be the element in the upper left-hand corner, and let M_1 be the minor of a_1 in $|A|$. Then, $a_1 M_1$ is the sum of the terms with a_1 as a factor in the expansion of $|A|$.*

Illustration 7. Let $|A| = \begin{vmatrix} a_1 & b_1 & c_1 \\ a_2 & b_2 & c_2 \\ a_3 & b_3 & c_3 \end{vmatrix}$. Then $M_1 = \begin{vmatrix} b_2 & c_2 \\ b_3 & c_3 \end{vmatrix}$, or

$M_1 = b_2 c_3 - b_3 c_2$. Property IX states that the sum of the terms with a_1 as a factor in the expansion of $|A|$ is $a_1(b_2 c_3 - b_3 c_2)$.

Proof of Property IX.   1. We shall deal with the special case where

$$|A| = \begin{vmatrix} a_1 & b_1 & c_1 & d_1 \\ a_2 & b_2 & c_2 & d_2 \\ a_3 & b_3 & c_3 & d_3 \\ a_4 & b_4 & c_4 & d_4 \end{vmatrix} ; \quad then \quad M_1 = \begin{vmatrix} b_2 & c_2 & d_2 \\ b_3 & c_3 & d_3 \\ b_4 & c_4 & d_4 \end{vmatrix}.$$

Any term with a_1 as a factor in the expansion of $|A|$ is seen to be of the form $T = \pm a_1 b_i c_j d_k$, where (i, j, k) is a permutation of $(2, 3, 4)$. Hence, there are *six* terms with a_1 as a factor, because $_3P_3 = 6$. Let the sum of these six terms be H. With the factors of T arranged as directed in Definition I, let s be the number of inversions in the subscripts $(1, i, j, k)$. We can also describe s as the number of inversions in (i, j, k), because the presence of 1 preceding (i, j, k) *does not alter the inversions*. Hence, each term in H is of the form

$$T = (-1)^s a_1 b_i c_j d_k. \tag{4}$$

2. Let τ be any one of the six terms in the expansion of M_1, with the factors of τ arranged as specified by Definition I. Then, if s is the number of inversions in the permutation (i, j, k) of $(2, 3, 4)$, each term τ is of the form

$$\tau = (-1)^s b_i c_j d_k. \tag{5}$$

We observe that there is a one-to-one correspondence between the terms of type T in H and τ in M_1, and that, for corresponding terms (T *and* τ), we have $T = a_1\tau$, becuase the exponent s is the same in (4) and in (5). Hence, we obtain $H = a_1 M_1$.

Property X.   *Let A be any $n \times n$ matrix, and let α be the element in the hth row and kth column of A. Then, if M is the minor of α in $|A|$, the sum of the terms in the expansion of $|A|$ having α as a factor is $\alpha \cdot [(-1)^{h+k}M]$, or αC, where C is the* **cofactor** *of α in $|A|$.*

Illustration 8.   In $|A|$ in Illustration 7, if $\alpha = c_2$ then $h = 2$ and $k = 3$; $h + k = 5$, which is *odd*. Then, Property X states that the sum of the terms with c_2 as a factor in the expansion of $|A|$ is

$$(-1)^5 c_2 \begin{vmatrix} a_1 & b_1 \\ a_3 & b_3 \end{vmatrix}, \quad or \quad -c_2(a_1 b_3 - a_3 b_1).$$

Proof of Property X.   1. In A, interchange the hth row with the one above it, then with the new one above it, etc., until, after $(h - 1)$ interchanges, the original hth row has become the 1st row. Then, interchange the kth column with the one at its left, then with the new column at its left, etc. until, after $(k - 1)$ interchanges, the original kth column has become the 1st column. Call the final matrix B. In B, element α is in the upper left-hand corner.

2. In $|B|$, the minor of α is M, just as was the case in $|A|$. Hence, by Property IX, the sum of the terms with α as a factor in the expansion of $|B|$ is αM.

3. Since B was obtained from A by $(h - 1 + k - 1)$, or $(h + k - 2)$ interchanges of rows and columns, on account of Property V, we have

$$|B| = (-1)^{h+k-2}|A| = (-1)^{h+k}|A|,$$

because $(-1)^{-2} = +1$. Thus,

$$(-1)^{h+k}(-1)^{h+k}|A| = (-1)^{h+k}|B|, \quad or \quad |A| = (-1)^{h+k}B,$$

because $(-1)^{2(h+k)} = +1$. Therefore, since αM is the sum of the terms with α as a factor in the expansion of $|B|$, the corresponding sum in the expansion of $|A|$ is $\alpha \cdot [(-1)^{h+k}M]$.

Property XI. *If A is any $n \times n$ matrix, and $(p_1, p_2, \cdots p_n)$ are the elements in a column of A, then*

$$|A| = p_1 C_1 + p_2 C_2 + \cdots + p_n C_n, \tag{6}$$

where C_i is the cofactor of p_i in $|A|$.

Proof. Each term in the expansion of $|A|$ has as a factor just one element from the specified column. Hence, the expansion is the sum of all terms having p_1 as a factor, which accounts for $p_1 C_1$ in (6); plus the sum of all terms having p_2 as a factor, which gives $p_2 C_2$ in (6); $\cdots$; plus the sum of all terms having p_n as a factor, which gives $p_n C_n$ in (6). Therefore, (6) has been proved.

We note that Property XI states as a *theorem* the fact about $|A|$ which was phrased as Definition III for $|A|$ on page 272.

NOTE 7

Review of Trigonometric Functions of Angles

Suppose that a ray or half line, issuing from a point O in a plane, rotates about O in the plane in either a clockwise or a counterclockwise sense from an initial position OA to a terminal position OB. Then, this rotation is said to form or generate an *angle AOB* with *vertex O, initial side OA,* and *terminal side OB,* as illustrated in Figure 116. The measure of $\angle AOB$ is defined as a

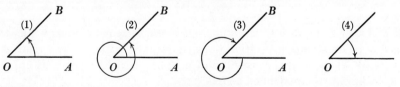

Figure 116

measure of the amount of rotation used in forming the angle. As a measure of rotation, one degree $(1°)$ is defined as $1/360$ of a complete revolution, one minute (1′) as 1/60 of 1°, and one second (1″) as 1/60 of 1′. Regardless of the unit of measurement, an angle is assigned *positive measure*, and is called a *positive angle*, if it is generated by **counterclockwise rotation**; the angle is assigned *negative measure*, and is called a *negative angle*, if it is generated by **clockwise rotation.** An angle can be said to have *zero measure* if the initial and terminal sides of the angle coincide. In representing an angle in a figure, we may indicate the corresponding amount of rotation by a curved arrow, as in Figure 187. We may say that an *angle* is the *configuration* resulting from a rotation as just described, or that an *angle* is an *amount of rotation* of a *ray* (a *half line*) about its initial point. In either case, we shall refer to an angle as a *geometric entity*.

Illustration 1. In (1) of Figure 116, the measure of ∠*AOB* is 45°, called the *value* of the angle, and we write ∠*AOB* = 45°. We do not call "45°" a *number;* "45°" abbreviates "45 *degrees.*" We also permit use of a symbol like 45° to represent the angle involved. In (2) of Figure 116, we verify that ∠*AOB* = 360° + 45° = 405°.

A positive angle is called an **acute angle** when its value lies between 0° and 90°, and an **obtuse angle** when the value lies between 90° and 180°. To state that an angle is a **quadrantal angle** means that its value is $k \cdot (90°)$ where k is some integer. If at any time an angle is shown by merely drawing two rays radiating from the vertex, without indicating rotation and sense, it will be assumed that the angle has positive measure, at most 180°. Thus, in any triangle, each angle will be considered to have a positive measure.

An angle θ is said to be in its **standard position** on an xy-system* of rectangular coordinates in a plane in case the vertex of θ is at the *origin* and the *initial side of θ lies on that half of the horizontal axis which represents positive numbers, x.* A few angles are shown in standard positions in Figure 117. An

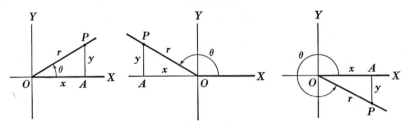

Figure 117

angle θ is said to be *in a certain quadrant* if the terminal side of θ falls there when θ is in its standard position on a coordinate system. Now, consider θ as a variable whose *domain* consists of *all angles*. For each angle† θ, six numbers, sine θ, cosine θ, etc. are defined as follows.

---

* In all of this note of the Appendix, the scale units will be equal on the axes of any coordinate system, and the same unit will be used for distance in an arbitrary direction.

† With the exception of certain quadrantal angles in the case of tan θ, cot θ, sec θ, and csc θ, when some denominator becomes zero in (1) on page 383.

DEFINITION I. *Place angle θ in standard position on a coordinate system. Choose any point P, not the origin, on the terminal side of θ; let the coordinates and radius vector of P be (x, y) and r, respectively. Then,*

$$
\begin{aligned}
sine\ \theta &= \frac{ordinate\ of\ P}{radius\ vector\ of\ P}, & or && \sin \theta &= \frac{y}{r}; \\[2mm]
cosine\ \theta &= \frac{abscissa\ of\ P}{radius\ vector\ of\ P}, & or && \cos \theta &= \frac{x}{r}; \\[2mm]
tangent\ \theta &= \frac{ordinate\ of\ P}{abscissa\ of\ P}, & or && \tan \theta &= \frac{y}{x}; \\[2mm]
cotangent\ \theta &= \frac{abscissa\ of\ P}{ordinate\ of\ P}, & or && \cot \theta &= \frac{x}{y}; \\[2mm]
secant\ \theta &= \frac{radius\ vector\ of\ P}{abscissa\ of\ P}, & or && \sec \theta &= \frac{r}{x}; \\[2mm]
cosecant\ \theta &= \frac{radius\ vector\ of\ P}{ordinate\ of\ P}, & or && \csc \theta &= \frac{r}{y}.
\end{aligned}
\tag{1}
$$

The six functions, as defined in (1), are called the basic (direct) *trigonometric functions of angles.* We recall that $\tan \theta$ and $\sec \theta$ are not defined when θ is a quadrantal angle whose terminal side, in standard position, is vertical; $\cot \theta$ and $\csc \theta$ are not defined when the terminal side is horizontal. For instance, we write $\tan 90°$ *is infinite,* meaning that (a) $\tan 90°$ *does not exist* and (b) $|\tan \theta| \to \infty$, or *the absolute value of* $\tan \theta$ *grows large without bound if* $\theta \to 90°$.

Two angles are said to be **coterminal** if their terminal sides coincide when both angles are placed in their standard positions on the same coordinate system. Since Definition I involves only the terminal side of the angle, if follows that, *if two angles θ and φ are coterminal, each trigonometric function of θ is equal to the same function of φ.*

DEFINITION II. *Let θ be an angle in any quadrant, and let θ be placed in its standard position in a coordinate plane. Then, the* **reference angle** *for θ is the acute angle, α, between the terminal side of θ and the horizontal axis.*

Various reference angles are indicated in Figure 118. We recall the following useful theorem, which can be proved by use of (1) above.

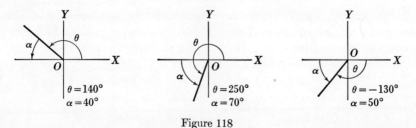

$$\theta = 140° \qquad \theta = 250° \qquad \theta = -130°$$
$$\alpha = 40° \qquad \alpha = 70° \qquad \alpha = 50°$$

Figure 118

THEOREM I. *The value of any trigonometric function of an angle θ in any quadrant is numerically equal to the value of the same-named function of the reference angle, α, for θ. That is,*

(any function of **θ**) = ±(same function of reference angle **α**),   (2)

with "+" or "−" according as the function of θ is positive or negative.

By Theorem I, the values of the trigonometric functions of an angle of any size can be found by use of a table of the function values for just acute angles. We disregard quadrantal angles in the preceding statement, since the trigonometric functions of a quadrantal angle are the same as the functions for 0°, 90°, 180°, or 270°.

Illustration 2. To find tan 140°, notice that $\alpha = 40°$ in Figure 118. Also, the tangent is negative in quadrant II. Hence, from (2) and Table IV for acute angles, tan 140° = −tan 40° = −.839.

For many purposes, particularly in calculus and certain fields of applied mathematics, the convenient unit for angular measurement is one *radian*.

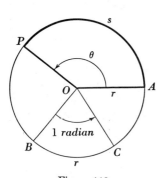

Figure 119

DEFINITION III. *One* **radian** *is the measure of a positive angle which, if its vertex is at the center of a circle, intercepts on the circle an arc whose length is the radius of the circle.*

Illustration 3. In Figure 119, $\angle BOC = 1$ rad.

Let K be the measure in radians of a complete counterclockwise rotation of OB, in Figure 119, about O. Then, the angle K radians intercepts the whole circumference, of length $2\pi r$, and 1 radian intercepts arc BC, of length r. Hence,

$$\frac{K}{1} = \frac{2\pi r}{r}, \quad or \quad K = 2\pi. \quad (3)$$

Since the angle K radians also has the measure 360°,

360° = (2π radians),   *or*   180° = (π radians).   (4)

Notice that equalities like (4) are *not equations* in the usual sense of expressing the equality of two *numbers*. Thus, (4) abbreviates *an angle of 360° also has the measure 2π radians*, etc. From (4), on dividing by 180, and by π,

$$1° = \left(\frac{\pi}{180} \text{ radians}\right) = (.0174533 \text{ radian}), \text{ } approximately; \quad (5)$$

$$(1 \text{ radian}) = \frac{180°}{\pi} = 57.2958°, \text{ } approximately. \quad (6)$$

From (5), to change degree measure to radian measure, *multiply the number of degrees by* $\pi/180$. To change radian measure to degree measure, *multiply the number of radians by* $180/\pi$. Frequently, it is useful to recall simply that any multiple of 180° is the same multiple of π radians. Thus, $30° = (\frac{1}{6}\pi \text{ rad.})$.

In a circle of radius r, as in Figure 119 on page 384, a central angle of 1 radian intercepts on the circle an arc of length r. Hence, a central angle of θ radians intercepts on the circle an arc of length s where $s = \theta r$. That is

$$s = r\theta, \quad or \quad \textbf{arc} = \textbf{(radius} \times \textbf{angle, in radians).} \tag{7}$$

Illustration 4. If $r = 25$ and $s = 75$, then $\theta = s/r = \frac{75}{25} = 3$, radians.

Hereafter, if simply a numeral, such as x, is used as a symbol for an angle, it will be understood that the measure of the angle is x radians. That is, when the unit of measurement is 1 radian, no indication of this unit need be shown with the number, say x, representing the measure of the angle. In most of the applications of trigonometry in this text, degree measure for angles will be more convenient than radian measure.

Illustration 5. "sin 1.2" means the sine of 1.2 radians. From Table VI, $\sin 1.2 = .93204$.

In the following trigonometric identities, α and β are symbols for *any* angles, with a few exceptions due to the fact that two of the trigonometric functions of an angle θ are undefined if θ is a quadrantal angle. We shall interpret α and β as symbols such as 45°, $-75°$, etc., showing degree measure. However, the identities may be used unaltered in form if α and β represent real numbers, and thus are symbols for angles in *radian* measure. Only those identities which might be useful in this text are listed. In (X), n represents any integer.

$$\csc \alpha = \frac{1}{\sin \alpha} ; \quad \sec \alpha = \frac{1}{\cos \alpha} ; \quad \cot \alpha = \frac{1}{\tan \alpha} ; \quad \tan \alpha = \frac{1}{\cot \alpha} . \tag{I}$$

$$\sin^2 \alpha + \cos^2 \alpha = 1; \quad \tan^2 \alpha + 1 = \sec^2 \alpha. \tag{II}$$

$(\text{"}+\text{" } with \text{ "}+\text{"}) \qquad \sin (\alpha \pm \beta) = \sin \alpha \cos \beta \pm \cos \alpha \sin \beta. \tag{III}$

$(\text{"}+\text{" } with \text{ "}-\text{"}) \qquad \cos (\alpha \pm \beta) = \cos \alpha \cos \beta \mp \sin \alpha \sin \beta. \tag{IV}$

$$\sin (-\alpha) = -\sin \alpha; \quad \cos (-\alpha) = \cos \alpha; \quad \tan (-\alpha) = -\tan \alpha. \tag{V}$$

$$\tan (\alpha + 90°) = -\cot \alpha. \tag{VI}$$

$$\tan (\alpha \pm 180°) = \tan \alpha; \quad \cot (\alpha \pm 180°) = \cot \alpha. \tag{VII}$$

$$[\textit{Any trig. function of } (90° - \alpha)] = (\textit{cofunction of } \alpha). \tag{VIII}$$

$$[\textit{Any trig. function of } (\alpha \pm 360°)] = (\textit{same function of } \alpha). \tag{IX}$$

$$\begin{bmatrix} \textit{Any trig. function} \\ \textit{of } (\pm\alpha + n \cdot 90°) \end{bmatrix} = \begin{bmatrix} \pm \ (\textit{same function of } \alpha), \ n \ \textbf{even;} \\ \pm \ (\textit{cofunction of } \alpha), \ n \ \textbf{odd.} \end{bmatrix} \tag{X}$$

Note 1. Suppose that α represents an angle with measure α radians. Then, in (VI)–(X), 90°, 180°, and 360° should be replaced by $\frac{1}{2}\pi$, π, and 2π, respectively.

TRIGONOMETRIC FUNCTIONS OF CONVENIENT ANGLES

The function values in the following table were read from Figures 120 and 121. These figures, or the table, or both, should be memorized.

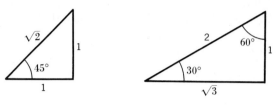

Figure 120   Figure 121

ANGLE	SIN	COS	TAN	COT	SEC	CSC	ANGLE (*rad.*)
0°	0	1	0	*none*	1	*none*	0
30°	$\dfrac{1}{2}$	$\dfrac{\sqrt{3}}{2}$	$\dfrac{1}{\sqrt{3}}$	$\sqrt{3}$	$\dfrac{2}{\sqrt{3}}$	2	$\frac{1}{6}\pi$
45°	$\dfrac{1}{\sqrt{2}}$	$\dfrac{1}{\sqrt{2}}$	1	1	$\sqrt{2}$	$\sqrt{2}$	$\frac{1}{4}\pi$
60°	$\dfrac{\sqrt{3}}{2}$	$\dfrac{1}{2}$	$\sqrt{3}$	$\dfrac{1}{\sqrt{3}}$	2	$\dfrac{2}{\sqrt{3}}$	$\frac{1}{3}\pi$
90°	1	0	*none*	0	*none*	1	$\frac{1}{2}\pi$

NOTE 8

*Introduction to Matrix Algebra**

1. Addition of matrices. On page 265, the concept of a matrix was introduced. If H is an $m \times n$ matrix, we call "$m \times n$," read "*m by n*," the **order** of H. Hereafter, if we refer to a *number*, we shall mean a *complex number*, unless otherwise specified. Sometimes a number will be called a **scalar,** to emphasize that it is not a matrix. We agree that capital letters will be reserved as symbols for matrices. In this section, all matrices mentioned will be of some fixed order $m \times n$, where $m \geqq 1$ and $n \geqq 1$.

DEFINITION I. *If H and K are matrices with the elements h_{ij} and k_{ij}, respectively, in row i and column j, the **sum** of H and K, or the result of **adding** them, is represented by $(H + K)$ and is the matrix with the element $(h_{ij} + k_{ij})$ in row i and column j.*

* Any student reading this note would be helped by having studied Note 2 of this Appendix previously.

Illustration 1. $\begin{bmatrix} 2 & 3 & 2 \\ 4 & -5 & 6 \end{bmatrix} + \begin{bmatrix} -1 & 3 & 1 \\ 4 & -1 & 0 \end{bmatrix} = \begin{bmatrix} 1 & 6 & 3 \\ 8 & -6 & 6 \end{bmatrix}.$

The **zero matrix,** represented by **O,** is defined as that matrix where each element is *zero.* Two matrices H and K, of the same order, **are said to be equal,** or $H = K,$ in case, in the notation of Definition I, we have $h_{ij} = k_{ij}.$

Note 1. If we know that H has m rows and n columns, with h_{ij} as the element in row i and column j, we may write merely $H = [h_{ij}]$ instead of, more fully,

$$H = [h_{ij}]_{i=1,2,\cdots,m; j=1,2,\cdots,n}. \tag{1}$$

In any symbol such as $H = [h_{pq}]$ for a matrix, we agree that the *first* subscript, p, indicates the *row*, and the *second* subscript, q, indicates the *column* where h_{pq} is situated in H.

If $H = [h_{ij}]$, we define $-H = [-h_{ij}]$. Then, by Definition I, $(H + (-H)) = $ **O.** The student may verify that the matrix equation $H + W = $ **O** is satisfied if and only if $W = -H$. The **difference** of two matrices H and K, and the terminology of **subtraction** for matrices, is defined as in Definition I on page 365, with the letters there representing matrices. Thus, the difference of H and K is $(H + (-K))$, and this is rewritten, by definition, as $(H - K)$.

With only negligible effort, the student may verify that Axioms I_1–I_5 of pages 362–3 are satisfied for the set S of all matrices of order $m \times n$, with x, y, and z of I_1–I_5 representing matrices. In this case, $-H$ is the *additive inverse* of H, and the *zero matrix,* **O,** is the *additive identity* element for S. Hence, by terminology at the bottom of page 366, S is a *group*, with *matrix addition* as the *group operation.* Since matrix addition is commutative, S is called a *commutative* group.* Thus, we have met three important commutative groups with an operation called *"addition"* as the group operation: the set R of all real numbers; the set C of all complex numbers, and the set S of all $m \times n$ matrices.

2. Multiplication of matrices by scalars. If r is a scalar, and H is any matrix of order $m \times n$, with general element h_{ij}, then rH is defined as the matrix of order $m \times n$ with the element rh_{ij} in row i and column j. If r and s are scalars, and H and K are of order $m \times n$, it is very easy to prove that the following results are true:

$$\left\{ \begin{array}{l} (1)(H) = H; \quad -H = (-1)(H); \quad (0)(H) = \mathbf{O}; \\ \qquad r\mathbf{O} = \mathbf{O}; \quad r(sH) = (rs)H; \\ (r+s)H = rH + sH; \quad r(H+K) = rH + rK. \end{array} \right\} \tag{1}$$

Let S be *any* set of elements (not necessarily matrices) for which a binary operation, called *addition*, is defined. Assume that, with respect to this operation, S is a *commutative group*. Also, suppose that, if r is a scalar, for any element H

---

* A commutative group also is called an **Abelian group,** thus named in honor of Niels Henrik Abel (see page 224).

in S the product rH is defined as an element of S in such a way that conditions (1) are satisfied. Then, S is referred to as a **vector space** over the field of numbers (complex numbers in (1)) to which r and s belong.

3. Row and column matrices. An $n \times 1$ matrix is called a **column matrix,** or a **column vector** of order n. A $1 \times m$ matrix is called a **row matrix,** or a **row vector** of order m.

Illustration 1. The matrix $[2 \quad -1 \quad 4]$ is a *row vector* of order 3. The matrix $\begin{bmatrix} -3 \\ 2 \end{bmatrix}$ is a *column vector* of order 2. We verify that

$$[a \quad b] + [c \quad d] = [(a + c) \quad (b + d)]. \tag{2}$$

Any row vector $[a \quad b]$ of order 2 can be represented by an *arrow* (or, a *vector*) from the origin in an xy-plane to the point $P:(a, b)$. Then, from (2), it can be verified that, if each row vector is represented as just specified, the sum of $[a \cdot b]$ and $[c \quad d]$ is represented by the diagonal of the parallelogram with the corresponding geometrical vectors $[a \quad b]$ and $[c \quad d]$ as adjacent sides. Thus, vectors in a plane can be studied by use of row (or column) matrices of order 2. Vectors in space of three dimensions can be studied by use of row (or column) matrices of order three. These facts account for the name *vector space* as met in Section 2.

4. Matrix multiplication. A system of three linear equations in three variables (x_1, x_2, x_3) can be abbreviated by

$$\sum_{j=1}^{3} a_{ij}x_j = b_i; \quad (i = 1, 2, 3). \tag{1}$$

Let $A = [a_{ij}]$, a 3×3 matrix; $X = \begin{bmatrix} x_1 \\ x_2 \\ x_3 \end{bmatrix}$ and $B = \begin{bmatrix} b_1 \\ b_2 \\ b_3 \end{bmatrix}$, which are column vectors. Then, we may abbreviate (1) by

$$AX = B, \tag{2}$$

where AX is the *"product"* of A and X as described below. This illustration shows that the apparently strange definition to be given for the product of two matrices is dictated by the most natural applications of matrices in connection with systems of linear equations.

DEFINITION II. *Let $A = [a_{ij}]$ be an $m \times n$ matrix and $B = [b_{jk}]$ be an $n \times t$ matrix. Then, the product AB is an $m \times t$ matrix whose element in row i and column k is $\sum_{j=1}^{n} a_{ij}b_{jk}$, or*

$$AB = \left[\sum_{j=1}^{n} a_{ij}b_{jk} \right]_{i=1,2,\cdots,m;\, k=1,2,\ldots,t}. \tag{3}$$

We remember (3) by stating that, to obtain the product AB, we multiply *"rows of A by columns of B."* Thus, in AB, the element in row i and column k is the sum of the products of the elements in *row i of A by corresponding elements in the kth column of B.*

Illustration 1. $\begin{bmatrix} 1 & -2 & 3 \\ 2 & 4 & -1 \end{bmatrix} \begin{bmatrix} 1 & 4 \\ -3 & 1 \\ 2 & 3 \end{bmatrix} = \begin{bmatrix} 13 & 11 \\ -12 & 9 \end{bmatrix}$, because

$$1(1) + (-2)(-3) + 3(2) = 13; \quad 1(4) - 2(1) + 3(3) = 11;$$
$$2(1) + 4(-3) + (-1)(2) = -12; \quad 2(4) + 4(1) + (-1)(3) = 9.$$

From this point on, we shall consider only the set of *all square matrices of a given order*, that is, the set of $n \times n$ matrices for some $n \geq 1$.

Illustration 2. Multiplication of matrices is *not commutative*. The student may prove this by showing that $AB \neq BA$ for the following A and B:

$$A = \begin{bmatrix} 1 & 3 \\ 2 & 5 \end{bmatrix}; \quad B = \begin{bmatrix} -1 & 4 \\ 2 & -1 \end{bmatrix}.$$

If $A = [a_{ij}]$, $B = [b_{ij}]$, and $C = [c_{ij}]$ are $n \times n$ matrices, it is found that

$$(AB)C = A(BC) \quad and \quad A(B + C) = AB + AC. \tag{4}$$

A student who has good appreciation of the sigma notation for sums should be able to verify (4), which shows that matrix multiplication (for $n \times n$ matrices) is *associative*, and *distributive with respect to matrix addition.*

A square matrix in which all elements not in the *main* (or, *principal*) *diagonal* are zero is called a **diagonal matrix.** Thus, $\begin{bmatrix} 4 & 0 \\ 0 & -3 \end{bmatrix}$ is a 2×2 diagonal matrix. Let I be the $n \times n$ diagonal matrix with 1 in each place in the main diagonal. Then, if A is any $n \times n$ matrix, it is simple to verify that $IA = AI = A$. The student should show that I is the only $n \times n$ matrix with this property. We call I the **multiplicative identity element** for the set of $n \times n$ matrices.

THEOREM I. *Let $A = [a_{ij}]$ be an $n \times n$ matrix for which $|A| \neq 0$, and let A_{ij} be the cofactor of a_{ij} in $|A|$. Let H be the $n \times n$ matrix whose element h_{ij} in row i and column j is defined as follows:*

$$h_{ij} = \frac{A_{ji}}{|A|}. \tag{5}$$

Then, $AH = HA = I$, where I is the unit diagonal $n \times n$ matrix.

Proof. (For the case $n = 3$.) We have

$$A = \begin{bmatrix} a_{11} & a_{12} & a_{13} \\ a_{21} & a_{22} & a_{23} \\ a_{31} & a_{32} & a_{33} \end{bmatrix}.$$

In H, the elements in the second column, for instance, are

$$h_{12} = \frac{A_{21}}{|A|}; \quad h_{22} = \frac{A_{22}}{|A|}; \quad h_{32} = \frac{A_{23}}{|A|}.$$

Hence, by Definition II, the element in row 2 and column 2 of AH is

$$\frac{a_{21}A_{21} + a_{22}A_{22} + a_{23}A_{23}}{|A|}. \tag{6}$$

The numerator in (6) is the expansion of $|A|$ by elements and cofactors of row 2 of A. Hence, (6) is equal to $|A|/|A|$, or 1. The element in row 1 and column 2 of AH is

$$(a_{11}A_{21} + a_{12}A_{22} + a_{13}A_{23})/|A|, \tag{7}$$

where the numerator could be obtained from that in (6) by replacing the elements of row 2 of A by row 1 of A. Hence, by Theorem III on page 279, the numerator in (7) is 0. Similarly, we find that each element in the main diagonal of AH is 1, and each element outside the main diagonal is zero. Hence, $AH = I$. Similarly, $HA = I$.

Hereafter, the matrix H found in Theorem I will be represented by A^{-1}, and will be called the **multiplicative inverse** of A. We read A^{-1} as "*A inverse.*" Because of (5), we may describe A^{-1} as follows: *First replace each element of A by the cofactor of that element in $|A|$. Then, take the* **transpose** *of the new matrix, and divide each element by $|A|$ to obtain A^{-1}.* We have

$$\boldsymbol{AA^{-1} = I} \quad and \quad \boldsymbol{A^{-1}A = I.} \tag{8}$$

THEOREM II. *If $|A| \neq 0$ and B is such that $AB = I$, then $B = A^{-1}$. If C is such that $CA = I$, then $C = A^{-1}$.*

Proof. Suppose that $I = AB$. Then,

$$A^{-1}I = A^{-1} = A^{-1}(AB) = (A^{-1}A)B = IB = B.$$

Similarly, we find that $C = A^{-1}$.

Let (x, y, z) in system (I) on page 280 be replaced by (x_1, x_2, x_3), and let the notation in (I) be changed to that in system (1) on page 388. Then, Theorem IV on page 280 states that, if $|A| \neq 0$, the solution of (1) is

$$x_1 = \frac{\sum_{i=1}^{3} b_i A_{i1}}{|A|}; \quad x_2 = \frac{\sum_{i=1}^{3} b_i A_{i2}}{|A|}; \quad x_3 = \frac{\sum_{i=1}^{3} b_i A_{i3}}{|A|}. \tag{9}$$

The numerators above were represented by $|K_1|$, $|K_2|$, and $|K_3|$ on page 280. On pages 280 and 281, we only proved that, **IF** system (1) has a solution, then it is given by (9). We are prepared, now, to prove that (9) *actually is a solution of* (1). Essentially, we shall give a completely new and exceedingly simple proof of Theorem IV on page 280.

Proof of (9). 1. In matrix form, we have seen that (1) becomes

$$AX = B, \tag{10}$$

where X and B are column matrices with elements (x_1, x_2, x_3) and (b_1, b_2, b_3), respectively. With the assumption that $|A| \neq 0$, the matrix A possesses the unique inverse A^{-1}. Hence, **IF** X satisfies (1), then

$$A^{-1}(AX) = A^{-1}B, \text{ or}$$
$$(A^{-1}A)X = IX = X = A^{-1}B, \text{ or} \tag{11}$$

$$\begin{bmatrix} x_1 \\ x_2 \\ x_3 \end{bmatrix} = \frac{1}{|A|} \begin{bmatrix} A_{11}b_1 + A_{21}b_2 + A_{31}b_3 \\ A_{12}b_1 + A_{22}b_2 + A_{32}b_3 \\ A_{13}b_1 + A_{23}b_2 + A_{33}b_3 \end{bmatrix}. \tag{12}$$

In (12), we have $X = A^{-1}B$. In writing (12), we used (5) to obtain

$$A^{-1} = \frac{1}{|A|} \begin{bmatrix} A_{11} & A_{21} & A_{31} \\ A_{12} & A_{22} & A_{32} \\ A_{13} & A_{23} & A_{33} \end{bmatrix}, \tag{13}$$

and then employed Definition II to write $A^{-1}B$. Hence, **IF** (1) has any solution, it is given by (12), which is the same as (9).

2. In order to prove that (9), or (12), actually is a solution, we substitute $X = A^{-1}B$ on the left in (10), and obtain

$$AX = A(A^{-1}B) = (AA^{-1})B = IB = B.$$

Hence, (9) *is* a solution, and therefore *is the only solution* of (1). This completes our proof of Theorem IV on page 280.

An $n \times n$ matrix A is said to be **nonsingular** in case $|A| \neq 0$. In Theorem I we proved that *each nonsingular matrix A has an inverse*, A^{-1}. In an advanced discussion of determinants, it is shown then that A^{-1} *is nonsingular*. Also, it is proved that, if A and B are nonsingular then AB is nonsingular. The set of all nonsingular matrices of a given order $n \times n$ has many interesting properties, which are discussed in texts on matrix theory.

EXERCISE 97

1. If S represents the set of all $m \times n$ matrices, for fixed m and n, prove that addition of matrices in S is associative and commutative. Perhaps first write the proof for the case of 3×2 matrices. Finally write the proof for any values of m and n, with the general notation of (1) in Section 1 on page 387 usually abbreviated.

2. Prove the results in (1) of Section 2 on page 387.

Obtain the indicated products.

3. $\begin{bmatrix} 3 & 1 \\ -2 & 4 \end{bmatrix} \begin{bmatrix} -1 & 3 \\ 2 & -1 \end{bmatrix}$.

4. $\begin{bmatrix} 1 & -2 \\ 5 & 0 \end{bmatrix} \begin{bmatrix} -3 & 4 \\ 2 & -1 \end{bmatrix}$.

5. $\begin{bmatrix} 3 & -1 & 2 \\ 0 & 2 & -1 \end{bmatrix} \begin{bmatrix} 2 & -1 \\ -3 & 2 \\ 4 & 2 \end{bmatrix}.$

6. $\begin{bmatrix} -2 & -4 & 1 \\ 3 & 5 & 2 \end{bmatrix} \begin{bmatrix} -2 & 1 \\ 3 & 2 \\ 0 & 4 \end{bmatrix}.$

7. $\begin{bmatrix} 3 & -2 \\ 4 & 1 \end{bmatrix} \begin{bmatrix} -1 \\ 5 \end{bmatrix}.$

8. $\begin{bmatrix} -2 & 1 \\ 3 & 2 \end{bmatrix} \begin{bmatrix} -2 \\ 3 \end{bmatrix}.$

9. $\begin{bmatrix} 3 & 4 \end{bmatrix} \begin{bmatrix} -2 & 2 \\ 3 & -1 \end{bmatrix}.$

10. $\begin{bmatrix} 2 & 2 & -1 \\ -1 & 3 & 2 \\ 3 & -1 & 4 \end{bmatrix} \begin{bmatrix} x_1 \\ x_2 \\ x_3 \end{bmatrix}.$

11. $\begin{bmatrix} -2 & 4 & 1 \\ 3 & 2 & 3 \\ -1 & 3 & 2 \end{bmatrix} \begin{bmatrix} x_1 \\ x_2 \\ x_3 \end{bmatrix}.$

12. If $B = \begin{bmatrix} b_{11} & b_{12} & b_{13} \\ b_{21} & b_{22} & b_{23} \\ b_{31} & b_{32} & b_{33} \end{bmatrix}$, $X = \begin{bmatrix} x_1 \\ x_2 \\ x_3 \end{bmatrix}$, and $D = \begin{bmatrix} d_1 \\ d_2 \\ d_3 \end{bmatrix}$,

obtain in usual form, without matrix notation, the system of equations in the variables (x_1, x_2, x_3) abbreviated by $BX = D$.

Obtain the multiplicative inverse of the matrix, if it is nonsingular.

13. $\begin{bmatrix} 3 & -2 \\ 1 & 4 \end{bmatrix}.$

14. $\begin{bmatrix} 2 & -4 \\ 3 & 1 \end{bmatrix}.$

15. $\begin{bmatrix} -2 & 2 \\ 3 & 5 \end{bmatrix}.$

16. $\begin{bmatrix} a & c \\ b & d \end{bmatrix}.$

17–19. The matrices of the determinants in Problems 2–4 on page 273.

20–25. Let A represent the matrix of coefficients of the variables in Problems 1–6, respectively, of Exercise 73 on page 267. First, obtain A^{-1} if A is nonsingular. Then, let B represent the column matrix (or, column vector) of order 3 whose elements are the right-hand sides of the equations, when they are written in the form (10) of page 391. Finally, obtain the solution for the problem by calculating $X = A^{-1}B$, where X is the column vector with elements (x, y, z).

Tables

I. SQUARES AND SQUARE ROOTS: 1—200

N	N²	√N	N	N²	√N	N	N²	√N	N	N²	√N
1	1	1.000	51	2,601	7.141	101	10,201	10.050	151	22,801	12.288
2	4	1.414	52	2,704	7.211	102	10,404	10.100	152	23,104	12.329
3	9	1.732	53	2,809	7.280	103	10,609	10.149	153	23,409	12.369
4	16	2.000	54	2,916	7.348	104	10,816	10.198	154	23,716	12.410
5	25	2.236	55	3,025	7.416	105	11,025	10.247	155	24,025	12.450
6	36	2.449	56	3,136	7.483	106	11,236	10.296	156	24,336	12.490
7	49	2.646	57	3,249	7.550	107	11,449	10.344	157	24,649	12.530
8	64	2.828	58	3,364	7.616	108	11,664	10.392	158	24,964	12.570
9	81	3.000	59	3,481	7.681	109	11,881	10.440	159	25,281	12.610
10	100	3.162	60	3,600	7.746	110	12,100	10.488	160	25,600	12.649
11	121	3.317	61	3,721	7.810	111	12,321	10.536	161	25,921	12.689
12	144	3.464	62	3,844	7.874	112	12,544	10.583	162	26,244	12.728
13	169	3.606	63	3,969	7.937	113	12,769	10.630	163	26,569	12.767
14	196	3.742	64	4,096	8.000	114	12,996	10.677	164	26,896	12.806
15	225	3.873	65	4,225	8.062	115	13,225	10.724	165	27,225	12.845
16	256	4.000	66	4,356	8.124	116	13,456	10.770	166	27,556	12.884
17	289	4.123	67	4,489	8.185	117	13,689	10.817	167	27,889	12.923
18	324	4.243	68	4,624	8.246	118	13,924	10.863	168	28,224	12.962
19	361	4.359	69	4,761	8.307	119	14,161	10.909	169	28,561	13.000
20	400	4.472	70	4,900	8.367	120	14,400	10.954	170	28,900	13.038
21	441	4.583	71	5,041	8.426	121	14,641	11.000	171	29,241	13.077
22	484	4.690	72	5,184	8.485	122	14,884	11.045	172	29,584	13.115
23	529	4.796	73	5,329	8.544	123	15,129	11.091	173	29,929	13.153
24	576	4.899	74	5,476	8.602	124	15,376	11.136	174	30,276	13.191
25	625	5.000	75	5,625	8.660	125	15,625	11.180	175	30,625	13.229
26	676	5.099	76	5,776	8.718	126	15,876	11.225	176	30,976	13.266
27	729	5.196	77	5,929	8.775	127	16,129	11.269	177	31,329	13.304
28	784	5.292	78	6,084	8.832	128	16,384	11.314	178	31,684	13.342
29	841	5.385	79	6,241	8.888	129	16,641	11.358	179	32,041	13.379
30	900	5.477	80	6,400	8.944	130	16,900	11.402	180	32,400	13.416
31	961	5.568	81	6,561	9.000	131	17,161	11.446	181	32,761	13.454
32	1,024	5.657	82	6,724	9.055	132	17,424	11.489	182	33,124	13.491
33	1,089	5.745	83	6,889	9.110	133	17,689	11.533	183	33,489	13.528
34	1,156	5.831	84	7,056	9.165	134	17,956	11.576	184	33,856	13.565
35	1,225	5.916	85	7,225	9.220	135	18,225	11.619	185	34,225	13.601
36	1,296	6.000	86	7,396	9.274	136	18,496	11.662	186	34,596	13.638
37	1,369	6.083	87	7,569	9.327	137	18,769	11.705	187	34,969	13.675
38	1,444	6.164	88	7,744	9.381	138	19,044	11.747	188	35,344	13.711
39	1,521	6.245	89	7,921	9.434	139	19,321	11.790	189	35,721	13.748
40	1,600	6.325	90	8,100	9.487	140	19,600	11.832	190	36,100	13.784
41	1,681	6.403	91	8,281	9.539	141	19,881	11.874	191	36,481	13.820
42	1,764	6.481	92	8,464	9.592	142	20,164	11.916	192	36,864	13.856
43	1,849	6.557	93	8,649	9.644	143	20,449	11.958	193	37,249	13.892
44	1,936	6.633	94	8,836	9.695	144	20,736	12.000	194	37,636	13.928
45	2,025	6.708	95	9,025	9.747	145	21,025	12.042	195	38,025	13.964
46	2,116	6.782	96	9,216	9.798	146	21,316	12.083	196	38,416	14.000
47	2,209	6.856	97	9,409	9.849	147	21,609	12.124	197	38,809	14.036
48	2,304	6.928	98	9,604	9.899	148	21,904	12.166	198	39,204	14.071
49	2,401	7.000	99	9,801	9.950	149	22,201	12.207	199	39,601	14.107
50	2,500	7.071	100	10,000	10.000	150	22,500	12.247	200	40,000	14.142
N	N²	√N	N	N²	√N	N	N²	√N	N	N²	√N

N	Log N	N	Log N
1.0	.000	5.5	.740
1.1	.041	5.6	.748
1.2	.079	5.7	.756
1.3	.114	5.8	.763
1.4	.146	5.9	.771
1.5	.176	6.0	.778
1.6	.204	6.1	.785
1.7	.230	6.2	.792
1.8	.255	6.3	.799
1.9	.279	6.4	.806
2.0	.301	6.5	.813
2.1	.322	6.6	.820
2.2	.342	6.7	.826
2.3	.362	6.8	.833
2.4	.380	6.9	.839
2.5	.398	7.0	.845
2.6	.415	7.1	.851
2.7	.431	7.2	.857
2.8	.447	7.3	.863
2.9	.462	7.4	.869
3.0	.477	7.5	.875
3.1	.491	7.6	.881
3.2	.505	7.7	.886
3.3	.519	7.8	.892
3.4	.531	7.9	.898
3.5	.544	8.0	.903
3.6	.556	8.1	.908
3.7	.568	8.2	.914
3.8	.580	8.3	.919
3.9	.591	8.4	.924
4.0	.602	8.5	.929
4.1	.613	8.6	.935
4.2	.623	8.7	.940
4.3	.633	8.8	.944
4.4	.643	8.9	.949
4.5	.653	9.0	.954
4.6	.663	9.1	.959
4.7	.672	9.2	.964
4.8	.681	9.3	.968
4.9	.690	9.4	.973
5.0	.699	9.5	.978
5.1	.708	9.6	.982
5.2	.716	9.7	.987
5.3	.724	9.8	.991
5.4	.732	9.9	.996
5.5	.740	1.00	1.000
N	Log N	N	Log N

→	L Sin *	L Tan *	L Cot	L Cos *	
0°	——	——	——	10.000	90°
1°	8.242	8.242	1.758	10.000	89°
2°	.543	.543	.457	10.000	88°
3°	.719	.719	.281	9.999	87°
4°	.844	.845	.155	.999	86°
5°	8.940	8.942	1.058	9.998	85°
6°	9.019	9.022	0.978	9.998	84°
7°	.086	.089	.911	.997	83°
8°	.144	.148	.852	.996	82°
9°	.194	.200	.800	.995	81°
10°	9.240	9.246	0.754	9.993	80°
11°	9.281	9.289	0.711	9.992	79°
12°	.318	.327	.673	.990	78°
13°	.352	.363	.637	.989	77°
14°	.384	.397	.603	.987	76°
15°	9.413	9.428	0.572	9.985	75°
16°	9.440	9.458	0.543	9.983	74°
17°	.466	.485	.515	.981	73°
18°	.490	.512	.488	.978	72°
19°	.513	.537	.463	.976	71°
20°	9.534	9.561	0.439	9.973	70°
21°	9.554	9.584	0.416	9.970	69°
22°	.574	.606	.394	.967	68°
23°	.592	.628	.372	.964	67°
24°	.609	.649	.351	.961	66°
25°	9.626	9.669	0.331	9.957	65°
26°	9.642	9.688	0.312	9.954	64°
27°	.657	.707	.293	.950	63°
28°	.672	.726	.274	.946	62°
29°	.686	.744	.256	.942	61°
30°	9.699	9.761	0.239	9.938	60°
31°	9.712	9.779	0.221	9.933	59°
32°	724	.796	.204	.928	58°
33°	.736	.813	.187	.924	57°
34°	.748	.829	.171	.919	56°
35°	9.759	9.845	0.155	9.913	55°
36°	9.769	9.861	0.139	9.908	54°
37°	.779	.877	.123	.902	53°
38°	.789	.893	.107	.897	52°
39°	.799	.908	.092	.891	51°
40°	9.808	9.924	0.076	9.884	50°
41°	9.817	9.939	0.061	9.878	49°
42°	.826	.954	.046	.871	48°
43°	.834	.970	.030	.864	47°
44°	.842	.985	.015	.857	46°
45°	9.849	10.000	0.000	9.849	45°
	L Cos *	L Cot *	L Tan	L Sin *	←

* Subtract 10 from each entry in this column.

IV. THREE-PLACE VALUES OF TRIGONOMETRIC FUNCTIONS
AND
DEGREES IN RADIAN MEASURE

Rad.	Deg.	Sin	Tan	Sec	Csc	Cot	Cos	Deg.	Rad.
.000	0°	.000	.000	1.000	——	——	1.000	90°	1.571
.017	1°	.017	.017	1.000	57.30	57.29	1.000	89°	1.553
.035	2°	.035	.035	1.001	28.65	28.64	0.999	88°	1.536
.052	3°	.052	.052	1.001	19.11	19.08	.999	87°	1.518
.070	4°	.070	.070	1.002	14.34	14.30	.998	86°	1.501
.087	5°	.087	.087	1.004	11.47	11.43	.996	85°	1.484
.105	6°	.105	.105	1.006	9.567	9.514	.995	84°	1.466
.122	7°	.122	.123	1.008	8.206	8.144	.993	83°	1.449
.140	8°	.139	.141	1.010	7.185	7.115	.990	82°	1.431
.157	9°	.156	.158	1.012	6.392	6.314	.988	81°	1.414
.175	10°	.174	.176	1.015	5.759	5.671	.985	80°	1.396
.192	11°	.191	.194	1.019	5.241	5.145	.982	79°	1.379
.209	12°	.208	.213	1.022	4.810	4.705	.978	78°	1.361
.227	13°	.225	.231	1.026	4.445	4.331	.974	77°	1.344
.244	14°	.242	.249	1.031	4.134	4.011	.970	76°	1.326
.262	15°	.259	.268	1.035	3.864	3.732	.966	75°	1.309
.279	16°	.276	.287	1.040	3.628	3.487	.961	74°	1.292
.297	17°	.292	.306	1.046	3.420	3.271	.956	73°	1.274
.314	18°	.309	.325	1.051	3.236	3.078	.951	72°	1.257
.332	19°	.326	.344	1.058	3.072	2.904	.946	71°	1.239
.349	20°	.342	.364	1.064	2.924	2.747	.940	70°	1.222
.367	21°	.358	.384	1.071	2.790	2.605	.934	69°	1.204
.384	22°	.375	.404	1.079	2.669	2.475	.927	68°	1.187
.401	23°	.391	.424	1.086	2.559	2.356	.921	67°	1.169
.419	24°	.407	.445	1.095	2.459	2.246	.914	66°	1.152
.436	25°	.423	.466	1.103	2.366	2.145	.906	65°	1.134
.454	26°	.438	.488	1.113	2.281	2.050	.899	64°	1.117
.471	27°	.454	.510	1.122	2.203	1.963	.891	63°	1.100
.489	28°	.469	.532	1.133	2.130	1.881	.883	62°	1.082
.506	29°	.485	.554	1.143	2.063	1.804	.875	61°	1.065
.524	30°	.500	.577	1.155	2.000	1.732	.866	60°	1.047
.541	31°	.515	.601	1.167	1.942	1.664	.857	59°	1.030
.559	32°	.530	.625	1.179	1.887	1.600	.848	58°	1.012
.576	33°	.545	.649	1.192	1.836	1.540	.839	57°	0.995
.593	34°	.559	.675	1.206	1.788	1.483	.829	56°	0.977
.611	35°	.574	.700	1.221	1.743	1.428	.819	55°	0.960
.628	36°	.588	.727	1.236	1.701	1.376	.809	54°	0.942
.646	37°	.602	.754	1.252	1.662	1.327	.799	53°	0.925
.663	38°	.616	.781	1.269	1.624	1.280	.788	52°	0.908
.681	39°	.629	.810	1.287	1.589	1.235	.777	51°	0.890
.698	40°	.643	.839	1.305	1.556	1.192	.766	50°	0.873
.716	41°	.656	.869	1.325	1.524	1.150	.755	49°	0.855
.733	42°	.669	.900	1.346	1.494	1.111	.743	48°	0.838
.750	43°	.682	.933	1.367	1.466	1.072	.731	47°	0.820
.768	44°	.695	0.966	1.390	1.440	1.036	.719	46°	0.803
.785	45°	.707	1.000	1.414	1.414	1.000	.707	45°	0.785
Rad.	Deg.	Cos	Cot	Csc	Sec	Tan	Sin	Deg.	Rad.

N	0	1	2	3	4	5	6	7	8	9
10	.0000	0043	0086	0128	0170	0212	0253	0294	0334	0374
11	.0414	0453	0492	0531	0569	0607	0645	0682	0719	0755
12	.0792	0828	0864	0899	0934	0969	1004	1038	1072	1106
13	.1139	1173	1206	1239	1271	1303	1335	1367	1399	1430
14	.1461	1492	1523	1553	1584	1614	1644	1673	1703	1732
15	.1761	1790	1818	1847	1875	1903	1931	1959	1987	2014
16	.2041	2068	2095	2122	2148	2175	2201	2227	2253	2279
17	.2304	2330	2355	2380	2405	2430	2455	2480	2504	2529
18	.2553	2577	2601	2625	2648	2672	2695	2718	2742	2765
19	.2788	2810	2833	2856	2878	2900	2923	2945	2967	2989
20	.3010	3032	3054	3075	3096	3118	3139	3160	3181	3201
21	.3222	3243	3263	3284	3304	3324	3345	3365	3385	3404
22	.3424	3444	3464	3483	3502	3522	3541	3560	3579	3598
23	.3617	3636	3655	3674	3692	3711	3729	3747	3766	3784
24	.3802	3820	3838	3856	3874	3892	3909	3927	3945	3962
25	.3979	3997	4014	4031	4048	4065	4082	4099	4116	4133
26	.4150	4166	4183	4200	4216	4232	4249	4265	4281	4298
27	.4314	4330	4346	4362	4378	4393	4409	4425	4440	4456
28	.4472	4487	4502	4518	4533	4548	4564	4579	4594	4609
29	.4624	4639	4654	4669	4683	4698	4713	4728	4742	4757
30	.4771	4786	4800	4814	4829	4843	4857	4871	4886	4900
31	.4914	4928	4942	4955	4969	4983	4997	5011	5024	5038
32	.5051	5065	5079	5092	5105	5119	5132	5145	5159	5172
33	.5185	5198	5211	5224	5237	5250	5263	5276	5289	5302
34	.5315	5328	5340	5353	5366	5378	5391	5403	5416	5428
35	.5441	5453	5465	5478	5490	5502	5514	5527	5539	5551
36	.5563	5575	5587	5599	5611	5623	5635	5647	5658	5670
37	.5682	5694	5705	5717	5729	5740	5752	5763	5775	5786
38	.5798	5809	5821	5832	5843	5855	5866	5877	5888	5899
39	.5911	5922	5933	5944	5955	5966	5977	5988	5999	6010
40	.6021	6031	6042	6053	6064	6075	6085	6096	6107	6117
41	.6128	6138	6149	6160	6170	6180	6191	6201	6212	6222
42	.6232	6243	6253	6263	6274	6284	6294	6304	6314	6325
43	.6335	6345	6355	6365	6375	6385	6395	6405	6415	6425
44	.6435	6444	6454	6464	6474	6484	6493	6503	6513	6522
45	.6532	6542	6551	6561	6571	6580	6590	6599	6609	6618
46	.6628	6637	6646	6656	6665	6675	6684	6693	6702	6712
47	.6721	6730	6739	6749	6758	6767	6776	6785	6794	6803
48	.6812	6821	6830	6839	6848	6857	6866	6875	6884	6893
49	.6902	6911	6920	6928	6937	6946	6955	6964	6972	6981
50	.6990	6998	7007	7016	7024	7033	7042	7050	7059	7067
N	0	1	2	3	4	5	6	7	8	9

Prop. Parts

	28	27	26
1	2.8	2.7	2.6
2	5.6	5.4	5.2
3	8.4	8.1	7.8
4	11.2	10.8	10.4
5	14.0	13.5	13.0
6	16.8	16.2	15.6
7	19.6	18.9	18.2
8	22.4	21.6	20.8
9	25.2	24.3	23.4

	22	21	20
1	2.2	2.1	2.0
2	4.4	4.2	4.0
3	6.6	6.3	6.0
4	8.8	8.4	8.0
5	11.0	10.5	10.0
6	13.2	12.6	12.0
7	15.4	14.7	14.0
8	17.6	16.8	16.0
9	19.8	18.9	18.0

	16	15	14
1	1.6	1.5	1.4
2	3.2	3.0	2.8
3	4.8	4.5	4.2
4	6.4	6.0	5.6
5	8.0	7.5	7.0
6	9.6	9.0	8.4
7	11.2	10.5	9.8
8	12.8	12.0	11.2
9	14.4	13.5	12.6

	13	12	11
1	1.3	1.2	1.1
2	2.6	2.4	2.2
3	3.9	3.6	3.3
4	5.2	4.8	4.4
5	6.5	6.0	5.5
6	7.8	7.2	6.6
7	9.1	8.4	7.7
8	10.4	9.6	8.8
9	11.7	10.8	9.9

	43	42	41	40	39		38	37	36	35	34		33	32	31	30	29	
1	4.3	4.2	4.1	4.0	3.9	1	3.8	3.7	3.6	3.5	3.4	1	3.3	3.2	3.1	3.0	2.9	1
2	8.6	8.4	8.2	8.0	7.8	2	7.6	7.4	7.2	7.0	6.8	2	6.6	6.4	6.2	6.0	5.8	2
3	12.9	12.6	12.3	12.0	11.7	3	11.4	11.1	10.8	10.5	10.2	3	9.9	9.6	9.3	9.0	8.7	3
4	17.2	16.8	16.4	16.0	15.6	4	15.2	14.8	14.4	14.0	13.6	4	13.2	12.8	12.4	12.0	11.6	4
5	21.5	21.0	20.5	20.0	19.5	5	19.0	18.5	18.0	17.5	17.0	5	16.5	16.0	15.5	15.0	14.5	5
6	25.8	25.2	24.6	24.0	23.4	6	22.8	22.2	21.6	21.0	20.4	6	19.8	19.2	18.6	18.0	17.4	6
7	30.1	29.4	28.7	28.0	27.3	7	26.6	25.9	25.2	24.5	23.8	7	23.1	22.4	21.7	21.0	20.3	7
8	34.4	33.6	32.8	32.0	31.2	8	30.4	29.6	28.8	28.0	27.2	8	26.4	25.6	24.8	24.0	23.2	8
9	38.7	37.8	36.9	36.0	35.1	9	34.2	33.3	32.4	31.5	30.6	9	29.7	28.8	27.9	27.0	26.1	9

Prop. Parts	N	0	1	2	3	4	5	6	7	8	9
	50	.6990	6998	7007	7016	7024	7033	7042	7050	7059	7067
	51	.7076	7084	7093	7101	7110	7118	7126	7135	7143	7152
	52	.7160	7168	7177	7185	7193	7202	7210	7218	7226	7235
	53	.7243	7251	7259	7267	7275	7284	7292	7300	7308	7316
	54	.7324	7332	7340	7348	7356	7364	7372	7380	7388	7396
	55	.7404	7412	7419	7427	7435	7443	7451	7459	7466	7474
	56	.7482	7490	7497	7505	7513	7520	7528	7536	7543	7551
	57	.7559	7566	7574	7582	7589	7597	7604	7612	7619	7627
	58	.7634	7642	7649	7657	7664	7672	7679	7686	7694	7701
	59	.7709	7716	7723	7731	7738	7745	7752	7760	7767	7774
	60	.7782	7789	7796	7803	7810	7818	7825	7832	7839	7846
	61	.7853	7860	7868	7875	7882	7889	7896	7903	7910	7917
	62	.7924	7931	7938	7945	7952	7959	7966	7973	7980	7987
	63	.7993	8000	8007	8014	8021	8028	8035	8041	8048	8055
	64	.8062	8069	8075	8082	8089	8096	8102	8109	8116	8122
	65	.8129	8136	8142	8149	8156	8162	8169	8176	8182	8189
	66	.8195	8202	8209	8215	8222	8228	8235	8241	8248	8254
	67	.8261	8267	8274	8280	8287	8293	8299	8306	8312	8319
	68	.8325	8331	8338	8344	8351	8357	8363	8370	8376	8382
	69	.8388	8395	8401	8407	8414	8420	8426	8432	8439	8445
	70	.8451	8457	8463	8470	8476	8482	8488	8494	8500	8506
	71	.8513	8519	8525	8531	8537	8543	8549	8555	8561	8567
	72	.8573	8579	8585	8591	8597	8603	8609	8615	8621	8627
	73	.8633	8639	8645	8651	8657	8663	8669	8675	8681	8686
	74	.8692	8698	8704	8710	8716	8722	8727	8733	8739	8745
	75	.8751	8756	8762	8768	8774	8779	8785	8791	8797	8802
	76	.8808	8814	8820	8825	8831	8837	8842	8848	8854	8859
	77	.8865	8871	8876	8882	8887	8893	8899	8904	8910	8915
	78	.8921	8927	8932	8938	8943	8949	8954	8960	8965	8971
	79	.8976	8982	8987	8993	8998	9004	9009	9015	9020	9025
	80	.9031	9036	9042	9047	9053	9058	9063	9069	9074	9079
	81	.9085	9090	9096	9101	9106	9112	9117	9122	9128	9133
	82	.9138	9143	9149	9154	9159	9165	9170	9175	9180	9186
	83	.9191	9196	9201	9206	9212	9217	9222	9227	9232	9238
	84	.9243	9248	9253	9258	9263	9269	9274	9279	9284	9289
	85	.9294	9299	9304	9309	9315	9320	9325	9330	9335	9340
	86	.9345	9350	9355	9360	9365	9370	9375	9380	9385	9390
	87	.9395	9400	9405	9410	9415	9420	9425	9430	9435	9440
	88	.9445	9450	9455	9460	9465	9469	9474	9479	9484	9489
	89	.9494	9499	9504	9509	9513	9518	9523	9528	9533	9538
	90	.9542	9547	9552	9557	9562	9566	9571	9576	9581	9586
	91	.9590	9595	9600	9605	9609	9614	9619	9624	9628	9633
	92	.9638	9643	9647	9652	9657	9661	9666	9671	9675	9680
	93	.9685	9689	9694	9699	9703	9708	9713	9717	9722	9727
	94	.9731	9736	9741	9745	9750	9754	9759	9763	9768	9773
	95	.9777	9782	9786	9791	9795	9800	9805	9809	9814	9818
	96	.9823	9827	9832	9836	9841	9845	9850	9854	9859	9863
	97	.9868	9872	9877	9881	9886	9890	9894	9899	9903	9908
	98	.9912	9917	9921	9926	9930	9934	9939	9943	9948	9952
	99	.9956	9961	9965	9969	9974	9978	9983	9987	9991	9996
	N	0	1	2	3	4	5	6	7	8	9

Prop. Parts

	25	24	23
1	2.5	2.4	2.3
2	5.0	4.8	4.6
3	7.5	7.2	6.9
4	10.0	9.6	9.2
5	12.5	12.0	11.5
6	15.0	14.4	13.8
7	17.5	16.8	16.1
8	20.0	19.2	18.4
9	22.5	21.6	20.7

	19	18	17
1	1.9	1.8	1.7
2	3.8	3.6	3.4
3	5.7	5.4	5.1
4	7.6	7.2	6.8
5	9.5	9.0	8.5
6	11.4	10.8	10.2
7	13.3	12.6	11.9
8	15.2	14.4	13.6
9	17.1	16.2	15.3

	10	9
1	1.0	0.9
2	2.0	1.8
3	3.0	2.7
4	4.0	3.6
5	5.0	4.5
6	6.0	5.4
7	7.0	6.3
8	8.0	7.2
9	9.0	8.1

	8	7
1	0.8	0.7
2	1.6	1.4
3	2.4	2.1
4	3.2	2.8
5	4.0	3.5
6	4.8	4.2
7	5.6	4.9
8	6.4	5.6
9	7.2	6.3

	6	5	4
1	0.6	0.5	0.4
2	1.2	1.0	0.8
3	1.8	1.5	1.2
4	2.4	2.0	1.6
5	3.0	2.5	2.0
6	3.6	3.0	2 4
7	4.2	3.5	2.8
8	4.8	4.0	3.2
9	5.4	4.5	3.6

α Rad.	Degrees in α	Sin α	Cos α	Tan α	α Rad.	Degrees in α	Sin α	Cos α	Tan α
.00	0° 00.0′	.00000	1.0000	.00000	.60	34° 22.6′	.56464	.82534	.68414
.01	0° 34.4′	.01000	.99995	.01000	.61	34° 57.0′	.57287	.81965	.69892
.02	1° 08.8′	.02000	.99980	.02000	.62	35° 31.4′	.58104	.81388	.71391
.03	1° 43.1′	.03000	.99955	.03001	.63	36° 05.8′	.58914	.80803	.72911
.04	2° 17.5′	.03999	.99920	.04002	.64	36° 40.2′	.59720	.80210	.74454
.05	2° 51.9′	.04998	.99875	.05004	.65	37° 14.5′	.60519	.79608	.76020
.06	3° 26.3′	.05996	.99820	.06007	.66	37° 48.9′	.61312	.78999	.77610
.07	4° 00.6′	.06994	.99755	.07011	.67	38° 23.3′	.62099	.78382	.79225
.08	4° 35.0′	.07991	.99680	.08017	.68	38° 57.7′	.62879	.77757	.80866
.09	5° 09.4′	.08988	.99595	.09024	.69	39° 32.0′	.63654	.77125	.82534
.10	5° 43.8′	.09983	.99500	.10033	.70	40° 06.4′	.64422	.76484	.84229
.11	6° 18.2′	.10978	.99396	.11045	.71	40° 40.8′	.65183	.75836	.85953
.12	6° 52.5′	.11971	.99281	.12058	.72	41° 15.2′	.65938	.75181	.87707
.13	7° 26.9′	.12963	.99156	.13074	.73	41° 49.6′	.66687	.74517	.89492
.14	8° 01.3′	.13954	.99022	.14092	.74	42° 23.9′	.67429	.73847	.91309
.15	8° 35.7′	.14944	.98877	.15114	.75	42° 58.3′	.68164	.73169	.93160
.16	9° 10.0′	.15932	.98723	.16138	.76	43° 32.7′	.68892	.72484	.95045
.17	9° 44.4′	.16918	.98558	.17166	.77	44° 07.1′	.69614	.71791	.96967
.18	10° 18.8′	.17903	.98384	.18197	.78	44° 41.4′	.70328	.71091	.98926
.19	10° 53.2′	.18886	.98200	.19232	.79	45° 15.8′	.71035	.70385	1.0092
.20	11° 27.5′	.19867	.98007	.20271	.80	45° 50.2′	.71736	.69671	1.0296
.21	12° 01.9′	.20846	.97803	.21314	.81	46° 24.6′	.72429	.68950	1.0505
.22	12° 36.3′	.21823	.97590	.22362	.82	46° 59.0′	.73115	.68222	1.0717
.23	13° 10.7′	.22798	.97367	.23414	.83	47° 33.3′	.73793	.67488	1.0934
.24	13° 45.1′	.23770	.97134	.24472	.84	48° 07.7′	.74464	.66746	1.1156
.25	14° 19.4′	.24740	.96891	.25534	.85	48° 42.1′	.75128	.65998	1.1383
.26	14° 53.8′	.25708	.96639	.26602	.86	49° 16.5′	.75784	.65244	1.1616
.27	15° 28.2′	.26673	.96377	.27676	.87	49° 50.8′	.76433	.64483	1.1853
.28	16° 02.6′	.27636	.96106	.28755	.88	50° 25.2′	.77074	.63715	1.2097
.29	16° 36.9′	.28595	.95824	.29841	.89	50° 59.6′	.77707	.62941	1.2346
.30	17° 11.3′	.29552	.95534	.30934	.90	51° 34.0′	.78333	.62161	1.2602
.31	17° 45.7′	.30506	.95233	.32033	.91	52° 08.3′	.78950	.61375	1.2864
.32	18° 20.1′	.31457	.94924	.33139	.92	52° 42.7′	.79560	.60582	1.3133
.33	18° 54.5′	.32404	.94604	.34252	.93	53° 17.1′	.80162	.59783	1.3409
.34	19° 28.8′	.33349	.94275	.35374	.94	53° 51.5′	.80756	.58979	1.3692
.35	20° 03.2′	.34290	.93937	.36503	.95	54° 25.9′	.81342	.58168	1.3984
.36	20° 37.6′	.35227	.93590	.37640	.96	55° 00.2′	.81919	.57352	1.4284
.37	21° 12.0′	.36162	.93233	.38786	.97	55° 34.6′	.82489	.56530	1.4592
.38	21° 46.3′	.37092	.92866	.39941	.98	56° 09.0′	.83050	.55702	1.4910
.39	22° 20.7′	.38019	.92491	.41105	.99	56° 43.4′	.83603	.54869	1.5237
.40	22° 55.1′	.38942	.92106	.42279	1.00	57° 17.7′	.84147	.54030	1.5574
.41	23° 29.5′	.39861	.91712	.43463	1.01	57° 52.1′	.84683	.53186	1.5922
.42	24° 03.9′	.40776	.91309	.44657	1.02	58° 26.5′	.85211	.52337	1.6281
.43	24° 38.2′	.41687	.90897	.45862	1.03	59° 00.9′	.85730	.51482	1.6652
.44	25° 12.6′	.42594	.90475	.47078	1.04	59° 35.3′	.86240	.50622	1.7036
.45	25° 47.0′	.43497	.90045	.48306	1.05	60° 09.6′	.86742	.49757	1.7433
.46	26° 21.4′	.44395	.89605	.49545	1.06	60° 44.0′	.87236	.48887	1.7844
.47	26° 55.7′	.45289	.89157	.50797	1.07	61° 18.4′	.87720	.48012	1.8270
.48	27° 30.1′	.46178	.88699	.52061	1.08	61° 52.8′	.88196	.47133	1.8712
.49	28° 04.5′	.47063	.88233	.53339	1.09	62° 27.1′	.88663	.46249	1.9171
.50	28° 38.9′	.47943	.87758	.54630	1.10	63° 01.5′	.89121	.45360	1.9648
.51	29° 13.3′	.48818	.87274	.55936	1.11	63° 35.9′	.89570	.44466	2.0143
.52	29° 47.6′	.49688	.86782	.57256	1.12	64° 10.3′	.90010	.43568	2.0660
.53	30° 22.0′	.50553	.86281	.58592	1.13	64° 44.7′	.90441	.42666	2.1198
.54	30° 56.4′	.51414	.85771	.59943	1.14	65° 19.0′	.90863	.41759	2.1759
.55	31° 30.8′	.52269	.85252	.61311	1.15	65° 53.4′	.91276	.40849	2.2345
.56	32° 05.1′	.53119	.84726	.62695	1.16	66° 27.8′	.91680	.39934	2.2958
.57	32° 39.5′	.53963	.84190	.64097	1.17	67° 02.2′	.92075	.39015	2.3600
.58	33° 13.9′	.54802	.83646	.65517	1.18	67° 36.5′	.92461	.38092	2.4273
.59	33° 48.3′	.55636	.83094	.66956	1.19	68° 10.9′	.92837	.37166	2.4979
.60	34° 22.6′	.56464	.82534	.68414	1.20	68° 45.3′	.93204	.36236	2.5722

VI. RADIAN MEASURE: VALUES OF FUNCTIONS

α Rad.	Degrees in α	Sin α	Cos α	Tan α
1.20	68° 45.3′	.93204	.36236	2.5722
1.21	69° 19.7′	.93562	.35302	2.6503
1.22	69° 54.1′	93910	.34365	2.7328
1.23	70° 28.4′	.94249	.33424	2.8198
1.24	71° 02.8′	.94578	.32480	2.9119
1.25	71° 37.2′	.94898	.31532	3.0096
1.26	72° 11.6′	.95209	.30582	3.1133
1.27	72° 45.9′	.95510	.29628	3.2236
1.28	73° 20.3′	.95802	.28672	3.3413
1.29	73° 54.7′	.96084	.27712	3.4672
1.30	74° 29.1′	.96356	.26750	3.6021
1.31	75° 03.4′	.96618	.25785	3.7471
1.32	75° 37.8′	.96872	.24818	3.9033
1.33	76° 12.2′	.97115	.23848	4.0723
1.34	76° 46.6′	.97348	.22875	4.2556
1.35	77° 21.0′	.97572	.21901	4.4552
1.36	77° 55.3′	.97786	.20924	4.6734
1.37	78° 29.7′	.97991	.19945	4.9131
1.38	79° 04.1′	.98185	.18964	5.1774
1.39	79° 38.5′	.98370	.17981	5.4707
1.40	80° 12.8′	.98545	.16997	5.7979

α Rad.	Degrees in α	Sin α	Cos α	Tan α
1.40	80° 12.8′	.98545	.16997	5.7979
1.41	80° 47.2′	.98710	.16010	6.1654
1.42	81° 21.6′	.98865	.15023	6.5811
1.43	81° 56.0′	.99010	.14033	7.0555
1.44	82° 30.4′	.99146	.13042	7.6018
1.45	83° 04.7′	.99271	.12050	8.2381
1.46	83° 39.1′	.99387	.11057	8.9886
1.47	84° 13.5′	.99492	.10063	9.8874
1.48	84° 47.9′	.99588	.09067	10.983
1.49	85° 22.2′	.99674	.08071	12.350
1.50	85° 56.6′	.99749	.07074	14.101
1.51	86° 31.0′	.99815	.06076	16.428
1.52	87° 05.4′	.99871	.05077	19.670
1.53	87° 39.8′	.99917	.04079	24.498
1.54	88° 14.1′	.99953	.03079	32.461
1.55	88° 48.5′	.99978	.02079	48.078
1.56	89° 22.9′	.99994	.01080	92.620
1.57	89° 57.3′	1.0000	.00080	1255.8
1.58	90° 31.6′	.99996	− .00920	− 108.65
1.59	91° 06.0′	.99982	− .01920	− 52.067
1.60	91° 40.4′	.99957	− .02920	− 34.233

DEGREES IN RADIANS

1°	0.01745	16°	0.27925	31°	0.54105	46°	0.80285	61°	1.06465	76°	1.32645
2	0.03491	17	0.29671	32	0.55851	47	0.82030	62	1.08210	77	1.34390
3	0.05236	18	0.31416	33	0.57596	48	0.83776	63	1.09956	78	1.36136
4	0.06981	19	0.33161	34	0.59341	49	0.85521	64	1.11701	79	1.37881
5	0.08727	**20**	0.34907	**35**	0.61087	**50**	0.87266	**65**	1.13446	**80**	1.39626
6	0.10472	21	0.36652	36	0.62832	51	0.89012	66	1.15192	81	1.41372
7	0.12217	22	0.38397	37	0.64577	52	0.90757	67	1.16937	82	1.43117
8	0.13963	23	0.40143	38	0.66323	53	0.92502	68	1.18682	83	1.44862
9	0.15708	24	0.41888	39	0.68068	54	0.94248	69	1.20428	84	1.46608
10	0.17453	**25**	0.43633	**40**	0.69813	**55**	0.95993	**70**	1.22173	**85**	1.48353
11	0.19199	26	0.45379	41	0.71558	56	0.97738	71	1.23918	86	1.50098
12	0.20944	27	0.47124	42	0.73304	57	0.99484	72	1.25664	87	1.51844
13	0.22689	28	0.48869	43	0.75049	58	1.01229	73	1.27409	88	1.53589
14	0.24435	29	0.50615	44	0.76794	59	1.02974	74	1.29154	89	1.55334
15	0.26180	**30**	0.52360	**45**	0.78540	**60**	1.04720	**75**	1.30900	**90**	1.57080

$$1° = .01745329 \text{ rad.} \qquad \log .01745329 = 8.24187737 - 10.$$
$$1′ = .0002908882 \text{ rad.} \qquad \log .0002908882 = 6.46372612 - 10.$$
$$1″ = .0000048481368 \text{ rad.} \qquad \log .0000048481368 = 4.68557487 - 10.$$

MINUTES IN RADIANS

1′	0.00029	11′	0.00320	21′	0.00611	31′	0.00902	41′	0.01193	51′	0.01484
2	0.00058	12	0.00349	22	0.00640	32	0.00931	42	0.01222	52	0.01513
3	0.00087	13	0.00378	23	0.00669	33	0.00960	43	0.01251	53	0.01542
4	0.00116	14	0.00407	24	0.00698	34	0.00989	44	0.01280	54	0.01571
5	0.00145	15	0.00436	**25**	0.00727	**35**	0.01018	**45**	0.01309	**55**	0.01600
6	0.00175	16	0.00465	26	0.00756	36	0.01047	46	0.01338	56	0.01629
7	0.00204	17	0.00495	27	0.00785	37	0.01076	47	0.01367	57	0.01658
8	0.00233	18	0.00524	28	0.00814	38	0.01105	48	0.01396	58	0.01687
9	0.00262	19	0.00553	29	0.00844	39	0.01134	49	0.01425	59	0.01716
10	0.00291	**20**	0.00582	**30**	0.00873	**40**	0.01164	**50**	0.01454	**60**	0.01745

VII. COMMISSIONERS 1941 STANDARD ORDINARY MORTALITY TABLE

Age	Number Living l_x	Number Dying d_x	Rate of Mortality q_x	Age	Number Living l_x	Number Dying d_x	Rate of Mortality q_x
0	1,023,102	23,102	.02258	50	810,900	9,990	.01232
1	1,000,000	5,770	.00577	51	800,910	10,628	.01327
2	994,230	4,116	.00414	52	790,282	11,301	.01430
3	990,114	3,347	.00338	53	778,981	12,020	.01543
4	986,767	2,950	.00299	54	766,961	12,770	.01665
5	983,817	2,715	.00276	55	754,191	13,560	.01798
6	981,102	2,561	.00261	56	740,631	14,390	.01943
7	978,541	2,417	.00247	57	726,241	15,251	.02100
8	976,124	2,255	.00231	58	710,990	16,147	.02271
9	973,869	2,065	.00212	59	694,843	17,072	.02457
10	971,804	1,914	.00197	60	677,771	18,022	.02659
11	969,890	1,852	.00191	61	659,749	18,988	.02878
12	968,038	1,859	.00192	62	640,761	19,979	.03118
13	966,179	1,913	.00198	63	620,782	20,958	.03376
14	964,266	1,996	.00207	64	599,824	21,942	.03658
15	962,270	2,069	.00215	65	577,882	22,907	.03964
16	960,201	2,103	.00219	66	554,975	23,842	.04296
17	958,098	2,156	.00225	67	531,133	24,730	.04656
18	955,942	2,199	.00230	68	506,403	25,553	.05046
19	953,743	2,260	.00237	69	480,850	26,302	.05470
20	951,483	2,312	.00243	70	454,548	26,955	.05930
21	949,171	2,382	.00251	71	427,593	27,481	.06427
22	946,789	2,452	.00259	72	400,112	27,872	.06966
23	944,337	2,531	.00268	73	372,240	28,104	.07550
24	941,806	2,609	.00277	74	344,136	28,154	.08181
25	939,197	2,705	.00288	75	315,982	28,009	.08864
26	936,492	2,800	.00299	76	287,973	27,651	.09602
27	933,692	2,904	.00311	77	260,322	27,071	.10399
28	930,788	3,025	.00325	78	233,251	26,262	.11259
29	927,763	3,154	.00340	79	206,989	25,224	.12186
30	924,609	3,292	.00356	80	181,765	23,966	.13185
31	921,317	3,437	.00373	81	157,799	22,502	.14260
32	917,880	3,598	.00392	82	135,297	20,857	.15416
33	914,282	3,767	.00412	83	114,440	19,062	.16657
34	910,515	3,961	.00435	84	95,378	17,157	.17988
35	906,554	4,161	.00459	85	78,221	15,185	.19413
36	902,393	4,386	.00486	86	63,036	13,198	.20937
37	898,007	4,625	.00515	87	49,838	11,245	.22563
38	893,382	4,878	.00546	88	38,593	9,378	.24300
39	888,504	5,162	.00581	89	29,215	7,638	.26144
40	883,342	5,459	.00618	90	21,577	6,063	.28099
41	877,883	5,785	.00659	91	15,514	4,681	.30173
42	872,098	6,131	.00703	92	10,833	3,506	.32364
43	865,967	6,503	.00751	93	7,327	2,540	.34666
44	859,464	6,910	.00804	94	4,787	1,776	.37100
45	852,554	7,340	.00861	95	3,011	1,193	.39621
46	845,214	7,801	.00923	96	1,818	813	.44719
47	837,413	8,299	.00991	97	1,005	551	.54826
48	829,114	8,822	.01064	98	454	329	.72467
49	820,292	9,392	.01145	99	125	125	1.00000

VIII. VALUES OF e^x

x	e^x	x	e^x	x	e^x	x	e^x
0.00	1.0000	0.45	1.5683	.90	2.4596	2.75	15.643
.01	1.0101	.46	1.5841	.91	2.4843	2.80	16.445
.02	1.0202	.47	1.6000	.92	2.5093	2.85	17.288
.03	1.0305	.48	1.6161	.93	2.5345	2.90	18.174
.04	1.0408	.49	1.6323	.94	2.5600	2.95	19.106
.05	1.0513	.50	1.6487	.95	2.5857	3.00	20.086
.06	1.0618	.51	1.6653	.96	2.6117	3.05	21.115
.07	1.0725	.52	1.6820	.97	2.6379	3.10	22.198
.08	1.0833	.53	1.6989	.98	2.6645	3.15	23.336
.09	1.0942	.54	1.7160	.99	2.6912	3.20	24.533
.10	1.1052	.55	1.7333	1.00	2.7183	3.25	25.790
.11	1.1163	.56	1.7507	1.05	2.8577	3.30	27.113
.12	1.1275	.57	1.7683	1.10	3.0042	3.35	28.503
.13	1.1388	.58	1.7860	1.15	3.1582	3.40	29.964
.14	1.1503	.59	1.8040	1.20	3.3201	3.45	31.500
.15	1.1618	.60	1.8221	1.25	3.4903	3.50	33.115
.16	1.1735	.61	1.8404	1.30	3.6693	3.55	34.813
.17	1.1853	.62	1.8589	1.35	3.8574	3.60	36.598
.18	1.1972	.63	1.8776	1.40	4.0552	3.65	38.475
.19	1.2092	.64	1.8965	1.45	4.2631	3.70	40.447
.20	1.2214	.65	1.9155	1.50	4.4817	3.75	42.521
.21	1.2337	.66	1.9348	1.55	4.7115	3.80	44.701
.22	1.2461	.67	1.9542	1.60	4.9530	3.85	46.993
.23	1.2586	.68	1.9739	1.65	5.2070	3.90	49.402
.24	1.2712	.69	1.9937	1.70	5.4739	3.95	51.935
.25	1.2840	.70	2.0138	1.75	5.7546	4.00	54.598
.26	1.2969	.71	2.0340	1.80	6.0496	4.10	60.340
.27	1.3100	.72	2.0544	1.85	6.3598	4.20	66.686
.28	1.3231	.73	2.0751	1.90	6.6859	4.30	73.700
.29	1.3364	.74	2.0959	1.95	7.0287	4.40	81.451
.30	1.3499	.75	2.1170	2.00	7.3891	4.50	90.017
.31	1.3634	.76	2.1383	2.05	7.7679	4.60	99.484
.32	1.3771	.77	2.1598	2.10	8.1662	4.70	109.95
.33	1.3910	.78	2.1815	2.15	8.5849	4.80	121.51
.34	1.4049	.79	2.2034	2.20	9.0250	4.90	134.29
.35	1.4191	.80	2.2255	2.25	9.4877	5.00	148.41
.36	1.4333	.81	2.2479	2.30	9.9742	5.20	181.27
.37	1.4477	.82	2.2705	2.35	10.486	5.40	221.41
.38	1.4623	.83	2.2933	2.40	11.023	5.60	270.43
.39	1.4770	.84	2.3164	2.45	11.588	5.80	330.30
.40	1.4918	.85	2.3396	2.50	12.182	6.00	403.43
.41	1.5068	.86	2.3632	2.55	12.807	7.00	1096.6
.42	1.5220	.87	2.3869	2.60	13.464	8.00	2981.0
.43	1.5373	.88	2.4109	2.65	14.154	9.00	8103.1
.44	1.5527	.89	2.4351	2.70	14.880	10.00	22026.

Answers to Exercises

Note. Answers to most of the odd-numbered problems are given here. Answers to even-numbered problems are furnished in a separate pamphlet, when ordered by the instructor.

Exercise 1. Page 16

1. 5. **3.** 168. **5.** $-2a + 5b - c$. **7.** $-5x$. **9.** $-2a + 3$. **11.** $4y - 12$.
13. $2a - 3 - (c - 5b)$. **15.** 17; 46; $\frac{3}{4}$; 1.48. **17.** -7; 4; $\frac{2}{3}$; 8; 0. **29.** .5.
31. .3125. **33.** .$\dot{3}0\dot{7}6\dot{9}\dot{2}$. **35.** $-\frac{4}{7}$. **37.** 3. **39.** $\frac{45}{7}$. **41.** $\frac{21}{8}$. **43.** $\frac{35}{4}$. **45.** $3a/2$.
47. $5d$. **49.** $7/15a$. **51.** $\frac{3}{2}$. **53.** $-10/9d$. **55.** $-x/4$. **57.** $\frac{7}{25}$. **59.** $2/9d$.
61. $\frac{35}{4}$. **63.** $5c/3$. **65.** $2/5b$. **67.** $8/5dk$.

Exercise 2. Page 24

1. 1. **3.** $\frac{1}{81}$. **5.** $\frac{81}{256}$. **7.** $1,000,000,000,000$. **9.** 144. **11.** a^9. **13.** u^8. **15.** a^6x^3.
17. $h^5/32$. **19.** x^4/y^6. **21.** y^2. **23.** $1/x^3$. **25.** a^2/b. **27.** 1. **29.** $8x^2y^3$.
31. $-8h^5r^3$. **33.** $6 - x^2 - 15x^4$. **35.** $6 - 5x - 6x^2 - x^3$. **37.** $x^{3n} - 27y^{3k}$.
39. ± 11. **41.** ± 10. **43.** $\frac{7}{8}$. **45.** $7z^3$. **47.** $8/w^3$. **49.** $9a/y^2z$.

51. $37x$; $142a^5$; $659z^3$. **53.** $\dfrac{1}{6xy} - \dfrac{1}{2x^2y^3} + \dfrac{1}{3xy^2}$. **55.** $2x^2 - 3x + 5$.

57. $x^3 - x^2 - 4$. **59.** $h^2 + 2hk + k^2$. **61.** $a^2 - 9x^2$. **63.** $24 - 5x - x^2$.
65. $9 - 9r - 10r^2$. **67.** $9x^2 - 30x + 25$. **69.** $9x^2 + 6xy^3 + y^6$.
71. $4x^2 + 4x^3 + x^4$. **73.** $x^8 - 16y^4$. **75.** $4 + 4a + 4b + a^2 + 2ab + b^2$.
77. $a^2 + 2aw + w^2 - 16$. **79.** $x^2 + y^2 + z^2 + 2xy + 2yz + 2xz$.
81. $\{1\}$, $\{2\}$, $\{3\}$, $\{4\}$, $\{1, 2\}$, etc., $\{2, 3, 4\}$, etc., but not $\{1, 2, 3, 4\}$.

Exercise 3. Page 28

1. $x(b - a)$. **3.** $t(t - 4a - ct^2)$. **5.** $(1 - 5x)(1 + 5x)$. **7.** $(\frac{1}{3} - w)(\frac{1}{3} + w)$.
9. $4(3ab - 4x)(3ab + 4x)$. **11.** $(a + 2)^2$. **13.** $(d + y)^2$. **15.** $(a - 7b)^2$.
17. $(4 - y)(3 - y)$. **19.** $(9 - w)(3 + w)$. **21.** $(8 + a)(2 - a)$.
23. $(3a + 5)(a + 1)$. **25.** $(5a + 9b)(a + b)$. **27.** $(3x + 2y)(x + y)$.
29. $x^2(4x - 3)(2x - 1)$. **31.** $(w - z)(3h - 1)$. **33.** $4(h - 2c)(x - b)$.
35. $(x - 1)(x + 1)(x - 2)$. **37.** $2c(2a - 3c)(2a + 3c)$.
39. $(9c^2 + 4d^2)(3c - 2d)(3c + 2d)$. **41.** $(y + z - 2x)(y + z + 2x)$.
43. $(3w + 2a + b)(3w - 2a - b)$. **45.** $(z + 10)(z^2 - 10z + 100)$.
47. $(6x - yz)(36x^2 + 6xyz + y^2z^2)$. **49.** $(2x - 5y)(4x^2 + 10xy + 25y^2)$.
51. $(x - 7y)(x^2 + 7xy + 49y^2)$. **53.** $(y^2 + 9)(y - 3)(y + 3)$.
55. $(a - 3x^2)(a^2 + 3ax^2 + 9x^4)$. **57.** $(a - 2)(a + 2)(a^2 - 2a + 4)(a^2 + 2a + 4)$.
59. $(2x - y^2)(2x + y^2)(4x^2 + y^4)$. **61.** $1 - 27x^3$. **63.** $125 - 75y + 15y^2 - y^3$.
65. $c^3 + 9c^2b^2 + 27cb^4 + 27b^6$. **67.** $8x^3 + 12x^2w + 6xw^2 + w^3$.
69. $c^3 - 18c^2z^3 + 108cz^6 - 216z^9$. **71.** $x^2 - 2xy + 4y^2$.
73. $x^4 - x^3y + x^2y^2 - xy^3 + y^4$.

Exercise 4. Page 32

1. $\dfrac{19x - 24}{35}$. 3. $\dfrac{40u - 3}{12}$. 5. $\dfrac{20b - 15ay + 3a}{15a^2b}$. 7. $\dfrac{4y - 12x + 7xy}{6x^2y^2}$.

9. $\dfrac{1}{35(x + y)}$. 11. $\dfrac{-2x^2 - 7x - 10}{6x(x + 1)}$. 13. $\dfrac{3x^2 - 3xy + 8}{2(x^2 - y^2)}$.

15. $\dfrac{x^2 - 17x + 1}{x^2 + x - 12}$. 17. $\dfrac{2n + 14}{3(1 - n)(n + 4)}$. 19. $\dfrac{9 + 9x - 12x^2}{2(2x + 3)^2}$.

21. $\dfrac{3 - 5x - 10x^2}{4x^2 - 1}$. 23. $\frac{1}{5}$; $-\frac{7}{4}$; $\dfrac{d}{3c}$. 25. $\dfrac{y^2 - y - 6}{y}$. 27. $\dfrac{2(2x - y)}{3(x - y)}$.

29. $\dfrac{(x + 3)(x - 5y)}{2x}$. 31. $\dfrac{xy}{2x + 3y}$. 33. $\dfrac{wx(4 - x)}{ch(5 - x)}$. 35. $\dfrac{5 + 3x}{x(x + 3)}$.

37. $\dfrac{4x + 5}{3x + 1}$. 39. $\dfrac{(x - 1)(x + 4)}{x}$. 41. $\dfrac{50ab - 15}{a^2b}$. 43. $\dfrac{1 + x + x^2}{2 + 2x}$.

45. $\dfrac{(b - a)(2a - 3b)}{a + b}$.

Exercise 5. Page 39

1. 11; $\frac{2}{7}$; $\frac{5}{6}$. 3. 5; 10; 4; no principal 4th root is defined for $-.0001$.
5. a^2b. 7. 3. 9. 3. 11. 57. 13. $3ab^3$. 15. -3. 17. 5. 19. 2. 21. 10.
23. 30. 25. $\frac{6}{7}$. 27. $3h$. 29. $\frac{10}{3}$. 31. $\frac{3}{2}$. 33. a^3b^2. 35. $-3x$. 37. $-2a^2$.
39. $.5$. 41. $\dfrac{2x}{ab^2}$. 43. $\dfrac{6}{bx^2}$. 45. 1. 47. 3. 49. $\frac{1}{25}$. 51. $\frac{1}{216}$. 53. 2. 55. 11.
57. -2. 59. $\frac{1}{3}$. 61. $\frac{1}{2}$. 63. 5. 65. 1728. 67. 27. 69. 625. 71. $\frac{3125}{243}$.
73. $\frac{1}{8}$. 75. $2y^{-3}$. 77. $4^{-1}x$. 79. $2(9^{-1})a^3y^{-4}$. 81. $6\sqrt[5]{x^2}$. 83. $b\sqrt[4]{x^3}$.
85. $x^{\frac{7}{3}}$. 87. x^2. 89. $\sqrt{27a^3}$. 91. $\frac{1}{6}$. 93. $\frac{3}{16}$. 95. $\frac{6}{25}$. 97. $\frac{16}{5}$. 99. $a^{\frac{10}{3}}$.
101. y^5. 103. 256. 105. 729. 107. $1/81x^4$. 109. $a^{\frac{5}{2}}$. 111. $1/a^{\frac{1}{3}}$. 113. y^4/x^6.
115. $7i$. 117. $i\sqrt{17}$. 119. $\frac{1}{3}i$. 121. ai. 123. $\frac{11}{5}i$. 125. $\pm\frac{2}{5}i$. 127. $\pm\frac{5}{4}i$.
129. 5. 131. $2 + 11i$. 133. -1. 135. i. 137. -24. 139. -16. 141. -12.

Exercise 6. Page 42

1. $3\sqrt{3}$. 3. $10\sqrt{3}$. 5. $z^4\sqrt[4]{z^3}$. 7. $3xy^2\sqrt{2x}$. 9. $-xy\sqrt[5]{xy^2}$. 11. $\dfrac{9u^2}{5v^2}\sqrt{\dfrac{u}{v}}$.

13. $-\dfrac{3x}{y^2}\sqrt[3]{\dfrac{1}{4}}$. 15. $\sqrt{6}$. 17. $2\sqrt[3]{3}$. 19. $\sqrt{5}$. 21. $\frac{1}{2}\sqrt{\dfrac{a}{c}}$. 23. $10x$.

25. $2xy\sqrt[3]{3xy}$. 27. $6 - 9\sqrt{2}$. 29. $\frac{1}{5}\sqrt{5}$. 31. $\frac{1}{5}\sqrt[3]{15}$. 33. $\frac{1}{10}\sqrt[3]{30}$. 35. $\frac{1}{10}\sqrt{10}$.

37. $\frac{1}{2}\sqrt[3]{6}$. 39. $\frac{1}{3}\sqrt[3]{6}$. 41. $\frac{1}{6}(6 - \sqrt{6})$. 43. $\frac{1}{2}\sqrt{2a}$. 45. $\dfrac{1}{a}\sqrt{2ac}$. 47. $\dfrac{1}{3d}\sqrt[3]{9cd}$.

49. $\dfrac{1}{a}\sqrt[4]{a}$. 51. $\dfrac{x}{y^2}\sqrt{y}$. 53. $\dfrac{1}{2x}\sqrt{2ax^2 - 20x}$. 55. $\dfrac{1}{2bx}\sqrt{2bx(4b + x^2)}$.

57. $\sqrt[15]{a^8}$. 59. $a^2b^2\sqrt[3]{b}$. 61. $xyz^3\sqrt[6]{y^4z^3}$. 63. $\sqrt{z}$. 65. $\sqrt[3]{u^2}$. 67. $\sqrt[3]{4}$.
69. $\sqrt[6]{2x}$. 71. $\sqrt[3]{3a}$. 73. $z\sqrt{z}$; $z^{\frac{3}{2}}$. 75. $3\sqrt[3]{3}$; $3^{\frac{4}{3}}$. 77. $7\sqrt[3]{49}$; $7^{\frac{5}{3}}$.
79. $216\sqrt{6}$; $6^{\frac{7}{2}}$. 81. $\sqrt[3]{4a^2}$; $2^{\frac{2}{3}}a^{\frac{2}{3}}$. 83. $5a\sqrt[3]{5a}$; $5^{\frac{4}{3}}a^{\frac{4}{3}}$. 85. $\sqrt[8]{a}$; $a^{\frac{1}{8}}$. 87. $\sqrt[9]{x}$; $x^{\frac{1}{9}}$.
89. $\sqrt[4]{a}$; $a^{\frac{1}{4}}$. 91. $\sqrt[3]{a^2}$; $a^{\frac{2}{3}}$. 93. $\sqrt[4]{8}$; $2^{\frac{3}{4}}$. 95. $\sqrt[10]{x^7}$; $x^{\frac{7}{10}}$. 97. $2\sqrt[15]{4}$; $2^{\frac{17}{15}}$.

99. $\frac{1}{5}\sqrt{10}$; $2^{\frac{1}{2}}/5^{\frac{1}{2}}$. **101.** $\sqrt[4]{a}$; $a^{\frac{1}{4}}$. **103.** $\frac{1}{b}\sqrt[4]{b^3}$; $b^{-\frac{1}{4}}$. **105.** $\frac{1}{5}\sqrt{15}$; $3^{\frac{1}{2}}5^{-\frac{1}{2}}$.

107. $\frac{1}{2x^2}\sqrt[3]{2x}$; $2^{-\frac{2}{3}}x^{-\frac{5}{3}}$. **109.** $\frac{1}{x^3}\sqrt{x}$; $x^{-\frac{5}{2}}$. **111.** $\sqrt[4]{d}$; $d^{\frac{1}{4}}$. **113.** $\frac{3}{x^2}\sqrt[3]{3x^2}$, $3^{\frac{4}{3}}x^{-\frac{4}{3}}$.

115. $\sqrt[4]{3x}$; $3^{\frac{1}{4}}x^{\frac{1}{4}}$. **117.** $\frac{1}{xy}\sqrt[3]{x^3+y^3}$; $x^{-1}y^{-1}(x^3+y^3)^{\frac{1}{3}}$. **119.** $\sqrt[18]{a}$; $a^{\frac{1}{18}}$.

Exercise 7. Page 47

1. $\frac{2}{5}$. **3.** $\frac{2}{3}$. **5.** $\frac{3}{2}$. **7.** 2. **9.** $y = \frac{4a+5c}{2a-3b}$. **11.** $x = \frac{2ab}{3c}$. **13.** $x = \frac{1}{12}ABC$.

15. $y = \frac{k}{c+b}$. **17.** $z = b^2 - 4b + 16$. **19.** $y = -\frac{a^2+3a+9}{a+2}$. **21.** 6.

23. $-\frac{3}{2}$. **25.** 2. **27.** -2. **29.** -13. **31.** -1. **33.** 75%. **35.** 1 gal.
37. $x = \frac{5}{4}$. **39.** 6″ and 14″. **41.** 14 and 12.6. **43.** Solution set is $\{5, 1\}$.

Exercise 8. Page 52

7. $|\overline{AB}| + |\overline{BC}| = 6$; $\overline{AC} = |\overline{AC}| = 6$. **9.** $|\overline{AB}| + |\overline{BC}| = 10$; $|\overline{AC}| = 2$.

Exercise 9. Page 57

5. $x > 4$. **7.** $\frac{13}{5} < x$. **9.** $-\frac{12}{7} < x$. **11.** $-\frac{20}{3} < x$. **13.** $x \geqq \frac{5}{6}$.
15. $x \leqq -3$.

17. If $(a - 2b) > 0$, $x \geqq \frac{3(2b + 5a)}{10(a - 2b)}$.

If $(a - 2b) < 0$, $x \leqq \frac{3(2b + 5a)}{10(a - 2b)}$.

If $a - 2b = 0$, the statement is true or false for all values of x according as $(2b + 5a) \leqq 0$ or $(2b + 5a) > 0$.

Exercise 10. Page 64

1. $A \cap B = \{5, 6, \cdots, 10\}$. $A \cup B = \{1, 2, 3, \cdots, 20\}$.
$A \setminus B = \{1, 2, 3, 4\}$. $B \setminus A = \{11, 12, \cdots, 20\}$.
$A \cup T = T$. $B \cap T = B$.
3. In order: $\{1, 2, \cdots, 20\}$; $\{5, 6, \cdots, 10\}$; $\{1, 2, \cdots, 25\}$; $\{8, 9, 10\}$.
5. $U = \{x \mid -1 < x\}$; $V = \{x \mid x < 4\}$.
7. $U = \{x \mid -4 < x\}$; $V = \{x \mid x \leqq 6\}$.
9. $G = \{x \mid x \geqq 3\}$; $H = \{x \mid x \leqq -3\}$; $W = G \cup H$.
11. $G = \{x \mid x < 4\}$; $H = \{x \mid x > -4\}$; $W = G \cap H$.
13. $A \cup B = \{x \mid -4 < x < 6\}$; $A \cap B = \{x \mid 0 < x \leqq 3\}$.
15. $\{x \mid 1 < x \leqq 3\}$. **17.** $\{x \mid -5 \leqq x \leqq 5\}$.
19. In order: $\{x \mid -1 < x \leqq 5\}$; $\{x \mid 2 \leqq x < 4\}$; $\{$all $x\}$.

Exercise 11. Page 66

1. $2 < x \leqq 3$. **3.** $1 \leqq x < 2$. **5.** Inconsistent. **7.** $-\frac{20}{3} < x < \frac{11}{24}$.
9. $-5 < x < 1$.
11. With $A = \{x \mid x \leqq 1\}$ and $B = \{x \mid x \geqq 7\}$, the solution set is $A \cup B$.

Exercise 12. Page 66

1. 27; 16. **3.** −6; 12; −12. **5.** $x \leqq 6$. **7.** $\frac{1}{2} < x \leqq \frac{7}{2}$.

9. In order: $\{x \mid -4 \leqq x < 15\}$; $\{x \mid 3 \leqq x < 12\}$; $\{x \mid 12 \leqq x < 15\}$; $\{x \mid -4 \leqq x < 3\}$.

11. $A = \{x \mid -3 < x\}$; $B = \{x \mid x \leqq 2\}$; $K = A \cap B$.

13. $A = \{x \mid x \leqq 6\}$; $B = \{x \mid -6 \leqq x\}$; $K = A \cap B$.

15. $A = \{x \mid x > 3\}$; $B = \{x \mid x < 1\}$; $K = A \cup B$.

Exercise 13. Page 69

11. $\overline{AB} = -6$. **13.** $\overline{AB} = 7$. **15.** $\overline{AB} = y_2 - y_1$. **17.** 13. **19.** 13. **21.** $\sqrt{65}$.
23. 6. **31.** 12.

Exercise 14. Page 73

1. 3.271. **3.** −1. **5.** 1. **7.** 71.6°. **9.** 116.6°. **11.** $\frac{7}{5}$. **13.** 3. **15.** −4.
27. $y = -\frac{5}{2}$.

Exercise 16. Page 80

1. $(-4, 16), (-3, 9), \cdots, (0, 0), \cdots, (2, 4), (3, 9), (4, 16)$. **9.** 7. **11.** −1.
13. 25. **15.** 3525. **17.** $32c^4 - 12c^2$. **19.** 12. **21.** $3b^2 + 2a - ab$.
23. 175; 9; $-\frac{7}{3}$; $(2x^3 - 1)$; $(x^3 + 6x + 7)$; $(8x^3 + 36x^2 + 54x + 25)$.
25. $(2 + k)^3$; $8x^3$; $(x - 3)^3$.

Exercise 17. Page 83

1. $y = \frac{1}{3}(12 - 4x)$; $x = \frac{1}{4}(12 - 3y)$. **3.** $y = \frac{1}{6}(3x - 8)$; $x = \frac{1}{3}(8 + 6y)$.
7. $y = -x^2 + 6x - \frac{3}{2}$. **9.** $y = \pm 2\sqrt{4 - x^2}$.

Exercise 18. Page 87

1. $y = -5$. **3.** $y = 3x + 2$. **5.** $\frac{x}{2} + \frac{y}{3} = 1$. **7.** $y = -\frac{2}{3}x + 4$.

9. $y = \frac{1}{3}x\sqrt{3} + 2$. **11.** $y = x + 3$. **13.** $5x - y = 14$. **15.** $x + 4y = 2$.
17. $x = 5$. **19.** $x - y = -4$. **21.** $x - 3y = -11$. **23.** $x = -1$.
25. $6x + y = -3$. **27.** $y = -x\sqrt{3} + 6$. **29.** $y = -x + 5$.
31. $2x - y = -11$; $x + 2y = 12$. **35.** $y = -\frac{2}{3}x + 2$. **37.** $y = \frac{5}{12}x - \frac{1}{2}$.
39. $y = \frac{6}{5}x + 2$.

Exercise 19. Page 90

11. $h = \frac{6}{5}$; $h = -\frac{10}{3}$. **13.** $h = 8$; $h = -\frac{9}{2}$. **15.** $h = \frac{3}{2}$; $g = 4$.
17. x-int., $-C/A$; y-int., $-C/B$.

Exercise 20. Page 94

1. $x = -\frac{2}{3}, y = -\frac{5}{3}$. **3.** $x = 2, y = 5$. **5.** $x = -\frac{8}{3}, y = 3$.
7. $x = -\frac{7}{3}, y = -\frac{5}{6}$. **9.** $x = -1, y = 1$. **11.** Inconsistent. **13.** Inconsistent.
15. Infinitely many solutions; dependent. **17.** $x = 2, y = 3$. **19.** $x = \frac{1}{2}, y = 5$.

21. $x = 5, y = 4.$ **23.** $v = \dfrac{2}{a+b^2}, w = \dfrac{2}{a+b^2}.$ **25.** $v = \dfrac{1}{a}, w = -\dfrac{b}{2}.$

27. $v = \dfrac{3a^2 - b^2}{3}, w = \dfrac{2b}{3}.$ **29.** $x = 2, y = 3.$ **31.** Not concurrent.

Exercise 22. Page 99

1. $W = ku/v^3.$ **3.** $R = kvz^{\frac{3}{2}}\sqrt{u}.$ **5.** $z - 3 = k(x+5).$ **7.** $V = kr^3.$
9. $W = k/d^2.$ **11.** $H = \frac{5}{2}x^3.$ **13.** $w = 10.$ **15.** 1936 ft. **17.** 25,000 ft.-lb.
19. 12 ft.

Exercise 23. Page 100

1. $\sqrt{106}.$ **3.** $\sqrt{41}.$ **5.** $-\frac{6}{5}.$ **11.** $x = -5.$ **13.** $4x - y = -12.$
15. $y = -2x - 2.$ **17.** $3x - 5y = 9.$
19. Slope $= -\frac{4}{5}$; y-int. $= 4$; $5x - 4y = 30.$
21. $14; 0; 9; -6y + 8y^2; 8x^2 + 18x + 9.$ **23.** $y = \frac{1}{3}(x^2 - x + 5).$
25. (a) $h = -\frac{6}{5}$; (b) $h = \frac{15}{2}.$ **27.** Inconsistent.

Exercise 24. Page 104

1. $V:(0,0)$; axis, $x = 0$; min., 0. **3.** $V:(-1,8)$; axis, $x = -1$; max., 8.
5. $V:(0,0)$; axis, $x = 0$; max., 0. **7.** $V:(2,11)$; axis, $x = 2$; max., 11.
9. Min., 2. **11.** Max., 1. **15.** 100 ft. by 100 ft.

Exercise 25. Page 107

1. $\pm\frac{5}{2}i.$ **3.** $\pm\frac{1}{7}\sqrt{35}.$ **5.** $\pm\frac{1}{3}\sqrt{a}.$ **7.** $\pm\dfrac{1}{2a}\sqrt{2ab}.$ **9.** $\pm\frac{7}{2}i.$ **11.** $\pm\frac{3}{2}i\sqrt{2}.$

13. $7, -2.$ **15.** $4, -7.$ **17.** $\pm 4.$ **19.** $0, \frac{5}{2}.$ **21.** $\frac{3}{4}, \frac{3}{4}.$ **23.** $-3, -3.$
25. $-\frac{1}{3}, -2.$ **27.** $0, -b/2a.$ **29.** $3a, -2a.$ **31.** $a, -\frac{3}{4}a.$ **33.** $b/c, -2b/3c.$
35. $3a, 3a.$ **37.** $4, -\frac{3}{2}.$ **39.** $6, -4.$ **41.** $\frac{1}{4}(1 \pm \sqrt{41}).$ **43.** $5, -\frac{1}{3}.$
45. $\frac{3}{2}, -\frac{4}{3}.$ **47.** $\frac{2}{3}, \frac{2}{3}.$ **49.** $\frac{1}{12}(-3 \pm i\sqrt{15}).$ **51.** $\pm\frac{2}{3}i.$ **53.** $\frac{1}{2}(1 \pm \sqrt{7}).$
55. $\frac{1}{4}(-2 \pm i\sqrt{10}).$ **57.** $\frac{1}{2}(-1 \pm 3i\sqrt{2}).$ **59.** $-\frac{3}{2}, \frac{5}{6}.$ **61.** $\frac{1}{4}(3 \pm 2\sqrt{7}).$
63. $-k, \frac{3}{2}k.$ **65.** $(-c \pm \sqrt{c^2 + 24ab})/4b.$ **67.** $(5 \pm \sqrt{25 - 24k^2})/4k.$
69. $8, -5.$ **71.** $-\frac{1}{2}, \frac{3}{7}.$ **73.** $\frac{1}{3}(2 \pm i\sqrt{5}).$ **75.** $\frac{1}{4}(1 \pm 3i\sqrt{2}).$
77. $\pm\frac{1}{3}\sqrt{3(a^2 + ab + b^2)}.$ **79.** $y = \frac{1}{3}x, y = \frac{1}{2}(2x + 3).$
81. $1, -4, \frac{1}{2}(-3 \pm i\sqrt{7}).$

Exercise 26. Page 112

1. Disc., -36; roots not real and unequal. **3.** Disc., 0; roots real, equal, and rational.
5. Disc., 64; roots real, unequal, and rational. **11.** $k = 0, -\frac{12}{13}.$
13. $k = -2, k = -10.$ **15.** $-1, -9.$ **17.** Sum, $-\frac{3}{7}$; prod., $-\frac{4}{7}.$
19. Sum, d/c; prod., $-h/c.$ **21.** Sum, $\frac{1}{3}c$; prod., $\frac{1}{3}a.$ **23.** $16x^2 + 9 = 0.$
25. $x^2 + 20 = 0.$ **27.** $x^2 - 6x + 34 = 0.$ **29.** $x^2 - 4x - 14 = 0.$
31. $h = -4.$

Exercise 27. Page 116

1. $\pm i$; $\pm\sqrt{3}$. **3.** ± 2; $\pm 2i$. **5.** -1; $\frac{1}{2}$. **7.** ± 2, ± 3. **9.** $\pm i$; $\pm\frac{3}{2}$.
11. 1, $\frac{2}{3}$. **13.** 2, $(-1 \pm i\sqrt{3})$. **15.** $\pm\frac{2}{3}$, $\pm\frac{2}{3}i$. **17.** $-\frac{14}{3}$. **19.** 6. **21.** 3.
23. 4. **25.** No sol. **27.** 2. **29.** 2. **31.** -8, $\frac{1}{64}$. **33.** $\frac{1}{9}$.

Exercise 28. Page 118

1. $x < \frac{7}{5}$.
3. If $A = \{x \mid x > 2\}$ and $B = \{x \mid x < -2\}$, the solution set is $A \cup B$.
5. $2 < x < 3$. Or, if $A = \{x \mid 2 < x\}$ and $B = \{x \mid x < 3\}$, the solution set is $A \cap B$.
7. No sol., or inconsistent. **9.** Union of $\{x \mid x < -3\}$ and $\{x \mid x > \frac{1}{2}\}$.
11. If $A = \{x \mid x < 0\}$ and $B = \{x \mid x > \frac{5}{3}\}$, then the solution set is $A \cup B$.
13. $.586 \leqq x \leqq 3.414$. **15.** Inconsistent.
17. All x in $\{x \mid x \leqq -\frac{5}{2}\} \cup \{x \mid x \geqq \frac{5}{2}\}$. **19.** All x in $\{x \mid x \geqq 3\} \cup \{x \mid x \leqq -3\}$.
21. All x in $\{x \mid x \leqq 1\} \cup \{x \mid x \geqq 4\}$. **23.** $-1 < x < 2$. **25.** $\frac{3}{2} < x < 2$.

Exercise 29. Page 121

1. (Why?) **5.** 13. **7.** 14. **9.** 151. **11.** $23\frac{1}{2}$. **13.** -67; -459. **15.** .78; 46.86.
17. -35; -1215. **19.** $n = 65$; 1235. **21.** $n = 21$; 525. **23.** 36,270.
25. 24,750. **27.** $\frac{108}{5}$, $\frac{101}{5}$, $\frac{94}{5}$, $\frac{87}{5}$. **29.** $\frac{17}{12}$, $\frac{25}{12}$, $\frac{33}{12}$, $\frac{41}{12}$, $\cdots$, $\frac{65}{12}$, $\frac{73}{12}$. **31.** 35.
33. 2. **35.** $15,840. **37.** 14. **39.** 36. **41.** $7560.

Exercise 30. Page 124

9. $(1.03)^{13}$, $(1.03)^{16}$. **11.** $(1.01)^{-2}$, 1. **13.** $\frac{7}{4}$. **15.** $\frac{6}{5}$. **17.** 768. **19.** $-\frac{7}{128}$.
21. $l = 18(10^{-8})$; $S = 18(.90909091)$. **23.** $l = 2a^9$; $S = \dfrac{2 - 2a^{10}}{1 - a}$. **25.** 4372.
27. $r = -3$; $n = 6$. **29.** $S = \frac{4372}{3}$; $n = 7$. **31.** .0025.
33. $\frac{5}{4}$, 25, 500; or $-\frac{5}{4}$, 25, -500. **35.** 2, 6, 18, 54. **37.** 3. **39.** -10.
41. $\dfrac{(1.04)^{64} - 1}{.04}$. **43.** $\dfrac{(1.02)^{53} - (1.02)^5}{(1.02)^3 - 1}$.

Exercise 31. Page 126

1. 17. **3.** $409.50. **5.** $360. **7.** $375; $30,375. **9.** n^2. **11.** $(x - x^{51})/(1 - x)$.
13. 2740. **17.** $4(10^7)[(1.05)^{10} - 1]$. **19.** $33\frac{1}{3}\%$. **21.** $33\frac{1}{3}\%$.
23. $\frac{1}{6}$, $\frac{1}{10}$, $\frac{1}{14}$, $\frac{1}{18}$, $\frac{1}{22}$. **25.** $\frac{1}{3}$, $\frac{3}{11}$, $\frac{3}{13}$, $\frac{1}{5}$. **27.** $\frac{16}{3}$. **29.** 8.

Exercise 32. Page 133

1. $-\frac{3}{4}$. **3.** 0. **5.** $+\infty$. **7.** 2. **9.** 2. **15.** No limit. **17.** No limit. **19.** 15.
21. $\frac{15}{2}$. **23.** $x_1y_1 + x_2y_2 + x_3y_3 + x_4y_4 + x_5y_5$.
25. $c(x_1 + x_2 + x_3 + x_4 + x_5 + x_6)$. **27.** 25; 5; 75. **29.** 55.
31. $b(1 - r^{15})/(1 - r)$. **33.** $3\sum_{k=1}^{9} 2^{k-1}$.

Exercise 33. Page 139

1. $\frac{15}{2}$. **3.** 30. **5.** $\frac{2}{9}$. **7.** $\frac{2}{3}$. **9.** $\frac{1}{6}$. **11.** $\frac{1}{11}$. **13.** $\frac{7}{33}$. **15.** $\frac{28}{9}$. **17.** $\frac{4}{11}$. **19.** $\frac{332}{33}$.
21. $\frac{600}{37}$. **23.** $\frac{860}{33}$. **27.** $\frac{10}{3}$. **29.** $\frac{4}{5}$. **31.** $\frac{3}{2}$.

Exercise 34. Page 141

1. $a^5 + 5a^4b + 10a^3b^2 + 10a^2b^3 + 5ab^4 + b^5$.
3. $x^8 - 8x^7y + 28x^6y^2 - 56x^5y^3 + 70x^4y^4 - 56x^3y^5 + 28x^2y^6 - 8xy^7 + y^8$.
5. $16 + 32a + 24a^2 + 8a^3 + a^4$.
7. $729b^6 - 1458b^5y + 1215b^4y^2 - 540b^3y^3 + 135b^2y^4 - 18by^5 + y^6$.
9. $a^3 + 3a^2b^2 + 3ab^4 + b^6$.
11. $a^{12} - 6a^{10}b^2 + 15a^8b^4 - 20a^6b^6 + 15a^4b^8 - 6a^2b^{10} + b^{12}$.
13. $x^5 - \frac{5}{2}x^4 + \frac{5}{2}x^3 - \frac{5}{4}x^2 + \frac{5}{16}x - \frac{1}{32}$.
15. $x^3 - 6x^{\frac{5}{2}}y^{\frac{1}{2}} + 15x^2y - 20x^{\frac{3}{2}}y^{\frac{3}{2}} + 15xy^2 - 6x^{\frac{1}{2}}y^{\frac{5}{2}} + y^3$.
17. $a^4 - 4a^3y^{-2} + 6a^2y^{-4} - 4ay^{-6} + y^{-8}$. **19.** $x^2 - \dfrac{8x^{\frac{3}{2}}}{a} + \dfrac{24x}{a^2} - \dfrac{32x^{\frac{1}{2}}}{a^3} + \dfrac{16}{a^4}$.
21. $c^{25} - 75c^{24} + 2700c^{23}$. **23.** $1 + 20a + 180a^2$. **25.** $1 + 2.4 + 2.64$.
27. $1 - 54x^3 + 1377x^6$. **29.** $x^7 + 14x^{\frac{13}{2}}b + 91x^6b^2$.
31. $x^{11} - 11x^{10}a^{-2} + 55x^9a^{-4}$. **33.** $a^k + ka^{k-1}x + \frac{1}{2}k(k-1)a^{k-2}x^2$.
35. $w^{2h} + hw^{2h-2}z + \frac{1}{2}h(h-1)w^{2h-4}z^2$. **37.** 1.195. **39.** 1.220.

Exercise 35. Page 142

1. Axis, $x = 2$; roots, 3.2 and .8; $f(x) < 0$,
   $\{x \mid .8 < x < 3.2\}$; $f(x) \geqq 0$, $\{x \mid x \leqq .8 \text{ or } x \geqq 3.2\}$.
3. Axis, $x = \frac{7}{2}$; roots, $\frac{7}{2}$ and $\frac{7}{2}$; $f(x) < 0$, no sol.;
   $f(x) \geqq 0$, all real numbers x.
5. $(2, -4)$. **7.** $(1, 2)$. **9.** $-\frac{3}{2}, \frac{2}{3}$. **11.** $\frac{1}{3}(-1 \pm \sqrt{61})$. **13.** $\frac{1}{2}(-3 \pm 5i)$.
15. Real, unequal, irrational. **17.** Real, unequal, rational. **19.** $\frac{1}{2}(3 \pm \sqrt{2})$.
21. Term, -169; sum, -3600.   **23.** Term, -48; sum, -168.   **25.** 6.2.
27. 108. **29.** $a = 5, n = 7$. **31.** 6, 18, 54; or, $-6, 18, -54$. **33.** 25.
35. $64b^6 - 192b^5y^2 + 240b^4y^4 - 160b^3y^6 + 60b^2y^8 - 12by^{10} + y^{12}$.
37. $k = \pm 3$. **39.** $k = \frac{8}{3}$. **41.** $x = -1$. **43.** $2, \frac{14}{25}$. **45.** $\pm\sqrt{2}, \pm\frac{1}{3}i\sqrt{15}$.
47. $\pm 6, \pm 6i$.   **49.** 10.8 gal.
51. 91; $(x_1 + x_2 + x_3 + x_4 - 24)$; $(2n + n^2)$; $\frac{15}{2}$.

Exercise 37. Page 150

1. $(x - 3)^2 + (y - 4)^2 = 4$. **3.** $(x - 3)^2 + (y + 2)^2 = 16$.
5. $x^2 + y^2 = 16$. **7.** $x^2 + 4x + y^2 = 0$. **9.** $x^2 + y^2 - 2by = 0$.
11. $C:(3, 2)$; $r = 4$. **13.** $C:(-3, 2)$; $r = \sqrt{10}$. **15.** $C:(3, 0)$; $r = 2\sqrt{5}$.
17. $C:(-3, 2)$; $r = 0$. **19.** Imag. circle.   **21.** $x^2 \pm 8x + y^2 + 6y + 9 = 0$.
23. $x^2 + 10x + y^2 - 8y + 37 = 0$.

Exercise 39. Page 158

1. $y^2 = 16x$. **3.** $x^2 = 32 - 16y$.
21. $y^2 = -6x$; $x^2 = -6y$.
23. $y^2 = -54x$; $x^2 = 2y$.

Exercise 40. Page 162

1. $5x^2 + 9y^2 = 45$.

Exercise 41. Page 166

1. $16y^2 - 9x^2 = 144$.
3. Asym., $2x = \pm 3y$.
5. Asym., $x = \pm 3y$.
7. Asym., $x = \pm y$.
9. Asym., $5y = \pm 3x$.
21. $8x^2 - 80x - y^2 + 8y + 176 = 0$.

Exercise 42. Page 170

1. $(.5, 4.0)$; $(-2.9, -2.8)$. **3.** $(\frac{5}{2}, -\frac{3}{2})$. **5.** $(1.2, \pm 3.2)$; $(-1.2, \pm 3.2)$.
7. $(2.5, .8)$; $(-2.5, -.8)$. **9.** $(\pm 3, 0)$. **11.** $(3.8, 3.2)$.
13. $(5.1, 1.7)$; $(2.1, -.7)$; $(4.6, .2)$; $(-2.6, 3.8)$.

Exercise 43. Page 171

1. $(4, -3)$; $(-3, 4)$. **3.** $(-3, 5)$; $(-3, 5)$.
5. $[\frac{1}{7}(12 - 2i\sqrt{6}), \frac{1}{7}(8 + i\sqrt{6})]$; $[\frac{1}{7}(12 + 2i\sqrt{6}), \frac{1}{7}(8 - i\sqrt{6})]$.
7. $(2, 3)$; $(\frac{3}{2}, 4)$. **9.** $(5, \frac{3}{2})$; $(5, \frac{3}{2})$.
11. $[\frac{3}{2}(-2 + i\sqrt{6}), -(1 + i\sqrt{6})]$; $[\frac{3}{2}(-2 - i\sqrt{6}), (-1 + i\sqrt{6})]$.
13. $[\frac{1}{5}(-4 + \sqrt{26}), \frac{1}{10}(-2 + 3\sqrt{26})]$; $[\frac{1}{5}(-4 - \sqrt{26}), \frac{1}{10}(-2 - 3\sqrt{26})]$.

Exercise 44. Page 173

1. $(.790, \pm 1.837)$; $(-.790, \pm 1.837)$. **3.** $(\frac{2}{3}i\sqrt{7}, \pm \frac{4}{3}\sqrt{2})$; $(-\frac{2}{3}i\sqrt{7}, \pm \frac{4}{3}\sqrt{2})$.
5. $(\sqrt{5}, \pm \frac{1}{2})$; $(-\sqrt{5}, \pm \frac{1}{2})$. **7.** $(\sqrt{2}, \pm i\sqrt{2})$; $(-\sqrt{2}, \pm i\sqrt{2})$.
9. $(2, \pm \frac{3}{2})$; $(-2, \pm \frac{3}{2})$. **11.** $(\frac{1}{3}\sqrt{3}, \pm \frac{1}{2}\sqrt{2})$; $(-\frac{1}{3}\sqrt{3}, \pm \frac{1}{2}\sqrt{2})$.

Exercise 45. Page 175

1. $(4, 3)$; $(-4, -3)$; $(3, -4)$; $(-3, 4)$. **3.** $(2, 2)$; $(-2, -2)$; $(1, 2)$; $(-1, -2)$.
5. $(2, 1)$; $(-2, -1)$; $(7, -4)$; $(-7, 4)$. **7.** $(4, -1)$; $(-4, 1)$; $(1, -\frac{3}{2})$; $(-1, \frac{3}{2})$.
9. $(\frac{1}{2}\sqrt{2}, \sqrt{2})$; $(-\frac{1}{2}\sqrt{2}, -\sqrt{2})$; $(3, -4)$; $(-3, 4)$.
11. $(2, -1)$; $(-2, 1)$; $(\frac{1}{2}, -\frac{3}{2})$; $(-\frac{1}{2}, \frac{3}{2})$.
13. $(10, 2)$; $(-\frac{4}{3}, 2)$; $(\frac{15}{11}, \frac{3}{11})$; $(6, -9)$. **15.** $(0, 2)$; $(2, 0)$.
17. $(2, \frac{3}{2})$; $(-2, -\frac{3}{2})$; $(3, 1)$; $(-3, -1)$. **19.** $(6, \frac{1}{2})$; $(-2, -\frac{3}{2})$.
21. $(\frac{3}{7}, -\frac{2}{7})$; $(-\frac{1}{3}, -\frac{2}{3})$; $(\frac{1}{7}, \frac{4}{7})$; $(-\frac{1}{3}, \frac{1}{3})$.

23. $(\frac{1}{2}, -3)$; $(-3, \frac{1}{2})$; $(\frac{3}{2}, -1)$; $(-1, \frac{3}{2})$.
25. $(\pm i\sqrt{2}, \pm\sqrt{3}, \pm\sqrt{3})$, with all possible combinations of signs, giving eight solutions.
27. $(1, -27)$; $(-1, 27)$; $(-64, 8)$; $(64, -8)$. **29.** ± 2. **31.** $c = \pm\sqrt{9m^2 + 4}$.

Exercise 46.   Page 186

1. $11i$. **3.** $9ai$. **5.** $-\frac{5}{3}i$. **9.** -1. **11.** $-i$. **13.** $-3 + 10i$. **15.** $-6i$.
17. -9. **19.** -10. **21.** $-3\sqrt{5}$. **23.** $17 + 17i$. **25.** -9. **27.** $\frac{22}{41} + \frac{7}{41}i$.
29. $\frac{6}{25} + \frac{17}{25}i$. **31.** $\frac{13}{5} - \frac{1}{5}i$. **33.** $\frac{3}{5} - 12i$. **35.** $-\frac{6}{5}i$. **37.** $\frac{5}{4}i$. **39.** $3i$.
41. $-40i\sqrt{5}$. **43.** $-2i$. **45.** $2 + 11i$. **47.** $-10 + 9i\sqrt{3}$. **49.** $\frac{2}{29} + \frac{5}{29}i$.
51. $-\frac{1}{5}i$. **53.** $\frac{1}{2}(-3 \pm i)$. **55.** $x^2 - 6x + 34 = 0$. **57.** $(x = 3, y = 7)$.
59. $(x = \frac{8}{3}, y = 0)$. **61.** $(x = 1, y = -1)$. **63.** $a - bi$.

Exercise 48.   Page 192

1. $\frac{3}{2}\sqrt{3} + \frac{3}{2}i$. **3.** $2 + 0i$. **5.** $\frac{3}{2} - \frac{3}{2}i\sqrt{3}$. **7.** $-2\sqrt{2} - 2i\sqrt{2}$. **9.** $0 - 5i$.
11. $-2.180 + 3.356i$. **13.** $-\frac{1}{2}\sqrt{2} - \frac{1}{2}i\sqrt{2}$. **15.** $3(\cos 90° + i \sin 90°)$.
17. $8(\cos 180° + i \sin 180°)$. **19.** $2\sqrt{2}(\cos 45° + i \sin 45°)$.
21. $8\sqrt{2}(\cos 135° + i \sin 135°)$. **23.** $2(\cos 150° + i \sin 150°)$.
25. $8(\cos 120° + i \sin 120°)$. **27.** $5\sqrt{2}(\cos 225° + i \sin 225°)$.
29. $13(\cos 157.4° + i \sin 157.4°)$. **31.** $5(\cos 36.9° + i \sin 36.9°)$.
33. $5(\cos 240° + i \sin 240°)$.
35. $\overline{N} = r[\cos(-\theta) + i \sin(-\theta)]$; $N^{-1} = [\cos(-\theta) + i \sin(-\theta)]/r$.

Exercise 49.   Page 194

1. $6 + 6i\sqrt{3}$. **3.** $12(\cos 35° + i \sin 35°)$. **5.** $4\sqrt{2} + 4i\sqrt{2}$. **7.** $-64i$.
9. -64. **11.** $-16 - 16i\sqrt{3}$. **13.** $-8 + 8i\sqrt{3}$. **15.** $128 + 128i$.
17. $3(\cos 110° + i \sin 110°)$. **19.** $\frac{15}{2}\sqrt{2}(\cos 105° + i \sin 105°)$. **21.** $-\frac{2}{3}\sqrt{3} + \frac{2}{3}i$.

Exercise 50.   Page 197

1. $3(\cos 40° + i \sin 40°)$; other amplitudes are $130°, 220°, 310°$.
3. $3(\cos 76° + i \sin 76°)$; other amplitudes are $196°, 316°$.
5. $\frac{3}{2}\sqrt{2} + \frac{3}{2}i\sqrt{2}$; $-\frac{3}{2}\sqrt{2} - \frac{3}{2}i\sqrt{2}$. **7.** 3; $\frac{3}{2}(-1 + i\sqrt{3})$; $\frac{3}{2}(-1 - i\sqrt{3})$.
9. $2(\cos 18° + i \sin 18°)$; $2i$; $2(\cos 162° + i \sin 162°)$; other amplitudes are $234°$ and $306°$.
11. ± 3; $\pm 3i$.
13. $2(\cos 78.75° + i \sin 78.75°)$; other amplitudes are $168.75°, 258.75°, 348.75°$.
15. $2(\cos 75° + i \sin 75°)$; other amplitudes are $165°, 255°, 345°$.
17. $2(\cos 37.5° + i \sin 37.5°)$; other amplitudes are $127.5°, 217.5°, 307.5°$.
19. ± 2; $\pm 2i$. **21.** ± 2; $(1 \pm i\sqrt{3})$; $(-1 \pm i\sqrt{3})$.

Exercise 51.   Page 200

1. $f(3) = 77$; $f(-2) = -8$. **3.** Quot. $= 2x^2 + 8x + 16$; rem. $= 40 = f(2)$.
5. No; $f(2) = 12$. **7.** No; $f(-2) = 22$. **11.** $-\frac{7}{8}$. **13.** 5; -2.

Exercise 52. Page 202

1. $2x^2 + 4x + 6 + \dfrac{19}{x-2}$.   3. $4x + 10 + \dfrac{33}{x-3}$.   5. $3x^2 + 5x + 12 + \dfrac{17}{x-2}$.

7. $2x^2 - 9x + 18 - \dfrac{29}{x+2}$.   9. $2x^2 + 4x - 6 - \dfrac{2}{x+\frac{1}{2}}$.

11. $f(2) = 41; f(-3) = 316.$

13. $f(.7) = 4.113; f(-.4) = 3.816; f(1.2) = 7.848.$ 15. $x^2 - 6x + 1.$

17. $x^5 - cx^4 + c^2x^3 - c^3x^2 + c^4x - c^5.$

Exercise 53. Page 204

11. $-1.4; 1.1; 4.3.$ 13. $.4.$ 15. $-1; .8; -.6; -2.2.$

Exercise 54. Page 207

1. $3; -4; 8.$ 3. $0; \frac{2}{3}; \frac{1}{4}(5 \pm i\sqrt{47}).$ 5. $x^4 - x^3 - 7x^2 + 13x - 6 = 0.$

7. $x^3 - 4x^2 + 2x + 4 = 0.$ 9. $9x^4 - 12x^3 + 85x^2 - 108x + 36 = 0.$

11. $x^3 - 8x^2 + 22x - 20 = 0.$ 13. $2x^4 - x^3 - 38x^2 + 16x + 96 = 0.$

15. $18x^3 - 51x^2 + 50x - 21 = 0.$ 17. $x^3 - 6x^2 + 12x - 8 = 0.$

19. $4x^4 + 16x^3 + 15x^2 - 4x - 4 = 0.$ 21. $-4 - 3i.$ 23. $8 + 4i.$

25. $x^3 - x^2 + 17x + 87 = 0.$

27. $x^5 - 11x^4 + 53x^3 - 119x^2 + 196x = 300.$

Exercise 55. Page 209

5. $3 < x < 5.$ 7. The solution set is $S = \{x \mid x < -3\} \cup \{x \mid 1 < x < 2\}.$

9. $x > 3.$ 11. The solution set is $S = \{x \mid -3 < x < 2\} \cup \{x \mid 4 < x < 6\}.$

Exercise 56. Page 213

1. $2x^4 + 3x^3 + 4x^2 + 6x = 5.$ 3. $2x^3 - 5x^2 + 7x + 3 = 0.$

5. $5x^6 - 4x^4 - x^2 + 7 = 0.$ 7. $2x^5 + 3x^4 - x^3 = 3x + 1.$

9. One positive and one negative.

11. One pos., one neg., and two not real.

13. One pos., two neg., and two not real; or, three pos. and two not real; or, three pos. and two neg.; or, one pos. and four not real.

15. One pos., one neg., and two not real; or, one pos. and three neg.

17. One neg. and two not real.   19. One pos. and two not real.

21. One pos. and six not real; or, one pos., two neg., and four not real; or, three pos. and four not real; or, three pos., two neg., and two not real.

23. One neg. and six not real.   25. One pos., one neg., and four not real.

27. Three pos. and three neg.   29. Zero, three pos., and one neg.

Exercise 57. Page 215

1. Upper $= 3$; lower $= -6$.   3. Upper $= 5$; lower $= -3$.

5. Upper $= 7$; lower $= 0.$ 7. Upper $= 9$; lower $= -6$.

9. Upper $= 5$; lower $= -2$.

Exercise 58. Page 218

1. 1; 2; −3. **3.** 3; $\frac{1}{4}(-3 \pm i\sqrt{7})$. **5.** 2; 2; −3. **7.** 2; 2; ±3. **9.** None.
11. $\frac{3}{2}$; $(-2 \pm \sqrt{2})$. **13.** $\frac{1}{2}$; $(-2 \pm i)$. **15.** None. **17.** $-\frac{1}{2}$; 2; −4.
19. $\frac{1}{4}$; $-\frac{1}{2}$; −2. **21.** None. **23.** 2. **25.** 3. **27.** $\frac{1}{4}$.
29. $3x^4 - 18x^2 + 189x - 324 = 0$. **41.** ±1; $\frac{1}{2}$; $\frac{3}{2}$. **43.** None.

Exercise 59. Page 221

Note. Some answers are given approximately to one more place than requested in the directions for the exercise.

1. 2.213. **3.** .426. **5.** 1.357; 1.692. **7.** 1.224. **9.** −.802; .555; 2.247.
11. .150; 1.724; −3.874. **13.** 2.107; .730; .162. **15.** 2; 1.154. **17.** 1.778.
19. −3.958. **21.** 2.32; 1.71; .54. **23.** 2.37″; .87″.

Exercise 60. Page 223

3. $x^4 + x^3 - 9x^2 - 3x + 18 = 0$. **5.** −4. **7.** 2; $\frac{5}{3}$; $-\frac{1}{3}$. **9.** 2; −3; −3.
11. $-\frac{1}{3}$; $-\frac{2}{3}$; −1. **13.** $-\frac{3}{4}$; $\frac{3}{2}$; −3.

Exercise 61. Page 228

1. 3.532; .120; 2.348. **3.** 3; $(\frac{3}{2} \pm \frac{3}{2}i\sqrt{3})$. **5.** 6.064; 3.696; −.760.
7. 2; −1; $\frac{1}{2}(5 \pm i\sqrt{3})$. **9.** $(1 \pm i)$; ±3i.

Exercise 62. Page 228

1. 317; 47. **3.** $2x^2 + 2x + 1$. **5.** −2.35; −1.40; 2.74.
7. $3x^3 - 2x^2 - x - 8 = 0$.
9. Upper bound, 2; lower bound, −21. Roots: one pos., one neg., and two not real.
11. −2; $\frac{1}{2}(1 \pm \sqrt{2})$. **13.** 3.3. **15.** 2.6.

Exercise 64. Page 238

33. 36. **35.** 10,000. **37.** 125. **39.** 15. **41.** $\frac{1}{5}$. **43.** b. **45.** 3. **47.** $\frac{1}{6}$. **49.** 9.
51. 2. **53.** 4. **55.** 2. **57.** 5. **59.** $\frac{1}{2}$. **61.** −1. **63.** −3. **65.** −3. **67.** 3.
69. 10. **71.** 4. **73.** 64. **75.** 20. **77.** 343. **79.** $\frac{1}{81}$. **81.** $\frac{1}{8}$.

Exercise 65. Page 241

1. 1.1461. **3.** 1.4771. **5.** 1.3222. **7.** .5441. **9.** −.3680 **11.** 0.843.
13. 2.3010. **15.** −1.0212. **17.** .6778. **19.** 1.5050. **21.** .2386. **23.** .1840.

Exercise 67. Page 247

1. Ch. = 3; man. = .5217. **3.** Ch. = −3; man. = .550.
5. Ch. = −4; man. = .8418. **7.** Ch. = −5; man. = .2891. **9.** 8.1356 − 10.
11. 6.5268 − 10. **13.** 4. **15.** −5. **17.** −6. **19.** 2.0934. **21.** 9.4166 − 10.
23. 8.7497 − 10. **25.** 4.3201. **27.** 9.9586 − 10. **29.** 4.1818. **31.** 5.3404 − 10.
33. 136. **35.** .523. **37.** 55.7. **39.** .0376. **41.** 3.31. **43.** .00293.
45. 32,900,000. **47.** .000429. **49.** (*a*) .000250; (*b*) .00400.

Exercise 68. Page 250

1. 3.2840. **3.** 3.7646. **5.** 0.9748. **7.** 9.8509 — 10. **9.** 7.7106 — 10.
11. 6.3025 — 10. **13.** 4.9036. **15.** 0.4950. **17.** 4.4113. **19.** 7.7934 — 10.
21. 45.22. **23.** .1053. **25.** 3.557. **27.** .04397. **29.** 108.6. **31.** .0001050.
33. .00008644. **35.** $1.088(10^7)$. **37.** 2298. **39.** .9008. **41.** 9.708. **43.** 36.71.

Exercise 69. Page 253

1. 2328. **3.** 2.868. **5.** .009780. **7.** —.04454. **9.** 35.80. **11.** .04926. **13.** 22.93.
15. 118.1. **17.** 647.3. **19.** .01699. **21.** .001421. **23.** $-4.769(10^{-7})$.
25. $1.857(10^{-5})$. **27.** 28.66. **29.** .006971. **31.** 87.78.
33. (a) $3.810(10^5)$; (b) 7.778.

Exercise 70. Page 255

1. 6537. **3.** .6737. **5.** 5.966. **7.** .9782. **9.** .2369. **11.** 6.310. **13.** 13.16.
15. .04642. **17.** —12.00. **19.** $-3.186(10^{-8})$. **21.** .7827. **23.** 57.65.
25. 53.40. **27.** 1.229. **29.** .01953. **31.** $2.233(10^9)$. **33.** (a) 50.12; (b) 50.50.
35. .2005. **37.** 1842. **39.** $1.529(10^{-5})$. **41.** $2.305(10^4)$. **43.** 6.006. **45.** 3.378.
47. 4.696. **49.** 2.282. **51.** .3322. **53.** 77.57. **55.** —.134.

Exercise 71. Page 256

1. 1.280. **3.** 1.369. **5.** —17.8. **7.** ±1.266. **9.** —1.982; .982. **11.** 17.
13. $3.418(10^5)$. **15.** 7.132. **17.** 2.303. **19.** 2.502. **21.** —8.980.
23. (a) .318; (b) at end 2.18 hr.

Exercise 73. Page 267

1. $x = 4, y = -5, z = 1$. **3.** $S = -1, t = -1, y = -\frac{1}{2}$.
5. $x = \frac{1}{2}, y = -\frac{3}{2}, z = -2$. **7.** $w = 2, x = 4, y = 1, z = -1$.
9. $x = 0, y = 0, z = 0$. **11.** Inconsistent.
13. $w = -2, x = 4, y = -2, z = -1$.
15. $u = 2, v = 1, x = \frac{1}{2}, y = -\frac{1}{2}, z = -\frac{1}{2}$.

Exercise 74. Page 270

1. —14. **3.** $-9 - c$. **17.** $x = \dfrac{bk + h^2}{bd + fh}, \ y = \dfrac{dh - fk}{bd + fh}$.

Exercise 75. Page 273

1. For 2d column, $\quad -m_1 \begin{vmatrix} c_2 & v_2 \\ c_3 & v_3 \end{vmatrix} + m_2 \begin{vmatrix} c_1 & v_1 \\ c_3 & v_3 \end{vmatrix} - m_3 \begin{vmatrix} c_1 & v_1 \\ c_2 & v_2 \end{vmatrix}$. **3.** —41.
5. —63. **7.** $x^2y^3 - x^3y^2 - xy^3 + x^3y + xy^2 - x^2y$. **9.** 146.

Exercise 76. Page 278

7. 176. **9.** —400.

Exercise 78. Page 285

11. 0; 1; $-\frac{9}{14}$. **13.** ± 2. **15.** $-10 : 7 : 8$.

Exercise 79. Page 289

1. 840; 480. **3.** 120. **5.** 60. **7.** 216. **9.** 15,120; 6720; 1680; 4200.
11. 1956. **13.** 288. **15.** 625; 120. **17.** 1440. **19.** 288. **21.** 59,999,400.

Exercise 80. Page 293

1. 120. **3.** 24. **5.** 720. **7.** 12,600. **9.** 1680. **11.** 24; 24. **13.** 20,160.
15. 560. **17.** 288. **19.** 144. **21.** 2880. **23.** 2. **25.** 44.

Exercise 81. Page 298

3. 70; 126. **5.** 20; 15. **7.** 1287; 495. **9.** 50; 525; 120; 36,750.
11. 1960; 35; 175. **13.** 15,625. **15.** 604,800. **17.** 1260. **19.** 5. **21.** 49. **23.** 64.
25. 1095; 435; 36,036. **27.** 9. **29.** 15. **31.** 1440. **33.** 4200. **35.** 1880.
37. 15,120. **39.** 35.

Exercise 82. Page 303

1. $x^6 + {}_6C_1 x^5 y^2 + {}_6C_2 x^4 y^3 + etc.$
3. $x^{15} - 3({}_5C_1)x^{12}y^2 + 9({}_5C_2)x^9 y^4 - 27({}_5C_3)x^6 y^6 + etc.$
5. $x^{\frac{8}{3}} - {}_8C_1 x^{\frac{7}{3}} y^{\frac{2}{3}} + {}_8C_2 x^{\frac{6}{3}} y^{\frac{4}{3}} - etc.$
7. $2^9 y^{-18} - 2^7({}_9C_1)y^{-16}x^{\frac{1}{4}} + 2^5({}_9C_2)y^{-14}x^{\frac{1}{2}} - etc.$ **9.** $28x^2 y^6$. **11.** $126{,}720 x^4 z^4$.
13. $5376(10^{-12})$. **15.** $448y^{\frac{1}{2}}x^{\frac{3}{2}}$. **17.** $25{,}344 x^{\frac{7}{2}}$. **19.** $\frac{35}{8}x^4 y^2$.
21. $462x^6 y^5$; $462x^5 y^6$. **23.** 255. **25.** 4095.

Exercise 83. Page 309

1. $\frac{3}{5}$; $\frac{2}{5}$; 1. **3.** $P(H) = \frac{5}{9}$; $P(H') = \frac{4}{9}$. **5.** $\frac{1}{3}$; $\frac{1}{2}$. **7.** $\frac{3}{28}$; $\frac{5}{14}$; $\frac{15}{28}$; $\frac{13}{28}$.
9. $\frac{1}{6}$; $\frac{1}{9}$; $\frac{1}{18}$; $\frac{5}{18}$. **11.** $\frac{4}{7}$; $\frac{3}{7}$; $\frac{1}{7}$; $\frac{3}{7}$. **13.** $\frac{2}{9}$; $\frac{2}{9}$; $\frac{5}{9}$; $\frac{7}{9}$. **15.** $11/6{,}431{,}950$.
17. $\frac{28}{585}$; $\frac{32}{117}$; $\frac{14}{117}$. **19.** $\frac{11}{30}$. **21.** .582; .650. **23.** $\frac{1}{24}$; $\frac{7}{24}$.
25. For (b): $\frac{1}{12}$; $\frac{1}{36}$; $\frac{7}{18}$; $\frac{7}{48}$. **27.** $\frac{5}{11}$. **29.** (a) .117; (b) .123. **31.** .368.

Exercise 84. Page 314

1. Domain of f is $\{3, 4, 5, \cdots, 18\}$; corresponding values of f are
$\{\frac{1}{36}, \frac{1}{36}, \frac{1}{18}, \frac{1}{18}, \frac{1}{12}, \frac{1}{12}, \frac{1}{12}, \frac{1}{12}, \frac{1}{12}, \frac{1}{12}, \frac{1}{12}, \frac{1}{12}, \frac{1}{18}, \frac{1}{18}, \frac{1}{36}, \frac{1}{36}\}$
3. Domain of f is $\{1, 2, 4\}$; values of f are $\{\frac{1}{3}, \frac{1}{6}, \frac{1}{2}\}$.
5. Domain of f is $\{2, 3, 4, 5, 6\}$; values of f are $\{\frac{1}{5}, \frac{2}{5}, \frac{1}{15}, \frac{1}{5}, \frac{2}{15}\}$.

Exercise 85. Page 316

1. $\frac{23}{4}$. **3.** 7. **5.** $\frac{5}{8}$. **7.** $E(X) = 3\frac{1}{2}$.
9. Domain of f is $\{0, 1, 2, 3, 4, 5\}$. Values of f are
$\{\frac{1}{6}, \frac{5}{18}, \frac{2}{9}, \frac{1}{6}, \frac{1}{9}, \frac{1}{18}\}$. $E(X) = \frac{35}{18}$.
11. $V = \{0, 1, 2, 3\}$. $E(X) = .75$.
13. Range of X is $\{2, 3, 4, 5\}$. Values of f are $\{\frac{1}{5}, \frac{3}{10}, \frac{2}{5}, \frac{1}{10}\}$. $E(X) = 3.4$.

Exercise 86.   Page 322

1. $25.   3. $\frac{5}{8}$; $\frac{3}{8}$; $62.50.   7. $\dfrac{883,342}{971,804}$.   9. $\dfrac{577,882}{924,609}$; $\dfrac{123,334}{924,609}$.

11. $\dfrac{2312}{951,483}$; $\dfrac{4161}{951,483}$.

13. $877, in money due at the end of 20 years.

17. 4.47(10^3)$, in money due at the end of 15 years.

Exercise 87.   Page 329

1. $\frac{7}{12}$.   3. $\frac{1}{32}$.   5. $\frac{1}{5832}$.   7. $\frac{3}{16}$; $\frac{3}{8}$; $\frac{7}{16}$; $\frac{9}{16}$.   9. $\frac{1}{4}$; $\frac{11}{24}$; $\frac{13}{24}$.

11. $\frac{9}{196}$; $\frac{25}{98}$; $\frac{47}{588}$; $\frac{55}{196}$.   13. $\frac{1}{24}$; $\frac{1}{4}$; $\frac{1}{4}$.   15. $\frac{7}{8}$.   17. $\frac{3}{64}$.

19. A, $\frac{1}{8}$; B, $\frac{1}{8}$; C, $\frac{1}{4}$; D, $\frac{1}{2}$.

21. $P(E') = .4$; $P(E \cap F) = .4$; $P(E \cup F) = .7$;
$P(E' \cup F') = .6$; $P(E' \cap F') = .3$

Exercise 88.   Page 333

1. $\frac{8}{27}$; $\frac{11}{27}$; $\frac{8}{9}$.   3. $\frac{5}{16}$; $\frac{21}{32}$; $\frac{11}{32}$; $\frac{5}{16}$.   5. $\frac{3}{64}$; $\frac{67}{256}$; $\frac{255}{256}$ 7. $\dfrac{392}{151,875}$.   9. 20.

11. 57.   13. .198.   15. .0595.   17. $\frac{7}{128}$; $_{n-1}C_{k-1}\left(\dfrac{1}{2^n}\right)$.

Exercise 89.   Page 339

1. P(boy) $= \frac{4}{9}$; P(girl) $= \frac{5}{9}$; $P(H) = \frac{1}{2}$; P(boy $\cap H$) $= \frac{1}{6}$;
P(girl $\cap H$) $= \frac{1}{3}$; $P_c(H$, given girl$) = \frac{3}{5}$;
$P_c(H$, given boy$) = \frac{3}{8}$; P_c(girl, given H) $= \frac{2}{3}$;
P_c(boy, given H) $= \frac{1}{3}$.   3. $\frac{2}{5}$.   5. .35; $\frac{5}{8}$.   7. (a) $\frac{9}{23}$; (b) $\frac{14}{23}$.

9. (α) $\frac{97}{382}$; (β) $\frac{285}{382}$.

11. $E \cap F = \{(1, 2), (1, 3), \cdots, (1, 6)\}$;
$E \cap G = \{(1, 1)\}$. $F \cap G = \{(2, 2), (3, 3), \cdots, (6, 6)\}$.
What are the outcomes in $E \cap F \cap G$?

Exercise 90.   Page 344

1. $\frac{2}{9}$.   3. $\frac{52}{315}$; $\frac{59}{315}$; $\frac{17}{35}$.   5. $\frac{2}{91}$; $\frac{1}{27}$.   7. $\frac{5}{26}$; $\frac{2}{7}$; $\frac{87}{182}$; $\frac{52}{87}$.   9. $\frac{72}{5525}$.

11. $P(H) = \frac{1}{2}$; $P(K) = \frac{59}{104}$; $P(H \cap K) = \frac{5}{26}$; $P_c(K$, given $H) = \frac{5}{13}$.

13. $\frac{3}{7}$; P_c(box I, given white ball$) = \frac{8}{15}$.   15. $\frac{14}{135}$.   17. .512; .256; .232.

Exercise 91.   Page 348

7. Inconsistent.   9. If "yes," give a counterexample.

11. $x \geq 3$, $y \geq 0$, $x \leq 6$, and $2x + 3y - 24 \leq 0$.

13. $y \leq 5$, $8x - y - 11 \geq 0$, $6x - y - 19 \leq 0$, and $y - x + 4 \geq 0$.

Exercise 92. Page 352

1. Max. = 5; min. = −23.

3. $x = 2 + 6t$, $y = 4 + 6t$; $(5, 7)$; $(4, 6)$ and $(6, 8)$.

5. $x = -8 + 6t$, $y = -3 + 6t$; $(-5, 0)$; $(-6, -1)$ and $(-4, 1)$.

7. $x = -10 + 6t$, $y = -2 + 7t$; $(-7, \frac{3}{2})$; $(-8, \frac{1}{3})$ and $(-6, \frac{8}{3})$.

9. $(\frac{7}{2}, \frac{11}{2})$, $(5, 7)$, $(\frac{13}{2}, \frac{17}{2})$.　**11.** $(21, -14)$.

13. $(6, 11)$.　**15.** $(5, 9)$.

17. $\phi(t) = 43 - 48t$; $M = 43$ at $(12, 0)$; $m = -5$ at $(0, 6)$.

19. $\phi(t) = 12t + 6$; $M = 18$ at $(9, 8)$; $m = 6$ at $(3, 5)$.

21. $x = \dfrac{k_1 x_2 + k_2 x_1}{k_1 + k_2}$, $y = \dfrac{k_1 y_2 + k_2 y_1}{k_1 + k_2}$.

Exercise 93. Page 355

1. Min. = −16; max. = 5.　**3.** Min. = 4; max. = 91.

5. Min. = −6; max. = 6.　**7.** Min. = −30; max. = 29.

Exercise 94. Page 358

1. 300 of A and 600 of B.　**3.** 75 lb. of A and 25 lb. of B.

5. In pounds: 30 of A, 40 of B, and 30 of C.

7. (In ounces per 100 ounces of the syrup, or the number of percent for each in any amount.) 30 of A, 60 of B, and 10 of C.

9. (i) 30% A, 60% B, and 10% C. (ii) Min. = \$48; max. = \$72.

11. Max., −14, at $(x = 3, y = \frac{3}{2})$.

13. Min., −2, at all points (x, y) on line $y - x - 2 = 0$ below point $(x = 1, y = 3)$.

15. Ship 150 to G from A and 50 from B; ship 150 to H from A; ship 250 to K from B.

Exercise 97. Page 391

3. $\begin{bmatrix} -1 & 8 \\ 10 & -10 \end{bmatrix}$.　**5.** $\begin{bmatrix} 17 & -1 \\ -10 & 2 \end{bmatrix}$.　**7.** $\begin{bmatrix} -13 \\ 1 \end{bmatrix}$.　**9.** $[6 \quad 2]$.

11. $\begin{bmatrix} -2x_1 + 4x_2 + x_3 \\ 3x_1 + 2x_2 + 3x_3 \\ -x_1 + 3x_2 + 2x_3 \end{bmatrix}$.　**13.** $A^{-1} = \dfrac{1}{14} \begin{bmatrix} 4 & 2 \\ -1 & 3 \end{bmatrix}$.

15. $\dfrac{1}{16} \begin{bmatrix} 5 & -2 \\ 3 & 2 \end{bmatrix}$.　**17.** $-\dfrac{1}{91} \begin{bmatrix} 33 & -34 & 6 \\ -18 & 2 & 5 \\ -26 & 13 & -13 \end{bmatrix}$.

19. $\dfrac{1}{42} \begin{bmatrix} -3 & -4 & 6 \\ 21 & -14 & 0 \\ 18 & -4 & 6 \end{bmatrix}$.　**21.** $\dfrac{1}{11} \begin{bmatrix} 5 & 7 & -8 \\ 4 & -1 & -2 \\ -1 & 3 & -5 \end{bmatrix} = A^{-1}$.

23. $A^{-1} = \dfrac{1}{8} \begin{bmatrix} -5 & 7 & 9 \\ 4 & -4 & -4 \\ 7 & -5 & -11 \end{bmatrix}$.　**25.** $A^{-1} = \dfrac{1}{48} \begin{bmatrix} -10 & -7 & -27 \\ 48 & 24 & 72 \\ 14 & 5 & 33 \end{bmatrix}$.

Index

419

234567890